A
History
of the
Ordnance
Survey

A
History
of the
Ordnance
Survey

EDITED BY W A SEYMOUR

with contributions by J H Andrews, R C A Edge, J B Harley,
J S O Jelly, I Mumford, Yolande O'Donoghue, K M Papworth,
E J S Parsons, C W Phillips, W A Seymour and others

DAWSON

First published in 1980

Wm Dawson & Sons Ltd, Cannon House
Folkestone, Kent, England

British Library Cataloguing in Publication Data

A history of the Ordnance Survey.
  1. Ordnance Survey – History
  I. Seymour, W A
  GA793.7.A1   526′.06′141

ISBN 0–7129–0979–6

Printed in Great Britain
by W & J Mackay Limited, Chatham

Contents

List of Plates   *page* xi
List of Principal Contributors   xiii
Preface   xv
Publisher's Note   xvi

1 The Origins of the Ordnance Survey   1
The Board of Ordnance and the Development of Military Cartography in Britain   2
The Civilian Contribution to the Foundation of the Ordnance Survey   9
The Scientific Tradition and the Establishment of the Ordnance Survey   12
2 The Resumption of the Trigonometrical Survey   21
First Appointments to the Trigonometrical Survey   22
The Directorate of William Mudge 1798–1820   23
The Apprenticeship of Thomas Colby   27
The Trigonometrical Operations and the Scientific Image of the early Ordnance Survey   28
3 The Geodesy of Roy, Mudge and Kater 1784–1823   33
The Connection of the Observatories of Greenwich and Paris 1784–90   33
The Triangulation of Great Britain 1791–1822: Instruments – Bases – Observation of
    the Triangulation – Calculation   36
The Dunnose – Clifton Arc of Meridian   40
The West European Arc of Meridian 1816–23: The Remeasurement of the Greenwich
    – Paris Connection 1821–3   40
4 The Birth of the Topographical Survey   44
The Reorganization of 1787   44
Early Surveys for the Maps of Kent and Essex   45
The Royal Military Surveyors and Draftsmen 1800–17   48
The Topographical Survey as a Training Ground for Royal Engineers   50
The Beginnings of Reform 1816–20   53
5 Early Methods of Topographical Survey   57
Field Surveying   57
Hill-Sketching   60
Ordnance Survey Orthography   60
The Archaeological Survey: The Work of Roy – Archaeology on the Old Series
    One-Inch   62
6 The Ordnance Survey becomes a Map-Publisher 1801–1820   67
The Development of an Engraving Service   69
The Prohibition of Publication 1811–16   70
Relationships with other Map-Sellers   73
7 The Survey of Ireland to 1847   79
The Spring Rice Committee and its Antecedents   79
The Military System 1825–8   81
Colby in Trouble 1826–33   84
Colby Triumphant 1833–46   87
Geology and Statistics 1826–45   91
The Aftermath 1842–7   94
8 Colby's Reforms in Great Britain 1820–1840   99
Publication and Marketing   99
The Reform of the Topographical Survey: The One-Inch Survey of Southern Scotland –
    Revision and the Geological Survey – Cartography, the Old Series One-Inch –
    Advances in the Treatment of Place-Names   100
The Completion of the Primary Triangulation of Scotland   107
9 Changing Needs in Great Britain   109
The Introduction of the Six-Inch Scale: The Survey Act 1841   109
The Fire in the Tower   111

New Uses for Maps: Tithes, Inclosures and Railways – Sanitary Reform   112
The Beginning of the Scales Controversy   114
The Staff   115
The End of the Colby Era: An Appreciation of Colby   115
10 The Superintendency of Lewis Alexander Hall   119
Colby's Successor   119
The Scales Dispute: Hall and Yolland in Concert – the Quarrel between Hall and
    Yolland – the Scales Dispute Resumed   119
Hall's Successor   127
11 The Scales Dispute – Henry James 1854–1863   129
The Conclusion of the Scales Dispute   129
The One-Inch Map in Disgrace   134
The End of the Board of Ordnance   135
The Staff – the Clash of Military and Civilian Interests   136
James and Technical Developments   137
12 Clarke and the Principal Triangulation   139
Alexander Ross Clarke   139
Instruments and Observations: Angular measurements – Improvements in Base
    measurement – Latitude and Longitude   139
Calculation and Adjustment of the Principal Triangulation: Standards of Length –
    Adjustment   141
The Figure of the Earth   143
The Initial Levelling of Great Britain   145
The Resignation of Colonel Clarke 1881   145
13 The Irish Survey under Hall and James   147
Devolution – the Irish Survey under Hall 1847–54   147
Assimilation – Sir Henry James and after   150
14 The Surveys of Jerusalem and Sinai   154
The Survey of Jerusalem 1864–5   154
The Sinai Survey 1868–9   157
15 The Last Years of James's Superintendency and the Transfer to Civil Control 1864–1880   158
The Last Years of War Office Control 1864–70: The Movement towards Civil Control
    – Progress of the Survey 1864–70 – Map Sales and Agents   158
A New Broom: The Board of Works Committee of Enquiry – Progress 1870–80   161
Methods and Processes of the Ordnance Survey   165
James – his Departure and his Successors   166
16 The Mature Topographical Survey   168
The Large-Scale Plans – Function and Content   168
Topographical Methods: The Chain Survey – Plotting and Examination   169
The Depiction of Relief: Contouring – Hill-Sketching   171
The Archaeological Survey for the Large-Scale Plans of Great Britain   173
Place-Names – the Mature System   175
17 The Expansion 1880–1891   178
Cause and Effect   178
Staffing Problems of the Expansion   179
Revision   182
More Changes in Map Distribution   183
18 The Dorington Committee   185
The Ordnance Survey under Attack   185
The Dorington Committee 1892   189
The Results of the Inquiry   192
19 A Period of Consolidation 1894–1913   195
Wilson's Successors   195
Maps Sales and Agents: Crown Copyright   196
Land Registration   198
Cartographic Developments: Accommodation and Machinery – The Engraved
    One-Inch Map – The One-Inch Map in Colour – More New Maps   200
Progress in the Field   203

The South African War 1899–1902   204
A Revival – the First Years of Close's Directorship   204
A Pre-War Summary   207

20 Ireland – The Land Question and After, 1871–1918   209
The Land Question   209
Colour and its Problems   211
Towards Home Rule   212

21 A Geodetic Revival – The Test of the Triangulation and the Second Geodetic Levelling 1909–1921   214
The Test of the Triangulation 1909–12   214
Minor Triangulation and Meridians   215
The Magnetic Survey 1913–15   216
The Second Geodetic Levelling of England and Wales 1912–21   217

22 The Ordnance Survey 1914–1918   220
The Survey and the First World War: The Western Front – the Overseas Branch of the
     Ordnance Survey – the Home Front   220
The Olivier Committee 1914   225
Domestic Mapping 1914–18: The Small-Scale Maps – the Large-Scale Plans   227
The Effect of the War   228

23 Reconstruction after The First World War 1919–1922   230
The Economy Cuts and the Large-Scale Plans   230
The Small-Scale Maps   231
The Establishment of the Whitley Council   232
The Separation of the Irish Surveys   233
Two New Posts for the Ordnance Survey   233
The Beginning of the Debate on Air Survey   234
The End of an Era – Sir Charles Close retires   235

24 Archaeology – The Crawford Period   237
The First Archaeology Officer   237
Period Maps   239
The Beginnings of Archaeology Branch   240

25 The Lean Years 1922–1934   241
Close's Successors   241
Staff Problems: The Abolition of Engraving   242
Cost Accounting for the Ordnance Survey   244
A National Compromise: the Ordnance Survey in the Military Context   245
The Changing Face of Post-War Britain and the Large-Scale Plans: The Large-Scale
     Plans and Air Photography – Government Acts and the Large-Scale Plans   248
The Small-Scale Maps: The One-Inch Map – The Half-Inch and Smaller Scales   251
Scientific Work   254

26 MacLeod and the Davidson Committee 1935–1939   257
The Interim Report of the Davidson Committee   258
The Final Report of the Davidson Committee   260
The Eve of War   266

27 The Retriangulation 1935–1939   268
The Need for a new Triangulation: The National Grid   268
The Primary Triangulation: Execution of the Triangulation – Marking of Stations –
     Observation of the Angles of the Triangulation   269
The Ridge Way and Lossiemouth Bases   272
Computation of the Primary Triangulation   272

28 The Second World War 1939–1945   274
The Ordnance Survey at Southampton 1939–40   274
The Ordnance Survey and the War Office   275
The Blitz at Southampton in 1940   277
The Dispersal 1941–3   279
Map Production 1936–45: Pre-War Military Mapping – Maps for the Expanding
     Theatre of War – Maps for the Invasion of Europe 1944–5   280

Other War-time Work in Great Britain 1939–45: Work in the Field – Maps for the
    Public – The Heathrow Cannon   283

29 The Restoration of the Survey – Expansion 1945–1950   286
Planning for the Post-War Period 1941–5: Planning for Air Photography   286
The Administrative Background 1945–50   288
The Short-Term Plan   291
The Long-Term Plan: Field-work – Publication   293
Science and Research   296

30 The Restoration of the Survey – Consolidation and Recession 1950–1960   298
Staffing and Accommodation   298
Consolidation: Copyright   299
Pressure on Resources: Expedients – New Methods – New Maps, a Retreat from
    Austerity   300

31 The Post-War Trigonometrical Survey and the Third Geodetic Levelling 1945–1960   307
Post-War Triangulation: Primary Triangulation – The Secondary and Lower Order
    Triangulation – Ancillary Operations – Electromagnetic Distance-Measurements
    and the Scale of the Triangulation – Azimuth Observations – Other Supplementary
    Work – Comparison with the Principal Triangulation – Connections with Other
    Countries   307
Post-War Levelling: The Second Geodetic Levelling of Scotland – The Third Geodetic
    Levelling – Lower Order Levelling   312

32 The Restoration of the Survey – The Reappraisal 1961–1968   318
Revision   318
The Estimates Committee 1962–3: Staffing – Consultation – Marketing and Revenue –
    Ministerial Responsibility for the Ordnance Survey   319
Field Survey – a Reappraisal: Place-names – Land Registration   324
Metric Maps   327
Map Production and Publication: Repayment Work   327
Basic Ordnance Survey Policy   330

33 The Topographical Survey After The Second World War   332
New Methods: 1:1250 Resurvey – Six-Inch Resurvey – Contours   332
Revision: The Overhaul Revision – The Revision of the National Grid Plans – The
    Control of Continuous Revision – Field Methods for One-inch Revision   336
Tide Lines   339
Archaeology and the Post-War Survey: Research and Recording – Field
    Reconnaissance and Survey   340

34 Geodetic Developments 1960–1974   344
The Readjustment of the Triangulation   344
Satellite Geodesy   346
Geoidal Sections   347
Levelling Connections with Europe   347
The National Gravity Reference Net   348

35 The Restoration of the Survey – A New Home and New Aims 1968–1978   350
The New Headquarters Building   350
Staff Affairs and Training   351
Mapping: Automated Cartography   352
Computerized Planning   354
Marketing   354
Management Accounting and Accountable Management   355
New Aims   356

Plates

Appendices   361

  I   Roy's General Instructions for the Officers of Engineers employed in Surveying, with
     Appendix containing practical observations on Surveying   363
 II Dawson's Course of Instructions in Military Surveying and Plan Drawing   366
III Colby's Instructions for the Interior Survey of Ireland, 1825   367

IV   Ordnance Survey Contours 1847–90   373
 V   Recommendations of the Dorington Committee   376
VI   Recommendations of the Davidson Committee   378

Index   379

List
of
Plates

Roy's Triangulation 1787–8   1
Ramsden's 3-foot 'Royal Society' theodolite   2
Ramsden's Zenith Sector   3
Part of one-inch map of Kent (1801) (a)   4
Old Series one-inch map, part of sheet 1, Essex (1805)
Surveyors' 2-inch drawings for Old Series, drawing no. 7 (1810) (a)   5
                                        drawing no. 321 (1822) (b)
Six-inch map of Ireland, part of sheet 19, County Monaghan (1836)   6
Old Series one-inch map, part of sheet 52 (1835)   7
Part of 1:528 plan of Sunderland, surveyed 1856   8
Colby's Compensation Bars   9
Airy's Zenith Sector   10
The Principal Triangulation with adjustment figures   11
1:2500 sheet, Wilts 48/8 (1880), showing Ludgershall Castle   12
The one-inch map in colour, part of sheet 21 (1903)   13
Fundamental Bench Mark   14
Part of Killarney Tourist Map (1913)   15
One-inch Popular Edition, England and Wales, part of sheet 119 (1918)   16
Part of Map of Roman Britain, 4th edition (1978)   17
The Primary Retriangulation, with adjustment figures   18
1:10 000, Regular Derived Series, part of sheet TQ 20 NW (1972)   19
Thompson-Watts stereoplotter mark I   20
One-inch Seventh Series, part of sheet 55 (1969)   21
Quarter-inch Fifth Series, part of sheet 11 (1978)   22
Geodimeter 8 and Tellurometer MRA2   23
1:25 000 Second Series, part of sheet SY 29/39 (1973)   24
1:1250 instrumental survey, tacheometric survey and air survey   25
The new building at Maybush, Southampton   26
1:50 000 Second Series, part of sheet 94 (1976)   27

List
of
Principal
Contributors

	Chapters
Dr J. H. ANDREWS, Associate Professor of Geography, Trinity College Dublin, author of *A Paper Landscape – the Ordnance Survey in Nineteenth-Century Ireland* (OUP)	7, 13, 20
MAJOR-GENERAL R. C. A. EDGE CB, former Director General, Ordnance Survey	27, 31, 34
Dr J. B. HARLEY, Montefiore Reader in Geography, University of Exeter; author of *Ordnance Survey Maps – A Descriptive Manual*	1 (with Y. O'Donoghue) 2, 4, 6; (with W. A. Seymour) sections on place-names in 5, 8, 16, 32
LIEUTENANT-COLONEL J. S. O. JELLY, formerly of the Survey of India and of the Ordnance Survey	sections on topographical surveying in 5, 16
I. MUMFORD, Mapping and Charting Establishment, Royal Engineers; Past President of the British Cartographic Society	15*, 17*, 18*, 19*
YOLANDE O'DONOGHUE, British Library Map Library	22, 23*, 25*, 26; (with J. B. Harley) 2, 4, 6
BRIGADIER K. M. PAPWORTH OBE, MC, formerly of the Ordnance Survey and former Chief Survey Officer, Ordnance Survey of Northern Ireland	3, 12, 21*
E. J. S. PARSONS, Deputy Librarian and Secretary of the Library, Bodleian Library, Oxford	8*, 9*, 10, 11*
C. W. PHILLIPS OBE, former Head of Archaeology Division, Ordnance Survey; directed excavation of the Sutton Hoo burial ship	14, 24*, 28*, sections on archaeology in 5, 16, 33
COLONEL W. A. SEYMOUR OBE, former Assistant Director, Training and Information, and former Deputy Director, Field Survey, Ordnance Survey	29, 30, 32, 35; sections on cartography in 5, 18, 19, 25 and on field surveying in 33; (with J. B. Harley) sections on place-names in 5, 8, 16, 32

Note: Chapters marked * contain short sections by other main contributors

Other contributors

Major-General A. H. Dowson, formerly Director General, Ordnance Survey, Lieutenant-Colonel H. E. M. Newman, Brigadier D. E. O. Thackwell, Brigadier R. P. Wheeler, all formerly of the Ordnance Survey	miscellaneous material
Marjorie Seymour	index

Acknowledgements

The Assistant Director, Ordnance Survey of the Republic of Ireland, for permission to make use of the records at the Ordnance Survey Office, Dublin.
Harry Margary, Lympne Castle, Kent, for permission to use parts of the text accompanying Volumes 1 and 2 of *The Old Series Ordnance Survey Maps of England and Wales*.
Diana Marshallsay, of the University of Southampton, for advice on the referencing of Parliamentary Papers.

Preface

No comprehensive history of the Ordnance Survey has hitherto existed. Short accounts were written by Captain H. S. Palmer in 1873 and by Lieutenant-Colonel Pilkington White in 1886, but both books dealt only superficially and briefly with the earlier history. Sir Charles Close's *Early Years of the Ordnance Survey*, covering the period 1784–1846, is of great historical value as he quotes from important documents since lost, but the subject matter is incomplete and the treatment of it uneven. The Progress Reports of the Survey itself do not provide a continuous record, since the first did not appear until 1856 and none were published during the ten years after the Second World War.

Much of the material for the new *History* has therefore had to be obtained from sources such as documents in the Public Records Office and Parliamentary papers. There was no lack of original material, and the editor and authors became increasingly aware that, had there been more time for research, many other matters of interest might have been disclosed. However, as the authors' work was voluntary, the time at their disposal was usually limited.

The present *History of the Ordnance Survey* was first conceived in 1963 by E. J. S. Parsons of the Bodleian Library, together with J. B. Harley, then of Liverpool University, and R. A. Skelton, of the Map Room, British Museum, as a collaborative collection of essays by various authors. Initially it was intended that the book should be published as a private venture, and during 1963 and 1964 Parsons invited several potential authors to contribute. At the same time he sought advice and assistance from the Director General of the Ordnance Survey, Major General A. H. Dowson, who suggested, as an alternative, that the work might be undertaken as an official history and published by HM Stationery Office. Parsons at once accepted this proposal, and the Ordnance Survey set about obtaining the government's approval. This was eventually given in 1967, after the support of the Royal Society, the Royal Geographical Society and the Institution of Royal Engineers, had been successfully invoked.

Once approval had been obtained, the project was put on a more formal basis by the appointment of R. A. Skelton as editor, whose main task was to co-ordinate the work of the authors, and by the creation of a History Board, under the Director General, to monitor progress. Skelton continued as editor until his death in 1970, which tragically occurred in a road accident when he was on his way to a History Board meeting in Southampton. The editorship then passed to Major General R. C. A. Edge, but in 1974 pressure of other work compelled him to withdraw.

Progress so far had been disappointingly slow; although several chapters were being written, only three had been completed, and a few were still without authors. The Director General, Major General B. St G. Irwin, concluded that a full-time editor was needed if the *History* was to be finished within a reasonable time. Accordingly, he offered this post to W. A. Seymour – who was about to retire from the Ordnance Survey – for two years, on the understanding that a final draft of the manuscript would be completed within this time.

This draft was ready in July 1976, but a further difficulty had arisen. The original plan for the *History* had divided it into two parts: a chronological narrative covering historical events, followed by a series of technical chapters on geodesy, cartography, administration, etc. The plan had undergone modification in detail but not in structure, the 1976 draft consisting of eight narrative and eight technical chapters. The fatal disadvantage of the plan – the unavoidable duplication of subject matter – was now revealed. Dr R. P. Beckinsale of Oxford University, who kindly read and commented on the draft, considered that the text needed to be substantially restructured and recompiled into shorter chapters. The History Board accepted this criticism and advice, and the editor undertook to rearrange the text into a single chronological narrative in – as far as possible – a consistent style. The revised draft, consisting of thirty-five chapters, was finished early in 1978. Some technical episodes from the original technical section were retained as separate chapters in correct time sequence, but others lost their identity on being absorbed into the general narrative. One consequence of this was that the work of several authors became dispersed throughout the book, making it difficult to acknowledge their contributions in any simple way.

In 1978 the Ordnance Survey was undergoing a major governmental review, and there appeared to be no possibility of publication by HM Stationery Office, as originally planned, or by the Ordnance Survey itself. In these circumstances the present Director General, Mr W. P. Smith, decided to seek the co-operation of a private publisher.

W.A.S.
March 1980

Publisher's Note

The notes are of two kinds: footnotes on the page, which are explanatory notes on points in the text, and references to sources, listed at the end of each chapter. The main abbreviations used in the references are:

CR = Ordnance Survey Central Registry File
OS = Ordnance Survey
OSLB = Ordnance Survey Letter Book
OSR = Ordnance Survey Report
Phil. Trans. = Philosophical Transactions of the Royal Society
PP = Parliamentary Papers
PRO = Public Records Office
RS = Royal Society

1
The Origins
of the
Ordnance
Survey

... every Prince should have ... a Draught of his Country and Dominions, to see how the ground lies in the several parts of them, which highest, which lowest; what respect they have to one another, and to the Sea; how the Rivers flow, and why; how the Mountains lie, how Heaths, and how the Marches. Such a Map or Survey would be useful both in time of War and Peace, and many good observations might be made by it, not only as to Natural History and Philosophy, but also in order to the perfect improvement of a Country.

Thomas Burnet, *The Theory of the Earth* ... (London 1684)

In the latter part of the eighteenth century official mapping in Britain had fallen behind that in other European countries such as Austria, Denmark and France, and even in parts of her own colonial possessions, especially those in India and eastern North America. That England – the first industrial nation – should find herself in the lagging sector was beginning to attract the notice of some professional observers of her scientific progress. Sir Joseph Banks, for example, in his presidential address in 1791 on the occasion of the award of the Copley Medal of the Royal Society to Major James Rennell*, compared the situation in India, an underdeveloped country, with the state of regional mapping in Britain:

> Would I could say that England proud as she is of being esteemed by surrounding nations the Queen of Scientific improvement, could boast of a general Map as well executed as the Majors delineation of Bengal and Baher, a tract of Country considerably larger in extent than the whole of Great Britain and Ireland; ... the accuracy of his particular surveys stands unrivaled by the most laboured County Maps this nation has hitherto been able to produce.[1]

It was in the same year that the Board of Ordnance decided to continue the trigonometrical survey in southern England started under General William Roy, and it is possible, in view of Banks's intimate association with that enterprise, that his remarks contain a political note of exhortation as well as one of censure. In explaining the lateness of government intervention in British map-making it would be wrong to attribute this solely to official apathy. Users of maps – both official and private – were frequently satisfied with the range and quality of the surveys available to them. The age into which the national survey was born was already one of considerable cartographic sophistication; improved maps of counties, towns, estates, enclosures, parklands, rivers, canals and turnpike roads, as well as marine charts, to name only the most familiar types, were becoming available in ever increasing numbers. The land surveyor had acquired a greatly enhanced professional status in the eighteenth century, while the London map trade had emerged from a period of stagnation to become a world centre of map engraving and publication. These facts suggest that the Ordnance Survey could have been conceived on the crest of a wave of improvement rather than being born out of despair with the existing provision for maps.

Reality lies somewhere between the two interpretations. It is true that there were periodical complaints about the topographical maps of the British regions, but the effect of public opinion, at a local and even a national level, was to spark off imaginative proposals for their improvement. Step by step, from Tudor to Georgian times, better maps replaced the inferior in a piecemeal fashion. All that can be said is that neither public opinion nor official expediency was sufficient to force the government to shoulder responsibility for the basic surveys required by the nation. The existing ways of providing maps – by a haphazard blend of private surveys, military mapping when invasion scares arose, and

---

* James Rennell, Major, Bengal Engineers, appointed first Surveyor General of Bengal by Clive in 1767.

scientific observations (occasionally helped along by a little official patronage) – must have been perceived as adequate in method and end-product.

A result of this slow drift towards better maps was that when a national survey was finally founded in Britain, it was not so much a new beginning as a fusion of existing trends. Three sets of influences, often overlapping, were of particular importance in establishing the Survey and in shaping the characteristics it assumed in the early nineteenth century. These were military surveying particularly under the auspices of the Board of Ordnance, the developments in civilian cartography as represented in the work of county surveyors in the second half of the eighteenth century, and surveying done with scientific objectives, supported either directly or implicitly by the Royal Society.

The Board of Ordnance and the Development of Military Cartography in Britain

The Board of Ordnance, to which the national survey of Great Britain owes its name, was one of the more ancient institutions of the country. Its roots have been traced to the Middle Ages and its beginnings were connected with the establishment of the Royal Arsenal at the Tower of London. In Elizabethan times it was made a Department of State and subsequently it was maintained by a separate vote from Parliament, with the power of making payments not previously sanctioned when unforeseen emergencies arose. This financial flexibility was to be a critical advantage in the permanent establishment of the national survey under the Board of Ordnance for, until 1811, it was supported out of the Board's contingency funds rather than by annual Parliamentary grant.[2] The Board had a permanent organization long before a standing army was created in Britain,[3] and was headed by a powerful office-holder, the Master General of the Ordnance, sometimes a distinguished soldier and often a person with cabinet rank. His powers of patronage and persuasion, as well as the limits of his influence in the face of a tightening Treasury control of all military expenditure, are neatly illustrated by some of the conflicting policies to which the Ordnance Survey was subjected in its early years.

The Board of Ordnance was a shambling, complex, and even contradictory organization, but it is necessary to understand at least its basic structure and functions to appreciate how the Ordnance Survey was contained within this administrative giant. The most important fact is that throughout the period of the Board's control of the national survey (up to 1855), cartography represented only a small and virtually insignificant sector of its total responsibilities. Even with respect to map-making, home surveys were only part of much wider duties, especially in the late eighteenth and early nineteenth centuries. The primary responsibilities of the Board of Ordnance, as described by its historians, were to act as a custodian of the lands, depots and forts required for the defence of the realm and its overseas possessions, and as the supplier of munitions and equipment to both the Army and the Navy.[4] At the same time the Board was a civil organization. The confusing aspect is that by the mid eighteenth century, this civil body had started to pay, maintain, educate and organize military forces of its own. These were the so-called Ordnance Corps (of which the Artillery and Engineers are the best known) who were to provide the officers for the Ordnance Survey. These Corps were quite independent from the Army and its administrators, a fact of some relevance to the technical development of the Ordnance Survey, especially after the reforms of the late eighteenth century, when the Army began to develop an independent cartographic service within the Quartermaster-General's Department. Even in appearance, the blue-coated Ordnance officers were boldly distinguished from the redcoats of the Army.

The Board of Ordnance also maintained a series of ancillary establishments. Abroad there was a chain of Ordnance depots and stations to match the spread of Empire and its staging posts. In Britain there were also Engineer stations for a territorial organization based on 'Districts',[5] and specialist buildings such as powder-mills and laboratories at Faversham and Waltham Abbey, as well as the Royal Observatory at Greenwich. The Tower of London was used for a variety of activities ranging from the manufacture of arms to the copying of maps and plans, and at Woolwich a Royal Military Academy existed to train officers for the Artillery and Engineers. Only small parts of this vast structure are of direct relevance to the history of the Ordnance Survey.

As far as cartography is concerned, the most consistently important aspects of the Board's responsibilities were those connected with military engineering. From the reign of Henry VIII onwards the principal energies of the military surveyors and engineers were directed to fortification and harbour improvement. The essence of Tudor warfare lay in the attack and defence of fortified places, and because in England the principal threat came from the sea, it was the strong points along the 'invasion coasts' that produced the most notable examples of the military surveyor's art. Nowhere is this more evident than in the detailed series of plans which characterize the cartographic records of such towns as Dover, Portsmouth, Plymouth, Hull and Berwick,[6] which provided, for a map-minded statesman such as William Cecil, Lord Burghley, information vital for the planning of national defence. The relationship to the present argument is that here was an aspect of cartography which owed its existence largely to the Crown, because the principal opportunities for practising military architecture and engineering – of which the making of 'plats' was an integral part – lay in the royal service. From the mid sixteenth century onwards, the office of 'Surveyor of the King's (or Queen's) works', held by practitioners such as Richard Lee, John Rogers and Richard Popinjay, played a central role in the work of fortification.[7]

For most of the seventeenth century similar offices were held under the Crown, but it was not until the Board of Ordnance was reorganized in 1683 that a major step forward was taken in rationalizing the engineering service. In a warrant of that year, there was set out a codification of the engineer establishment in terms both of personnel and of the distribution of Ordnance depots such as those at the Tower of London, Chatham, Portsmouth, Tilbury, Sheerness, Woolwich, Plymouth and Hull.[8] These regulations did much to determine the geographical pattern as well as the character of military surveying in eighteenth-century Britain. Geographically, the locations of the main Ordnance depots, as at Portsmouth and Plymouth, emerged as nuclei of mapping operations which retained their significance long after the foundation of the Ordnance Survey. The cartographic qualifications demanded of the Chief Engineer in 1683 speak for themselves:

> . . . to be well-skilled in all the parts of the Mathematicks, more particularly in Stereometry, Altemetry, and Geodœsia. To take Distances, Heights, Depths, Surveys of Land, Measures of solid Bodies, and to cut any part of ground to a proportion given; . . . and to be perfect in Architecture, civil and military, . . . to draw and design the situation of any place, in their due Prospects, Uprights, and Perspective; . . . To keep perfect draughts of . . . the Fortifications, Forts, and Fortresses of Our Kingdoms, their situation, figure, and profile . . .
> To make Plots or Models of all manner of Fortifications, both Forts or Camps, commanded by Us to be erected for Our Service . . .[9]

It was to this office that Sir Bernard de Gomme,* a veteran of the Civil War, was appointed in the same year, but even the two 'ordinary Engineers' on the establishment were to be 'young men . . . bred up in the art and knowledge of Fortification'.[10]

From such foundations was built a 'scientific corps' under the Board of Ordnance during the course of the eighteenth century. Its two principal branches were the Artillery, the Royal Warrant for the first two companies of which was granted in 1716,[11] and the Corps of Engineers (consisting only of officers), which was given military establishment in 1717 and military rank from 1757 onwards.[12] From 1720, too, there were the beginnings of a systematic technical education for officers entering these Corps. The first proposal to set up an academy dates from 1720, but the Royal Military Academy as it is generally understood was founded at Woolwich by a Royal Warrant of 30 April 1741.[13] For military engineering and its cartographical by-products, the importance of the Woolwich Academy was that it helped to transmit some of the theory and practice of European military science into the British service, both through the medium of recommended text-books and in the employment on its staff of expert foreign instructors.[14] Such was John Muller, born in Germany in 1699, first employed by the Board of Ordnance in the Tower of London and, after the foundation of the Woolwich Academy, engaged as its headmaster and later as professor of fortifications and artillery.[15] He was justifiably described by a contemporary as 'the scholastic father of all the great engineers this country employed for forty years'. For the future Ordnance Survey, the Academy was to train a nucleus of scientifically-minded officers sufficiently versed in mathematics to be able to direct the Trigonometrical Survey. As a result of their education and training, the officers of the Ordnance Corps were often closely associated with the scientific life of the nation, sometimes appearing to have stronger links with the Royal Society than with the Army. The Duke of Richmond, who became Master General in 1782, and William Roy were both Fellows, and this degree of identification provides a background to the events leading to the formation of the Ordnance Survey.

Until they were moved to Southampton in 1841 the offices of the Survey, the drawing room and its stores, were all located in the Tower of London. The Drawing Room of the Tower, apart from its notable contribution to the training of British military surveyors and draughtsmen in the eighteenth century, was an integral part of the prehistory of the national survey. Although its origins are obscure, it may already have been functioning as a cartographic establishment in the days of De Gomme who died at the Tower in 1685, and certainly, from the early eighteenth century there are occasional

___

* Sir Bernard de Gomme, 1620–85. A Dutch military engineer who fought in the Civil War on the Royalist side. In 1661 he was made Engineer-in-Chief of all the king's castles and fortifications in England and Wales and in 1683 was appointed Surveyor General of Ordnance.

references to 'clerks' and draughtsmen employed there.[16] It was administered by the Board of Ordnance as part of its headquarters services in the Tower and after the middle of the century the numbers who worked and trained there rose sharply from around a dozen in the 1750s to nearly fifty at times in the early 1780s.[17] Although there were other drawing rooms maintained by the engineer establishment, both in Britain and abroad, a particular function of that in the Tower was to train and supply surveyors and draughtsmen. Young cadets were taken on from the age of eleven or twelve,[18] and instructed by the chief draughtsman and suitable 'mathematical masters' in elementary mathematics, drawing, and especially in the draughting and copying of fortification plans and military topographical maps.[19] Through the continuous copying of fairly standard models the Tower draughtsmen developed a recognizable style, which was retained when they were posted to other engineer establishments, or even into staff appointments in the Army when an influential commander-in-chief was successful in prizing a suitable candidate out of the Board of Ordnance. The Tower draughtsmen held civilian status in the eighteenth century, although some were later commissioned into the Engineers. Although there was no hard-and-fast distinction, the practical skills of these draughtsmen were complementary to the somewhat more theoretical training of the Woolwich cadets and it was logical that they should work in harness. Most engineer establishments, as the contemporary military text-books advocated, employed draughtsmen in both surveying and map-copying duties.

The availability of such skilled personnel, although it would be wrong to imply that the Tower of London was their sole source, helped to underpin a second tradition in British military map-making, that of the survey of topographical maps. In some respects this is of more direct relevance than the mapping of fortifications and arsenals to the genesis of the Ordnance Survey, for the purpose of such surveys was to furnish smaller-scale maps of the countryside through which armies might have to move. Even in Tudor times, when fortification was the main focus of military engineering, the beginnings of military topographical surveying can be observed. In some European countries it was sufficiently recognized by the end of the sixteenth century to have a number of text-books devoted primarily to its practice,[20] and even in Britain, heavily dependent on Europe for its military innovations, the manuals of such mathematical exponents as Leonard Digges provided instruction in topographical maps and in drawing 'plats of cities'.[21] Although there are a number of sixteenth century maps of fairly extensive stretches of coastline in southern England – for example the 1587 map of parts of Sussex covering 'all the places of descente' along the sea coast[22] – the seventeenth century saw little progress in Britain in this type of cartography. One reason for this may have been that the new county maps, especially those of Christopher Saxton, were regarded as adequate for military planning on a regional scale. This seems to have been the case in the Civil War and not until the mid eighteenth century was there a marked expansion of British military surveying, which thereafter, in one theatre of war or another, continued unabated.

Among these new military surveys, in which Britain shared the experience of other European lands, one of the most remarkable and perhaps the most formative for the Ordnance Survey was that of Scotland undertaken between 1747 and 1755. Some historians have, indeed, regarded it as almost *the* founding episode.[23] At a scale of one inch to 1000 yards, and covering the whole mainland of Scotland, it was the most extensive survey of its kind to be made in eighteenth-century Britain, and it had no real precursor or successor. From the contemporary accounts of the map by William Roy and Aaron Arrowsmith, and from modern studies by R. A. Skelton and D. G. Moir,[24] it appears that it originated in the aftermath of the 1745 rebellion. It was in fact initiated not by any far-seeing government minister, but by the engineer officer on the spot, Lieutenant-Colonel David Watson (1713?–61), who was serving in 1747 as Deputy Quartermaster-General in the military district of North Britain. He was faced with a dearth of adequate maps in connection with a programme of road building and fort construction,* and his proposal for making a military map to aid the pacification of the Highlands, put forward in July or August 1747, received the full support of his commander-in-chief, the Duke of Cumberland. However, for the future of national mapping, by far the most seminal appointment was that of William Roy to execute the survey. Although little is known of Roy's early life it has been established that he was born on 4 May 1726 at Miltonhead, Lanarkshire (now Strathclyde), Scotland.[25] The only formal education he received was at Carluke parish school and the grammar school at Lanark where he was presumably 'soundly drilled in the elements of Latin and mathematics'.[26] Both his father and grandfather were factors to the lairds of Milton and under such tutelage he might have

---

* The best available map of Scotland, albeit only at a scale of one inch to 13½ miles, was probably the single sheet 'A New and Correct Mercator's Map of North Britain' by John Elphinstone. Printed for A. Millar, London 6 March 1745. John Elphinstone, a Practitioner Engineer, brought out the map on the eve of the Jacobite rebellion, and despite its limitations it was extensively used by both sides.

picked up the rudiments of estate surveying which were later to be adapted with such good effect in the survey of Scotland. In addition, and in view of his later career this seems probable, he may also have been apprenticed as a civilian draughtsman by the Board of Ordnance, finding employment in the drawing room of the engineer establishment in Edinburgh.[27] But however he acquired his carto-graphic training there is no doubt that Roy brought to bear, on the Scottish survey, techniques and styles which were being developed at the same time in the Tower of London. This influence was reinforced when he was later joined by a recruit directly from the Tower establishment, Paul Sandby, 'the chief Draftsman of the plan',[28] later to become famous as the 'Father of English water colour art', who had followed his elder brother Thomas into the Ordnance service.[29]

It was Roy's contribution to the organization of the project which marked him out as a future leader in cartographic matters. As he recalled later, as an Assistant Quartermaster to Watson 'it fell to my lot to begin . . . the execution of that map'.[30] For almost two years he was apparently the only trained surveyor engaged in field work – which is perhaps a measure of his technical competence – but in 1748, following an increase in the engineer establishment in Scotland, he was joined by several junior surveyors: Hugh Debbeig, William Dundas, Howse, John Manson and John Williams;[31]* and eventu-ally six field parties were at work. The finished maps represent a British variant of a contemporary European map culture, both in the methods of survey[32] and in the drawing conventions employed.[33] Skelton describes the surviving fair copies of Roy's maps as

> . . . drawn in pen-and-ink and wash. The customary colour conventions are used: blue-green for water features, green for woodland, yellow for land under cultivation, buff for moors, grey washes of various tones for relief, solid red for houses, red outline for formal grounds, brown (a single line) for roads. Hill features are delineated by brush strokes laid in the direction of the slope, supplemented here and there by rock- or cliff-drawing; gradient is carefully differentiated, the steeper slopes being indicated by strokes of darker tone laid more closely. The vocabulary of symbols is very small, and limited almost entirely to land-cover: trees for woodland, parallel hatching for tilled land, the usual moorland symbol, stipple for sands or shoals.[34]

The influence of this remarkable survey on the development of military cartography in Britain and, in particular, on the establishment of the national survey, is by no means obvious, and it is sometimes difficult to reconstruct the channels by which the ideas it embodied were carried forward into the rest of the eighteenth century. In a sense the Scottish survey was overtaken by events and before it was completed and (in Roy's words) 'many of its imperfections no doubt remedied',[35] the rumours of war in America and Europe meant that the trained engineers employed on it were transferred to more urgent tasks. The ending of the Scottish survey was also a turning point in Roy's life for he was to begin a military career which, although it eventually set him in a senior position in which he could influence the establishment of the national survey, for many years kept him preoccupied with duties that gave him little chance to capitalize on his experience.

In December 1755 Roy was appointed a Practitioner-Engineer[36] and less than a fortnight later, in January 1756, he was commissioned Lieutenant in the 53rd (Shropshire) Regiment of Foot; there-after throughout his career he held double rank – and even simultaneous appointments – in the Army and the Corps of Engineers, the former rank always being the higher. In 1756 Roy, together with David Dundas, accompanied Colonel Watson as he toured the country from Dover to Milford Haven, reconnoitring the coastal areas in preparation for the expected French invasion.[37]

The Seven Years War (1756–63) was to provide Roy with his only experience of active service. He took part in the unsuccessful expedition against Rochefort in 1757 and in the Battle of Minden in 1759. His printed plan of the battle,[38] used in the trial of Lord George Sackville, is the only surviving document of the many sketches, plans and notes which he made at this time. Evidently distinguishing himself in Germany, Roy was appointed in quick succession Captain in the Engineers (1759), Deputy Quartermaster-General of the British Forces in Germany (1760), Major of Foot and Deputy Quartermaster-General of the Forces in South Britain (1761) and Lieutenant-Colonel in the Army (1762)**.

One result of the transfer of British military activity to the European theatre was that interest in Scotland waned and the need for a comprehensive military map of that country largely vanished. Copies of many of the Scottish maps were retained by David Watson until his death in 1761, when they passed into the Royal Library at Windsor; others were in the possession of the Duke of

---

* At this time only three out of this team of seven – Debbeig, Manson and Williams – were Practitioner Engineers (the lowest commissioned rank given by the Board of Ordnance in the Corps of Engineers: until 1757 the engineer officers had no recognized military rank, but after this date Practitioner Engineer equated to Ensign in the Army).

** His subsequent promotions in the Army were to Colonel (1777), and Major-General (1781); in the Corps of Engineers he remained Lieutenant-Colonel.

Cumberland but again, on his death in 1765 they were deposited in the Royal Library. Thus the maps ceased to be working military documents. Although they were referred to from time to time, they served neither as a model for similar surveys in Great Britain nor, until Arrowsmith obtained permission to consult them in the first decade of the nineteenth century, were they used to improve the published cartography of Scotland.[39] On the face of it Roy's map seemed destined to become almost a forgotten survey; but for two circumstances this could well have been so.

The first was the expansion of the geographical area of activity of British military surveyors in the second half of the eighteenth century. After 1756 they were transferred from Scotland to regions where, owing to military and colonial aspirations, British interest was concentrated. Viewed in this light the survey of Scotland belongs to the same stemma as the Murray map of Quebec (1760–1), the Holland survey of the east coast of North America (1764–75), the De Brahm map of Florida (1765–71), the Rennell survey of Bengal (1765–77) and the Vallancey map of Ireland (1778–90). It is true that these surveys varied in their precise objectives and execution but they represented a similar basic response to the same perceived needs of underdeveloped 'colonial' territories. And even when their sponsors varied, as from the Board of Trade to the East India Company, much of the work was entrusted to military surveyors. One of the engineers who had worked under Roy in Scotland, Debbeig, was posted to North America, and in the mid 1760s he submitted a proposal for a military survey of the eastern part of that country. Although it was not adopted, it is of interest that as part of the summary of his career, presumably offered as a *curriculum vitae* to indicate his competence to carry out the project, he referred to his work under Roy:

> . . . he was seven years employed upon the Survey of Scotland (the greatest work of this sort ever performed by British Subjects and perhaps for the fine Representations of the Country not to be equaled in the World).[40]

Clearly the Highland survey had not been forgotten in North America, and to this direct reference there can be added the stylistic similarities between the Murray Map of the St Lawrence and the Roy map of Scotland. The value of such surveys being made by the military engineers abroad can hardly have been lost on the influential men in England who were subsequently to play a leading role in the establishment of the Ordnance Survey. Copies of surveys certainly found their way into the collections of George III. The Duke of Richmond, who was Master General of the Ordnance at the time of the revival of the trigonometrical survey in 1791, had received copies of some of Samuel Holland's North American plans; and Sir Joseph Banks was fully informed about developments in the survey of India. Once the geographical context is broadened there is no real hiatus in British military topographical surveying from the 1750s to the 1780s. The plans of Kent and of the Plymouth and Portsmouth districts, made after 1780, which were later embodied into the published Ordnance Survey maps, belong to the same cartographical family as Roy's map of Scotland.

The second and more important factor which ensured the survival of the concepts underlying the Scottish survey was Roy himself. It is clear that his experience as a young man had left an indelible impression. At some date after 1763 he found a pretext for borrowing the complete set of the maps of Scotland from George III (he retained them for the rest of his life), which he used for archaeological purposes, and which seemed to serve as a reminder of the need for extending such a survey into England. But it was his professional military career as a staff officer at Army Headquarters and in the Corps of Engineers which gave him most opportunity for canvassing the need for adequate national surveys. In the work both of the Board of Ordnance (directed from the Tower of London) and of the Quartermaster-General's Department (at the Horse Guards) maps were accepted as part of the most advanced military thinking of the day. In his role as Deputy Quartermaster-General, Roy's duties included the planning of marches and encampments, as well as the organization of the subsistence of the army in the field. It was about this time, according to his own later testimony, that he formulated a plan for the triangulation of the whole country, into which the map of Scotland was to be integrated:

> On the conclusion of the peace of 1763, it came for the first time under the consideration of government, to make a general survey of the whole island at the public cost. Towards the execution of this work, the direction of which was to have been committed to our author, the map of Scotland was to have been made subservient, by extending the great triangles quite to the northern extremity of the island, and filling them in from the original map. Thus that imperfect work would have been effectually completed, and the nation would have reaped the benefit of what had already been done, at a very moderate expense.[41]

The maps arising from this compilation were to be at a scale of one inch to one mile and based on accurate triangulation: Roy had already conceived the basic design for the early Ordnance Survey. The scheme did not go further, perhaps because it would have been (in his own words) a 'Work of much time and labour, and attended with great Expence to the Government'.[42]

The next instance of Roy's advocacy of a national survey is recorded in 1766. By this date he had been appointed, under a Royal Warrant of 19 July 1765, to 'inspect, survey and make Reports from time to time of the state of the Coasts and Districts of the Country adjacent to the Coasts of this Kingdom and Islands thereunto belonging';[43] but the term 'surveys' did not apply solely to maps: it was a generic word referring to the whole process – written and graphic – of inspecting and reporting on fortifications, which was a normal Board of Ordnance function. To Roy, however, maps were so fundamental to any professional assignment that his report on the defensive state of the nation was accompanied by a 'General Map of the Southeast Part of England'.[44] In the associated written document he explained how the 'Positions of Camps represented by streight lines' were strategically placed 'where the several great Roads . . . to the Capital do cross the Rivers or Ranges of Hills'. Conscious of what might be 'defective with regard to the expression of the Ground', Roy noted that 'an Attempt is made at the bottom of the Map, to represent something of the General Section of the Country'.[45] It is clear that his mind was again dwelling on the need for better surveys, and in the following year he took the opportunity to resubmit his earlier scheme in a modified and less expensive form. In a paper entitled 'Considerations on the Propriety of making a General Military Map of England, with the Method proposed for carrying it into Execution, & an Estimate of the Expence',[46] he outlined a scheme in 1766 which must be regarded as one of the basic documents in the establishment of the Ordnance Survey.

The principal economy in the revised scheme was to make use of the new printed county surveys, many of them at a scale of one inch to one mile or larger, which were beginning to be published at the time. Roy was obviously impressed by the revolution in privately sponsored regional cartography and he noted:

> THERE are already good Surveys made by different people, of the undermentioned Counties. Viz: Middlesex, Herfordshire, Berkshire, Hampshire, Dorsetshire, Devonshire, Herefordshire and Shropshire; There is also a tolerable Map of Sussex and another of Cornwall; That of Surrey is almost finished; Kent, Bedfordshire, Buckinghamshire, Oxfordshire, Northamptonshire, Huntingdonshire, Worcestershire, Cumberland & the Bishoprick of Durham, are carrying on in the same manner.
>
> SUCH a number of Counties being already either surveyed or surveying, it is not to be doubted, but that in time, the others will likewise be done, especially if Subscriptions for the County Surveyors, are set on Foot in each County, & encouraged by Government, or even by people of Influence in the respective Districts.[47]

At the same time he reviewed the maps not only as a geodesist but also as a military topographer:

> THESE County Maps are sufficiently exact, in what regards their geometrical measurement, for common purposes, but are extremely defective with respect to the topographical representation of the ground, giving scarcely any Idea, or at least but a very imperfect one, of what is remarkable strong or weak in the nature of the Country.[48]

The main criticism concerning the lack of adequate relief-portrayal on the county maps was a fair one. It was based on Roy's experience as a staff officer and engineer; he recognized that a representation of only two dimensions of landscape was of little value either for the selection of 'strong ground' for field fortification as advocated in contemporary text-books, or for the movement of troops through a countryside under attack. This deficiency, together with the absence of over-all geodetic control owing to the piecemeal nature of the private surveys, led Roy to recommend that the county maps ought to be strengthened and supplemented. In the first place, again foreshadowing developments after the foundation of the Ordnance Survey, he proposed to measure a British arc of meridian to assist the accurate determination of latitudes and longitudes and to provide additional information about the figure of the Earth:

> IN carrying on the Serieses of Triangles, it would be useful to trace one grand Meridian line, thro' the whole extent of the Island, marked by Obelisks from distance to distance like that thro' France. And that the Northern Extremity of this Meridian might fall to the Westward of Dungsbay Head in Caithness, it would be necessary to carry the South-End (where it is supposed to be begun) at least as far west as Dorsetshire. The prolongation of the Meridian of the Royal Observatory at Greenwich, would fall into the sea in Norfolk.[49]

In the second place, equally anticipating the early work of the Trigonometrical Survey, Roy saw that a proper scientific triangulation of the whole country would be required. This would begin with a measurement of the 'great Base of the first Triangle'. It was to be

> six or Eight miles in length, measured with the utmost exactness on the Sands of the Sea Shore, or in one of the open level Counties, such as Cambridgeshire or Wiltshire, and afterwards reduced to the Level of the Sea.[50]

From this foundation the principal and secondary triangulations could be extended. Only 'proper persons' were to be employed, 'furnished with good Instruments', and they were to observe 'Serieses of Triangles along the Coast, and along the remarkable Ridges of Hills and principal Rivers'. In this way 'the Situations of all the material points would be truely fixed with regard to one another, and thence the Great Outlines of the Country would be truely determined'.[51]

Additional topographical information would have been provided in several ways. First, detail on the county maps would be used to fill in 'the smaller Interior parts of each triangle'. Second, no doubt to ensure that the military specification of the survey was adequate, 'the Line of the Coast and the Country for two miles parallel to it' were to be 'very minutely surveyed, even in the Counties where the ordinary Surveys may have taken place'.[52] Third, Roy envisaged that with or without Admiralty assistance there ought to be a hydrographic element to the surveys as far as the inshore waters were concerned:

> SUCH Soundings as it might seem necessary to take along the Coast in general, or at any particular parts thereof, might be done at the same time as the plan of the Country was carrying on, or afterwards as a separate Operation; Tho' it is presumed that the Admiralty have been employed for several years, in making a Sea Chart of the Coasts and Islands, and as their observations might be inserted into the great plan, it would therefore seem unnecessary to repeat them.[53]

Once again this was a question which was not to be resolved until much later. The map of Kent published by William Faden (1801), and also the first regular Ordnance Survey sheets of Essex (1805) were alike in embodying hydrographic information.

Roy's comprehensive plan, emanating as it did from a highly-placed officer within the Ordnance department, naturally put the direction of the survey in the hands of the Engineers. It could be said that Roy's background made such an approach inevitable, but he was also following a wider European model, for a number of countries had already initiated official surveys by military departments of government to serve the strategic or tactical requirements of national defence. In Britain, however, with no long-established standing army, the matter was still open to argument. Although it was probably unthinkable to Roy that others than Engineers should direct the survey and undertake the scientific work, he raised the matter of

> whether it would be proper to employ Soldiers (as was done in taking the Plan of Scotland) to assist the Engineers in measuring &c, instead of Labourers hired in the Country. The former would be more useful as being subject to Military Command, and would be the cheapest as they would only receive an additional Allowance of pay for their Work, and would be entitled to Quarters in the Towns and Villages where the Several Parties were employed. – Whereas Country-Labourers would not be so obedient, and not being entitled to Quarters, would (excepting when they were at Work very near the places of their abode) be obliged to pay for their Lodging, which would consequently give them a Right to demand and expect greater Wages.[54]

The relative merits of civilian versus military assistants in the development of the national survey was yet another subject first broached by Roy.

As with similar proposals for surveys put to the Crown in the mid eighteenth century, Roy ended his 'Considerations' with a 'General Estimate' of the expense of completing such a military map of England. In the first year the total cost was to be £2778. 12s., made up of a dozen items, but if Roy's headings are simplified into four categories, the different types of expenditure are put into clearer perspective.

ESTIMATED COSTS FOR ROY'S 1766 PROPOSAL FOR A GENERAL SURVEY OF ENGLAND

Type of expenditure	amount £	s	% of total
Instruments	400	00	14.4
Engineers, draughtsmen, clerks, labourers, horses	2128	12	76.6
Drawing Room and stationery	150	00	5.4
Contingent expenses for signals	100	00	3.6
Totals	2778	12	100

While it would be wrong to read too much into these figures, it appears that in the mid eighteenth century the principal running costs of a national survey were believed to lie in the salaries of trained surveyors and their assistants, together with the horses needed to transport the surveying parties in the field. Roy further estimated that 'Perhaps in 6 or 8 years, at the Rate of £2500 p^r Annum, viz for £15 000 or £20 000, the Work might be finished'.[55] If soldiers were employed instead of labourers, there could be a possible saving of £200 per annum, but this still left man-power as by far the greatest expense. In 1766, although the documents are silent on this point, £15 000–£20 000 might have seemed excessive to the Government, especially at a time when they were being offered military surveys of much more extensive areas in North America at seemingly bargain prices.[56] Roy's proposals were not taken up and in the 1770s, if not already forgotten by those with power to implement them, they were overtaken by the more pressing military needs of the War of American Independence, both in its North American and European aspects.

It was not until 1783 that Roy was again given an opportunity, albeit under completely different circumstances, to pursue his cherished aim of creating a national survey, but meanwhile the trends in military cartography were helping to build a suitable environment for its foundation. The Board of Ordnance was an organization with financial resources adequate to undertake a national survey and, being a powerful department of State, was clearly capable of taking a domestic survey under its wing; it was also capable of offering important technical services. By the closing decade of the eighteenth century, the military engineers and draughtsmen through their experience in Scotland, on foreign stations, and in parts of southern England, had accumulated a considerable knowledge of both trigonometrical and topographical survey, which was capable of adaptation in a national context, especially when a general officer of the calibre of Roy could codify existing practices. In his 'General Instructions for the officers of Engineers employed in surveying',[57] written in the 1780s for the surveying company of Engineers* there can be discerned the embryo of a technical charter for the Ordnance Survey.

The Civilian Contribution to the Foundation of the Ordnance Survey

Although the Ordnance Survey originated under a military department of State, other aspects of the mapping of Britain also exerted a significant influence on its foundation and early character. British military survey in the eighteenth century was seldom closed to civilian influences, and the teachers at the Woolwich Academy were often drawn from civilian backgrounds. This was true of its leading mathematicians who were the intellectual mainspring of the geodetic activities of the Trigonometrical Survey. John Bonnycastle (1750–1821), Charles Hutton (1737–1823) and Olinthus Gregory (1774–1841) all fell into this category and their influence was to be important both in the training and selection of Ordnance Survey officers.

Even more far-reaching was the influence of published county cartography. From Tudor times to the late eighteenth century it was mainly a handful of county cartographers who kept alive the prospect of producing a national set of topographical maps which would be suitable for private use and could also serve the needs of national defence. Their contribution to the development of the idea of a national survey and to its implementation included the making of county maps, surveyed and engraved largely at private expense, and then sold through the normal commercial channels of the map trade. Such maps, just as much as the military survey of Scotland, are an integral part of the prehistory of the Ordnance Survey, particularly perhaps because some members of the Government, as well as many private map-users, believed that the commercial sector was capable of producing those very maps which in the course of the nineteenth century became largely the province of the Ordnance Survey.

The model for such county surveys was undoubtedly that of Saxton. The thirty-four county maps and one general map were engraved from 1574 to 1579 for publication in atlas form – the 'first national atlas' in this country. Saxton's maps, which 'inaugurated English regional cartography from field observations' were in a sense a government survey, although the mode of their financing and support was indirect:

> The evidence of the documents makes it clear beyond dispute that this was an official survey, promoted by the Crown on the advice of the Queen's ministers, as an act of policy, and designed to produce maps for the purpose of national administration.[58]

In the 1570s Elizabeth's ministers were faced with the need to organize national defence, for which reliable geographical intelligence, including that which could be obtained from maps, was indispensable. Saxton's Atlas, when it appeared, and later in its reprinted variants and in the plagiarized copies of Speed and others, served to introduce and consolidate the habit of using maps in national and local administration as well as for a variety of private purposes. The Atlas was already anticipating the role of the Ordnance Survey.

The later history of Saxton's maps and their successors up until the mid eighteenth century reveals that the energetic attitude of some of Elizabeth's ministers towards the nation's maps was not

* In 1784 the survey officers who formed this company were:
William Roy, in command   Lieutenant-Colonel and Director
Archibald Robertson   Captain and Engineer in Ordinary
John Eveleigh   Captain/Lieutenant and Engineer Extraordinary
Charles Holloway   First Lieutenant and Sub-Engineer
James Fiddes   First Lieutenant and Sub-Engineer
Peter Coutre   Second Lieutenant.
(Porter, *History of the RE* vol. 1, pp. 215–16).

sustained. There is, to be sure, a sporadic record of Crown support for county mapping ventures, but this was usually half-hearted with the main responsibility for financing surveys always resting with the map trade, and with a narrowly based map-buying public who had to be carefully wooed as subscribers to each new atlas or map. There is no better illustration of this tendency than the unfulfilled projects for county atlases which followed the Restoration of Charles II. These abortive schemes included those of John Ogilby for an atlas of English county maps based on original survey, to follow his road book *Britannia* (1675), and of John Seller, Hydrographer to Charles II, whose folio *Atlas Anglicanus* was also to contain new maps of the English counties. Neither cartographer received more than the most marginal financial support – mainly in the form of relief from customs duty on imported paper – and between them they only managed to survey nine counties. Outside the London map trade, too, the late seventeenth century was marked by a number of cartographical initiatives. From Oxford, for example, Moses Pitt projected an ambitious *English Atlas* (which had it got off the ground would have included a volume of county maps), while Dr Robert Plot regarded maps as an integral part of his design for a Natural History of England. In Scotland there were similar attempts at new maps with John Adair trying to implement the proposals of Moses Pitt, and with Sir Robert Sibbald also projecting an, unsuccessful, atlas of Scotland. These schemes again resulted in relatively few maps but, inasmuch as they kept alive a prospect of better maps eventually replacing the ageing surveys of the Tudor cartographers, they may be regarded as a contribution to the history of cartographical ideas.

In the first half of the eighteenth century much the same approach to the mapping of Britain seems to have prevailed. Although the commercial risks of a national survey clearly remained beyond the resources of private capital, there is no evidence of official support for the schemes of county cartographers, and there was little improvement in the basic printed map-cover of Britain. One factor in this situation was that the London map trade was experiencing one of its less innovative phases compared with European cartography in general. It tended to be weakly organized and under-capitalized; its best county maps, such as those in the *Large English Atlas* which began to appear serially from the workshops of Emanuel Bowen and Thomas Kitchin in the later 1740s, were secondary compilations lacking the authority of new surveys. Not surprisingly, in an age of improvement and of the early industrial revolution, dissatisfaction was beginning to be voiced about the relatively poor quality of the available maps.[59] The few exceptions, such as the one inch to one mile surveys of Cornwall by Joel Gascoyne (1699), and of Warwickshire by Henry Beighton (1727), did little to remedy the general deficiency of county cartography. As earlier, there were ambitious proposals to undertake subscription surveys of the whole country, as in the 1720s by John Warburton and in the late 1740s by John Rocque, but it was not until the second half of the century that, taken together, such schemes began to achieve a substantial success.

The period from the 1750s to 1800 was one of remarkable progress in the private mapping of Britain. At the earlier date only a handful of counties had been mapped at a scale of one inch to one mile or larger; by the time the Ordnance Survey was established, much of Britain had been so surveyed in unprecedented accuracy and detail.[60] Indeed, it could be argued that so successful were these new county maps, and so widely used in practical affairs, that they retarded rather than advanced the emergence of the Ordnance Survey as a map-publishing organization. Even after the first Ordnance Survey maps had appeared there was still a body of opinion in favour of allowing private surveyors to fill in the detail of the survey on the basis of the Ordnance triangulation.

The causes of the improvements in county cartography were complex. They were often local, but in terms of a national impact, the decision of the Society of Arts to offer money prizes for new county surveys after 1759 must be rated above other initiatives in its long-term effects.[61] A basic document is the letter dated January 1755 in which Henry Baker FRS suggested that the Society of Arts ought to support cartography:

> I would submit to you as a friend, whether the state of British Geography be not very low, and at present wholly destitute of any public encouragement. Our Maps of England and its counties are extremely defective . . . and the head lands of all our shores are at this time disputed . . .

An improvement, he continued, was to 'be dispaired of till the Government interposes and attempts what would be so much for the honour as well as Commerce of this Island', and he went on to suggest that the Society of Arts, among its premiums, ought to offer a reward for 'the best plan measurement and actual Survey of city or District'. This, he believed,

> might move the attention of the public towards Geography, and in time, perhaps, incline the Administration to take this matter into their hands (as I am informed it does in some foreign Countries) and employ proper persons every year from actual surveys to make accurate Maps of Districts, till the whole Island is regularly surveyed.[62]

These remarks were a clear articulation of the case for a national survey and the Society's first reaction was an attempt to push the responsibility towards the Crown. In 1757 it was noted that 'some of their great Members have promised at a more convenient Season, to recommend it to the Ministers as a matter worthy the Government's attention',[63] but there is no further record of this approach. Like Roy's attempt to stimulate a military survey of the country some ten years later, it came to naught, and the Society was forced to act independently. It believed that by offering premiums to individual surveyors it could 'give proper surveyors such Encouragement as may induce them to make accurate Surveys of two or three Counties towards completing the whole',[64] so that, in time, a fairly standard map of the country would be produced in piecemeal fashion. The Society, in effect, was encouraging a privately-sponsored national survey and to this wider objective some surveyors at least felt they were contributing. In 1768 Peter Perez Burdett, whose map of Derbyshire had already been rewarded with a premium, was arguing in his proposals for a similar map of Lancashire:

> that by encouraging this Work, we shall contribute *our* Part to a more large and extensive one, – a correct Map of the whole Kingdom, (which we must not expect to see, till an actual Survey has thus been made of every County).[65]

And in the same year Robert Dossie, the agricultural writer, also recognized that the new county surveys were 'furnishing materials for a complete map of England'.[66] In the 1760s no-one seems to have seriously questioned if such surveys could be fitted together!

The specification of the Society of Arts for county surveys was also to exert an influence on the future format of the published maps of the Ordnance Survey. After some changes, the final wording of their advertisement announced their intention

> to give a Sum not exceeding one hundred Pounds, as a Gratuity to any Person or Persons, who shall make an accurate Survey of any County upon the Scale of one Inch to a Mile; the Sea Coasts of all Maritime Counties to be correctly laid down together with the Latitudes and Longitudes.[67]

These stipulations did much to standardize two aspects of the new regional cartography and the Ordnance Survey maps which followed. First, by offering awards for maps of counties, they confirmed the dominance of this basic area of local administration as the most suitable unit of regional map publication. This territorial emphasis was carried over into the nineteenth century and was still an influence in fashioning the design of large-scale Ordnance Survey maps in the Victorian era. Secondly, the choice by the Society of Arts of a scale of one inch to one mile did much to establish its popularity and also to ensure its eventual adoption by the Ordnance Survey. It has been said that one inch to one mile was a military scale but, although it was sometimes employed, none of the major British military surveys of the eighteenth century – in Scotland, in Ireland, in North America or in India – had adopted it extensively for either survey or fair-drawing. Nor was one inch to one mile, although used by Roy for several reconnaissance sketches in southern England, much favoured by Engineers on home stations: it was considered too small for field engineering, and the manuscript sheets incorporated into the first Ordnance Survey maps were at scales of two, three or six inches to one mile. It would seem, therefore, that the one-inch scale, first adopted for the 1801 map of Kent by its publisher, William Faden, an experienced county cartographer, owed its selection as much to civilian traditions as to any military influence.

The origin of the Ordnance Survey scales again illustrates how, when the national survey finally emerged, it brought together a wide range of cartographical traditions. That this was possible was partly owing to the fact that surveying had not yet been subdivided into a number of specialist branches. There was a strong element of common practice, and the able practitioner could easily move between different types of assignment. Civilian and military topographical surveying were not always as far apart as independent studies of either one or the other might suggest. Some surveyors at different points in their career had a foot in both camps. Daniel Paterson, an Assistant Quartermaster-General at Army headquarters in Whitehall, was also the compiler of a popular road book for civilian use;[68] and Andrew Armstrong, who in 1768 described himself as 'Lieut. on half pay from the 32nd Regt.' (and had presumably learnt his surveying in the King's service), went on to become one of the more prolific of the new county surveyors.[69] Or, in a reverse direction, Andrew Skinner and George Taylor, having established a reputation as regional surveyors in Scotland, were recruited to Sir Henry Clinton's New York staff during the War of American Independence;[70] while Peter Perez Burdett was sufficiently qualified through his English county surveys to be given the direction of a military topographical survey in Baden after 1775.[71] Even more specifically, two of the future Ordnance surveyors, Thomas Yeakell and William Gardner, served an apprenticeship as county surveyors. The Yeakell and Gardner map of Sussex (the southern half only was published in four sheets between 1778 and 1783) was undertaken while both men were salaried land surveyors in the pay of the Duke of Richmond.[72] Shortly afterwards, still under the Duke's patronage, they were to enter the service of the Board of Ordnance as surveyors and draughtsmen – another example of a direct link between civilian and military developments.

Lastly it was Roy himself who proposed that the topographical detail of the county maps should be integrated into a national survey. In this and other respects he emerges as the common denominator linking together the separate elements of eighteenth-century cartography.

The Scientific Tradition and the Establishment of the Ordnance Survey

At the time of its establishment and for many years afterwards the Ordnance Survey was officially known as the 'Trigonometrical Survey', a fact which reflected not only its beginnings in an international geodetic operation, but also much of the emphasis of its early work. In carrying out the task assigned to it the Trigonometrical Survey was borne along by the broad stream of a European scientific culture in which geodesy and cartography had a recognized place. The membership of the Paris *Académie des Sciences*, for example, in the late seventeenth century, was 'composed of the most learned persons available in all the true sciences', and these included geometry, optics, astronomy, geography and navigation.[73] The interests of the Royal Society of London, founded shortly after the Restoration, were similar and during the eighteenth century it built up a record of research in the astronomical and geodetic sciences. A simple subject classification, such as that undertaken by the editors of the abridged *Philosophical Transactions* of the Royal Society in the early nineteenth century,[74] reveals the relative importance of research, often with a strong utilitarian bent, dealing with various aspects of astronomy, chronology, land surveying and navigation.

The debate surrounding such topics, the observations made in the course of their study, and the improved instruments on which they depended were all constituents of the scientific environment into which the Trigonometrical Survey was born. In particular it was heir to a long succession of enquiries into the method of determining longitude. This, apart from any intellectual interest, was a matter of considerable practical importance both for establishing longitude at sea and for improving the maps and charts used by the European powers who were competing to extend their empires. There is no doubt that the urgency with which longitude was viewed was a powerful stimulus to astronomy and its related sciences. It was a major influence in the establishment in 1675 of the Royal Observatory at Greenwich, and John Flamsteed, as first 'astronomical observator', was expected to provide accurate tables of lunar distances and a fuller catalogue of star places for use in marine navigation. Other astronomical observations, as of the eclipses of Jupiter's satellites, were aimed specifically at fixing the longitude of particular sites. They were undertaken not only in Europe but also in other continents and the flow of new geographical data from these observations was such that in the 1660s it was estimated that the latitudes and longitudes of about 2200 places had been fixed on the world map as 'certain or probable';[75] by the early nineteenth century this total had risen to over 6000.[76] In Britain, even the county surveyors carried out 'astronomical observations', especially after 1750, to determine latitudes and longitudes for their maps.

Another strand to these enquiries, equally essential to the construction of accurate maps and charts, was related to continuing attempts to establish the correct circumference and shape of the Earth and the length of a degree. The method of accomplishing this was by the measurement of an 'arc of the meridian', and – an augury of the future scientific work of the Trigonometrical Survey – Roy had proposed in 1766 the measurement of an English arc.

In some respects the making of terrestrial measurements and the building up of a data bank of geographical co-ordinates from observatories and other shore stations were relatively straightforward tasks. A far more intractable problem was to estimate longitude on a moving ship. In this case a major key to progress was seen to lie in accurate timekeeping and the eighteenth century is marked by a number of initially unsuccessful attempts to construct a clock or chronometer of adequate reliability. John Harrison, with his 'No.4' marine chronometer, was eventually able to accomplish this in the 1760s,* exemplifying the essential role of precision-instrument makers in the development of astronomical and geodetic science.[77] Indeed, the type of operation contemplated by Roy in the 1760s, and eventually carried out by him after 1783, would not have been possible but for significant

---

* In 1713 the British Government offered rewards for the construction of a chronometer that would determine longitude to within 1 degree (£10 000), 40 minutes (£15 000), or 30 minutes (£20 000). The Board of Longitude, consisting of 22 Commissioners, was set up in 1714 to administer the prize money. Harrison claimed the £20 000 reward but it was not paid in full until 1773. The Board was dissolved in 1828.

improvements in surveying instruments. By the late eighteenth century London was the leading European centre for the design and making of scientific instruments. The skill of men such as Jonathan Sisson, George Graham, John Bird, James Short and Jesse Ramsden – the last-named especially for the first operations of the Trigonometrical Survey – was a vital part of the infrastructure for scientific advance.[78] By 1780, many of the necessary conditions for a national geodetic project – in terms of skilled man-power, methods and instruments – were in being. Only a catalyst was required to bring them into a working relationship.

William Roy was certainly one of the more important components of this catalyst and his selection to undertake the first episode in a national triangulation was no historical accident. After 1763 Roy made his home in London,* and this enabled him to build up a network of scientific contacts within the capital. On 15 January 1767 he was proposed as a Fellow of the Royal Society 'from personal knowledge' by James Short, Dr John Bevis and William Harrison, and duly elected. In the intimately-linked society of the eighteenth century Roy's sponsors reflect both his earlier contacts and his interests in surveying. James Short, a fellow Scotsman, had been a tutor in mathematics to the fifteen-year-old Duke of Cumberland (later to become patron of the Scottish survey), and in 1759 had carried out a survey of the Orkneys for James Douglas, Earl of Morton and President of the Royal Society at the time of Roy's election.[79] By the 1760s Short had become a leading instrument maker; his reflecting telescopes were 'the best of their kind'[80] and his private observatory in Surrey Street was frequented by many scientific notables, among whom was John Bevis, the astronomer, who in 1767 became the Foreign Secretary of the Royal Society. William Harrison, son of the chronometer maker, was likewise an experienced astronomical observer and had travelled widely while testing his father's instruments.[81]

The opportunities of this new intellectual world were eagerly grasped by Roy and he was transformed from being a very competent military engineer, but one to whom map-making was a routine activity, into a geodesist of eventually international repute. He purchased his own scientific instruments, made by craftsmen as distinguished as Sissons, Short, the Dollond brothers and Jesse Ramsden, including several chronometers, telescopes, barometers and quadrants, a sextant and a '*capital large equitorial instrument*' (which can be identified as a telescope made by Ramsden, elaborately mounted, and which could be set by clockwork to follow the course of an observed heavenly body across the sky).[82] His barometers were used for his measurements of heights made during the five years from 1771 to 1776, which took him as far afield as Schiehallion in Scotland and Snowdon in Wales.[83] Moreover, it was to this same scientific method of field enquiry that Roy's archaeological interests – focused since the days of the Scottish survey on the Roman antiquities of 'North Britain' – can also be assigned.

If these activities were personal to Roy, their significance in relation to his future role in the establishment of the Trigonometrical Survey was that they firmly placed him within the horizon of a group of men who made most of the critical decisions about matters of scientific importance. Aristocrats such as the Duke of Richmond, with ample powers of patronage, were also Fellows of the Royal Society. And Roy became a firm friend of Sir Joseph Banks, botanist, wealthy landowner and President of the Society who, in company with such other prominent members as Charles Blagden and Dr Lind,** had looked in on his experiments to measure altitudes. It was indeed an intimate circle to which he belonged by the 1770s. In 1775 Banks formed a new and select dining club, the 'Royal Society Club', of which Roy was one of the eight founder members.[84] Two of the other members, Blagden and John Lloyd, as well as Banks himself, were later closely associated with Roy's geodetic activities. Until the Club's dissolution in 1784 Roy attended 99 out of 141 dinners and such occasions provided an ideal forum for the discussion of his ideas for a national survey. Just as the Board of Ordnance had provided an umbrella organization for military cartography in the eighteenth century, and the Society of Arts for county mapping, so too the Royal Society was the obvious institution for fostering the advance of the scientific aspects of cartography. A breadth of outlook as well as of membership helped it to play a synthesizing and an influential role.

The historic opportunity arrived in 1783, the year in which peace was re-established between

---

* From 1765 his residence was at 32–5 Great Pulteney Street; in 1779 he moved to 12 Argyll Street where he remained until his death. The formation of Argyll Place in 1820, which followed the construction of Regent Street, led to the renumbering of the houses in Argyll Street. Roy's house became no. 10 and, although much altered, has survived in an identifiable state.

** Dr Charles Blagden, 1748–1820. Elected a Fellow of the Royal Society 1772; became Secretary of the Society in 1784 and was knighted in 1792.
James Lind, 1716–94. Scottish physician instrumental in improving health and hygiene in the Navy, notably by the use of lemon juice against scurvy.

Britain and France after the War of American Independence. The specific point at issue was the relative positions of the Royal Observatories in Paris and Greenwich, with a difference of opinion between English and French astronomers that amounted to nearly 11 seconds for longitude and 15 seconds for latitude. The fact that such a matter could generate an international debate at all illustrates how the scientific community in eighteenth-century Europe maintained close contact across national frontiers. The location of the two observatories was in any case not a new question, for the *Philosophical Transactions* had reported earlier attempts to resolve the difference by means of astronomical measurements.[85] In October 1783, however, Cassini de Thury,[86] Director of the Paris Observatory and a foreign member of the Royal Society of London, proposed an alternative way to settle the sometimes acrimonious disagreement. Its essence was that the English scientists should undertake a triangulation from the vicinity of the Greenwich Observatory to the coast near Dover and, from there, by means of cross-Channel observations, link up with the French triangulation already completed to the area of Calais. These arguments were contained in a mémoire submitted to the British Government through the Comte d'Adhémar, the French Ambassador in London;[87] this was received by Charles James Fox, a principal Secretary of State who, after consultation with George III, passed the paper to Sir Joseph Banks in his capacity as President of the Royal Society. Banks, as his extensive correspondence makes clear,[88] was certainly no stranger to developments in geodesy and cartography but, in a matter of such technical complexity and with national prestige at stake, he turned for advice to Roy, his friend and scientific associate, and a high-ranking officer in the Ordnance department. From this moment were linked together the highest scientific authority and the organization having the resources and the specialists for carrying out the work.

In the summer of the year when Cassini's mémoire arrived Roy, as if by an uncanny coincidence, had, for his own 'private amusement', measured

> a base of 7744.3 feet, across the fields between the Jews-Harp, near Marybone, and Black-Lane, near Pancras; as a foundation for a series of triangles, carried on at the same time, for determining the relative situations of the most remarkable steeples, and other places, in and about the Capital, with regard to each other, and the Royal Observatory at Greenwich.

He went on:

> The principal object I had here in view (besides that it might possibly serve as a hint to the public, for the revival of the now almost forgotten scheme of 1763) was, to facilitate the comparison of the observations, made by lovers of astronomy, within the limits of the projected survey; namely, Richmond and Harrow, on the west; and Shooter's Hill and Wansted, on the east.[89]

In short, Roy was already waiting in the wings in the autumn of 1783 and as he further explained, over the previous twenty years in the course of his 'ordinary military employments' he had 'not failed to observe . . . such situations as seemed to be best adapted for the measurement of bases for the formation of the great triangles'. Not surprisingly, he responded quickly and positively to Banks's consultation. Roy's reply, dated 28 November, not only gave further justification for Cassini's plan but also provided Banks with an estimate of its cost. These documents make it clear that to Roy at least the Anglo-French triangulation was not an end in itself but a new opportunity to establish a national survey which, to this extent, was inaugurated and first supported from public funds in 1784. After reinforcing the arguments in favour of the immediate project Roy continued:

> This is nevertheless, of but small moment compared with other advantages that will in all probability arise from the commencement of these operations in Britain. For the Base on Hounslow Heath is well situated for extending different serieses of Triangles from thence in all directions to the remotest parts of the Island; and even connecting them with others that may be carried over our Sister Kingdom. By these means the best foundation will be laid for an accurate Survey of the British Dominions.[90]

In a breakdown of the cost of operations, however, Roy confined himself to the immediate scheme and submitted to Banks the unrealistically low estimate of £350.[91]

	£	s	d
Mathematical instruments of the best Kinds about	200	,,	,,
A carriage on Springs (Secondhand or otherwise) for transporting the Instruments during the operation	25	,,	,,
Pay of six men for sixty days, one with Another at 2s.6d. each	45	,,	,,
Hire of Horses, &c, Carriages, &c, perhaps	80	,,	,,
	350	,,	,,

There was a hint of possible extra costs – such as an allowance 'to give the Computer after the Field Operation is over', the salary of an assistant to the director, and additional expenses incurred if the terminals of the base line and the trigonometrical station on Dover cliffs were to be permanently marked – but these did not appear in the main account. It is possible that such a cautious budget was a deliberate tactic, designed to disarm any critics in the Treasury, but clearly Roy believed that the Board of Ordnance would inevitably be drawn into the project to provide some of the resources needed, both in equipment and personnel. Although Roy's expenditure, as set out in a later account, reached £2000,[92] the Crown's initial commitment was indeed modest. The figures were put before George III and in April 1784 the Lords of the Treasury, who were to implement the payments, were informed that

> His Majesty has been pleased to approve of the Plan . . . for ascertaining a point of such Importance to the Science of Astronomy and to permit Major General Roy to proceed in the Execution of it under the Direction of the President & Council of the Royal Society.[93]

The Royal Society confirmed the arrangement at a Council meeting held on 24 June 1784.[94]

The base measurement and angular observations occupied Roy for much of the remaining six years of his life. Throughout the measurement of the base line on Hounslow Heath and the subsequent triangulation to the coast to join with the work of the French, it is possible to detect the dominance of those same influences which created the environment in which the Trigonometrical Survey could be initiated. First of all, with Roy in control of the day-to-day conduct of the operations and the Duke of Richmond as Master General, it was natural that the execution of the work would be largely in the hands of the Ordnance. For preparing the site of the Hounslow Heath base line Roy repeated the same preference which he had spelled out in 1766. He had, as he later explained,

> judged [it] to be a right measure to obtain and employ soldiers, instead of country labourers, in tracing the base, clearing the ground, and assisting in the subsequent operations. For, at the same time that this was obviously the most frugal method, it was evident, that soldiers would be more attentive to orders than country labourers; and by encamping on the spot would furnish the necessary centinels, particularly during the night, for guarding such parts of the apparatus, as it was foreseen must remain carefully untouched . . . Accordingly, a party of the 12th regiment of foot, consisting of a serjeant, corporal and 10 men, were ordered to march from Windsor to Hounslow Heath, where they encamped on the 26th of May, close by Hanworth Summerhouse.[95]

However, in this first operation of the Survey the military supporting party was not composed of Ordnance troops; it was evidently obtained from the regiment which was most conveniently close at hand. When the triangulation was started three years later a party of artillerymen was provided, a practice that was to be maintained for over fifty years.

The employment of Ordnance officers is confirmed in the official *Return Book of Royal Engineers for the Years 1786 [to] 1792*: William Roy is recorded as 'Directing Surveys' in 1786; in 1787 Lieutenant James Fiddes is also recorded as surveying and, in the following year, is listed as 'employed by General Roy'.[96] Roy wrote of this fellow officer that 'it was impossible for any person to fulfil the duties entrusted to him better than he did';[97] and of his assistant, Lieutenant Bryce of the Artillery, that he was 'an attentive officer and mathematician'.*

In spite of these facts, significant as they were for the future organization of the national survey, the trigonometrical operations of the 1780s were permeated by the ethos of the Royal Society. At a superficial level the measurements on Hounslow Heath in the summer of 1784 almost took on the air of a scientific carnival. 'The work excited very general interest'[98] and in mid-July the onlookers included 'Sir Joseph Banks, accompanied by Messrs Blagden, Cavendish, Lloyd, and Smeaton,** all ready to lend their assistance in the subsequent mensuration',[99] and

> On Saturday the 21st August . . . about noon, his Majesty deigned to honour the operation by his presence, for the space of two hours, entering very minutely into the mode of conducting it, which met with his gracious approbation.[100]

The focus of these gatherings seems to have been Banks and his entourage:

> With that liberality of mind which distinguishes all his actions, [he] ordered his tents to be continually pitched near at hand, where his immediate guests, and the numerous visitors whom curiosity drew to the spot, met with the most hospitable supply of every necessary and even elegant refreshment. It will be easily imagined, how greatly this tended to expedite the work, and how much more comfortable and pleasant it rendered the labour to all who obligingly took part in it.[101]

This popularization of the operations did not, however, detract from the consistent application of the most thorough scientific methods known to Roy and his contemporaries.[102] Of the Hounslow

---

* Lieutenant Bryce was transferred to the Engineers, and later became Major-General Sir Alexander Bryce and Inspector-General of Fortifications in 1829.

** Henry Cavendish, 1731–1810, chemist and physicist, carried out a series of experiments to determine the density of the Earth. The Cavendish Physical Laboratory at Cambridge was named after him.
John Smeaton, 1724–92. Civil Engineer who rebuilt Eddystone Lighthouse in 1759. He made improvements to instruments used in astronomy and navigation.

Heath Base, one historian has written: 'Seldom, if ever, had there been a line measured with such care'.[103] Banks, amid his hospitality, was 'ever zealous in the cause of science' and 'gave his attendance from morning to night in the field, during the whole progress of the work'.[104] Indeed, the importance attached by the Royal Society to its general surveillance of the project is shown by the length in which the minutest details were later reported in the *Philosophical Transactions*. And in November 1785 the Royal Society's Copley Medal for Science was presented to Roy, 'this very skilful engineer' for the 'accurate and satisfactory manner in which he has measured a base, for operations of Trigonometry, upon Hounslow Heath'. Sir Joseph Banks, in his presentation address, referred to Roy as the 'one Person at least we possess in this Island . . . willing to undertake and able to execute, the most difficult operations of mensuration'.[105]

After the speed with which the base line had been measured, the delays in commencing the triangulation towards the coast of Kent were evidently a great disappointment to Roy. Observations were not begun in earnest until the summer of 1787; the main reason for the gap – the need to design and construct a much better instrument than any which were then available – typifies another constraint to geodesy in the late eighteenth century. In order to attain the highest levels of accuracy as much in the angular as in the linear measurements, Roy had placed an order with Jesse Ramsden in 1784 for a large theodolite. After two years had passed without its completion, Roy, a man of sixty and no longer in good health, was unable to bottle up his frustration. In September 1786 he complained:

> It is hard upon me to have this operation hanging over my head for another year, without any fault of mine; But with such a man as Ramsden there is no help for it.[106]

and in July 1787, with the instrument still not actually in his hands, he again wrote: '. . . with such a man as Ramsden, it is altogether impossible to answer for what may happen'.[107] These strictures were made in the privacy of a letter but, with his exasperation growing, Roy carried his censure into the open at a Royal Society meeting. In a paper setting out his plans 'to be followed in determining the relative Situation of the Royal Observatories of Greenwich and Paris', he made his complaint public by charging Ramsden with being 'in the outset remiss and dilatory' and having failed to employ enough workmen in the construction of the theodolite.[108]

Whatever the rights and wrongs of this wrangle Roy, as a result, was given more than ample time to plan what was to be the final scientific survey of his career. From his account of expenditures of money received through Banks from the Treasury, it can be seen how, from 1785, he was making a series of meticulous preparations.[109] Scaffolds to mount the theodolite at various points were constructed, lamps were purchased (to illuminate the brass circle of the theodolite in night observations) and experiments were made with white lights. The composition of these latter, set out in a manuscript note in Sir Joseph Banks's copy of the *Philosophical Transactions*, was '28 parts of Nitre, 4 parts of Sulphur and two parts of orpiment [trisulphate of arsenic] powdered fine and mixed carefully'.[110] They were designed to be burnt in copper cups set on tripods and it was by this means alone, Roy claimed,

> that the most distant stations could be rendered visible; and there cannot be a doubt that, in great trigono-metrical operations of this sort, they will be universally adopted hereafter.[111]

Equally important was Roy's careful planning of the design of the triangles, and a diagram of their layout was submitted for approval by the Royal Society (Plate 1). Yet again we observe Roy with half an eye on the future. Just as he had explained that the base line on Hounslow Heath had been chosen as being 'commodiously situated for any future operations of a similar nature, which his Majesty may please to order to be extended from thence, in different directions, to the more remote parts of the island',[112] so too the triangles might serve as 'the foundation of a general survey of the British Islands'.[113] Still in the same vein, in a letter written in June 1787, he was already looking forward to the moment 'when H.M. may please to order the operations to be continued to the westward of Windsor'.[114]

The great theodolite which came to be known as the 'great circular instrument' was finally delivered to Roy in July 1787 (Plate 2). On 31 July it was placed on the trigonometrical station near Hampton Poor House at the end of the Hounslow Heath Base. From then on, most of the forces which had been either active or latent in the initiation of the Trigonometrical Survey were directed towards the completion of its first major operation. At a diplomatic level Sir Joseph Banks began corresponding, through the Marquis of Carmarthen, with the *Académie des Sciences* and it was agreed that the British and French observers should meet in September. In the Royal Society the renewal of operations caused a stir; Charles Blagden, whom Banks kept informed about progress, cancelled a summer tour of Germany to be available for the collaboration. The Board of Ordnance provided most of the resources, both before and during the triangulation. Lieutenant Fiddes worked on the measurement of the base of verification on Romney Marsh; 'an officer and a detachment of artillery-men' were sent to give labouring and semi-skilled assistance; the laboratory at Woolwich was instructed 'to supply whatever fire-works might be wanted for signals'; and on Ordnance property at Greenwich Observatory, Shooter's Hill and Dover Castle 'temporary scaffolds were erected . . . for the reception of the instrument'.[115]

Roy continued to worry and to organize; the weather was poor in August and he wrote with some anxiety from St Ann's Hill: 'It has blown so hard all day long and still continues to do so, that we have not been able to make any observation'.[116] As still worse weather could be near it was decided to give priority to the cross-Channel observations to France, although the triangles in Kent were incomplete. The French delegation was led by the Comte de Cassini (the fourth Cassini), Méchain and Legendre,* all distinguished members of the *Académie des Sciences*. They arrived at Dover on 23 September and, after two days of conferring, the details of the operation were agreed and Charles Blagden returned with the French party to Calais. By 17 October the operations had been successfully completed, 'thereby to establish for ever the triangular connection between the two countries'.[117]

It remained to close the gap in the chain of triangles between the coast and Wrotham Hill. Although the season was late Roy was 'eagerly wishing to bring the business to a conclusion'. By the beginning of November all but two stations had been observed, but Roy noted feelingly that the worsening weather 'at length became so tempestuous that it was utterly impossible to continue' when 'perched on the tops of high steeples such as Lydd and Tenterden, or on heights, such as Hollingborn Hill'.[118] By this time most of the helpers who had been so much in evidence on Hounslow Heath had fallen away and the triangulation had become almost exclusively an Ordnance operation. Probably this was largely accounted for by the contrast between the convenience of Hounslow Heath and the windy hill-tops of Kent.

The observations were completed in the following season. For good measure, 'with the view . . . of laying the foundation hereafter for a much more accurate plan of London than could possibly be obtained in any other way', some additional triangles were measured. His sights still set on the wider application of his work, Roy returned to London in September 1788. But his health was clearly deteriorating and this was to be his last field season.

Roy's last days can hardly have been very satisfying. The acrimonious dispute with Ramsden had dragged on to the next round of papers read before the Royal Society. Roy had widened his attack on the instrument maker, alleging serious faults in the chain apparatus used on Romney Marsh in 1787. 'If the maker had not been very negligent', Roy declared, the defect 'might easily have been prevented';[119] this was typical of the derogatory references in his paper on the triangulation of south-east England as it was read to a meeting of the Royal Society in February 1790. Ramsden, for his part, did not take lying down such slurs on his 'professional character', the more so because they were uttered in so 'respectable a place'. By means of a 'Memorial' sent to the Royal Society and to George III he mounted a spirited defence. He (Ramsden) was the 'more affected', he explained, because the attack came 'from a gentleman with whom I considered myself in friendship and, who had many obligations to me for my assistance in the business'.[120] His main excuse was the cumulative improvement he had made to the design of the instrument (the 3-foot theodolite); moreover, as he added with a touch of commercial realism 'within a fixed price' and 'to the neglect of more lucrative business'. As a result of these explanations Ramsden was finally able to secure the erasure of some of the more provocative passages from Roy's paper prior to its publication.

The whole incident is out of character with Roy's usually generous references to his scientific associates, and the truth is that he was already a sick man. As his health permitted he was busily engaged in preparing the results of the triangulation for publication in the *Philosophical Transactions* but, suffering from a lung complaint, he went to Lisbon in November 1789 to recuperate in a warmer climate. Before leaving he engaged Isaac Dalby, a civilian mathematician who had been employed on the triangulation since 1787, to help in correcting the proofs of his paper.[121] In April 1790 Roy returned to London from Lisbon. Still in harness (he was working at the War Office on the previous evening) he died suddenly at his home in Argyll Street in the early hours of 1 July of the same year. Only three pages of the proofs of his account of the triangulation remained to be corrected but, as in his other endeavours, he was denied the satisfaction of seeing their permanent substance. Even the triangulation had not resolved all the issues of the latitude and longitude differences,[122] but despite

---

* Pierre Méchain, 1744–1804: French astronomer who, with Delambre, measured the arc of meridian from Dunkerque to Barcelona in 1792–8, to establish a length for the metre.
Adrien Marie Legendre, 1752–1833: mathematician who wrote in 1783 the first comprehensive treatment of the method of least squares (q.v. Ch. 12).

unanswered questions it had a profound effect on the future of British map-making. It had brought scientific enthusiasm and military organization into a loose partnership and, while revealing new imperfections in the maps of England, had pointed the way to their improvement through a trigonometrical survey. These successes enabled Roy to reiterate the case for a national survey, a cause which he had espoused over a quarter of a century earlier. In his last paper, published posthumously, he wrote:

> the writer of this account cannot but help considering it as being incumbent on him to recommend that the trigonometrical operation, so successfully begun, should certainly be continued, and gradually extended over the whole island. Compared with the greatness of the object, the annual expense to the public would be a mere trifle ... The honour of the nation is concerned in having at least as good a map of this as is of any other country.[123]

That it was accomplished by others was truly his epitaph.

Notes

1 RS Journal, Book 34, 1790–3, pp. 389–90.
2 *Returns relative to the Ordnance Survey*, p. 2: PP 1846 (423) xxvi.
3 J. R. Western, *The English Militia in the Eighteenth Century* (London 1965), p. xiv.
4 C. M. Clode, *The military forces of the crown: their administration and government* (London 1869), 2 vols., and A. Forbes, *A History of the Army Ordnance Services* (London 1929), 3 vols.
5 PRO WO 55/2281.
6 A. H. W. Robinson, *Marine Cartography in Britain. A history of the sea chart to 1855* (Leicester 1962).
7 *Ibid.* pp. 145–9.
8 Clode, *The military forces*, vol. 1, pp. 456–70.
9 *Ibid.* pp. 464–5.
10 *Ibid.* p. 470.
11 O. F. G. Hogg, *The Royal Arsenal: Its Background, Origin and Subsequent History* (London 1963), vol. 1, p. 305.
12 W. Porter, *History of the Corps of Royal Engineers* (Chatham, reprinted 1951), vol. 1, pp. 143–4, 180.
13 *Records of the Royal Military Academy* (Woolwich 1851), p. 2.
14 *Records of RMA*, pp. 13–15, 19–20, 22–23, for the Woolwich syllabus and text-books, and PRO WO 30/120: Rules and Orders for the Royal Military Academy at Woolwich, 1776.
15 John Muller, 1699–1784. His first book, on conic sections, was dedicated to the Master General of the Ordnance.
16 PRO WO 54/199, 54/207, 54/208.
17 A 'List of the Drawing Room at the *Tower*', giving the grades of the draughtsmen, with salaries, was printed in the *Court and City Register*, beginning in 1758.
18 PRO MPH 14, MPH 15 tabulate names, ages, lengths of service of Drawing Room personnel.
19 PRO MPH 14, MPH 15 and WO 34/206: Report of the Drawing Room, for March 1782.
20 Maurice J. D. Cockle, *A Bibliography of English Military Books up to 1642 and of Contemporary Foreign Works* (London 1900), pp. 243–6.
21 E. G. R. Taylor, *The Mathematical Practitioners of Tudor and Stuart England* (Cambridge 1967); A. W. Richeson, *English Land Measuring to 1800: Instruments and Practices* (Cambridge, Massachusetts 1966).
22 M. A. Lower (ed.), *A Survey of the Coast of Sussex, made in 1587* (Lewes 1870).
23 C. F. Close, *The Early Years of the Ordnance Survey* (reprinted Newton Abbot 1969), pp. 2–5; Yolande O'Donoghue, *William Roy 1726–1790: Pioneer of the Ordnance Survey*, Catalogue of an Exhibition held at the British Library (London, the British Library 1977).
24 William Roy, 'An Account of the Measurement of a Base on Hounslow-Heath', *Phil. Trans.* 1785, LXXV, pp. 385–7; A. Arrowsmith, *Memoir relative to the construction of a map of Scotland* (London 1809); R. A. Skelton, *The Military Survey of Scotland* (Edinburgh 1967), Royal Scottish Geographical Society Special Publication no. 1; D. G. Moir, *The early Maps of Scotland*, third edition, revised ... with a history of Scottish maps (Edinburgh 1973), pp. 103–13.
25 Carluke Parish Register of Baptisms, Scottish Record Office, Edinburgh.
26 G. MacDonald, 'General William Roy and his Military Antiquities of the Romans in North Britain', *Archaeologia second series* 1917, XVIII, p. 163.

27 That such opportunities existed is confirmed by the maps and plans listed for the engineer 'Division' of 'North Britain' in PRO WO 55/2281, ff. 12–17. The earliest map drawn by Roy is a sketch of Culloden House and Moor, undated, but probably originally surveyed soon after the battle on 16 April 1746: British Library Map Library K. Top. L. 44–1.

28 Skelton, *Military Survey of Scotland*, quoting Arrowsmith, p. 4.

29 PRO WO 54/208 records Thomas Sandby as attending in the Drawing Room in 1743.

30 Roy, *Phil. Trans.* 1785, LXXV, p. 386.

31 Moir, *Early maps of Scotland*, p. 107.

32 See Ch. 5.

33 See J. B. Harley, Barbara Bartz Petchenik and Lawrence W. Towner, *Mapping the American Revolution* (Chicago 1977) Ch. 1, for a discussion on the wider eighteenth century context of such military topographical surveys.

34 Skelton, *Military Survey of Scotland*, p. 5.

35 Roy, *Phil. Trans.* 1785, LXXV, p. 387.

36 Roy's original appointment to this rank 'By the Right Honourable Sir John Ligonier . . . Lieutenant General, and the rest of the Principal Officers of his Majesty's Ordnance. To William Roy Gent', dated 23 December 1755, is in the OS Office, Southampton.

37 Maps resulting from the reconnaissance include British Library Map Library K. Top. V1. 103 and 110.

38 British Library Map Library 30520 (1).

39 MacDonald, *Archaeologia second series* 1917, XVIII, pp. 202–10.

40 PRO CO 325/1 f 199v.

41 Roy, *Phil. Trans.* 1785, LXXV, p. 387.

42 R. A. Skelton, 'The Origins of the Ordnance Survey of Great Britain', *Geographical Journal* 1962, CXXVIII, p. 419.

43 MacDonald, *Archaeologia second series* 1917, XVIII, p. 177.

44 British Library Map Library K. Top. V1. 97.; In similar fashion a visit to Ireland in the summer of 1765 resulted in a 'General Map of the South Part of Ireland': BL Map Library K. Top. L1. 30a.

45 British Library Map Library C 7 d 12.

46 J. Fortescue, *The Correspondence of King George the Third from 1760 to December 1783* (London 1927), vol. 1, pp. 328–34.

47 *Ibid.*

48 *Ibid.*

49 *Ibid.*

50 *Ibid.*

51 *Ibid.*

52 *Ibid.*

53 *Ibid.*

54 *Ibid.*

55 *Ibid.*

56 Debbeig's estimate for his 'Military Survey of the Great Harbours in North America', extending over 8 years, amounted to only £23 426 (PRO CO 325/1 f 200v); Samuel Holland's estimate in 1764 for carrying on the 'General Survey of the American Colonies' was even more modest and 'would not amount to above £700 yearly': PRO AO 3/140.

57 PRO WO 30/54, art. 22, and PRO WO 30/115 ff 175–88. See Appendix I.

58 R. A. Skelton, *Saxton's survey of England and Wales. With a facsimile of Saxton's wall-map of 1583* (Amsterdam 1974), pp. 7–8.

59 *Gentleman's Magazine* 1747, vol. 17, p. 406.

60 J. B. Harley, 'The re-mapping of England 1750–1800', *Imago Mundi* 1965, vol. 19, pp. 56–67; Paul Laxton, 'The Geodetic and Topographical Evaluation of English County Maps, 1740–1840', *The Cartographic Journal* 1976, vol. 13, pp. 37–54.

61 J. B. Harley, 'The Society of Arts and the surveys of English counties 1759–1809', *Journal of the Royal Society of Arts* 1963–4, vol. 112, pp. 43–6, 119–24, 269–75, 538–43.

62 Rylands English MS 19, VI, 178.

63 W. Borlase, Original Letters IV, p. 180, 2 July 1757, Library in the Morrab Gardens, Penzance, quoted in W. L. D. Ravenhill, Introduction to *Benjamin Donn. A map of the county of Devon 1765* (facsimile edition, Devonshire Record Society and Exeter University, 1964), p. 3.

64 Royal Society of Arts, Min. Comm. (Polite Arts), 15 March 1759.

65 Lancashire Record Office DDHe 61/22, 'Proposals of P. P. Burdett's *Map of Lancashire*', September 1768.

66 Robert Dossie, *Memoirs of Agriculture, and other Oeconomical Arts*, vol. 1 (London 1758), p. 309.

67 Harley, *Journal of the Society of Arts* 1963–4, vol. 112, p. 45.

68 H. G. Fordham, 'Paterson's roads. Daniel Paterson, his maps and itineraries, 1738–1825', *The Library* Fourth Series, 1925, vol. 5, pp. 332–56. (Transactions of the Bibliographical Society).

69 Harley, *Journal of the Royal Society of Arts*, 1963–64, vol. 112, p. 270.

70 P. J. Guthorn, *British maps of the American Revolution*, (Monmouth Beach N.J. 1972), pp. 42, 46.

71 J. B. Harley and P. Laxton, *A Survey of the County Palatine of Chester, P. P. Burdett 1777*, (Historic Society of Lancashire and Cheshire 1974), p. 5.

72 Skelton, *Geographical Journal* 1962, CXXVIII, p. 417.

73 R. Hahn, *The anatomy of a scientific institution. The Paris Academy of Sciences, 1666–1803* (Los Angeles and London 1971), p. 11.

74 Charles Hutton, George Shaw and Richard Pearson, *The Philosophical Transactions of the Royal Society of London . . . Abridged, with notes and biographic illustrations*. 18 vols. (London 1809).

75 Skelton, 'Cartography 1750–1850', Ch. 20 in C. Singer (ed.) *et al.*, *A History of Technology* (Oxford 1958), vol. IV, p. 596.

76 Skelton, *A History of Technology,* p. 599.

77 *Ibid.* p. 598.

78 Richeson, *English Land Measuring*, pp. 142–88.

79 R. A. Gardiner, 'William Roy, Surveyor and Antiquary', *Geographical Journal* 1977, vol. 143, pp. 439–50.

80 Taylor, *The Mathematical Practitioners of Hanoverian England 1714–1840* (Cambridge 1966), pp. 190–1.

81 Gardiner, *Geographical Journal* 1977, vol. 143, pp. 445–6.

82 Taylor, *Mathematical Practitioners 1714–1840*, pp. 216, 279. See also J. B. Harley and G. Walters, 'William Roy's Maps, Mathematical Instruments and Library: the Christie's Sale of 1790', *Imago Mundi* 1977, vol. 29, pp. 9–22.

83 Roy, 'Experiments and Observations made in Britain, in order to obtain a Rule for measuring Heights with the Barometer', *Phil. Trans.* 1777 LXVII, pp. 653–788.

84 T. E. Allibone, *The Royal Society and its Dining Clubs* (Oxford 1976), pp. 106–16.

85 'A letter from P. Wargentin F.R.S. Secretary to the Royal Academy of Sciences at Stockholm to . . . Maskelyne . . . Astronomer Royal; concerning the Difference of Longitude of the Royal Observatories of Paris and Greenwich', *Phil. Trans.* 1777, LXVII, p. 162.

86 For the Cassini family, see p. 33.

87 RS 'Triangulation letters and papers', DM4, t3.

88 W. R. Dawson (ed.), *The Banks letters, a calendar of the manuscript correspondence of Sir Joseph Banks* (London 1958).

89 Roy, *Phil. Trans.* 1785, LXXV, p. 388.

90 RS DM 4 f 6.

91 RS DM 4 f 5.

92 RS DM 4 f 23.

93 RS DM 4 f 8.

94 RS DM 4 f 9.

95 Roy, *Phil. Trans.* 1785, LXXV, pp. 391–2.

96 PRO WO 54/248: 'Surveyor General's Office, Return Book of Royal Engineers for the years 1786, 1787, 1788, 1789, 1790, 1791 and 1792.'

97 William Roy, 'An Account of the Trigonometrical Operation, whereby the Distance between the Meridians of the Royal Observatories of Greenwich and Paris has been determined', *Phil. Trans.* 1790, LXXX, p. 111.

98 Close, *Early Years*, p. 17.

99 Roy, *Phil. Trans.* 1785, LXXV, p. 425.

100 *Ibid.* p. 456.

101 *Ibid.* p. 425.

102 See p. 34.

103 Lloyd A. Brown, *The Story of Maps* (Boston 1949), p. 257.

104 Roy, *Phil. Trans.* 1785, LXXV, p. 425.

105 RS Journal [Copy], vol. 32, 1785–7.

106 Roy to Lind, Sept. 1786, quoted in Close, *Early Years*, p. 19.

107 Roy to Lind, 2 July 1787, quoted in Close, *Early Years*, p. 19.

108 William Roy, 'An Account of the Mode proposed to be followed in determining the relative Situation of the Royal Observatories of Greenwich and Paris', *Phil. Trans.* 1787, LXXVII, p. 189.

109 RS. DM 4 f 23.

110 Sir Joseph Banks's copy of *Phil. Trans.* 1790, LXXX, part I is in the British Library, pressmark L.R. 292.

111 Roy, *Phil. Trans.* 1790, LXXX, p. 170.

112 Roy, *Phil. Trans.* 1785, LXXV, p. 390.

113 Roy, *Phil. Trans.* 1787, LXXVII, p. 188.

114 Roy to Lind, 23 June 1787, quoted in Close, *Early Years,* p. 20.

115 Roy, *Phil. Trans.* 1790, LXXX, p. 114.

116 Roy to Lind, 17 Aug. 1787, quoted in Close, *Early Years,* p. 21.

117 Roy, *Phil. Trans.* 1790, LXXX, p. 114.

118 *Ibid.* p. 115.

119 RS Letters and Papers, Decade IX, no. 168.

120 RS MM. 3.30: Ramsden to the Council of the Royal Society, 13 May 1790.

121 Dawson, *The Banks Letters*, p. 720.

122 See p. 36.

123 Roy, *Phil. Trans.* 1790, LXXX, p. 262.

2
The Resumption
of the
Trigonometrical
Survey

Know . . .
That on the summit whither thou art bound
A geographic Labourer pitched his tent,
With books supplied and instruments of art,
To measure height and distance; lonely task,
Week after week pursued!

Wordsworth, 1813, from 'Written with a slate pencil on a stone on the side of the Mountain of Black Comb'.

When General William Roy died in July 1790 the immediate result was a suspension of the trigonometrical activities in south-east England on which he had been engaged. Mudge and Dalby, writing in 1799, noted that a 'considerable time had elapsed since the General's decease without any apparent intention of renewing the business',[1] and Portlock, the nineteenth-century biographer of Colby, remarked that the 'subject of a survey seemed, for a time, to be overlooked'.[2] That the work was in fact resumed with an interruption of only eleven months was largely owing to the personal initiative of the Duke of Richmond as Master General of the Ordnance. It was entirely consistent with his interest in cartography that he should have used the weight of his office to help promote such an undertaking at a national level. As a landowner and public administrator he was acutely map conscious and was incurably enthusiastic for schemes of military engineering.[3] In the 1780s he had shown himself to be much in sympathy with the objectives of Roy's work and there can be little doubt that sooner or later he intended to carry it on.

An immediate spark for his action in 1791 is more difficult to locate. Once again, Mudge and Dalby, the commentators closest in time to the events they describe, seem to have been convinced that it was almost a chance occurrence. They wrote of the 'casual opportunity' which had

> presented itself to the Duke of Richmond of purchasing a very fine instrument, the workmanship of Mr Ramsden, of similar construction to that which was used by General Roy, but with some improvements.[4]

The 'instrument' was a second three-foot theodolite which, together with two one-hundred-foot chains of steel, had been especially constructed to the order of the East India Company for triangulation in India. In a rather curious and indirect way, these can be regarded as yet another legacy from Roy to the trigonometrical activities which were resumed after his death. In 1787 he had read a paper to the Royal Society on the design of the triangulation he intended to execute in linking the observatories of Greenwich and Paris; part of his argument drew attention to the scientific value of accurate measurements of chains of triangles covering several degrees of latitude and longitude in different parts of the world. In particular he believed that 'the British dominions in the East-Indies' offered an especially favourable location 'for the measurement of five degrees of latitude on the coast of Choromandel' and that 'Two degrees of longitude, at each extremity of this arc, should likewise be measured'.[5] In pressing this suggestion Roy had sent a copy of his paper to the Court of Directors of the East India Company who referred it to two experts, Alexander Dalrymple and James Rennell, both of whom had first-hand knowledge of the region.[6] It was their support which led the East India Company to order a duplicate of the three-foot theodolite which had already been constructed for Roy, but Ramsden, always a perfectionist, had included a number of improvements derived from Roy's experience with the earlier design. To cover these sophistications Ramsden had asked for a price higher than his original estimate and the East India Company had thereupon refused to buy the theodolite.[7]

This was the 'casual opportunity' seized by the Duke of Richmond in 1791, but it is open to question whether it provides a complete explanation for the date of resumption of the trigonometrical survey. To Sir Charles Close at least it seemed 'quite inadequate'.[8] He preferred to stress the military advantages of resuming the work at this moment; yet in the summer of 1791 there was no immediate threat of war with France, and only months later Pitt was to introduce his budget of 1792 with a somewhat guarded prophecy of fifteen years of peace.[9] But if the truth is more complex than any single factor and if the Duke had several motives including (as Colby wrote many years later) 'to support the scientific reputation of the Country, and to improve the Corps under his command',[10] the availability of Ramsden's theodolite can still be regarded as the immediate cause of his decision.

First Appointments to the Trigonometrical Survey

The records of the Board of Ordnance enable a little flesh to be put on the bare bones of these speculations. In relation to the argument above it is probably only marginally significant that the first official reference to the Duke of Richmond's initiative should have been a small entry in the Expense Ledger of the Board on 21 June 1791 to the effect that £373. 14s. had been paid to Jesse Ramsden for the theodolite for the Trigonometrical Survey.[11] And in the Minutes of the Board, a day later, the fuller scope of the Duke's action is revealed:

> George William Phipps Esq., Under Secretary to the Master General, having by letter of this date signified that his Grace having taken His Majesty's Pleasure for proceeding with the Trigonometrical Operation begun by the late Major General Roy, and having procured a proper Instrument for that purpose, He had found it necessary to appoint a fit Person to take charge thereof and to attend to the various Calculations, that his Grace had fixed upon Mr Dalby for that Employment, who was to be allowed 100 Guineas per Annum from the 1st inst. exclusive of six shillings per diem when in the Field, and his Travelling Expenses for moving from Place to Place at the usual rate of 1/3d. p. mile, for which Mr Dalby would from time to time make out a Bill to be certified by the Officer who had the chief Direction of the Operation.[12]

It emerges from this entry that, apart from the chance to procure the 'proper Instrument', a central part of Richmond's strategy had been to obtain the blessing of the Crown for the resumption of the trigonometrical activities. George III had given full support to Roy's schemes and while a contemporary description of him as

> A generous and beneficent Monarch, whose knowledge and love of the sciences are sufficiently evinced by the protection which HE constantly affords them[13]

may be rather flowery, his continuing interest in the trigonometrical work could have tipped the opinion of the Government in its favour.

The Minute of 22 June 1791 also records the first appointment to the Survey by the Duke. That it should have been a civilian, Isaac Dalby, who became the earliest recorded employee of the national survey was probably a matter of coincidental timing rather than of any deep symbolic significance. Dalby, born in 1744, was already in his mid-forties at the time of his appointment and he was obviously brought onto the Ordnance pay-roll to strengthen the mathematical expertise available to the Survey. His main experience was as a teacher of mathematics – at Archbishop Tenison's grammar school, near Charing Cross, and at the naval school at Chelsea – but he had also been employed by Topham Beauclerk in making astronomical observations; he belongs to that wider group of mathematical practitioners who did much to underpin the scientific and technological advances of the eighteenth century. Of equal relevance to this post with the Trigonometrical Survey was that, following a recommendation by Ramsden, he had been employed by Roy from 1787 until 1790 in making calculations in connection with the observations to relate the meridians of Paris and Greenwich. Thus, as well as being the 'connecting link between the preceding and the successive stages of this great work',[14] he was probably a fairly obvious choice as first mathematician to assist with the primary triangulation. Dalby remained with the Trigonometrical Survey until, 'no longer able to endure the fatigues incident to the service', he resigned in 1799 on becoming Professor of Mathematics in the Royal Military College at High Wycombe.[15] He was succeeded in his post as observer and mathematician by another civilian, Simon Woolcot from South Molton in Devon, who was employed by the Survey until he died in the field in 1819.[16] These appointments were outstanding examples of the continuing Ordnance Survey tradition of employing civilians as well as military personnel within the same organization. Later, especially in the survey of Ireland, the role of civilian assistants was to be a contentious issue, but in the early years the need to import skilled man-power from outside the ranks of the Board of Ordnance does not seem to have been questioned.

In any case the Duke of Richmond quickly and firmly placed the executive direction of the Survey in military hands. His next action, on 12 July 1791, was to appoint

> Major Williams and Lieut. Mudge, of the Royal Regiment of Artillery, to carry on the Trigonometrical Survey with the assistance of Mr Dalby, and desired that they might receive an Extra Allowance equal to their pay and half-pay whilst actually in the field.[17]

Once again, careful thought seems to have been given to these key appointments; the Duke had consulted Dr Charles Hutton, Professor of Mathematics at the Royal Military Academy, Woolwich, as to the best officers of Artillery and Engineers to take charge of the Survey. In recommending Williams and Mudge, Hutton

> sincerely believed he had named the best mathematicians in the two Corps, and the fittest officers for this duty . . . it would have been very difficult to have found persons better qualified anywhere,[18]

but it would seem that his judgment of the potential of the two men was not wholly sound for Williams failed to live up to expectations. Neither contemporaries who worked with him nor later historians seem to have had much to say in his favour. His career in the Artillery was fairly orthodox; after passing through the Royal Military Academy at Woolwich he saw service at the siege of Belle Isle in 1761 and in North America during the War of Independence.[19] In eight years with the Survey, he seems to have made little impact and even if he did not unduly inhibit the attainment of its scientific objectives, he had little of the infectious enthusiasm which was a hallmark of the leadership of both Mudge and Colby; a few surviving letters convey a precise and bureaucratic mind.[20] His severest critic was probably Dalby who wrote in 1821:

> . . . truth compels me to drop eulogy in noticing our colleague Col. W. who nominally was the principal; I say *nominally*, because he never made an observation, or calculation, nor did he write a line of any of the printed accounts; in fact, he proved a dead weight in the undertaking by frequently retarding its progress: and the only time he benefited the service, was when he took his departure to the next world.[21]

Williams had died in 1798 and, in default of a more charitable notice, this must remain the obituary for the Survey's first director.

The Directorate of William Mudge 1798–1820

The first effective director of the Ordnance Survey was William Mudge, a Devonshire man born in 1762, who held this office for twenty-two critical years from 1798 until his death in 1820. Although the biographer of the Mudge family[22] provides only meagre information on William's early years in Plymouth, there can be little doubt that his family circle, which included Samuel Johnson (his godfather), Sir Joshua Reynolds and John Smeaton, helped to direct him towards a career in which he achieved some distinction as director of the national survey, and international recognition as a geodesist.

William Mudge's grandfather, who can be regarded as the founder of the Mudge dynasty, was Zachariah Mudge (1694–1769), a celebrated divine, and vicar of St Andrew's in Plymouth.[23] His father was John Mudge (1721–93), a physician (and author of a *Dissertation on the Inoculated Small Pox*) who in 1777 had been awarded the Copley Medal of the Royal Society for his metallurgical and optical research into the metal and lenses most appropriate for use in reflecting telescopes.[24] Added to this parental influence on William Mudge's interests were the ideas and enthusiasms of his uncle, Thomas Mudge (1717–94), the horologist. Thomas had been apprenticed to George Graham, the London instrument maker,[25] and had then become a master clock-maker before quitting active business in 1771 and retiring to Plymouth in order to concentrate on the improvement of chronometers designed to ascertain, with the aid of a sextant, longitude at sea. His failure to obtain Parliament's reward for his chronometer (a further £10 000 offered by the Board of Longitude in about 1773) and his long dispute with Nevil Maskelyne, the Astronomer Royal, were among the scientific *causes célèbres* of the late eighteenth century.[26] The young William Mudge must have been deeply impressed by this scientific environment; when he came to make a series of observations in Devon and Cornwall in 1795 and 1796, on several occasions he was careful to compare his own measurements with those made earlier by scientists who had worked in the region when he was a boy.[27]

Mudge entered the Royal Military Academy as a cadet on 17 April 1777, and would have received, in line with the contemporary syllabus, a basic education in elementary mathematics, the principles of artillery and fortification, and at least an introduction to the survey and drawing of military maps and plans.[28] In July 1779 he was commissioned as Second Lieutenant in the Royal Artillery and was posted to serve under Cornwallis in the War of American Independence. Afterwards he returned to the headquarters of the Board of Ordnance in the Tower of London and it was during this period that 'he began studying mathematics and mechanics'. Some of this knowledge, in the family tradition, he applied to the 'construction of some clocks for his private amusement'. But he was a serious student of mathematics and, 'perceiving the advantage of this branch of science, he set to work sedulously . . . applying to Dr Hutton* for assistance, when he found himself in any difficulty . . . [and] by perseverance became at last a first-rate mathematician'.[29]

It was undoubtedly this additional training undertaken in his twenties, coupled with the scientific charisma of the family name, which finally groomed Mudge for his career in the Ordnance Survey. And it was through the same network of patronage and friendship that, upon the establishment of the Trigonometrical Survey under the Board of Ordnance, he came to be recommended as one of the first officers of its small staff. As the only other military officer on the Survey, Mudge was Williams's natural successor as director, but his appointment was by no means automatic, for Cornwallis, Master General of the Ordnance, thought it necessary to consult the Duke of Richmond (who had retired from office in 1795) as to his suitability. Mudge's letter of appointment from Mr Apsley, the Master General's secretary, ran:

> I have the commands of the Master General to acquaint you that, sensible of the zeal and ability you have shewn in that part of the Trigonometrical Survey, which it has fallen to your lot to execute on the death of Lieut. Col. Williams, it was his Lordship's intention to have intrusted to you the conduct of its continuation; and it is with additional satisfaction and confidence that Lord Cornwallis now appoints you to that situation, assured of its coinciding with the wishes of his Grace the Duke of Richmond.
>
> His Lordship desires that you will accordingly take on yourself the charge, as it has hitherto been held by Colonel Williams.[30]

It would be an unduly harsh verdict on Mudge's twenty-two years of office merely to record that he failed to advance significantly either the geodetic concepts of the age of Roy or the techniques of geodetic measurement. In this matter, as in his comparative failure to regulate the work of the topographical survey, his performance has first to be weighed against the fact that until 1815 the country was at war with France. In several fundamental respects the conduct of the Survey was subservient to the demands of war.

After 1793, when hostilities with France were formally started, the national role of the Survey underwent a sharp change. In Roy's day, and even after 1791, the trigonometrical activities were largely a scientific operation undertaken for the 'progress of geography' and sponsored by the Royal Society, but by the date when Mudge took office the Survey's priorities were mostly bound up with the defence of the country. Even the progress of the primary triangulation came to be partly fashioned by military expediency, which became an important consideration in the spread of the triangulation during the 1790s in Kent and Essex, and in the West Country in particular. Writing in 1795, reviewing the progress of the four previous years, Mudge noted how in the 'early stages of the survey, the first object in view [had] been to determine the situations of the principal points on the sea coast, and those objects . . . near to it'.[31] Rather than continuing the early triangulation northwards, it was now a deliberate policy to fix points along the whole length of the invasion coasts, in the knowledge of their potential value in constructing military maps at short notice, and it was this requirement, 'to consider the survey of the sea coast',[32] which brought the primary triangulation to Land's End by 1796, much earlier than might otherwise have been the case.

Against such pressures Mudge's greatest contribution may perhaps be seen as the extent to which he managed to preserve the scientific and cartographic objectives of the Survey. The initial advantage of being sponsored by such a powerful and prestigious body as the Board of Ordnance could easily evaporate in war-time. Together with the Quartermaster-General's Department (with which there was rivalry) the Board of Ordnance had responsibility for organizing counter-measures and constructing defensive works against the threat of invasion.[33] The Board's adviser on the matter of fortification was the senior Royal Engineer officer, the Chief Engineer; in 1802 his title was changed by Royal Warrant to 'Inspector-General of Fortifications and Works'.[34] The fledgling Ordnance Survey came under the orders of the Inspector-General of Fortifications, and Mudge, as a relatively junior officer, could do little to moderate the demands made on it, even when they interfered with the programme of geodetic and cartographic work. As it was, both Mudge and the handful of trained men under his command were frequently diverted to assignments outside the normal course of the Survey.

* Dr Charles Hutton FRS, 1737–1823, professor at the RMA, was one of the most esteemed mathematical teachers of the period.

In the last ten years or so of Mudge's directorate he accepted various public offices outside the Survey. Among these appointments the most important was that in 1809 as Lieutenant-Governor of the Royal Military Academy at Woolwich.[35] When he first took stock of the situation there he described the Academy as being 'in ruins', and to 'remedy the state of things he at once struck at the root of the evil, and set to work to bring about better discipline, and management, among the Cadets'.[36] His success can be judged, not only from the detailed records of the Academy, but also from a letter to him in 1817 from Lord Chatham who was Master General at the time of his appointment, expressing gratification

> to learn that the Royal Military Academy has so fully answered all that was expected from it, and that it has attained that degree of perfection, the accomplishment of which was, he was confident, best insured, when it was placed under Colonel Mudge's auspices.[37]

It was no doubt this appointment which led in the following year to Mudge's being nominated as public examiner of the newly-established college of the East India Company at Addiscombe which was to be responsible for training its artillery and engineer officers in the Woolwich mould.[38] And as if three jobs – the Survey, Woolwich and Addiscombe – were not sufficiently demanding, Mudge was also a member of the Council of the Royal Society, and a Commissioner of the Board of Longitude.[39]

In one sense this public recognition may be taken as a confirmation of Mudge's ability and political acumen but, at the same time, the fact cannot be ignored that after 1809 the amount of time he could devote to the day-to-day running of the Survey was progressively curtailed. By 1811 pressures were building up and were accompanied by a deterioration of his health which marred the rest of his period in office. He wrote:

> My labours are great and I am without strength to carry my chains. I can assure you that I am a slave, and not wearing golden chains.[40]

and again, in the same year,

> I have more business on my hands that I have strength for, or if I had strength, even time to perform, and this has always been the case.[41]

The holding of plural office under a body as bureaucratic as the Board of Ordnance naturally had its frustrations and on occasions Mudge even had to obtain leave of absence from Woolwich to attend to the business of the Survey. In June 1814, for example, it was noted that the Master General had no objection to his surrendering

> the charge of the Royal Military Academy to Colonel Phipps (Inspector) till the end of October, to admit of Colonel Mudge inspecting the Trigonometrical Survey carrying on under the immediate superintendence of Captain Colby.[42]

It is in the light of the demands of war and of Mudge's multiple responsibilities that he must be judged. Dalby, capable of reminiscing in bitter mood, was unstinting in his praise for Mudge as 'always . . . zealous, active, and indefatigable in carrying on the Survey'.[43] At times it is clear that Mudge had to maintain a balancing act in moving the Survey along at a brisk enough pace to satisfy his masters, yet at the same time safeguarding scientific standards. In 1805, for example, he urged Colby not to make

> a practice of going to all the three points of every triangle, if observation made at two of them will be sufficient. Work round spires, staffs on mountains or any other proper objects, that the Survey may get on rapidly.[44]

In spite of this apparent departure from sound principles, there can be few doubts either of his competence as a surveyor or of his grasp of scientific method. When stationed in the Tower of London, in which the drawing-room became the headquarters of the Survey, he continued to keep a watchful eye on activities in the field, and his correspondence with Thomas Colby, his young deputy, provides many small insights into the thoroughness with which he directed the scientific observations. In one note, Simon Woolcot was to be reminded 'in observing the star', not to 'lean with his arm, or rest his breast on the Cover of the Instrument'.[45]

The same attention to detail was applied to the internal management of the Survey. Even when in the field Mudge maintained a flow of official letters,[46] and his administrative meticulousness did much to lay a secure foundation for the organization in its formative years. The financial accounts of the fieldwork and engraving were always regularly and scrupulously presented to the Board of Ordnance, and Mudge's probity in the public service was such that from 'his entrance into office until the day of his decease' he retained the 'cover of every letter charged for by him' so that he could easily prove that he 'had never placed the postage of a single private letter to the public account'.[47] This can be taken as a comment on his systematic habit of mind as much as on his honesty. To one historian at least such methodical virtue amounted to dullness and while accepting that Mudge was 'indomitable' and 'unbeatable at his job' felt him to be

> dreary with the inescapable dullness of any one-track-minded fanatic with a tedious subject; there is not a trace of lightness, brightness, or wit in the numerous and heavy pages of his published accounts of the survey work.[48]

As an assessment this appears to be wide of the mark, perhaps because it was derived, as the quotation implies, from a perusal of the published reports of the trigonometrical work, understandably written in a dry-enough style. Mudge's personal correspondence – as with Richard Rosedew,[49] his brother-in-law, or with Colby – brings the man alive. Far from being dull or narrow he is revealed as a warm and lively correspondent, with a keen sense of humour, keeping fully abreast of cultural, political and scientific matters which transcended the routine work of the Survey. Nor can there be much doubt about his kindly nature and consideration for those who worked under him. Perhaps the most sincere tribute to this quality came from Robert Dawson, the topographical draughtsman, who shortly after Mudge's death wrote:

> the connection of 18 years is dissolved and we are left in sorrow and reflection. The General's kind and amiable disposition, his mildness of temper, gentleness of command, and many marks of attachment and regard given to me particularly, and evidently always ready for his Friends, have created and nourished a Love for him in my heart, which will ever be the first impulse with which I shall cherish his memory.[50]

The words surpass the convention of a sad occasion. Not the least of Mudge's strong points, especially critical perhaps in a small and embryo organization, was that by tactful delegation he could get the best out of his assistants.

But was this enough? Perhaps the fairest verdict on Mudge is that, although he was administratively and technically competent, his vision of the future of the Survey seems to have been relatively narrow when compared with that of Roy and some of his nineteenth-century successors, notably Colby and Henry James. Mudge's ambitions were seldom focused beyond the job in hand. Thus, while Roy at one point envisaged a survey of the 'British Islands', it was with evident relief that in 1805 Mudge remarked to Colby: 'The Irish Military Survey Bill has no reference to us!'[51]

An obituary of Mudge referred to him as 'almost penuriously careful of the public money'. It continued:

> he was fearful lest his character should suffer by making applications for assistance, that might be deemed superfluous to those who were unacquainted with the necessities of his department, and who might, in the hurry of business, neglect to give him the opportunity of affording full explanations. This disposition deprived him of those means which would, had he possessed them, have enabled him to display his abilities to much greater advantage, both for his own fame, and the progress of the work. The public expected much more from the Conductors of the Trigonometrical part of the Survey, than it was possible for the number of individuals employed to perform; and whilst a continual arrear of business was unavoidably accumulating, the ardour of Science could not but suffer an abatement. Before General Mudge could make up his mind to apply for any new assistant, the aid of that assistant had been long required.[52]

In short, Mudge was a ponderously cautious man. While he was prepared to fight in public for what he considered to be the just dues of the Survey, he privately admitted to Colby in 1816 that it was his desire not to have more of the public money in his hands than was actually wanted.[53] Except perhaps in the matter of a geological survey, for which John MacCulloch was appointed geologist to the Trigonometrical Survey in 1814,[54] there is little evidence that Mudge attempted to extend the scope of the national survey in any significant direction.

On occasions Mudge acted as though he were the victim of a conspiracy against the Survey. In 1816 he wrote feelingly to Colby:

> that I have more difficulties thrown in my way as to the progress of the map making by Ignorance, Avarice, and Cupidity than you have by the intervention of Mountains, Morasses with all the local difficulties peculiar to Scotland put together.[55]

And in 1819, a little over a year before his death, he was again writing to Colby about the Duke of Wellington (by then appointed Master General of the Ordnance) who was complaining about imperfections in the published sheet (Old Series sheet 12) containing his country seat at Stratfield Saye:

> It is my intention to battle this matter inch by inch. To all appearances I shall See a great deal more of His Grace than will be pleasing. I am quite depressed under all these considerations.[56]

Perhaps he lacked the essential toughness so amply possessed by Colby; a director so beset, and in failing health, had little inclination to ponder long-term strategies for the Survey. Mudge was no innovator.

The Apprenticeship of Thomas Colby*

In one respect at least – in his choice of a deputy as able as Thomas Colby – Mudge did much to compensate for any deficiencies of his own. But it would be unfair to Colby not to give him credit for recognizing and learning from Mudge's comparative failures. Colby was to pay a great deal of attention to the technical and organizational weaknesses he inherited when he became Superintendent; from him the Survey was to derive much of the organization and most of the methods which were to be used for over a century. However, he had worked for nearly two decades under Mudge's directorate; these were his formative years and the mature 'Colby system' no doubt owed some of its characteristics to the kindly tutelage of Mudge.

Thomas Frederick Colby (1784–1852) was the eldest son of a military family with an estate near Newcastle Emlyn in South Wales and, like Mudge, he was well connected inasmuch as his mother was the sister of Major-General John Murray Hadden, sometime secretary to the Duke of Richmond, who was to become Surveyor General of the Ordnance from 1804 to 1810, at a critical juncture in the Napoleonic War.[57] Colby was an able pupil, mathematically and in other respects, and before reaching his seventeenth birthday had passed out of the Royal Military Academy to be commissioned as Second-Lieutenant of Royal Engineers on 21 December 1801.[58] In one sense he was the first true 'career' officer of the Ordnance Survey because while all its other founding fathers (as indeed nearly all of its principal officers subsequently) were posted to and from other duties, Colby was attached immediately to the Ordnance Survey and remained in its service for the rest of his professional life until his retirement in 1846. He and Mudge were able to work in undisturbed harness for almost twenty years, which were of the utmost importance in a critical period of the Survey's early history.

According to Portlock, Colby was very much the personal choice of Mudge. His appointment may have been smoothed by the fact that Hadden was secretary to the Master General at the time, but we know that it was Mudge who took the initiative; on 12 January 1802, in applying for Colby's services, he wrote:

> On examination I find him well grounded in the rudiments of mathematics, and, in other respects, perfectly calculated . . . to be employed in this Business . . . I beg to point out to your Lordship, the expediency of Lt. Colby being attached to me with some degree of permanency, and also to request, you be pleased to assign him to my orders on that principle.[59]

The appointment was made three days later in the manner Mudge had suggested; a Minute records that 'Second-Lieutenant Thomas Colby, of the Corps of Royal Engineers' was ordered to place himself under Mudge's command, 'to be employed on the Trigonometrical Survey'.[60] Here then was the first officer of the Royal Engineers to be appointed to the Survey, and from then until 1977, all directors of the Ordnance Survey were to be taken from this Corps.

Under Mudge, Colby received a thorough grounding in all aspects of a national survey. He had been appointed largely to assist with the trigonometrical observations and he worked throughout Mudge's term of office on the northward extension of the primary triangulation, but as the detailed mapping of England was extended after 1805 he was progressively drawn into the day-to-day administration and, in the Ordnance map office in the Tower of London, helped to organize computation, drawing, engraving and printing, and even to arrange the early attempts at wider publicity for the Survey's products. By 1820 his experience included all stages of map-making and he often had to assume full executive responsibility for the over-all quality of the work. This was necessary because of Mudge's frequent absences on other business, and was possible owing to the warm personal relationship between the two men. As early as 1805 Mudge could write to Colby:

> Glad I am that I have a man with me, who can think and act as you do . . . I wish you in all things to consult your own will, convenience and happiness, requiring you only to be punctual to writing me about all you do.[61]

and in September 1813 Mudge again remarked: '. . . how happy I am to account myself, that Providence has placed to my hand so able and so firm a friend'.[62] As the relationship ripened so the degree of delegation increased to the extent that Colby was perhaps more intensively prepared for taking over the leadership than any other Director of the Survey.

Many incidents in Colby's career, if amply confirming Mudge's assessment of his abilities and dedication to the work of the Survey, also reveal him as a man of sometimes unstable temperament. It is not that he lacked kindliness, but that he was often prickly, sensitive to criticism, and unable to work

---

* In *The Early Years of the Ordnance Survey* Close draws extensively on 'a considerable number of letters and documents, hitherto unpublished', consisting mainly of letters collected by Colby. These papers were presented to the Ordnance Survey by Close and were destroyed during the air raids on Southampton in 1940. Close to Phipps, 19 April 1952. Copy in Ordnance Survey Library.

well on occasions with those who, it must be said, seemed potentially most capable of stealing his thunder.[63] Such qualities are not unknown in successful men but in Colby they sometimes went beyond the bounds of wisdom; a possible explanation may lie in the serious accident which all but ended his career shortly after he joined the Survey. It occurred near Liskeard in Cornwall, on a day in December 1803 when he was inspecting the work of the trainee surveyors, and is described by Mudge in a letter to General Morse, the Inspector-General of Fortifications:

> On Monday last, L! Colby in the act of placing an over-loaded Pistol on the Ground, was severely wounded from its going off unexpectedly:– His left hand grasped the Barrel, and was so violently injured, that amputation became necessary:– It accordingly was taken off just above the wrist, the same Evening. The loss of his hand is not the only misfortune to be deplored, as his Skull received a violent blow, producing a Fracture in the Forehead . . . The Brain it seems remains free from any injury; nor any future evil apprehended beyond a scar.[64]

In a purely physical sense Colby clearly overcame his disability. His scientific colleagues later marvelled at the skill with which he was still able to make observations, even with Ramsden's zenith sector;[65] and if his reported feats in hill walking between trigonometrical stations in Scotland are anything to judge by, he was more determined than ever to prove his fitness. Despite Mudge's view, the effects of the accident on his personality are more difficult to assess. According to Portlock, he showed a 'reluctance to enter on long-continued mental exertion' and in other contexts 'a morbid apprehension of criticism' and occasionally an 'over-strained prejudice'.[66] There is no proof that such personality traits were owing to the injuries of 1803 yet, whatever the cause, Colby's later inability to get on with some of his most able junior officers reached irrational and even mildly paranoiac proportions. For the most part this side of Colby's nature was dampened down, or at least kept out of the public eye, under the equable leadership of Mudge.

After Mudge's death on 17 April 1820, the succession to his office remained for some time undecided, a matter on which, understandably enough, Colby was particularly sensitive from the points of view both of his military career and of his reputation as a scientist. It must have been obvious to all and sundry that Colby was the man to fill the vacant post, and indeed Olinthus Gregory, Professor of Mathematics in the Royal Military Academy, wrote soothingly that the Survey had been

> for so many years conducted and carried on so entirely by yourself, that I should have thought that the Master General would have settled the appointment the next day.[67]

The Duke of Wellington took no immediate steps to fill the vacancy and left Colby to carry the additional responsibility without certainty of promotion. It is likely that there was nothing more sinister in the delay than that Wellington was busy with his many other commitments, but Colby's anxiety built up to the extent that, after two months with no news, he took the bull by the horns, and addressed a letter to the Master General, reminding him of the unresolved state of affairs. He wrote:

> I have used no interest, I have solicited no one of your Grace's noble friends to paint my character or conduct on the Survey in glowing colours; but I have a firm but humble reliance that your Grace would, when the press of more important business allowed opportunity, enquire how far my conduct and character would render me deserving of confidence and enable me to conduct the Survey with efficiency and credit to the country.[68]

He mentioned several eminent persons to whom reference could be made, including Dr Charles Hutton, Professor of Mathematics at the Royal Military College; Professor Bonnycastle and Dr Gregory of the Woolwich Academy; Dr William Pearson of East Sheen; the Professors of Natural Philosophy and Mathematics at Edinburgh, Aberdeen and St Andrews. It is not clear how far this direct approach transgressed the proprieties of promotion in the Board of Ordnance, but the Duke of Wellington, fortunately for Colby and for the future of the Survey, does not seem to have reacted in any way against the obvious candidate. A month later, after some of the references had been taken up, Colby was appointed to succeed Mudge.[69] He was already proving himself to be potentially the most independent and single-minded of the early directors.

The Trigonometrical Operations and the Scientific Image of the Early Ordnance Survey

In 1811, when Mudge was questioned by the Commissioners of Military Enquiry about the 'original objects' of the Survey he replied that it 'was to ascertain by a correct trigonometrical operation, the situation of all Head-lands upon the Channel, Eminences, and the remarkable objects throughout the Country, thereby preparing correct Materials for a geographical description of it'.[70]

Twenty years after the resumption of Roy's triangulation, the trigonometrical activities were still regarded as of paramount importance. Indeed to some observers they were an end in themselves; the triangulation, their argument ran, required neither the topographical survey nor the published maps to justify its existence.

The growth of such an attitude stemmed from the stress laid by early nineteenth-century scientists on the need for accurate locational data, at a time when many of the accepted values for the geographical co-ordinates of even familiar regional and national landmarks were at best shaky.[71]* The remedying of this situation, for military, maritime and scientific purposes, was initially the main *raison d'être* for the national survey and it is a measure of its importance that so many angles in the triangulation, distances between trigonometrical stations, and also tables of latitudes and longitudes should have been printed in a journal as prestigious as the *Philosophical Transactions*. In supplying such information, which could be used for the correction of other maps and in the rectification of marine charts, the Trigonometrical Survey was seen to be discharging its primary scientific responsibility.** It was quite content to provide a service for other map-makers and, to assist surveyors wishing to visit stations, 'small stakes [were] placed over the stones sunk in the ground, having their tops projecting a little above it'.[72] It was in the same spirit that the Commissioners of 1811 were able to suggest that 'after the public objects of the Trigonometrical Survey were attained, it might have been left to individual speculation to fill up the Triangles with a Local Survey'.[73] Such a philosophy was damaging to the prospects of surveying and publishing the official one-inch maps, but its short-term effect was to enhance the scientific reputation of the Trigonometrical Survey.

At a national level, the scientific momentum generated by Roy was to be restored with the very first act of the reconstituted Survey in 1791; the remeasurement of the base on Hounslow Heath. This operation, as in Roy's day, took place in the presence of several dignitaries of the scientific establishment, including Sir Joseph Banks, Dr Maskelyne the Astronomer Royal, Jesse Ramsden, Dr Charles Hutton and a number of other members of the Royal Society.[74] And Mudge's decision in 1801 to interrupt the continuity of the trigonometrical survey with the measurement of an arc of meridian was likewise taken for scientific reasons.[75]

Although the Survey was occasionally under fire from 'anonymous scribblers of despicable characters' who 'inserted some feeble attacks upon it, in one or two of the most contemptible and unprincipled of the daily newspapers',[76] in general the scientific community in Britain was convinced of its merit. In 1798, when Mudge was elected to the Royal Society, he was informed by the President, Sir Joseph Banks, that the Fellows 'were well aware of the zeal, diligence and ability, he had shown in executing the interesting duty in which he was engaged'.[77] And in 1805 the *Edinburgh Review* believed that the continuation of the Trigonometrical Survey of England gave cause for congratulation to all who were 'interested in the progress of science', especially when the country was engaged in 'long and expensive wars'.[78] Ten years later the gloss of these glowing opinions was still bright; John Playfair, the geologist and mathematician, reflecting on the geodetic operations, wrote:

> ... the British Army – in General Roy ... and the officers who have succeeded him in the conduct of the English Survey – will have the glory of doing more for the advancement of general science than has ever been performed by any other body of military men.[79]

The Trigonometrical Survey also maintained some of the international contacts which had been inaugurated with the Anglo-French triangulation in 1783. Throughout Mudge's directorate an awareness of the Survey's scientific work was not confined to Britain, and the published results of the main operations were examined carefully in several other countries, where they did not always escape criticism. A particularly acrimonious dispute developed after the Spanish astronomer, Don Joseph Rodriguez, had thrown doubt in the *Philosophical Transactions* for 1812 on some of the observations for the Dunnose to Clifton arc of meridian.[80] It was said that Mudge was too ill to reply personally so the cause was taken up by Olinthus Gregory;[81] a century later Sir Charles Close dismissed it as a 'wearisome small business'.[82] But whatever the geodetic rights and wrongs of the controversy it pointed to a continuing involvement of the Trigonometrical Survey in scientific questions at an international level. This was partly, at least, owing to the superb instruments designed by Ramsden which focused foreign eyes on the domestic survey. In 1816 Heinrich Schumacher, the eminent Danish astronomer, was so impressed with Ramsden's zenith sector that he requested its loan for celestial observations in his own country.[83] His letter to Mudge referred to the 'beautiful work you have just terminated'; at about the same time Mudge was also in touch with the leading French scientist, J. F. D. Arago, who mentioned the 'confidence with which your operations have inspired

---

* Mudge noted that even in the *Requisite Tables* published by order of the Board of Longitude the position of the Scilly Isles was incorrectly given and this he found surprising 'in a maritime country, like our own, where chronometers are in such constant use'.

** The publication of the results of triangulation was common in Europe.

those scientific men who are best able to appreciate them'.[84] The French had a high enough opinion of the work of the Trigonometrical Survey to see it as the means of extending the Spanish and French arc of meridian, and in 1817 the *Bureau de Longitudes* sent Jean Baptiste Biot to England to engage in joint observations with Mudge's party in the Shetlands. It is an indicator of Colby's tetchiness that, once Mudge had had to return south because of illness, the probability quickly receded of completing the objectives of the expedition. Biot and Colby, reacting like oil and water and even pitching their camps in different islands, failed to co-operate in any significant way.[85] Much the same could be said of the partly abortive Anglo-French observations made with Ramsden's zenith sector at Dunkerque in 1818.[86]

In August 1820, the month in which Colby was promoted to Major,[87] arrangements were complete for reobserving the cross-Channel connection made by Roy in 1787. Colby had been informed of the proposed combined operation by Sir Humphrey Davy:

> The French have measured an . . . arc of the meridian from Formentera to Dunkirk and the British surveys . . . extend from the south of England to Zetland. These arcs combined would give an admeasurement of more than 20 degrees of Latitude or about 1/18 of the whole circumference of the earth.[88]

Again this work had no immediate connection with the trigonometrical operations of the Survey, but was nevertheless officially approved by Wellington, who gave permission for a party of seven artillerymen to be attached to Colby and authorized the provision of necessary stores.[89]

Colby energetically set about filling the few gaps remaining in the primary triangulation, as in the Highlands and Orkney and along the east coast of England. In 1823 the Greenwich-Paris connection was completed, after which all trigonometrical work in Great Britain was suspended because of the Irish survey. But Colby was able to report to the Select Committee of 1824 that the trigonometrical survey was complete except for the eastern part of England, and the northern part of the west coast and the Western Islands of Scotland.[90] The triangulation of these areas was not resumed until fourteen years later.

More than any other branch of the Survey, the trigonometrical parties, consisting of both officers and men, developed a sense of purpose and of esprit de corps. The soldiers assisting in the field observations were, by long-established custom, artillerymen – as many as nineteen non-commissioned officers and men – who were well practised in the labouring and semi-skilled tasks of the triangulation.* Something of a departmental folklore surrounding the exploits of the field surveyors was already growing up. If Dalby, looking back in 1821, felt that their 'routine of proceedings year after year had so much sameness',[91] life in the field for some of his younger contemporaries, especially it would seem with Colby, was more of an adventure than a chore. This spirit was captured vividly in the correspondence of Lieutenant Robert Kearsley Dawson, the eldest son of Robert Dawson the draughtsman, who was attached in 1819 to Colby's party in the primary triangulation of Scotland. Portlock printed extensive extracts from letters sent to him by Dawson, which epitomize the hardships, fascinations and pleasures of a field season with the trigonometrical surveyors.[92] The base camp for the summer of 1819 on Corriehabbie, an offshoot of the Banffshire Grampians, was the centre for far-ranging explorations and observations. On Friday, 23 July, Dawson recorded how

> Captain Colby took me and a fresh party of the soldiers on a station-hunt, to explore the country to the westward and northward of west. Out first halting-place was to be Grant Town, at a distance of twenty-four miles; and Captain Colby having, according to his usual practice, ascertained the general direction by means of a pocket compass and map, the whole party set off, as on a steeple-chase, running down the mountain side at full speed, over Cromdale, a mountain about the same height as Corrie Habbie, crossing several beautiful glens, wading the streams which flowed through them and regardless of all difficulties that were not absolutely insurmountable on foot. Some-times a beaten road would fall in our course, offering the temptation of its superior facilities to the exhausted energies of the weary members of our party . . . The distance travelled by us that day was calculated at thirty-one miles.[93]

Dawson records that, by the end of this reconnaissance, the party had 'walked 586 miles in twenty-two days, including Sundays, and the days on which [they] were unable to proceed from bad weather'.[94]

Scientific forays continued into late September. By this date there were 'frequent and violent storms of hail, rain, and wind, which occasionally threw down some of the tents'. In the intervals, however, 'the atmosphere was clear, and allowed the instrument being constantly at work', so that September was 'considered one of the best months for the Trigonometrical Survey'.[95] On some days, observations

---

* Artillerymen continued to be employed on this work for many years after the surveying companies of the Royal Sappers and Miners had been formed; in the 1830s the number of gunners assisting the Survey was reduced, and in 1839 the last five were transferred to the Royal Sappers and Miners. T. W. J. Connolly, *History of the Royal Sappers and Miners* (London 1855), I, p. 318.

continued from six in the morning till seven at night but by 29 September the 'weather was . . . becoming more stormy and wet. The mountains were all covered with snow, and the trigonometrical season was declared to be at an end.'[96]

The instruments safely packed away, it remained 'according to established custom', as Dawson tells us, to prepare for the season's 'farewell feast'. In 1819 this consisted of an 'enormous plum-pudding', followed by a party, from which the officers 'withdrew' after drinking '*Success to the Trig*'. For them, and for many outside observers of its progress, the trigonometrical operations still represented the essence of the Survey.

Notes

1 William Mudge and Isaac Dalby, *An Account of the Operations Carried on For Accomplishing a Trigonometrical Survey of England and Wales 1784–1796* (London 1799), p. 204.

2 J. E. Portlock, *Memoir of the life of Major-General Colby* . . . (London 1869), p. 23.

3 R. A. Skelton, 'The origins of the Ordnance Survey of Great Britain', *Geographical Journal* 1962, CXXVIII, pp. 416–18.

4 Mudge and Dalby, *Account of the Trig. Survey 1784–1796*, p. 204.

5 William Roy, 'An Account of the Mode proposed to be followed in determining the relative Situation of the Royal Observatories of Greenwich and Paris', *Phil. Trans.* 1787, LXXVII, pp. 188–226.

6 Alexander Dalrymple and James Rennell to the 'Hon'ble the Court of Directors', 15 June 1787, E/1/80, Misc. Letters Received, India Office Library and Records, contains an estimate of the expenditure on the scheme as put forward by Roy.

7 R. H. Phillimore, *Historical Records of the Survey of India, Volume I, 18th Century* (Dehra Dun 1945), p. 166.

8 C. F. Close, *The Early Years of the Ordnance Survey* (reprinted Newton Abbot 1969), p. 29.

9 Richard Glover, *Peninsular Preparation. The Reform of the British Army 1795–1809* (Cambridge 1963), p. 78.

10 Thomas Colby, 'Precis relating to the Survey of England and Wales', dated 7 Jan. 1834: PRO T 1/4060.

11 PRO WO 48/266 (1791).

12 PRO WO 47/117 (1791).

13 Mudge and Dalby, *Account of the Trig. Survey 1784–1796*, p. 5.

14 Portlock, *Memoir of Colby*, p. 23.

15 William Mudge, *An Account of the operations carried on for accomplishing a Trigonometrical Survey of England and Wales, continued from the Year 1797, to the end of the Year 1799* (London 1801), p. 4.

16 PRO WO 47/2372 (1799) for his appointment. Close, *Early Years*, p. 52.

17 PRO WO 47/118 (1791).

18 Stamford Raffles Flint (ed.), *Mudge Memoirs: Being a Record of Zachariah Mudge, and Some Members of his Family; together with a genealogical list of the same* . . . (Truro 1883), p. 123.

19 Close, *Early Years*, p. 31.

20 Williams's letters: the largest group is in the RS, DM4 ff 27–33, 35, 41–3, 50–51.

21 Dalby to Colby, 5 Feb. 1821, quoted in Close, *Early Years*, p. 42.

22 Flint, *Mudge Memoirs*.

23 *Ibid.* pp. 1–32.

24 *Ibid.* pp. 79–120.

25 *Ibid.* pp. 33–66.

26 E. G. R. Taylor, *The Mathematical Practitioners of Hanoverian England, 1714–1840* (Cambridge 1966), pp. 66–9, 187.

27 Mudge and Dalby, *Account of the Trig. Survey 1784–1796*, p. 364, where Mudge refers to observations made by the astronomer James Bradley, at the Lizard. See also Mudge, *Account of the Trig. Survey 1797–1799*, pp. 131–3.

28 Records of the Royal Military Academy (Woolwich 1851), pp. 32–4.

29 Flint, *Mudge Memoirs*, pp. 122–4.

30 *Ibid.*

31 Mudge, *Account of the Trig. Survey 1797–1799*, p. 177.

32 *Ibid.* p. 178.

33 S. G. P. Ward, 'Defence Works in Britain, 1803–1805', *Journal of the Society for Army Historical Research*, 1949, XXVII, pp. 18–37, distinguishes between the defensive responsibilities, at least as they were laid down in theory, of the two bodies.

34 W. Porter, *History of the Corps of Royal Engineers* (Chatham, reprinted 1951), vol. 2, p. 94.

35 *Records of the RMA*, p. 84.
36 Close, *Early Years*, pp. 40–41.
37 *Ibid.* p. 41.
38 Flint, *Mudge Memoirs*, pp. 139–50.
39 *Ibid.*
40 *Ibid.*
41 *Ibid.*
42 Records of the RMA, pp. 103–4.
43 Dalby to Colby, 5 Feb. 1821, quoted in Close, *Early Years*, p. 56.
44 Mudge to Colby, 9 July 1805, quoted in *Ibid.* p. 56.
45 Mudge to Colby, 5 Sept. 1804, quoted in *Ibid.* p. 56.
46 OSLB; PRO WO 55/960.
47 Flint, *Mudge Memoirs*, p. 155.
48 Glover, *Peninsular Preparations*, p. 78.
49 Flint, *Mudge Memoirs*, pp. 130–38.
50 Dawson to Colby, quoted in Close, *Early Years*, p. 70.
51 Mudge to Colby, 9 July 1805, quoted in *Ibid.* p. 57.
52 Flint, *Mudge Memoirs*, pp. 127–8, quoted from a 'Memoir' of Mudge in *The Annual Biography and Obituary* (London 1820); another obituary of Mudge appeared in *Gentleman's Magazine,* 1820, vol. 90, p. 381.
53 Mudge to Colby, 2 Sept. 1816, quoted in Close, *Early Years*, p. 65.
54 Close, *Early Years*, pp. 61–3. See also V. A. Eyles, 'John MacCulloch F.R.S., and his Geological Map: an account of the first Geological survey of Scotland', *Annals of Science*, 1937, vol. 2, pp. 114–29.
55 Mudge to Colby, 2 Sept. 1816, quoted in Close, *Early Years*, p. 65.
56 Mudge to Colby, 21 Feb. 1819, quoted in *Ibid.* p. 70.
57 Portlock, *Memoir of Colby*, pp. 11–13.
58 *Ibid.*
59 Mudge to the Earl of Chatham, 9 Jan. 1802, PRO WO 47/2383.
60 PRO WO 47/2383 (1802).
61 Mudge to Colby, 9 July 1805, quoted in Close, *Early Years*, p. 57.
62 Mudge to Colby, 9 Sept. 1813, quoted in *Ibid.* p. 59.
63 Portlock, *Memoir of Colby, passim.*
64 Mudge to Morse, 16 Dec. 1803, PRO WO 55/960.
65 Portlock, *Memoir of Colby*, p. 105.
66 *Ibid.* pp. 15, 3, 7.
67 Gregory to Colby, quoted in Close, *Early Years*, p. 54.
68 Colby to the Duke of Wellington, 20 June 1820, quoted in *Ibid.* p. 83.
69 On 10 July 1820: *Ibid.* p. 83.
70 '*XVIIth Report of the Commissioners of Military Enquiry*': PP 1812 (5) IV, p. 242.
71 Mudge, *Account of the Trig. Survey 1797–1799*, p. 135.
72 Edward Williams and William Mudge, 'An Account of the Trigonometrical Survey carried on in 1791, 1792, 1793 and 1794', *Phil. Trans.* 1795, LXXXV, p. 474.
73 *XVIIth Report . . .*; PP 1812 (5) IV, pp. 168–9.
74 Mudge and Dalby, *Account of the Trig. Survey 1784–1796*, pp. 205–25.
75 Close, *Early Years,* pp. 46–9.
76 O. G. Gregory, *Dissertations and Letters, by Don Joseph Rodriguez, the Chevalier Delambre . . . and others: tending either to impugn or to defend the Trigonometrical Survey of England and Wales carrying on by Col. Mudge and Capt. Colby* (London 1815), p. 3.
77 Flint, *Mudge Memoirs*, p. 124.
78 'Mudge's Account of the Trigonometrical Survey', *The Edinburgh Review*, 1805, X, p. 390.
79 Portlock, *Memoir of Colby*, p. 46.
80 Close, *Early Years*, p. 63.
81 Gregory, *Dissertations*, p. 29.
82 Close, *Early Years*, p. 63.
83 Portlock, *Memoir of Colby*, pp. 66, 67.
84 *Ibid.* p. 66.
85 *Ibid.* p. 73–83.
86 *Ibid.* pp. 96–102.
87 T. W. J. Connolly and R. E. Edwards, *Roll of Officers of the Corps of the Royal Engineers from 1660 to 1898* (Chatham 1898).
88 OSLB f 359.
89 OSLB f 375.
90 *Report from the Select Committee on the Survey and Valuation of Ireland*, p. 13: PP 1824 (445) VIII.
91 Dalby to Colby, 5 Feb. 1821, quoted in Close, *Early Years*, p. 42.
92 Portlock, *Memoir of Colby*, pp. 131–55.
93 *Ibid.* pp. 138–9.
94 *Ibid.* p. 148.
95 *Ibid.* p. 152.
96 *Ibid.* p. 153.

3
The Geodesy
of Roy,
Mudge
and Kater
1784-1823

The Connection of the Observatories of Greenwich and Paris 1784-90

Towards the end of the seventeenth century theoretical speculation about the shape of the Earth had given way to serious attempts to determine it by measurement. In 1671 Picard* measured an arc of longitude in France which was accurate enough for Newton to confirm his theory of gravitation and which, combined with an arc in Cayenne, enabled the first Cassini** to calculate the sun's distance as 87 000 000 miles. The second Cassini extended the French arc from Perpignan in the south to Dunkerque in the north, although this arc showed the Earth to be prolate; however, the French obtained convincing proof of the Earth's oblateness from arcs measured in Peru in 1735 and Lappland in 1736. At the time of the Anglo-French operation of 1784-90 many of the problems of geodetic measurement were still imperfectly understood, and the method proposed for determining the differences in latitude and longitude between Greenwich and Paris could not possibly have given a wholly satisfactory result, a fact that was recognized at the time by Dr Maskelyne, the Astronomer Royal.

He had been sent a copy of the Cassini Mémoire of 1783 by the Royal Society and had commented that the latitude of Greenwich had been well observed and was 51° 28′ 40″ with an error of less than a second;[1] the proposed survey might give an improved value for the longitude difference but the latitudes of the two would best be found by direct astronomical observations. He considered that a survey would be unlikely to ascertain the difference of latitude accurately because of the uncertainty about the true figure and dimensions of the Earth. Further, the latitude depended on the direction of the plumb-line which would be affected by any irregular distribution of mass under the Earth's crust at Greenwich and Paris.

Maskelyne was right up to a point; but the uncertainty in the size and shape of the Earth and any deviation in the plumb-line at Greenwich and Paris would also affect the deduced difference of longitude between the two observatories.

There are two accounts of the base measurement and triangulation linking the observatories of Greenwich and Paris. One is by Roy himself, written at the time and published in the *Philosophical Transactions* of the Royal Society between 1785 and 1790.[2] The other is included in the *Account of the . . . Trigonometrical Survey . . . 1784-1796* by Mudge and Dalby, published in 1799. The latter version is based on Roy's Royal Society papers, but is condensed and incorporates work carried out after his death as, for example, the second measurement of the Hounslow Heath Base. There are several interesting differences between Roy's results and those obtained by Mudge and Dalby which arise either because of the inclusion of these later measurements or because of differences in the computational procedure.

In April 1784 the site for a base between King's Arbour, on Hounslow Heath, and Hampton Poor House, near Bushey Park, was reconnoitred, and the ends of the base were marked by wooden pipes

* Jean Picard (1620-82). French astronomer.

** The Cassinis were a remarkable family, being Directors of the Paris Observatory through four generations. They were of Italian origin: Giovanni Domenici Cassini, 1625-1712, first Director of the Paris Observatory founded about 1670; Jacques Cassini, 1677-1756; César François Cassini de Thury, 1714-84, wrote the Mémoire to the English Secretary of State in 1783; Jacques Dominique Cassini de Thury, 1748-1845, a member of the French delegation for the cross-Channel connection of 1787.

about 6 feet long with the lower end of the pipe passing through the nave of a buried wheel. A cast-iron box, driven into the top of the pipe, held a brass cup with covers through which a plummet could pass.

Meanwhile Ramsden had constructed a steel chain 100 feet long with one hundred links. In June a preliminary measurement of the base was made with this chain laid directly on the ground, which gave the length as 27 408.22 feet. The height of the base was determined with a spirit-level lent by Ramsden; the King's Arbour terminal was found to be 31.265 feet above Hampton Poor House which, in turn, was 36.1 feet above the Thames at Hampton.

In the most advanced contemporary practice, as exemplified by the French, both deal rods and iron bars were used for base measurement. It was decided to use wood for the Hounslow Heath Base and four rods of red Riga pine were prepared by Ramsden; three were trussed laterally and vertically to make them entirely rigid and the fourth, to be used as standard, was trussed laterally only.

Roy had previously purchased a 42-inch brass scale which had been divided by Bird;* this was found to agree with the Royal Society's brass scale over 36 inches at 65 °F. Roy's scale was then used with a beam compass to lay off a twenty-foot length on the standard rod; rather inexplicably, the length was laid off from the forty-inch mark which had not been compared with the Royal Society's scale. The rods could be used either butted together when each measured 20 feet 3 inches, or laid with marks in coincidence to give 20 feet. They were supported on two types of stand, one of which had a fixed height of 2 feet 7 inches above the ground and the other a height which could be adjusted between 2 feet and 2 feet 8 inches. As the base had a generally uniform slope it was divided into bays of 600 feet in each of which the deal rods were laid parallel with the slope. After a length of 300 feet had been measured with the rods laid in coincidence it was decided that the method was too slow and that the whole should be measured with the ends butted together. The operation, which took from 16 July to 3 August with a break of about seven days for bad weather, gave the length of the base as 27 406.26 feet when reduced to the height of Hampton Poor House.

But it was then found that the length of the rods varied considerably with the humidity, there being a difference of 0.5 inch in 300 feet when the rods were dry and when damp. This defect would also have affected the twenty-foot standard rod. A suggestion was made by Lieutenant-Colonel Calderwood** that the difficulty might be overcome by using glass rods instead of deal; accordingly a number of glass tubes were obtained and sent to Ramsden to be made up into lengths of 20 feet. They were housed in wooden boxes, from which their ends protruded, and were supported at each end and at three equally spaced points. One end of the tube carried a fixed stud and the other a spring-loaded stud with an ivory scale. When lines on the glass tube and the ivory scale were coincident the length between the two studs was 20 feet. Each box had two thermometers with the bulbs about 2 inches inside the box so that temperature corrections could be assessed. The measurement of the base with the glass tubes began on 18 August, was completed on the 30th, and was made in bays of 600 feet measured on the slope. The final value, reduced to 62 °F and corrected to a mean sea-level estimated to be 54 feet below Hampton Poor House, was 27 404.7219 feet. In Mudge's account, the length corrected to assumed mean sea-level is given as 27 404.0137 feet which agrees with the value accepted by Clarke;[3] the difference of 0.7082 foot was due to an error in the standardization correction used by Roy. Mudge, however, combined his value with the result of a later measurement to give a mean value for the base of 27 404.2 feet which was used in all his calculations.[4]

When the glass rods and the steel chain were tested against each other over a distance of 1000 feet, they were found to be equally accurate. It was therefore decided to use the chain, laid in coffers and strained with a 28 lb weight, for the check base on Romney Marsh. This base was measured between 15 October and 4 December 1787 and, when reduced to 62 °F, gave a length of 28 532.92 feet corrected to mean sea-level. Mudge calculated the length as 28 535.677 feet which must be assumed to be the correct value, as Roy's temperature and standardization corrections were erroneous.[5]

For the angular measurements the new three-foot theodolite, made by Ramsden and purchased by the Royal Society, was used. This theodolite, which is usually designated 'RS' to distinguish it from the similar instrument bought a few years later by the Board of Ordnance, and designated 'BO', was described by Sir Charles Close as the first instrument capable of detecting spherical excess (the amount by which the sum of the three angles of a triangle on the curved surface of a sphere exceeds 180°).[6] The horizontal circle, which was graduated to 15 minutes of arc, could be read to one second by two micrometers, 180° apart, and estimated to 0.1 second. The six-inch vertical circle was read by

---

* John Bird, 1700–76, trained under Sisson and Graham. He achieved European fame as an instrument maker. His standard yards of 1758 and 1760 were deposited in the House of Commons where they were destroyed in the fire of 1834.

** Lt.-Col. Calderwood served in the 1st Troop, Horse Guards. He was elected to the Royal Society in June 1776.

one micrometer to 30 seconds of arc. Below the horizontal circle was a second telescope, fixed to the mahogany table; this was pointed at the first object being observed in order to indicate if there had been any movement of the instrument during observation (Plate 2).

The theodolite weighed about 200 lb and was transported 'in a four-wheeled spring carriage'; during use it was protected from the weather by a tent. It could be raised either 16 or 32 feet above the ground by means of a timber framework made in two separate parts, one to take the instrument and the other the observers, so that the theodolite would not be affected by their movements. To change zero it was necessary to lift the whole instrument and turn it, which usually meant that it had to be recentred and relevelled.

It had been intended to take several measures of an angle and to change zero frequently but time was too short for this lengthy process to become standard practice, and as the record of the actual observations has not survived, it is uncertain how many pointings were included in any one angle. All stations on the ground were marked by buried wooden pipes which had, however, only a short life. Stations on the tops of buildings were marked by concentric circles drawn on the leads and defined by measurements to the side walls.

Three kinds of signal were used to mark the stations to which observations were being made: lamps, white lights or flags, on tripods 35 feet high; lamps or flags on posts 10 feet high; and white lights on _____ The white lights were short-burning chemical flares, looked after by artillerymen _____ could be lit in succession at stated times, but with some _____ ly several lights were burning at the same time. In general, _____ was then unhurried; white lights, however, were required _____

_____ rteen ground stations and nine on tops of buildings, such as _____ latter were called 'up-stations'; they were sometimes _____ ervations from surrounding stations only, when they were _____

_____ ated by subtracting a constant 9.326 7737 ($= \log a^2 \sin 1''$, _____ from the common logarithm of the area of the triangle in _____ was then the excess or defect of the sum of the three angles _____ thirty-two triangles used to fix the side Fairlight Down – _____ ved and the triangular misclosures of these averaged less _____ than one second of arc. The _____ and the spherical excess were divided between the three angles of the triangle often somewhat arbitrarily.[7] The resulting angles were called the 'angles corrected for calculation' and were used in computing the side lengths.

ERRATUM

Page 35, third paragraph from the bottom of the page, delete the last two sentences and substitute:

'Without this correction he estimated that the length of the Romney Marsh Base calculated from Hounslow Heath would have been 0.375 foot greater than its measured length'.

The whole angular adjustment was rather haphazard. Some corrected angles were given to whole seconds, others to one decimal place and a few to two decimal places of a second. Where there were centre-point figures, such as the triangle Hanger Hill Tower – Hundred Acres – Severndroog Castle with centre-point Norwood, one of the triangles was often left unsolved. Braced figures such as the quadrilateral Wrotham Hill – Goudhurst Spire – Frant Spire – Botley Hill were similarly treated, but the general geometrical conditions of the figures appear to have been met in the calculations.

Computation was carried forward as far as the side Lydd – Allington Knoll, the length of which was 47 849.27 feet. This agreed with its length as calculated from the Romney Marsh Base, but Roy remarked that the agreement was only obtained by correcting the angle at Hollingbourn Hill between Allington Knoll and Fairlight Down by −3.5 seconds. Without this correction he estimated that the length of which was first given as 141 744.4 feet (Roy: 141 747.1 feet). By making small corrections to greater than its measured length.

In Mudge's *Account* the calculation was taken to the side Hollingbourn Hill – Fairlight Down, the length of which was first given as 141 744.4 feet (Roy: 141 747.1 feet). By making small corrections to the angles of the triangles, another value of 141 747.6 feet was obtained, giving a mean value of 141 746 feet. The side was then calculated backwards from the Romney Marsh Base to give 141 758 feet. The mean of the last two values, 141 752 feet, was used to compute the side lengths of the triangles up to the line Allington Knoll – Lydd.

Roy carried forward the computation to give the side Fairlight Down – Dover Castle as 186 113.0 feet which was used to obtain the distances from Dover Castle and Fairlight Down to both Blancnez and Montlambert. Mudge's value was 186 119 feet. The quadrilateral Fairlight Down – Dover Castle – Blancnez – Montlambert was calculated with the deduced angles at Blancnez and Montlambert, ignoring the French observations as they had been made to Dover Castle only and not to Fairlight

Down. The angle at Blancnez between Montlambert and Dover Castle used by Roy was 119°41′ 41″.64, but the observed value was 119°41′ 28″.9, a difference of 12.7 seconds.

The French observations continued the English triangulation through Notre Dame, Calais, and Dunkerque Tower to the French base (Fort Revers – The Dunes) giving its deduced length as 39 808.7 feet against 39 801.7 feet as measured with deal rods. Roy questioned the latter length, which he excluded from his own calculations, because the base line was very wet and he thought the deal rods would have been affected. The French triangulation from Paris depended on a base near Paris and a check base at Amiens and gave a computed value of 39 809.94 feet for the Fort Revers – The Dunes base, which agreed well with the English calculations. Finally, a station was fixed at Point M which was where the meridian through the Paris Observatory intersected the line from Dunkerque to Calais.

The English origin for the rectangular co-ordinates of the triangulation stations was the centre of Bradley's transit instrument at Greenwich Observatory, with axes along the meridian and at right angles to it. The initial azimuth was to Severndroog Castle (73°49′34″); thereafter bearings and reverse bearings were taken as differing by 180° exactly and the bearings to new stations were obtained by adding or subtracting the 'angle corrected for calculation', but there are inconsistencies of a second or two. From a side length and its bearing the differences in eastings and northings were computed; these were then added to give the rectangular co-ordinates of each station referred to the origin. By this means the position of Point M was found to be 538 048.2 feet east and 154 938.2 feet south of Greenwich. From these co-ordinates the meridional distance between the parallels through Greenwich and Point M was calculated to be 163 489.2 feet which, added to the French distance of 800 392.8 feet between the parallels of Point M and Paris Observatory, gave a distance of 963 882.0 feet between the parallels through Greenwich and Paris, corresponding to an arc of 02°38′26″. The difference of longitude was given as 02°19′42″. It is not entirely clear how Roy calculated the latitudes of the various stations of the triangulation but it would appear that he used Bouguer's* Spheroid.[8] His method for obtaining the longitudes is even more obscure, but it is probable that he used an arbitrary value of 367 488 feet for the length of a degree of a great circle perpendicular to the meridian; certainly the results were significantly in error, all being too small by about 12 seconds per degree.

At the end of his account Roy lists the rectangular and geographical co-ordinates of all stations together with their heights. Similar co-ordinates are also given for thirty-two up-stations observed from the main stations, as well as the distances and bearings of a number of London spires and other tall objects, from St Paul's Cathedral.

The heights of King's Arbour, Hampton Poor House, High Nook, Severndroog Castle and Dover Castle were obtained by levelling from the sea or river. The heights of the remaining stations were obtained from reciprocal vertical angles, the refraction being calculated for each line separately.

The first British triangulation had been carried out with vigour and with skill, but its great weakness was in the calculation: the method of correcting the angles of a triangle was poor, and the whole chain was calculated as if it were on a plane.[9] The latitudes and longitudes were probably calculated from lengths of a degree along and at right angles to the meridian, obtained from two different and unrelated measures.

The Triangulation of Great Britain 1791–1822

INSTRUMENTS

The instruments used for the triangulation included two new one-hundred-foot steel chains purchased from Ramsden, as well as a new three-foot theodolite (BO). This differed from the Royal Society's instrument only in minor details. The horizontal circle was graduated to 10 minutes of arc and the micrometers were improved. In 1795 an eighteen-inch theodolite, virtually a half-scale model of the larger instrument, was also bought from Ramsden: the horizontal circle was divided to 5 minutes and was read by three micrometers to 2 seconds, the eight-inch vertical circle was divided to 10 minutes and read by verniers to 10 seconds.

When making the two new chains, which had links of 2½ feet and were designed for use with a straining weight of 56 lb, Ramsden laid off 20 feet from his scale in successive bays of 40 inches on a prism-shaped cast-iron bar (known as the 'prismatic bar') at a temperature of 54°F. Each chain was

* Pierre Bouguer, 1698–1758, was noted for his pendulum experiments and work on gravitation. He went with La Condamine to Peru.

placed on rollers and strained with the 56 lb weight. Its end was then brought into coincidence with the end mark on the prismatic bar and a mark made at 20 feet along the chain which was then moved forward four times until 100 feet had been marked. Both Roy's scale and Ramsden's had been compared and found to agree with the Royal Society's scale, but nevertheless later comparisons show small differences. At 62°F, the temperature at which the bases were computed, there would be differences because of the differing coefficients of expansion of the scales.

Ramsden also constructed a zenith sector for the determination of latitudes. The instrument was in two parts: an outer frame, braced both horizontally and diagonally, was formed by an open-ended pyramid 12 feet high on a base 6 feet square with a top 3 feet square; within this was the inner frame carrying the four-inch telescope of eight-foot focal length with arrangements for setting it vertically by means of a plumb-line and for reversing it. The telescope was pivoted about its top end, the movement in the meridian being read by micrometers on an arc divided to 5 minutes, with 0.1 second obtainable by estimation. In daylight on a clear day a third magnitude star could be seen with the telescope. It was an excellent instrument but very cumbersome to transport and handle[10] (Plate 3).

BASES

During the 1784 measurement of the Hounslow Heath Base with glass tubes it was found that there was some movement of the trestles on which the tube-boxes rested when a box was lifted for moving forward. It was also thought that the tubes might not have been truly aligned and that they might have sagged between the supports. Consequently, between 1791 and 1822 all the bases were measured with the steel chains laid under 56 lb tension in coffers, and their length calculated as at 62°F. Generally only one of the chains was used for the actual measurement, the other being kept for comparison. It was found that constant use of a chain wore the links, making it longer, and an allowance for this was made at each base. All measurements were given in terms of Ramsden's scale.

Hounslow Heath. The measurement was done in August and September 1791, giving a length of 27 404.3155 feet, but this does not appear to have been reduced to sea-level. This result was combined with the earlier measurement to give a mean value of 27 404.2 feet which was used in computing the triangulation. When remeasuring the base it was found that the wooden terminal marks had deteriorated, so they were replaced with cannon carefully centred over the old marks.

Salisbury Plain. The ends at Beacon Hill and Old Sarum were marked by cannon. The base was measured in the summer of 1794 and its length, corrected to the height of the Hounslow Heath Base, was 36 574.4 feet or, corrected to sea-level, 36 574.232 feet.[11]

Sedgemoor. The base between Lugshorn Corner and Greylock's Foss was measured in July and August 1798. The length, uncorrected to sea-level, was 27 680.1447 feet.

Misterton Carr. This base, marked with wood blocks, was measured in June and July 1801. Mudge gives its length as 26 342.712 feet. There was, however, an error in the temperature correction; the proper length corrected to sea-level was 26 342.19 feet.[12]

Rhuddlan Marsh. Measured in October 1806, the length was 24 514.26 feet. The base is about 25 feet above sea-level but no correction for height was made. It was marked with wood blocks which, like those of Misterton Carr, were not found again.

Belhelvie Sands. The measurement in 1817 gave a length of 26 515.6509 feet reduced to mean sea-level.[13]

OBSERVATION OF THE TRIANGULATION

The triangulation of Williams and Mudge joined that of Roy at St Ann's Hill, Botley Hill and Fairlight Down, and by the end of 1798, when Williams died, all observations south of a line from Greenwich to Bristol had been completed. Mudge, appointed to succeed him, immediately asked the Royal Society for the loan of its three-foot theodolite so that the triangulation might be speeded up, which, during the next four years, was extended northwards to Clifton in Yorkshire. By 1809 all of Wales and as far north as East Lomond and Largo Law in Scotland were covered with stations about 12 to 18 miles apart. Thereafter, reports in the *Philosophical Transactions* cease and there is little detailed information about the work between 1810 and 1822, by which time the triangulation had been continued along the east coast of Scotland into the Orkneys and Shetlands, and to the Western Isles.

A complete list of the stations does not exist. But from a draft map of the triangulation in the

Ordnance Survey records and from Portlock's *Memoir of the Life of Major-General Colby* it would appear that the following stations were occupied during this period:

1813   Cowhythe, Kellie Law.
1814   Blue Hill, Knock, Little Stirling, Bin of Cullen, Findlay Seat, Caerloch, Red Head, Mormonth, Mount Battock.
1815   Brown Carrick, Glasserton.
1816   Calton Hill, Hill of Stake, Allermuir, Tinto Hill, Hart Fell, Dunrich, Wisp.
1817   Balta, Saxavord, Dudwick, Brimmond, Craigowl, Layton Hill, Over Hill, Tarbathy, Mount Battock.
1818   Ben Lomond, Glashmeal, Ben Cleugh, Bin of Campsie, Carn na Leagh, East Lomond, Largo Law, Ben Turk, West Lomond.
1819   Ben Chielt, Ben Wyvis, Balnaskerrish, Ben Lundie, Corriehabbie, Ben Hutig.
1820   ?
1821   Brassa, Deerness, Fair Isle, Fetlar, Fitty Hill, Ronas Hill, Foula, South Ronaldsay, Stronsay, Yell, Wart Hill, Hoy.
1822   Ben Heynish, Ben More Mull, Ben Tartevil, Oa or Cairnard, Jura North Pap.

Although progress was accelerated after 1798 because both three-foot theodolites were in use, it is noticeable that the quality of the early work was not altogether maintained. Poorly-shaped triangles with only two angles observed became more frequent, although the closures of fully-observed triangles remained good. The angular measures were all recorded and there were usually four values for each angle, frequently on different zeros, but the triangulation was not consistently of geodetic standard. The large theodolites gave some trouble because of unequal expansion of the horizontal circles in changing temperatures, and variation in the micrometer runs; another difficulty was that the instruments tended to sink on their axes, and it became the practice to raise the axis and to test the micrometer runs at each station. From 1791 the triangulation stations, hitherto marked with wooden pipes, were marked with stones, each about 2 feet square, with a one-inch hole in the centre.

CALCULATION

The method of calculating the triangulation was generally similar to that adopted by Roy. The spherical excess of each triangle and its closing error were computed and the closing error was then somewhat arbitrarily distributed between the three angles. But the 'angles corrected for calculation' were obtained by reducing the spherical triangle to the equivalent chordal triangle using Dr Maskelyne's formula.[14] The side lengths were then computed. Where there were two or more values for any one side the mean was taken and used in succeeding calculations. The triangulation was not calculated from one base and closed on the next, but the calculation was carried forward from the first base as far as a side near the second base; the length of this side was then computed backwards from the second base, and the mean of the two values for the side was used for continuing the triangulation. For example, the length of the side Ash Beacon – Bradley Knoll as calculated forward from Beacon Hill – Wingreen, a side near the Salisbury Plain Base, was 68 650.6 feet. As calculated backwards from the Sedgemoor Base its length was 68 653.6 feet, from which a value of 68 652.2 feet was derived for use on the next stage. Mudge records that the Salisbury Plain Base as calculated by different routes from the Hounslow Heath Base lay between 36 574.8 and 36 573.8 feet, with a mean of 36 574.3 feet.[15] Similarly, the length of the Sedgemoor Base calculated through from the Salisbury Plain Base differed from its measured length by one foot, and the Misterton Carr Base calculated from Dunnose would have been about one foot longer than measured.[16] But these comparisons were only noted in passing; the mean value of a side near the new base was invariably used in calculating the succeeding triangulation.

From Mudge's triangulation the latitude and longitude of Beachy Head, where the station was marked by a cannon, were obtained with reference to Greenwich. The azimuth of the line Beachy Head – Dunnose (also marked by a cannon) had been observed at each end. The latitude of Dunnose was deduced from the triangulation, presumably by the same method as that used by Roy, and the distance Beachy Head – Dunnose obtained, also from the triangulation. The difference in longitude, calculated by solving the spherical triangle Beachy Head – North Pole – Dunnose for the apex angle, was found to be 01°26′47″.93. It was then deduced that the length of a degree of the great circle at right angles to the meridian in latitude 50°41′ N was 367 093.8 feet. From Roy's work Mudge obtained the length of a degree of latitude at 50°10′ N as 365 058 feet. From these two values he calculated a table giving the lengths of arcs in fathoms at different latitudes, from which a table can be derived:

| | LENGTH IN FEET OF A DEGREE OF ARC | |
Latitude	Along the meridian	Perpendicular to the meridian
° ′		
50 00	365 034	367 062
50 10	365 058	367 068
50 20	365 076	367 080
50 30	365 100	367 086
50 40	365 118	367 092
50 50	365 136	367 098
51 00	365 160	367 104
51 10	365 178	367 116
51 20	365 202	367 122
51 30	365 226	367 128
51 40	365 244	367 134
51 50	365 262	367 140
52 00	365 286	367 146

The distances along the meridians are all greater than those calculated later on Airy's Spheroid[17] by about 140 feet at 50° to 270 feet at 52°. Consequently Mudge's latitudes are less than those calculated on Airy's Spheroid by about 1″.6 per degree. The distances perpendicular to the meridian are greater by about 1180 feet than on Airy, and Mudge's longitudes are all too small by about 11″.6 per degree.

The rectangular co-ordinates of all the stations were computed with reference to the initial station at Greenwich, Beachy Head or Dunnose, and these were then turned into geographical co-ordinates with the aid of the table given above. In general, the following details were given for each station, including all intersected points:

1 In terms of the different meridians (Greenwich, Beachy Head or Dunnose) the bearing of each line and the rectangular co-ordinates of each station.
2 The latitude of each station and the difference of longitude between it and the relevant meridian.
3 The longitude referred to Greenwich, obtained by a straight addition of the Greenwich longitude of the relevant origin.

A comparison of some of Mudge's results with those of the Retriangulation of 1935–50 is interesting:[18]

| | Latitude North | | Longitude West | |
Station	Mudge	Retn	Mudge	Retn
Greenwich (Pond)	51°28′40″	38″.3	00°00′00″	00′00″.1†
Dunnose	50°37′07″.3	03″.7	01°11′36″	11′50″.1
Black Down	50°41′13″.8	10″.3	02°32′22″.4	32′52″.5
St Agnes Beacon	50°18′27″	24″.2	05°11′55″.7	12′58″.7
Clifton	53°27′32″	26″.7	01°12′52″.5	13′06″.2
				†Longitude East

It is probable that the error in Mudge's longitudes arose from calculating the difference of longitude between Beachy Head and Dunnose by Dalby's theorem,* since small errors in the azimuth, reverse azimuth and the assumed latitudes have considerable effect on the calculated differences in longitude. Any deviation of the vertical at Dunnose and Beachy Head would also affect the result.

Since the computations were being made on the assumption that the Earth's surface was plane, it was decided to calculate the triangulation on a number of meridians about 60 miles apart. In addition to the three already named, there were meridians through Black Down, Butterton Hill, St Agnes Beacon, Clifton, Burleigh Moor, Delamere Forest and Moel Rhyddlad. The latitudes and longitudes of these meridian origins were generally obtained by methods similar to those used for fixing

* If λ, λ^1 be the latitudes of two points on the surface of a spheroid, ω their difference of longitude, α, α^1 their reciprocal azimuths,

$$\tan \frac{\omega}{2} = \frac{\cos \dfrac{\lambda^1 - \lambda}{2}}{\sin \dfrac{\lambda^1 + \lambda}{2}} \cot \frac{\alpha^1 + \alpha}{2}$$

Dunnose. The longitude errors did not affect the one-inch map; latitudes and longitudes did not appear on it until, in the second half of the century, the map was derived from the six-inch.* Before this time, the positions of the triangulation stations used for controlling the one-inch survey were calculated and plotted as plane rectangular co-ordinates relative to the ten meridian origins.

The Dunnose – Clifton Arc of Meridian

The zenith sector ordered from Ramsden in 1795 was still unfinished when Ramsden died in 1801. It was completed in April 1802 by Berge, his head assistant, who had succeeded to the business, and was taken to Greenwich for the observation of a programme of stars. This was necessary to determine any instrumental errors and to get up-to-date positions of the stars to be used in measuring the English arc of meridian.

The purpose of the zenith sector was to determine astronomical latitude from stars near the zenith, where errors due to atmospheric refraction are minimized. Latitude is particularly important in the determination of the Figure of the Earth (i.e. the shape and dimensions of the oblate ellipsoid – or 'spheroid' – most closely resembling the Earth). Distance along the arc of the meridian is measured by the triangulation and this, with the observed astronomical latitudes, provides the data used in the calculations. But the process is complicated by 'local attraction' or 'deviation of the vertical' resulting from the irregularities of the Earth's surface and the distribution of mass beneath it, which deflect the plumb-line by as much as 30 seconds of arc in places, and hence affect the observed altitudes of stars. There is thus a lack of consistency between the measured arc differences, from which 'geodetic' latitudes are derived, and the latitudes derived from astronomical observations.

Mudge chose a meridian running north from Dunnose to Clifton in Yorkshire and during 1802 made zenith sector observations at five stations, in addition to Dunnose, which he believed from a study of the topography to be relatively unaffected by local attraction. But he was mistaken, as the table shows:

Station	Difference of Latitude from Dunnose observed by Sector	Meridional Distance from Triangulation	Deduced Length of 1° of arc of Meridian
	° ′ ″	feet	feet
Greenwich	00 51 31.39	313 696	365 304
Arbury Hill	01 36 19.98	536 320	365 184
Delamere Forest	02 36 12.2	930 189.9	364 983
Clifton	02 50 23.38	1 036 337	364 337
Burleigh Moor	03 57 13.1	1 442 852	364 840

For an oblate spheroid the meridional distance between parallels should increase from south to north but, from Mudge's results, they seemed to decrease. Mudge attributed this anomaly to local attraction and in this he was right, as Clarke was to demonstrate fifty years later.[19]

The West European Arc of Meridian 1816–23

The French proposal to extend the West European arc of meridian northwards through the British triangulation led to further astronomical determinations being made between 1816 and 1818 throughout the entire length of the system. In addition to the six stations used for the Dunnose–Clifton arc, observations for latitude were made with the zenith sector at Cowhythe, Kellie Law and Balta.

THE REMEASUREMENT OF THE GREENWICH–PARIS CONNECTION 1821–3

The correspondence between the Royal Society and the *Académie des Sciences* about the cross-Channel connection of 1821–3 seems to suggest that the work of 1784–7 had either been forgotten or was not regarded as of a high enough standard to form part of the arc of meridian from Formentera to

---

* Except for Part I of the Ordnance Survey (Essex) published in 1805. On sheets 1, 2, 47, 48 latitude and longitude values were engraved in the margin. The sheets carried the note: 'The scale of latitude and also that of longitude around this map being drawn and graduated on a plane projection, the latitudes and longitudes deduced therefrom can be only nearly true, near to the meridian of Greenwich.' Most of Essex was re-engraved in the 1830s and the latitude and longitude scales omitted.

the Shetlands. So Roy's observations were repeated,[20] this time by Colby and Captain Henry Kater[21] as British Commissioners, and by Arago and Mathieu* for the French. For the new connection with France, the three-foot RS theodolite was used. To avoid the difficulty and delay caused by changing zero, Kater had four additional micrometers added which, with one of the original micrometers, divided the horizontal circle into five equal parts. This arrangement, attributed to Pond (Astronomer Royal 1811–25),** meant that several different parts of the horizontal circle could be used on any one pointing, obviating to some extent the need for changing zero. The BO theodolite was also modified by adding two new micrometers and removing one of the originals.

For the cross-Channel rays Fresnel lamps with compound lenses 3 feet in diameter were used as signals; at a distance of 48 miles these appeared as stars of the first magnitude. Roy's marks could not be found at Fairlight Down or Folkestone Turnpike, so new stations, Fairlight and Folkestone, were chosen on which the lamps were set up. The whole observing party crossed the Channel on 24 September 1821 and observed at Blancnez where the wind was so strong that the men's tents were blown away and the theodolite had to be taken down in case it was damaged. At Montlambert work was held up because the Fairlight lamp failed to appear. Mathieu and James Gardner were sent to find out what was wrong, but on arrival at Calais they found there was no packet; so, undeterred by darkness and storm, they crossed the Channel in an open boat. At Fairlight they discovered that the glass chimneys of the lamp had been broken but they managed to piece them together sufficiently well for the lamp to operate. On completion at Montlambert the combined party returned to England and finished the cross-Channel observing at Fairlight and Folkestone, from where Dover Castle was intersected. While at Fairlight it was discovered that a new mill had been built since Roy's time but the foundations of the old mill were found and the wooden pipe marking Roy's station was eventually located.

The next year the stations at Hanger Hill, Fairlight, Folkestone (where Roy's station was found very decayed), Tolsford (with rays to Montlambert and Fiennes), Stede Hill, Crowborough, Leith Hill, Wrotham Hill and Severndroog Castle were occupied before the work was stopped for the winter. A stone about 4 feet long and one foot square was buried at each station. In 1823 the scheme was completed with observations at Chingford with the BO theodolite; in addition, a number of rays to steeples and suitable objects near by were taken so that the station could be recovered. It had been intended to join the triangulation to the Hounslow Heath Base but it was found that the base line was interrupted by buildings, so the scheme was made to rest on the line Severndroog Castle – Hanger Hill, strengthened by rays intersecting new stations on Westminster Abbey and St Paul's Cathedral.

In calculating each triangle, spherical excess was first obtained and the closing error equally distributed between the three angles, the average closing error of the nineteen fully-observed triangles being about 1.25 seconds of arc. The lengths of the sides were then computed by Legendre's theorem† instead of by the chordal method which had been used previously; angles and sides were given to two decimal places of a second and foot respectively. Many triangles were calculated twice with slightly different values for a side length, although the angles were unchanged. Other triangles were computed three, and in one case four, times. Where several values were obtained for a side, the mean was taken and used in later calculations.

Kater gave all his results in terms of the imperial foot. In 1820 he and Wollaston†† had compared various scales including Bird's 1760 imperial standard, Roy's scale, the Royal Society's scale and Ramsden's prismatic bar; Ramsden's brass scale had apparently been lost. They found that Roy's and Mudge's lengths, which were based on the Royal Society's scale, had to be multiplied by 1.000 069 1 to convert them to imperial feet.[22]

A comparison of some of Roy's and Kater's results is given below, after Roy's measures have been converted to imperial feet and reduced to the new stations at Fairlight and Folkestone:

* François Arago, 1788–1853, became Director of the Paris Observatory.
Claude Louis Mathieu, 1783–1875. Astronomer appointed to the Paris Observatory in 1817 and to the French Bureau de *Longitudes*.

** John Pond, 1767–1836, succeeded Maskelyne as Astronomer Royal. Changed and improved all the instrumental equipment at Greenwich Observatory.

† Legendre's theorem states that if the sides of a spherical triangle are small compared with the radius of the sphere, each angle of the spherical triangle exceeds by a third of the spherical excess the corresponding angle of the plane triangle whose sides are of the same length as the arcs of the spherical triangle.

†† William Hyde Wollaston, 1766–1828. Became Secretary and later Vice-President of the Royal Society. He served on the Board of Longitude from 1818 until its abolition in 1828.

Side	Roy	Kater	Kater–Roy
Fairlight–Frant	113 850.59	113 857.34	+ 6.75
Fairlight–Tenterden	71 577.24	71 580.75	+ 3.51
Fairlight–Folkestone	154 802.70	154 807.00	+ 4.30
Dover–Notre Dame, Calais	137 459.72	137 471.99	+12.27

Bearings of the lines were calculated from the corrected angles of the relevant triangle on an initial azimuth of 359°59′53″.83 for the line from Pond's transit instrument at Greenwich Observatory to Chingford; reverse bearings were taken as equal to the forward bearing ± 180°. Rectangular co-ordinate differences for each station were then computed and these were added together to give co-ordinates on Greenwich as origin, the whole scheme being developed on the tangent plane at Greenwich.

The latitudes and longitudes of the stations were calculated on a spheroid with semi-major axis of 3 962.439 miles and flattening of 1:300 by the method of Oriani.*[23] The latitude of Greenwich was taken as 51°28′38″.96 N which is 01″.04 less than the value used by Roy and Mudge. With the latitude corrected for this difference and the longitude increased by 12 seconds a degree, Roy's position for Notre Dame, Calais, can be compared with Kater's values:

	Latitude	Longitude
Roy	50°57′29″.63 N	01°51′11″.0 E of Greenwich
Kater	50°57′27″.95 N	01°51′18″.73 E

Kater observed azimuths from Polaris at a number of stations and obtained the differences in longitude by Dalby's theorem. From these and the corresponding distances on the ground, the length of a degree perpendicular to the meridian was calculated. The results were somewhat inconclusive since small errors in the observed azimuths cause large changes in the longitude. Kater decided that the method was unreliable and recommended that azimuths should be observed from stars near the east or west point. When he wrote his report the French had not published their results so that it was impossible to deduce the difference of longitude of the two observatories. But taking the longitude of Notre Dame, Calais, as 00°28′59″ west of Paris and 01°51′18″.73 east of Greenwich, the difference of longitude becomes 02°20′17″.73. Roy's value was 02°19′42″ but this must be corrected by adding 12 seconds for each degree to give 02°20′10″.

Largely owing to Kater, the remeasurement of 1821–3 was technically better than the previous work. The observing was of a high standard, as the triangular closing errors show and, although computation was still somewhat rudimentary, significant advances were made, including the use of a spheroid for calculating both latitudes and longitudes, considerably reducing the longitude errors of Mudge and Roy.

* Oriani, in his *Opusculi Astronomici*, dealt with the calculations of a polar triangle on a spheroid with axes a = 3 271 209 toises, b = 3 261 443 toises.

Notes

1 Nevil Maskelyne, *Phil. Trans.* 1787, LXXVII, p. 151.
2 William Roy, *Phil. Trans.* 1785, LXXV; 1787, LXXVII; 1790, LXXX.
3 A. R. Clarke, *Account of the Observations and Calculations of the Principal Triangulation, and the figure, dimensions and mean specific gravity of the Earth as derived therefrom* (OS 1858), p. 208, See Ch. 12.
4 William Mudge and Isaac Dalby, *An Account of the Operations Carried on For Accomplishing a Trigonometrical Survey of England and Wales . . . 1784–1796* (London 1799), p. 219.
5 *Ibid.* p. 106.

6 C. F. Close, *The Early Years of the Ordnance Survey* (reprinted Newton Abbot 1969), p. 15.

7 A. M. Legendre, *Mémoires de l'Académie Royale des Sciences* 1788, p. 753.

8 *Phil. Trans.* 1790, LXXX, p. 200.

9 Legendre, *Mémoires de l'Académie Royale*, 1788, pp. 753–4.

10 William Yolland, *Astronomical Observations made with Ramsden's Zenith Sector etc.* (1842).

11 Clarke, *Principal Triangulation*, pp. 210–12.

12 *Ibid.*

13 *Ibid.*

14 Mudge and Dalby, *Account of the Trig. Survey 1784–1796* (London 1799), p. 274.

15 *Ibid.* p. 280.

16 Mudge, *An Account of the Operations Carried on For Accomplishing a Trigonometrical Survey of England and Wales, continued from the Year 1797 to the end of the Year 1799* (London 1801), part 2, p. 54.

17 See pp. 141–3.

18 *History of the Retriangulation of Great Britain 1935–1962* (HMSO 1967), pp. 92–7.

19 Clarke, *Principal Triangulation*, p. 560 et seq.

20 Henry Kater, *Phil. Trans.* 1828, CXVIII, p. 153.

21 See D. S. Macmillan, *The Kater Family 1750–1965* (Sydney 1966).

22 Kater, *Phil. Trans.* 1828, CXVIII, p. 161.

23 *Ibid.* p. 181.

4
The Birth of the Topographical Survey

The original survey having been grafted, as it were, upon an independent scientific work, was local, and detached in order of performance, and as the importance of a great national survey was at first only partly recognised . . . the work proceeded under all the disadvantages of a slowly protracted survey, an interrupted publication of unconnected maps, and a tone of shading and style of execution varying, though improving, in its progress.

J. E. Portlock, *Memoir of the Life of Major-General Colby* (London 1869)

Apart from its scientific function, the trigonometrical survey formed the framework for the general map of England, the publication of which in sheet form began after 1801. The secondary and tertiary triangulation (to furnish a network of control points for the topographical surveyors) soon claimed a progressively larger share of the Survey's time and man-power. As early as 1792, with this lower-order triangulation specifically in mind, the Board had placed an order with Ramsden for an eighteen-inch theodolite (the so-called 'Small Circular Instrument') and in the same year, somewhat prematurely as it turned out, an initial selection of interior stations had been made at which it would be set up. The small theodolite which, because of its 'portable size', could be readily hoisted to 'the tops of steeples, towers &c.', was not brought into use until 1795.[1]

By the end of the decade Mudge was referring more frequently to the cartographic, as distinct from the purely geodetic, applications of his work. It was symptomatic of this change of emphasis that he began to criticize existing county maps, especially in terms of errors of distance and direction, and in 1799, he wrote in the Preface to the first volume of the *Account of the Trigonometrical Survey*:

In the prosecution of the General Survey, frequent opportunities have manifested themselves of enabling us to discover the very erroneous state of our maps. The work itself, will enable any one to draw the same conclusion; for, by laying down on the maps of counties, particularly on Taylor's Map of Dorsetshire, the distances of the intersected objects . . . an immediate proof is obtained of their great inaccuracy.[2]

Perhaps he still had to recognize the full immensity of the tasks which awaited him in mapping even as much of Britain as the private surveyors had done in the preceding half century. The difficulties he would have to face were of a twofold nature: first, to create a satisfactory organization to carry on the topographical survey in the field; and secondly, to secure the publication of the resulting manuscripts. Only to a limited extent was Mudge given an opportunity to put into effect a rational plan (if indeed such existed) for the orderly development of the detail survey. From the late 1780s until the end of his directorate in 1820 there were so many shifts of policy and related changes in organization that the development of the topographical survey proceeded by a series of *ad hoc* expediencies, so that from the point of view of quality even contemporaries were agreed that many of the maps fell short of an acceptable standard.[3]

The Reorganization of 1787

When he remarked of the topographical survey that it had 'been grafted, as it were, upon an independent scientific work',[4] Portlock had put his finger on a fundamental aspect of its organizational shortcomings in the early years. There were, in fact, two national surveys in progress: the scientifically-orientated trigonometrical survey, and the topographical survey (known variously as the 'internal,' 'local' or 'interior' survey) designed to clothe the framework of triangles. In 1811 the distinction was still very real as the Commissioners of Military Enquiry explained:

> Both Surveys have been carried on at the expense of the Ordnance, and under the superior Superintendence of Colonel Mudge, but by a different Establishment for each Service; we shall therefore make separate Statements respecting them.[5]

Much of the early history of the topographical survey was concerned with the characteristics and consequences of this 'different Establishment' and, increasingly, towards the end of Mudge's tenure of office, with how it started to become more effectively integrated into the Survey as a whole.

According to Mudge's testimony before the Commissioners of Military Enquiry, it was four years after the resumption of the trigonometrical survey in 1791 that 'directions were given, under the authority of the Duke of Richmond, for filling up the Triangles established by the former Survey, with a distinct Local Survey of the Country'.[6] This would give a date of 1795 for the inauguration of the topographical work. However, a topographical organization existed before this date, and pre–1795 surveys were later incorporated into the first one-inch maps published by the Ordnance Survey; there are cogent reasons, therefore, for accepting the 1780s rather than the 1790s as the founding decade for the topographical survey. For much of the eighteenth century the Board of Ordnance had looked to the Drawing Room of the Tower of London for its military surveyors and draughtsmen, but during the 1780s dissatisfaction began to be expressed with the organization of the service. In 1787 it was extensively altered and specific provision was made for a permanent cadre of men trained to make topographical surveys in areas where military maps were required. This reorganization of an existing service gave rise to the topographical branch in a form which was to remain until 1800.

Two main administrative steps were taken in 1787. First, the Master General created a new position, that of 'Chief Surveying Draftsman', which was to rank next to the 'Chief Draftsman' in the hierarchy of the Drawing Room. Secondly, a 'surveying party' was to be formed 'consisting of the Chief Surveyor and a certain Number of Draftsmen'.[7] This was the 'corps of draftsmen' to which Portlock referred as having been formed by the Duke of Richmond,[8] who thus had a hand in the foundation of the topographical as well as the trigonometrical branch of the national survey. The post of Chief Surveying Draftsman was filled by William Gardner who, like the elder Thomas Yeakell, the Chief Draftsman, was a protégé of the Duke of Richmond.[9] As a past employee of the Duke, Gardner had been given an appointment by the Board of Ordnance and in 1784 was recorded as working in the Plymouth district on military surveys when plans were needed to fortify Plymouth dockyard 'against a regular Siege'.[10] Although they were never published, the importance of these six-inch maps was that they became something of a prototype for future work by the Board's surveying draughtsmen. Such continuity between surveys executed before and after 1787 is made clear by the regulations issued by the Duke of Richmond for the conduct of the newly-established surveying party. Besides their Drawing Room pay, its members were to be allowed, when ordered out on surveys,

> Two pence an acre, Statute measure for surveying & drawing two fair and finished plans on a scale of six inches to a mile, in the same manner as those done by William Gardner of the environs of Plymouth.[11]

In this instruction can be traced the origin both of the system of payment for topographical surveyors on the early Ordnance Survey and of the cartographic model for future work.

Early Surveys for the Maps of Kent and Essex

The topographical surveys which were eventually to result in the maps of Kent (actually published by William Faden in 1801) and of Essex (the first regular sheets to be published by the Board of Ordnance in 1805) have a convoluted history (Plate 4).

The early surveys carried out by Gardner's party were undertaken for short-term military objectives and not with publication in mind. This was certainly true of the surveys of Jersey (1787) and of Guernsey (1788),[12] executed at the six-inch scale, and it was also true of the earliest work in Kent, likewise beginning in 1788 at the same scale.[13] Military surveys according to the 'Plymouth model' were thus being made in a piecemeal fashion in a succession of areas in southern England which were of potential strategic interest to the Board. In 1791 the Master General had ordered that 'Mr. William Gardner the Chief Surveying Draftsman . . . proceed with the survey of the Isle of Wight', and had approved his taking with him 'as many assistants as he might want, exclusive of Messrs Yeakell and McLauchan, from the Drawing Room at the Tower'.[14] A year later the surveying party was moved to the Bagshot area, again by direct order of the Master General, where the work for that season was carried out.

It was in the same year that a small but significant change of policy occurred when for the first time an attempt can be detected, albeit a minor one, to integrate the trigonometrical and topographical surveys under the Board's control. The instructions to the trigonometrical party from the Master General were explicit:

> to be minute in our Survey of Sussex; and to furnish Mr. Gardner . . . with materials for correcting a Map of that county, intended, at some future period, to be published under the patronage of his Grace.[15]

Mudge recorded that, during the following two years,

> Mr. Gardner generally attended us, having been supplied with sufficient materials for correcting all the southern and western parts of his Map[16]

and through this project there was forged another link between the county cartography of the late eighteenth century and the first Ordnance Survey maps of the early nineteenth century. The main strands of the history of the Sussex map are summarized in its title and dedication: 'A Topographical Map of the County of Sussex . . . Planned from an actual Survey by a scale of one inch to a Statute Mile; begun by W. Gardner and the late T. Yeakell, Completed by Thos. Gream, Land Surveyor . . . Engraved by Thos. Foot'; it was 'Published by W. Faden, Geographer to His Majesty' and dedicated 'To His Grace Charles Lennox, Duke of Richmond'. Yeakell and Gardner while still employed on the estate of the Duke of Richmond had published four sheets of the 'Great Survey' of Sussex before being drawn into the service of the Board of Ordnance; the combination of Gardner's position as Chief Surveying Draftsman and the Duke's enthusiasm for promoting cartography explain why the incomplete survey should have been taken up again in the 1790s as new material became available. If the Lindley and Crosley map of Surrey,[17] based on Roy's triangulation of the 1780s, is excluded, this was the first published county map to benefit from data from the official Trigonometrical Survey. It served also as a model for the map of Essex when the survey for that county began in 1799.

While work was in progress in Sussex the Drawing Room establishment was again reconstituted by a Royal Warrant dated 15 September 1794,[18] and shortly afterwards the Master General took advantage of the death of Thomas Chamberlain, the Chief Draftsman, to abolish the position of Chief Surveying Draftsman. It was more appropriate, he decided, 'that there should be only one Chief Draftsman to superintend the establishment of the Drawing Room'.[19] This left William Gardner in sole charge of the thirty-one draughtsmen, and immediate supervisor of the interior survey. His enhanced status may have contributed to a more formal recognition of the role and potential of the topographical survey. Between 1788 and 1795 surveying draughtsmen had been almost continuously engaged in making surveys which were later to be incorporated into published Ordnance Survey maps, without any specific authority for their employment on the national survey. However, this authority was soon granted, and the Duke of Richmond's instruction of 1795 to complement the triangulation with 'a distinct Local Survey of the Country' formally brought together the two branches. In the same year the need for 'completing the Map of Kent for the Board of Ordnance'[20] was accepted as a priority task; the trigonometrical operations

> were carried on in Kent, in conjunction with Mr. Gardner, from which, a very fine Map has been since formed, containing all that part of the country, which, from its proximity to the coast, may in process of time, become the seat of military operations.[21]

It is clear that the military utility of surveys still dominated official thinking but it is interesting that Mudge, writing in 1799, should have hinted at the incompatibility of the needs of military surveying for defensive purposes, and surveying for the purpose of publishing a general map of the country:

> hitherto, the Trigonometrical Survey has been made to answer, the private purpose of the Board of Ordnance, in preparing Materials for accurate Descriptions of Military Districts, at the same time that, Operations have been carried on for answering those of the Public. A great part of the County of Kent was originally ordered to be surveyed on the first of these principles, all the Fields, and every variety of ground being laid down on the Plan & The remaining parts have since been surveyed in the same particular manner. This survey, begun by order of His Grace the Duke of Richmond, was completed at the instance of the Marquis Cornwallis:— The great map is lodged in the Tower, and a smaller on is about to be published.[22]

This explanation confirms that the Ordnance map of Kent (1801) originated as a military survey rather than one tailor-made from the outset for publication. The 'great map' referred to the field sheets which were first surveyed on the six-inch scale by Gardner with Thomas Cubbitt, George Pink, Thomas Yeakell jun., and Thomas Gream. The work was finally completed on the three-inch scale in

1799 and was finished in a 'masterly manner' by Gardner. After reduction it was originally scheduled for publication in 1799 by Faden but it did not appear until 1801.

These events were only a first stage in a continuing search for an appropriate specification for topographical surveys for a general map of England and Wales. Once Kent had been completed attention was turned to Essex, the southern part of which had already been surveyed so that both sides of the Thames could appear in the Kent map. As the area of the survey was extended beyond the immediate military requirement, the high cost became a significant constraint in its execution. Kent, which took over ten years to complete, had proved to be an expensive undertaking and Mudge and Gardner were forced to search for methods of economizing on the proposed interior survey in Essex. Mudge wrote with new proposals to the Lieutenant-General (deputy to the Master General) of the Board, William, Fifth Viscount Howe, in April 1799:

> Conformably to the instructions received by the Chief Draftsman and myself we are about to commence the survey of Essex. It was originally proposed to be gone over in the same manner as was lately did the County of Kent. But, as it does not appear that any advantage will acrue to the Board, from surveying all the fields of it; and since it would be impossible to publish a portable Map of the County with those Fields, I am desirous of submitting to the opinion of the Lieutenant General . . . whether or not, it would be eligible to relinquish the prosecution of the very minute part of the Survey, and attend to what is of real use to the Public at large?[23]

Such a curtailed specification for the field work would, he believed, save both time and money:

> the county can be surveyed in the manner which I propose, for about one third of the sum which has been lately expended in making the map of Kent, and in less than a quarter part of the time – I think there can be no doubt of a proper Military Map, exactly similar to that of Sussex, being completed before February next.[24]

In his usual thorough manner, Mudge had also asked Gardner to prepare a supporting document, indicating how such ideas were to be put into practice, and this was also duly presented to Howe. Dated 9 April 1799, Gardner's short statement analysed the probable labour costs and provided a synopsis of the techniques to be employed on the survey of Essex:

> I propose after receiving the general Trigonometrical Distances from Captain Mudge, to make numerous intermediate Intersections and lay the whole down on a scale of Two Inches to a mile. Upon the Triangles each surveyor will plot his Measurements etc., represent the Towns, Villages, Woods, Rivers, Hills, omitting only *the true* forms of the Fields the whole to form what is termed a proper Military Survey. When the Survey is compleat on this scale it may with great exactness be reduced to an Inch to a Mile.[25]

So it was planned that the interior survey should consist essentially of two operations: a secondary triangulation, based on the results of the trigonometrical survey, would be provided by Gardner who would be followed in the field by a second party to fill in the detail. The basic scale of the survey, unlike that of Kent, was to be two inches to one mile, reverting to Roy's specification, and setting the cartographic pattern for the next two decades. That the work should form a 'proper Military Survey' emphasizes that the first obligation was still to answer military needs. The major economy in time, and therefore expense, was to sacrifice the accurate representation of field boundaries, the correct delineation of which had apparently taken so long for Kent.

Gardner's proposals were not immediately adopted. The Lieutenant-General's secretary, Robert Mackenzie, whose job it was to draft his superior's replies to correspondence, was evidently a man of some cartographic perception. He did not consider that Gardner's statement was detailed enough, and suggested his own alterations: 'Permit me', Mackenzie wrote to Lord Howe,

> to observe that, in enumerating the objects to be laid down in the survey, all are not expressed as should, I conceive, be done in a Paper of Instructions, so pointed as the present seems to require, namely – Roads of all descriptions – Bridges – Fords – Hills, and *duly surveyed*, i.e. not simply sketched.[26]

Had William Gardner been required, as a result of this suggestion, to rewrite his proposals in more detail, it would perhaps have prevented much confusion in later years, but unfortunately this was not to be the case. Lord Howe, in his reply to Mackenzie, mildly rebuked this enthusiasm for detailed written instructions:

> By the way – It does not appear to me requisite to make any addition to Capt. Mudge's instructions . . . as the work is to be done in a similar mode to that of the survey of Sussex, which is sufficiently minute.[27]

In this way Gardner's earlier survey of Sussex, rather than that of Kent at six inches to one mile, became the prototype of the Essex map. Lord Howe having provisionally approved Gardner's proposals, it remained only for Mudge to present a detailed estimate of the likely savings from the new procedures. This he did at the end of April 1799:

> Mr. Gardner, and the Draftsmen employed with him, have been heretofore allowed the sum of £5..6..8 for

surveying and planning each square mile: But as the Trigonometrical Survey greatly facilitates his operations, and it does not become necessary to describe the Fields individually, it appears this allowance may be reduced to £1..13..0.[28]

On these figures there would be an over-all saving of about £5000, a considerable economy.

As soon as Gardner had agreed to carry on the survey on these terms Mudge expressed concern that ready cash should be made available during the field season:

> Being of opinion that an accurate survey of this County, cannot be made at the expense of any private individual for a sum less than £2423, I humbly submit to the Honourable Board the propriety of allowing the Chief Draftsman to draw on their Treasurer for the sum of £160..0..0 at the expiration of two months from the commencement of the survey, and the like sums at equal intervals of time 'til the survey be completed, which sums so advanced, will necessarily be deducted, when the work is ordered to be cast, which it will be most convenient to perform once in six months, two castings only will be necessary, as the survey of any one county, excepting Yorkshire, may be completed in Twelve months from its commencement.[29]

Mudge estimated – with remarkable foresight as it turned out – that, if the interior survey were to be conducted county by county with his existing resources, it would take at least fifty years to complete a map of England and Wales. The 'castings' to which he referred were probably the calculations of the work accomplished by each surveyor which had to be done before a final payment could be made. It is typical of Mudge's careful ordering of the Survey's affairs that the request for funds was accompanied by a breakdown of proposed expenditure:

SURVEY OF ESSEX – ESTIMATE[30]

	£	s	d
The County of Essex contains 1563 square miles of which number 1250 remain to be surveyed–			
To surveying 1250 square miles at 33 shillings per sq. mile	2062	0	0
To carrying on the Trigonometrical Survey over the County	300	0	0
To travelling charges of Ten Draftsmen	60	0	0
	2422	0	0

This estimate comes out neatly at one pound less than Mudge's figure for the cost of a private survey, but, since some of the work had already been done, Mudge's survey would still have been the more expensive. No doubt this could be justified to the Board by the greater accuracy of the work. There are no comparable figures for the Kent survey, but as Mudge had reckoned that Essex could be done for one-third the amount, it may be supposed that Kent had cost about £8000 – almost as much as the total expenditure on the interior survey for the next seven years.

Finally, on 28 May 1799, the Board ordered that 'the Survey which is carrying on under the Direction of Mr Gardner be proceeded with upon the Terms Capt Mudge has proposed'.[31] Mudge's efforts in economy of public expenditure did not pass unnoticed by the Board who informed him that

> they very much applaud the zeal which he has shewed in producing so considerable a saving of expense as will be effected by the execution of his proposal and that they consider themselves much obliged to him upon the occasion.[32]

A cost-conscious philosophy, albeit to the detriment of the Survey on occasions, was to be a characteristic of its operations for the rest of the Mudge era.

The Royal Military Surveyors and Draftsmen 1800–17

William Gardner, the leading figure behind the surveys of both Kent and Essex, died early in 1800 and the event marked the end of a distinctive phase in the history of the topographical survey. It was in the same year that the civilian draughtsmen and surveyors employed in the Drawing Room at the Tower of London again underwent a change of status. No reasons were specified but it had been decided that the organization approved as recently as 1794 was 'not well calculated to afford the services which are required by Draughts'* and the expedient was adopted of reconstituting the service into a 'Corps of Royal Military Surveyors and Draftsmen'. The Drawing Room at the Tower was to remain the headquarters of the new Corps, but henceforth its members, under the command of the Chief Engineer, were to be 'subject to the Rules and Discipline of War'.[33] To make clear their military status,[34] which was no doubt thought necessary if they were to be employed on active service in the war with France, they were supplied with blue uniforms 'bearing a resemblance to the Uniforms worn by

---

* 'Draught' was a term for a detachment of men, often proceeding overseas.

the Corps of Royal Engineers'.[35] The Corps was to be recruited either by selecting from the existing 'Drawing Room Establishment ... Persons ... most competent to the Duties of Surveyors & Draftsmen'[36] or by bringing in suitably qualified outsiders and trainees. The warrant authorized the expense of the Corps to be £4033. 5s. per annum with a new establishment to consist of

One Chief Surveyor and Draftsman	15/- per diem
1st Assistant Surveyor and Draftsman	12/- per diem
2nd Assistant Surveyor and Draftsman	10/- per diem
1st Class –8 Surveyors and Draftsmen	7/6^d each
2nd Class–16 Surveyors and Draftsmen	5/- each
3rd Class– 8 Surveyors and Draftsmen	4/- each
6 Cadets	2/- each[37]

In 1805 a further warrant increased this establishment by allowing two extra draughtsmen in the 1st class category, four in the 2nd class, two in the 3rd class, and two additional cadets. At this date the total number in the Corps was fifty-one and an annual expenditure of £4891 was allowed for in the estimates of the Ordnance.[38] The Corps survived until 1817. It was then disbanded but for nearly two decades it had operated as a military unit, the members of which were exclusively employed in cartographical duties either in the field or in the drawing office.

The contribution of this Corps to the survey of southern England has to be seen in the context of its other duties both in Britain and on foreign stations. At first sight the militarization of the surveyors and draughtsmen might appear to offer a better chance of effective control by the Board of Ordnance over the topographical mapping of Britain (perhaps through the Chief Engineer) but, in practice, several influences were at work which reduced this potential benefit. Most important was that the Corps had not been set up with the needs of the interior survey of Great Britain in mind but as a complement to the engineering services of the Board whether on home or foreign stations. The needs of the topographical survey came second to other requirements; at times of crisis during the Napoleonic war, whether financial or military, the domestic survey was always the loser. Out of the total strength of the Corps, no more than nine or ten of its members were employed on surveys in southern England at any one time. In 1816, a year for which 'A List and Distribution of the Corps' has survived, only nine out of fifty-one enumerated personnel were recorded as being attached to the 'Survey of Great Britain'; nineteen (including eight cadets in training) were stationed in the Tower of London; a number were on home stations – Chatham, Dublin, Jersey, Plymouth, Portsmouth and Woolwich – and the remainder were on overseas postings in Canada, Gibraltar, Malta and the West Indies, with one draughtsman reported as 'With the Army in France'.[39]

The wider demands of the service on the small number of topographical surveyors contributed to a lack of continuity in the field-work for the one-inch maps. Indeed, only a handful of men were employed continuously on the Ordnance Survey throughout the life of the Corps from 1800 to 1817. They included (with their years in service in 1817) Thomas Yeakell (30 years) who was employed in the Drawing Room in the Tower reducing the plans and preparing tracings prior to their engraving, Robert Dawson (26 years), William Stanley (20 years), and Charles Budgen (23 years). These four, all recruited to the Corps from the old Drawing Room establishment, were 1st class 'surveyors and draftsmen'; among those of 2nd class rank in 1816 (but listed in February 1817 as 'Supernumerary on the First Class') were Edward B. Metcalf (13 years), William Hyett (12 years) and Henry Stevens (11 years);[40] while other surveyors were employed for various shorter periods on the Survey.

From the records of the Corps it is clear that Mudge was denied a free hand to retain an adequate number of surveyors for the mapping of southern England. In some ways the Master General and the Board kept a much tighter rein over the development of the topographical survey than over the trigonometrical activities. Separate authorization had to be obtained for its extension into new counties; authority for the detailed mapping of Devon, for example, was not given until February 1800, when the Lieutenant-General of the Ordnance wrote to Mudge:

> I also approve ... of your proposition for continuing the same in the present year, namely, to Survey the County of Devon with as much of Somersetshire and Cornwall as will square the Map.[41]

This was clearly a reference to the surveys needed to complete the regular sheets of the one-inch series for publication, but for the Board of Ordnance the immediate military use of the surveys often took precedence over the long-term objective. In 1803 Mudge reassured the Surveyor-General (the senior officer in the Board of Ordnance responsible for coastal defence) that the 'planning of a large proportion of the Devonshire Coast [had] been completed on a proper scale and made every way suitable for military purposes'.[42] For Dorset, too, separate authorization was given; in 1804 Mudge noted that 'the Survey of Dorset is taken up' and although, as he said, *'all* hands doubled',[43] at this date his experienced surveyors were scattered over three or four counties in the West Country. At this time the threat of a French invasion was always in the forefront of official thinking, but even after 1815 the Master General and the Board kept a particularly close watch on the directions of the extension of the topographical survey.[44]

The Topographical Survey as a Training Ground for Royal Engineers

By themselves the figures for men and their lengths of service offer only a crude index of the skilled man-power resources available, for Mudge and the handful of warrant officers of the Corps of Royal Military Surveyors and Draftsmen employed under him were assigned to a series of other duties under the Board. By far the most demanding was the requirement, dating from 1803, to train cadets intended for commission in the Royal Engineers, as well as cadets of the Royal Military Surveyors and Draftsmen, in the arts of field surveying and sketching. The scheme, which seems to have been the brainchild of Robert Morse, the Inspector-General of Fortifications, again reflected the short-term needs of the Board rather than the long-term good of the Survey. Once the cadets had completed their basic theoretical training – at Woolwich for the Engineers, and in the Drawing Room of the Tower for the Surveyors and Draftsmen – they were to be attached to the Royal Military Surveyors for a course of practical surveying under Mudge's direction. Agreement to the proposal was given on 1 March 1803 when it was noted that

> The Master-General approved of a proposition submitted to him ... by which the Candidates for the Engineers (instead of remaining at the Academy an extra six months as had been customary for the last few years) were, conformably to the suggestions of the Inspector-General, to be sent to the Royal Military Surveyors, who are under the direction of Major Mudge, Royal Artillery, to be instructed in Surveying.[45]

Nor was the training to be a mere formality, because a fortnight later it was confirmed that progression to an Engineer's commission and seniority in the Corps would 'ultimately depend on the reports made to the Inspector-General of Fortifications concerning their assiduity and proficiency'.[46] From that date until 1832, the Board of Ordnance minutes record a procession of cadets being sent into the country to be attached to the national survey.

Mudge's reaction to this innovation is not recorded, but the fact that it was implemented when the resources of skilled man-power were already stretched to their limit was to affect the mapping in three main ways. First, especially in the first two or three years, the training programme took up much of Mudge's time and personal attention which ordinarily would have been devoted solely to the Survey, and the impression emerges from his correspondence that he was sometimes more concerned with the proficiency of his cadets than with the accuracy of the topographical surveys in Devon and Cornwall. Certainly, he threw himself energetically into preparing for the first cadets and already, by 19 March 1803, his planning included

> a list of Instruments necessary to be supplied by the Ordnance for the service of the G. Cadets about to be taught Surveying. Please to give it to General Morse.[47]

Moreover, once the first cadets had been posted to the West Country, he himself moved into the area to be in close touch with their progress – there is no evidence that he considered a similarly close supervision of the topographical survey to be essential. Thus, from May to September, he was lodging at Chudleigh in Devon, before travelling to Haverfordwest to make observations for the trigonometrical survey. He returned to Liskeard in Cornwall in December and then went back to the Drawing Room in the Tower for part of the winter. But by February 1804 he was active again in Devon; his letters trace his movements for the whole of the field season – at Teignmouth from February to April, at South Molton in May (with a quick foray to Swansea on the trigonometrical survey), returning to Teignmouth in June, at Chudleigh and Newton Abbot in early July, and then alternating between Teignmouth and Liskeard for the rest of the summer before returning to the Tower of London in the autumn.[48] Mudge seemed to enjoy his duties as a peripatetic headmaster to his cadets, and this, combined with his reputation as a man who could be trusted with public money, helps to explain his subsequent appointment as Lieutenant-Governor of the Royal Military Academy, and his drift away from an effective control of the topographical survey.

A second way in which the training programme affected the topographical survey was that heavy demands were made on the time of some of the best surveyors. The immediate requirement of the new programme in 1803 was for suitable teachers, and of six surveyors attached to Mudge on the West Country survey, four – Charles Budgen, Robert Dawson, Richard Searle and William Stanley – were selected to teach the gentlemen cadets. All four were Royal Military Surveyors and Draftsmen, three in the 'Second Class' rank of the Corps, and Robert Dawson in the 'First Class'.[49]

Although only a young man of twenty-seven, Dawson's quality of leadership and his skill in surveying and cartography were already sufficiently proven for him to be selected as head of the team of topographical surveyors and draughtsmen answerable only to Mudge. He had first joined the Drawing Room at the Tower on 1 July 1791, and at the age of eighteen was in the third out of five classes of draughtsmen. There is no record of his being employed on the topographical survey before 1802, but for nearly three years previously he had served as a military draughtsman, teaching officers intended for staff duties in the Quartermaster-General's Department, at the Royal Military College at High Wycombe (later to develop into the Staff College) from its inception in 1799 to the end of 1801.

With such experience, nobody could have been better qualified to teach the cadet engineers than Dawson, and it was to him that Mudge entrusted the planning of the new cartographic curriculum. A measure of Dawson's wider military reputation was that after he had joined the topographers in the West Country, there was an attempt to woo him away from the Ordnance Survey. This was in February 1804, and when Mudge heard the rumour that Dawson was intending to leave the Survey, apparently either to return to the Royal Military College or to enter the Royal Staff Corps with the Quartermaster-General's Department, he intervened and, fearing that he might lose Dawson's services, sent him a glowing letter of appreciation. Dawson's reply was that he had 'no Inclination to quit the Ordnance Service' unless he were offered a 'Rank in the Army';[50] such an offer was not forthcoming and this was the end of the matter, but it shows how, in the Napoleonic period, the satisfactory staffing of the Ordnance Survey often hung on a slender thread.

When the initial training scheme was still in the experimental stage, cadets were assigned to each of the four surveyors. It is evident, however, that Mudge was careful to weigh up the capabilities of the instructors. Thus Budgen, 'tho' but an indifferent Draftsman', nevertheless 'an expert Surveyor', was assigned to teach cadets from the Drawing Room (who had already attained a higher standard of draughtsmanship than the Woolwich men). But Richard Searle, 'whatever his merits may be as a Surveyor' was but 'an indifferent Master'; while at the same time 'the advantage which Mr Stanley has [as] a Master over Mr Searle' was noticeable.[51] Clearly, Dawson stood head and shoulders above his colleagues; by the summer of 1803, when the training in Devon was only a few months advanced, Mudge had felt able to refer to him as 'That meritorious Gentleman', and no doubt one of the good marks beside his name was that he had trained the young Lieutenant Colby (by then aged nineteen and already a great favourite with Mudge) and 'in the space of about five months' had turned him into 'a good surveyor and fair draftsman'.[52] Dawson's responsibilities for training were quickly increased and by December 1803 he had five pupils under him, compared with only one or two with each of the other surveyors. In March of the following year Mudge had decided that Dawson's pupils 'for general Information, have the advantage' and 'in future, every candidate should be sent to him'.[53] The practical teaching generated administrative duties and from January 1804 Dawson had to compile a monthly report on each candidate.[54] There is no doubt that he discharged all these tasks efficiently, but the cadets' gain must have been the Ordnance Survey's loss, for it would certainly have benefited from the undivided energies of a man of such calibre.

The third way in which the training programme influenced the Ordnance Survey was through the effects of the cadet syllabus on techniques employed by the topographical surveyors. These effects are difficult to assess and in any case indirect; nevertheless it is almost certain that Dawson's ideas would have rubbed off on the Survey as a whole. By December 1803 he had compiled a 'Course of Instructions',[55] designed for the Engineer cadets; as a final test of their competence in surveying, the pupils were to accompany 'the Teacher for some time on the General Survey, for the purposes of getting a Habitude of using the Instruments, with readiness and accuracy; and of obtaining Information on the Process of conducting a topographical Survey'.[56] A blurring of the methods used in instruction and those practised in the detail survey for the one-inch maps was an inevitable consequence of this dual role of the field parties.

The most significant long-term effect of Dawson's attachment to the Ordnance Survey was in the style of relief representation which he pioneered. This was widely adopted in British military cartography and, in circles beyond the Ordnance Survey, came to be described as the 'British National Style'.[57] It was principally achieved by using brush and water-colour or ink, to depict a landscape in oblique or vertical light, and its main inspiration seems to have been the *Mémorial Topographique et Militaire* published in France in 1802.[58] The French recommended a thorough acquaintance with physical geography, and similarly Dawson advocated the 'natural-history-principle of drawing'. This, he wrote much later, 'will require the physical substance, and geological structure and formation of the land to be understood',[59] an approach in which he was supported by Mudge who, as early as 1803, in referring to the training of the cadets, had stated: 'I would have them all draw from nature'.[60] Herein lies one explanation for the Survey's early interest in geological mapping, and many of the Ordnance surveyors' drawings completed before 1820 reflect these precepts. By the time the field parties had reached Snowdonia in 1815 Dawson's ideas had been fully developed both in cadet training and in the preparation of the hill-sketches for the one-inch maps.[61] It was his work in this area that earned him the reputation of

> bringing topographical drawing to a degree of perfection, that had given to his plans a beauty and accuracy of expression, which some of our eminent artists had previously supposed unattainable.[62]

It must be said that not everyone was so enamoured of Dawson's approach to hill representation. Carmichael-Smyth was one who believed that it left too much 'to the taste, imagination and fancy' of the individual draughtsman.[63]

In the topographical surveys of southern England this tendency was undoubtedly increased by Mudge's lack of a sufficient number of fully-trained military surveyors to execute the work in a standard fashion. His letters, while not openly critical, certainly do not disguise the shortage of surveyors on occasions. In August 1804 he reported to Morse from Teignmouth:

> The Party of Draftsmen employed in this quarter, being abridged in number . . . I shall find myself rather deficient in means of carrying on the survey towards the East, so expeditiously as may be necessary.[64]

His request to retain the services of an extra surveyor – 'Mr Robinson (now perfect)'[65] – was refused, and he adopted the unmilitary expedient of employing local civilian land surveyors on the work for the one-inch maps. In July 1805, however, the Board of Ordnance sanctioned the employment on the survey under Mudge of

> Messr. John and Phillip Crocker and Henry Boyce at the rate of 4d. per diem, and 1d. a Mile for Travelling and also of a 4th Person upon similar terms as soon as the Lieutenant Colonel could find a proper person for the Employment. Ordered that the Arrangement proposed by Lieutenant Colonel Mudge be carried into Effect and that he be authorised to engage the Number of extra Surveyors upon the conditions he has mentioned.[66]

The number of these extra assistants was fixed at four and Mudge, in giving evidence on the Ordnance Survey to the Commissioners of Military Enquiry in 1811, noted that the 'Local Survey' was still 'carried on by the Royal Military Surveyors and Draftsmen, assisted by four professional Surveyors who are hired for the occasion'.[67]

So by the end of 1805 there were six classes of people at work on the Survey – Royal Artillery, Royal Engineers, Engineer cadets, Royal Military Surveyors and Draftsmen and the cadets for that Corps, and the civilian assistants – each of whom, despite their absorption into one military command, could bring a potentially different cartographic experience to their work. The civilian assistants, in particular, were something of an unknown factor and, employed as they were on a piece-work basis (according to the number of square miles completed), they were liable to deviate from a strict military specification once out of the sight of Mudge or Dawson. And although the Royal Military Surveyors and Draftsmen could be expected to turn out fairly uniform maps, the presence of cadets, and specially the incorporation of plans done in training into the mapping for the one-inch, added a less controllable element to the work. Although this practice is only occasionally documented – as with the 37 square miles completed at a scale of three inches to one mile by cadet Richard Holberton to the west of Plymouth[68] – it was probably more widely condoned.

The surveyors' manuscript drawings offer a primary record of the contribution of the Royal Military Surveyors and Draftsmen to the development of the topographical survey. In terms of area much was accomplished. After the surveyors left Essex in about 1800, the field parties not only completed two-inch surveys for all the West Country but, by the time the Corps was disbanded in 1817, they had also surveyed the whole of southern England, and a great deal of Wales and the Midlands. Mudge's enemies could hardly have found fault with the quantity of mapping accomplished in this period; subsequent recriminations were largely about the quality of the work.

Apart from the distractions of training, the main weakness in the system of local surveying which prevailed for much of the era of the Royal Military Surveyors and Draftsmen lay in a lack of supervision of the work of individual surveyors. Until 1809 it had been a responsibility of the Chief Draftsman to supervise the field work, but thereafter special payments for this work were discontinued. The plans seem to have suffered from the absence of a standard specification or, if such existed, from a failure to implement it. Even a casual inspection of the two-inch drawings reveals wide variations in planimetric accuracy, in attention to detail and in style of drawing. Marked contrasts exist in the effectiveness and care with which the hills were drawn on different sheets: some were executed to high standards of penmanship, others resulted from rapid strokes of the brush. And, despite the decision about field boundaries made in connection with the survey of Essex, local interpretations of the instruction continued to vary widely; in the Land's End peninsula, for example, they were often omitted whereas in other areas in the south-west they were mapped in a fair amount of detail. Mudge's claim made in 1811 that the local survey was carried on under his 'immediate superintendence and controul'[69] can hardly be upheld; he was weighed down with public office, and his most trusted assistants, Colby and Dawson, were also extremely busy, the former owing his primary loyalty to the conduct of the trigonometrical operations, the latter often preoccupied with the instruction of Engineer candidates. There was more than a grain of truth in a comment made by Portlock (himself trained by Dawson as a cadet Engineer) that 'the importance of a great national survey was at first only partly recognised'.[70]

That individual surveyors worked largely without supervision is confirmed by an account given by Samuel Burt Howlett,[71] a Royal Military Surveyor and Draftsman, of his life with the Corps from 1808 to 1817. After a cadetship in the Drawing Room at the Tower, where he had 'to attend . . . every day from ten to three o'clock, to learn plan drawing under the Chief Draftsman' and mathematics under the 'well known Mr. Bonnycastle', he was sent in 1811, as a 3rd class draftsman, upon 'the General Survey of England to learn Land-surveying, levelling, and sketching ground'.[72] For a month his work was supervised by William Stanley but from then on, after drawing lots with another surveyor to decide which area each would survey, he evidently worked alone while he 'filled up a large piece of country bounded on the North by the Wilts and Berks Canal, on the South by the Ridge Way, on the East by Kingston, and on the West by the straight Roman Military Road'.[73]

What was true of the Royal Military Surveyors, who were only under military discipline in a very loose sense, applied equally to the civilian assistants on the survey. While their attachment could sometimes enrich the scope of the survey (as in the recording of archaeological sites on Salisbury Plain by the Crockers),[74] it led to much imperfect mapping. Colby, giving evidence in 1824 before the Committee on the Survey and Valuation of Ireland, was particularly uncompromising in his indictment. 'When we employed persons not brought up in the ordnance department', he concluded, 'considerable inconvenience resulted.' Civilian surveyors, in his experience of the English survey in the second decade of the century, exhibited 'Want of sufficient skill, and want of sufficient integrity', and when asked to define 'integrity', he expanded his comment:

> They performed their work without a sufficient degree of accuracy . . . It arose from not being completely under superintendence at the time it was done; I had not the direction of the survey at the time they were employed.[75]

Colby seems to have forgotten the failings of the unsupervised Royal Military Surveyors, but whatever the combination of events – and there were other factors such as local hostility to the surveyors in some areas* – the constraints of trying to carry out a general survey in war-time meant that the early topographical survey fell short of the high standards achieved in the trigonometrical field.

The Beginnings of Reform 1816–20

With the ending of the Napoleonic War Mudge began to try to remedy some of the irregularities in the topographical survey. Concerning the lack of supervision in the field, he told the Master General in 1816 that he found

> the Interior Survey performed by the Surveyors in the Country required more time for examination & superintendence than now can be devoted to that purpose by Captain Colby without neglecting the important Trigonometrical Operations which form the Basis of the Survey.

He continued:

> My own duties at the Academy prevent me from personally examining the plans in the Field of the Surveyors who are employed across the whole breadth of the Island from Norfolk to South Wales:—that, repeated examinations of their plans before they come to the Tower are necessary in order to procure an accurate

---

* In 1804, Simon Woolcot had experienced 'insults and interruptions' when engaged in the survey of north Devon: Woolcot to Mudge, 4 May 1804, quoted in Close, *Early Years*, p. 50.

> delineation of the face of the Country, the long experience I have had in this matter has assured me and I trust his Lordship . . . to accede to my request that an officer in the Corps of Royal Engineers, be appointed to assist Captain Colby and myself in the execution of this Duty.

He concluded that he had 'for some time delayed this application that, it might not interfere with the many services for which Engineers were required during the War'.[76] Mudge had always been too reticent in pressing a claim for extra man-power, but by 1816 a point had been reached when urgent action was required to restore the credibility of the topographical mapping. It is possible that Colby was a force behind Mudge's change of policy. For over five years he had borne the brunt of Mudge's absences, and the dual responsibility for trigonometrical and topographical work was more than enough, as Portlock put it, to exhaust even Colby's considerable 'mental energies and . . . physical powers'. The result of Mudge's request was that in 1816 his son, Lieutenant Richard Mudge RE, was attached to the Survey and was

> stationed in the country, as nearly as possible in the centre of the surveying parties, of which he had the immediate superintendence . . . for several years.[77]

It was also in 1816 that Mudge attempted a more far-reaching reorganization of procedures with the aim of improving the quality of plans being submitted to the Tower. His instructions were issued from the Drawing Room in the form of a circular sent to all members of the Royal Military Surveyors and Draftsmen employed on the survey. The circular contained ten points:

1 Each plan sent to the Drawing Room was to carry the name and rank of its surveyor, the date of its completion, and the number of square miles it contained.

2 Particular attention was to be paid to the abutting edges of plans to counter the tendency for these junctions to be copied from previously surveyed plans – a practice which led to great 'inconvenience' at the stage of their reduction.

3 No work 'surveyed or sketched by any candidate for the Corps of Roy[l] Engineers, or by any Royal Military Surveyor & Draftsman, whilst under tuition' was to be 'laid down on the Plans' sent to the Drawing Room, 'except the same shall have been performed under the immediate observation and superintendence of the teaching Draftsman'. Moreover, 'nor shall any other person', it was stipulated, 'be employed in Surveying or Sketching for the Plans . . . except he shall, having been found duly qualified be authorized . . . by an express permission, in writing from Colonel Mudge or the Officers employed under his command upon the General Survey'.

4 Every surveyor was to send a monthly report to the Drawing Office for Colonel Mudge's inspection and this was to contain 'an account of the state of the plans he has in hand with the number of square miles surveyed and Plotted'.

5 Travelling allowances were not to be allowed 'during the performance of work within the district allotted', implying that surveyors were to be allowed expenses in travelling to particular areas but not for the day-to-day surveys within them which were already subsumed in other allowances.

6 It was re-emphasized that 'every road, boundary of a common and river and Town' was to be surveyed, and 'no one of these should depend for its situation on any local survey to which the individual may have had access'. Indeed, no recourse was to be had to local surveys of any kind 'except for the situation of alterations and improvements whilst in progress'.

7 'The writing in each Plan' was 'to be put in with the top towards the north as is usual of maps in General'.

8 No work was to be paid for until it had been properly measured on a fair drawing.

9 '. . . all remains of ancient Fortifications, Druidical Monuments, vitrified Forts, and all Tumuli & Barrows shall be noticed in the Plans wherever they occur'.

10 All orders 'coming from officers of the Corps of Royal Engineers, employed on the General Survey' were to 'be considered as given with the authority of Colonel Mudge and to be obeyed as such'.[78]

The issuing of these instructions – a mixture of administrative and general technical guidance – confirmed that a deterioration had occurred in the topographical survey by the end of the Napoleonic War. Mudge had put his finger on several abuses, including the incorporation of plans made by cadets in training or by unqualified civilian assistants, the uncritical acceptance of local plans of varying provenance, and the claiming of unjustified expenses by the surveyors. And although they were a step in the right direction, it is clear that the orders provided no short-term panacea for the troubles of the topographical survey. Indeed, as a technical blueprint they lacked comprehensiveness, and in some items they verged on the trivial. They offered too little too late for an improvement to occur during Mudge's directorate, and the fact that his son turned out to be a poor organizer led to the administrative orders being widely ignored by the surveyors, all of whom were experienced men, and doubtless resistant to change after so much service in the field with only the lightest of supervision.

Mudge's efforts at reform should have been helped by the return to peace-time conditions which quickly turned a shortage of skilled military man-power into a surplus. But in 1817 the Corps of Royal Military Surveyors and Draftsmen was disbanded and most of its warrant officers were put on half-pay.[79] The reduction took place from the end of February but Mudge was allowed to retain Thomas Yeakell, Charles Budgen, William Stanley, Robert Dawson, Henry Stevens, Charles Chaplin and John Field for service on the 'Trigonometrical Survey',[80] and they were able to continue their duties in mapping for the one-inch series. Predictably, steps were also taken in the spring of 1817 to terminate the contracts of the four civilian surveyors 'as soon as they shall have completed their present Districts',[81] although Edmund Crocker, of the Wiltshire surveying family, was permitted to remain on the Ordnance payroll until 1818.

The mapping carried out in Mudge's era left an unwelcome legacy for Colby. The problem of standardizing the topographical surveys presented a more intractable challenge than did the scientific work connected with the triangulation; instead of dealing with a small number of men as scientifically committed as himself, Colby entered a field of management where he could not always assume that everyone shared his own impeccable standards of perfection.

Notes

1 William Mudge and Isaac Dalby, *An Account of the Operations Carried on for Accomplishing a Trigonometrical Survey of England and Wales . . . 1784–1796* (London 1799), p. 411.

2 *Ibid.* p. xi.

3 See J. B. Harley, 'Error and revision in early Ordnance Survey maps', *The Cartographic Journal* 1968, vol. 5, pp. 115–24, for a selection of these criticisms.

4 J. E. Portlock, *Memoir of the life of Major-General Colby . . .* (London 1869), p. 161.

5 *XVIIth Report of the Commissioners of Military Enquiry*: PP 1812 (5) IV, p. 166.

6 *Ibid.*

7 PRO WO 47/109, 1 June 1787.

8 Portlock, *Memoir of Colby*, p. 14.

9 R. A. Skelton, 'The origins of the Ordnance Survey of Great Britain', *Geographical Journal* 1962, CXXVIII pp. 416–19.

10 PRO WO 46/18; copies of Gardner's plans have survived as PRO MR 1385 and MR 1199 and British Library, Map Library, K. Top. XI.80. 8.Tab.end.

11 PRO WO 47/109, 1 June 1787.

12 PRO WO 47/110, 18 July 1787; PRO WO 47/111, 17 March 1788.

13 PRO WO 47/113, 19 Jan. 1789.

14 PRO WO 47/117, f 755.

15 Mudge and Dalby, *Account of the Trig. Survey, 1784–1796*, pp. xi-xii.

16 *Ibid.*

17 Harley, 'English county map-making in the early years of the Ordnance Survey: the map of Surrey by Joseph Lindley and William Crosley', *Geographical Journal* 1966, vol. 132, pp. 372–8.

18 PRO WO 55/419.

19 PRO WO 47/2365, 23 Dec. 1794.

20 Mudge and Dalby, *Account of the Trig. Survey, 1784–1796*, p. 357.

21 *Ibid.* p. xii.

22 PRO WO 47/2372, 10 April 1799.

23 *Ibid.*

24 *Ibid.*
25 PRO WO 47/2372, 9 April 1799.
26 *Ibid.*, 15 April 1799.
27 *Ibid.*, 17 April 1799.
28 *Ibid.*, 28 April 1799.
29 *Ibid.*
30 *Ibid.*
31 *Ibid.*, 28 May 1799.
32 *Ibid.*
33 PRO WO 55/421.
34 Portlock describes them as 'Warrant Officers'. *Memoir of Colby*, p. 305.
35 PRO WO 55/450.
36 PRO WO 55/421.
37 PRO WO 47/2378, f 751, 16 Dec. 1800.
38 PRO WO 55/421.
39 PRO WO 44/517, 1 Oct. 1816.
40 *Ibid.*, Feb. 1817.
41 Howe to Mudge, 24 Feb. 1800, OSLB f 126.
42 Mudge to Lt.-Col. Hadden, 21 Sept. 1803, Kent Archives Office, U269 0193/17.
43 Stamford Raffles Flint (ed.), *Mudge Memoirs . . .* (Truro 1883), p. 131.
44 For various decisions to extend the area of the topographical surveys, see OSLB *passim*.
45 *Records of the Royal Military Academy* (Woolwich 1851), p. 75.
46 *Ibid.*
47 Mudge to Rowley 19 March 1803. PRO WO 55/960.
48 Mudge to Rowley and Morse from 27 Feb. 1803 to 17 Sept. 1804, PRO WO 55/960.
49 PRO WO 47/2378, f 751, 16 Dec. 1800.
50 Dawson to Mudge, 29 Jan. 1804, and Mudge to Rowley, 6 Feb. 1804, PRO WO 55/960.
51 Mudge to Morse, 6 Aug. 1803; Mudge to Rowley, 6 Feb. 1804, and 28 May 1804, PRO WO 55/960.
52 Mudge to Morse, 14 June 1803; PRO WO 55/960.
53 Mudge to Rowley, 10 March 1804, PRO WO 55/960.
54 PRO WO 55/960 contains several examples of these Reports, including three for Thomas A. Larcom, later to be employed on the Ordnance Survey.
55 PRO WO 55/960, 22 Dec. 1803. See Appendix II.
56 *Ibid.*
57 Yolande Jones, 'Aspects of relief portrayal on 19th Century British Military maps', *Cartographic Journal* 1974, vol. 11, no. 1, pp. 22–4.
58 *Mémorial Topographique et Militaire, rédigé au Dépôt de la Guerre* (L'Imprimerie de la République, Paris 1802), 6 vols.
59 *Correspondence respecting the Scale for the Ordnance Survey, and upon Contouring and Hill Delineation*; pp. 359–63: PP 1854 [1831] XLI.
60 Mudge to Rowley, 8 Sept. 1803. PRO WO 55/960.
61 See R. K. Dawson, 'Essays towards the Expression of Ground in Topographical Plans', MSS, Lichfield, 1815–16, British Library, Map Library, Maps C21.e.7. These exercises were done by Robert Dawson's son, when an Engineer cadet, in training on the Ordnance Survey.
62 Flint, *Mudge Memoirs*, p. 141.
63 Major-General Sir James Carmichael-Smyth, *Memoir upon the Topographical System of Colonel Van Gorkum . . .* (printed for T. Egerton, London, 1828), p. 58.
64 Mudge to Morse, 2 Aug. 1804, PRO WO 55/960.
65 *Ibid.*
66 PRO WO 47/2411, 15 July 1805.
67 *XVIIth Report of the Commissioners of Military Enquiry*: PP 1812 (5) IV, p. 243.
68 Dawson to Mudge, 19 Jan. 1805, PRO WO 55/960.
69 *XVIIth Report . . .* : PP 1812 (5) IV, p. 243.
70 Portlock, *Memoir of Colby*, p. 161.
71 Samuel Burt Howlett papers, in possession of Mrs Barbara Denness of Ipswich, (copies in OS Library, Southampton).
72 'Memoirs of S. B. Howlett', 1808–17, pp. 58, 64.
73 Howlett, 'Memorandums [of service] commencing Aug:' 20:th 1808', p. 3; the area was in the east part of Old Series sheet 34.
74 On Philip Crocker in this context see the references in Kenneth Woodbridge, *Landscape and Antiquity, Aspects of English Culture at Stourhead 1718 to 1830* (Oxford 1970).
75 *Report from the Select Committee on the Survey and Valuation of Ireland*, Minutes of Evidence, p. 27: PP 1824 (445) VIII.
76 Mudge to the Master General, the Earl of Mulgrave, 20 May 1816, OSLB f 2.
77 Portlock, *Memoir of Colby*, p. 64.
78 OSLB ff 224–6.
79 PRO WO 44/517.
80 Crew, Secretary to the Board of Ordnance, to Mudge, 3 April 1817, OSLB ff 134–5.
81 Lt.-Col. Chapman to Mudge, 7 March 1817, OSLB f 133.

5
Early
Methods
of
Topographical
Survey

Field Surveying

Although the organization of the topographical survey was giving trouble to Mudge and Colby, the field methods themselves were well established and, apart from the introduction of the control framework provided by the Trigonometrical Survey, had hardly changed since the days of Roy.

In his *Memoir relative to the construction of a Map of Scotland*, Aaron Arrowsmith described the method of survey used by Roy in 1747–55. Of the members of each surveying party 'One carried the Theodolite; Two measured with the Chain; Two for the fore and back Stations, and the remaining one acted as Batman'. The instruments were 'plain Theodolites* of Seven Inches Diameter' with 'common sights unfurnished with Telescopes' and chains '45 or 50 Feet in length'.[1] For the detail survey itself the

> courses of the Rivers and numerous streams were followed to the source, and measured; all the Roads and the many Lakes of Salt-water and Fresh were surveyed . . . and intersections . . . to the Right and Left ascertained innumerable minute situations.

The survey was evidently based on a series of compass traverses with some of the features away from the traverse lines fixed by intersecting compass bearings. The remaining detail, including the relief, had necessarily to be sketched by eye. It is not surprising to learn from Arrowsmith that 'the connection of the summer work of the several surveyors was often the subject of mutual discussion'.

Contemporary surveying text-books show that the field techniques of the latter half of the eighteenth century included the use of the theodolite for triangulation; theodolite, or circumferentor and chain, for traversing; plane-table for surveying detail; compass, often built into the theodolite or circumferentor, for the measurement of magnetic bearings; cyclometer or measuring wheel for distances; telescopic level and staff or theodolite or sextant for measuring heights.[2] Field books for recording angles, chained distances, offsets and sketches of the relevant detail, generally had a central column for distances, similar to the books used one hundred years later.[3]

As early as 1679 William Leybourn had published a table of latitudes (northings) and departures (eastings) for the rapid calculation of rectangular co-ordinates.[4] However, in his text-book published in 1812 John Ainslie, land surveyor of Edinburgh, commented on the time and trouble involved in 'laying down' (i.e. plotting) triangulations by distances obtained by logarithms, compared with the shorter time required for 'protracting' such survey frameworks using the angles.[5] It therefore seems likely that the graphical construction of triangulations and traverses at map scale, as adopted by Roy, was common practice in the eighteenth century. Evidently, until the start of Mudge's country-wide triangulation, the control frameworks were all of such limited extent that plotting by co-ordinates was not always considered essential for reasonable accuracy at map scale.

For the Old Series one-inch maps the control points were plotted by plane rectangular co-ordinates related to a local meridian passing through a triangulation station at which the azimuth of one of the triangle sides had been astronomically determined. South of the Hull-Preston line there were no less than ten local meridians and local origins, and there could have been no uniform and precise way of linking these distinct co-ordinate systems to produce a continuous topographical map. The connections

---

* A 'plain theodolite' was a 'circumferentor', or surveying compass.

must have been made by approximate or empirical methods which introduced local errors too small to be significant at the scale of the published maps.

On the other hand, the sheet-line system appears to have been fundamentally arbitrary. From the occasional marginal notes stating that a map edge is parallel to a given meridian and from the measurement of sheet sides on paper copies, in the borders of which meridian lines are sometimes shown, it is evident that many of the north to south sheet-lines east of the centre of sheet 14 are parallel to the Greenwich meridian, whilst many of those to the west are nearly but not exactly parallel to the Butterton Hill (Devon) meridian. This arrangement ensured that the eastern and western edges of sheets would nowhere be very deviant from the direction of true north. Most of the sheets are rectangular, about 35 inches east to west by 23 inches north to south. Sheets narrower than this are used for the three columns northwards from sheets 11, 16 and 17, and in the central column the sheets are not rectangular but taper to the north.

Very soon the irregularities in the sheet-lines brought forth critical comment. In July 1821 Mr James Powell wrote to William Faden about some of the one-inch sheets he had bought:

> The mounting is so inaccurately done that the bottom from Edge to Edge is one and a quarter inches wider than the top and the left or Western side of the canvas is one and three-eighths inches longer than the opposite side, consequently the Angles at the bottom are not right angles and it is impossible to hang it so as not to offend a moderately accurate eye.

Captain Richard Mudge was invited by Faden to reply and did so in detail:

> When the idea of making maps from the Ordnance Trigonometrical operations originated it was first proposed to publish the work in County maps – Kent and Essex were the first engraved, and the meridian of Greenwich was selected as the most proper to project from. In the course of time, however, the intention of continuing the publication merely as County maps was laid aside and it was determined to lay down what should follow on the principle of one uniform map of the whole island. To accommodate the meridian of Greenwich to the meridian of the centre of the Island being an impossibility, in order to introduce as little error as possible on account of convergence, three meridians were established, one at the centre of the Kingdom, the other two for the East and West parts of it. Thus the South edges of the sheets being made at right angles to the respective meridians and the East and West edges parallel to the same, they cannot of course in all cases be rectangular and the other particulars which you noticed to Mr Faden are accounted for on the same principle.[6]

Mudge's reference to a meridian 'at the centre of the Kingdom' is rather obscure, but he probably had in mind the central column of trapezoidal sheets north of sheet 16, the south edges of which are roughly at right angles to a meridian through their centres, whereas the southern edges of the sheets to the east and to the west of this column are at right angles to the meridians respectively of Greenwich and Butterton Hill. Fortunately Mr Powell appeared to be well satisfied with Mudge's explanation.

All the evidence goes to show that the methods of working used by the early surveyors of the Ordnance were no different in their essentials from those of contemporary surveyors in private practice who produced maps of the English counties. A surveyor would normally produce three sets of documents for a given area. These were his field books containing measurements, then his sketches which in the very early period might be made on blank pages of field books but which later were done on paper, sometimes transparent, mounted in a sketching case, and finally his fair-drawn maps on thick drawing-paper.[7] The Ordnance Survey fair-drawings were usually at the scale of two inches to one mile, except for some parts of southern England where the three-inch and sometimes six-inch scales were used to provide material for military and fortification maps. The areas allocated to each surveyor were irregular in shape and varied in extent from a few square miles to upwards of two hundred square miles. The surveyor was entirely responsible for the survey of topographical detail and the depiction of relief in his area. The fair-drawn maps were called 'plans' and were normally constructed by the surveyors in the field and not at the Ordnance Survey Office in the Tower of London.[8] Nearly all these plans or copies of them are preserved in the Map Library, British Library, together with many ancillary drawings and sketches.* It appears that none of the field books has survived, and it is possible that they may have been systematically destroyed after the publication of the relevant one-inch maps.**

The appearance of these fair-drawn maps confirms that they were essentially personal productions of the individual surveyors; there are considerable variations in style, in colouring and in the use of symbols (Plate 5). There are no obvious grids or graticules. The surveyors were merely sent a 'sheet of points', which suggests that the triangulation points for a particular area were plotted on paper at the

---

* The original field and hill-shading drawings were deposited in the British Library Map Library in 1955.

** Plan no. 347 on scale two inches to one mile, probably by H. Stevens and dated 1837, covering parts of *Old Series* one-inch sheets 72 and 81, carries the pencilled remark, 'Field Books destroyed 1872'.

headquarters in the Tower at the two-inch scale, and sent to the surveyor in that form to be pricked through onto his sheets.[9] This basic control for the topographical field-work was provided by secondary or 'interior' triangulation, connected to the geodetic framework and observed either at the time of the main triangulation, or subsequently by men such as William Gardner and James Gardner. It was supplemented by the topographical surveyors themselves who used theodolites for fixing additional intersected points.

Frome's text-book *Trigonometrical Survey*, First Edition, although not published until 1839, contains probably the earliest account in any detail of the methods by which the interior or detail survey for these early Ordnance Survey maps was done.[10] Frome describes filling in the interior of triangles 'partly by measurement and partly by sketching as was practised by the Ordnance Survey of England' for the production of one inch to one mile maps. It appears that in England the road network of a piece of country was surveyed by traverses with theodolite and chain, connected to available triangulation points. In the course of this work 'all conspicuous objects to the right and left of the traverse lines' were 'fixed by intersections with the theodolite, either from the extremities of these lines, or from such intermediate points as appear best adapted for determining their positions'. There is no mention of the topographical surveyors doing any trigonometrical computations and it is probable that these local traverses and the intersected points fixed from them were plotted graphically by means of a protractor and a scale. Points on the traverses and the intersected points were terminals for additional chain lines; points of detail near to but not actually on chain lines were fixed by offsets from these lines. The field books were 'kept in the same method as when the entire county is laid down by measurement', that is, with a column for chainages down the centre of each page, and offsets and angles to intersected points recorded on both sides of the column.

Points fixed by intersection together with those fixed by offsets from chain lines provided a framework sufficiently dense for supplying the remaining detail by sketching so that the 'errors indispensable from sketching' were 'confined within very narrow limits'. The points and the detail connected to them were plotted from the field books in correct relationship to the controlling triangulation, at the chosen scale, and portions of this plotted work suitable to the size of the surveyor's sketching portfolio were then transferred to sheets of cardboard or drawing-paper. Alternatively the surveyor would trace an area of plotted work onto a large sheet of thin bank-post paper. This was folded over a piece of Bristol-board cut to the size of the portfolio, with the part to be worked on exposed as required. The use of a large sheet of paper had an advantage in that triangulation points remote from the working area could be plotted and so be available for occasional use. Specially prepared paper called 'asses' skin' was used when sketching in wet weather.[11]

The portable instruments generally used in sketching were 'the small four-inch or box sextant' (or some small reflecting instrument as a substitute for it) and 'the azimuth prismatic compass'. The process of sketching was similar to that of rigorous surveying except that lines were paced and offsets, if small, estimated. Pencil lines drawn on the various sketches which have been preserved slant to the west of true north by an amount about equal to the contemporary magnetic variation, affording additional evidence of the use of the compass in filling in minor detail.[12] It seems also that the method of surveying detail by the intersections of alignments between previously fixed points of detail, supplemented by short linear measurements, was well understood by the surveyors of these early maps.[13] In sketching, all the work was drawn on the paper held in the surveyor's portfolio and no formal field book was used.

Although the plane-table is frequently described in the surveying text-books of the eighteenth and early nineteenth centuries, it is practically certain that this instrument was never used in the field-work for the Old Series maps. Frome refers to it as being of a size which 'renders it too inconvenient to be termed portable', and he goes on to remark that 'its use is now almost universally superseded by the sketching portfolio and compass'.[14] But in his *Course of Instruction in Military Surveying*, Robert Dawson explains that after 'roads, rivers and particular boundaries had been surveyed instrumentally' – presumably by traversing – and the results plotted, the 'accidents of the interior ground would be filled in by plane-table'.[15] It is possible that this reference to the plane-table relates to Roy's method of sketching in which the drawing-board carrying the sketch was mounted 'on the top of a strong stick shod with iron to stick into the ground'.[16] Nowhere in the surviving Ordnance Survey letter book (June 1815 to July 1822) is there any mention of plane-tables amongst the miscellany of references to surveyors' requirements in the field, although in 1821 Robert Dawson himself specified in detail the sketching portfolios required for Assistant Engineers (military officers) attached to him on surveying courses in the mountains of North Wales.[17] By 1820 the use of Roy's 'plane-table' had probably declined; instead minor detail was more usually fixed by compass bearing and distance or by intersecting compass bearings.

Once they had received the 'sheet of points', the surveyors were expected to produce their plans as individual craftsmen. Any shortcomings were due not to lack of soundness in the field methods used, but to laxity by some of the surveyors in applying those methods. In field-work designed for small-scale mapping only, one inch or less to one mile, the measurement of short distances by pacing and by estimation was quite legitimate and a better map would not have been produced by increasing the amount of precise measurement on the ground beyond that judged to be sufficient by a competent surveyor. The procedure of sketching used by these early surveyors and the surveying of detail by visual alignments and short measurements did not imply an inaccurate map as the result. Comparison of several early Old Series sheets with Seventh Series one-inch maps shows in general remarkably close agreement in major detail such as main roads and churches. However, relative to the major detail within a limited locality, errors of up to 100 metres can be found and evidently some of the minor detail must have been fixed rather casually. A sheet published in 1811 containing part of south Dorset shows errors in the coastline of up to 300 metres and a rather wooden delineation of the coast such as might have been obtained by connecting a number of fixed points in an arbitrary fashion rather than by taking proper account of the minor features during sketching. But the triangulation prevented any large accumulation of error and it is safe to say that the early Old Series maps were as good if not better than the best of the independently published county maps of that era.

Hill-sketching

Hill-sketching, whether based on horizontal form-lines, vertical hachures or graduated shading, can only indicate the local shape of the ground and either the slope or – in a general way – the relative heights, but not both in any strict sense. The principle has to be either 'the darker the steeper' or 'the darker the higher'. If a visual effect is sought by depicting the landscape as if it were illuminated from a particular direction, even this simple rule cannot be applied. Attempts were made in military circles in the early nineteenth century to introduce a quantitative element into the hill-sketching. The system known as the 'scale of shade' – the darker the steeper – had its attractions for the military topographer but the practical difficulties of applying the scale when drawing the sketches and of using it in the heat of battle were discouraging. The Ordnance Survey was never completely committed to the scale of shade although it became the basis of the later horizontal field-sketching. On some of the first one-inch sheets the surveyors sketched by eye using the vertical system, but there was no uniformity about this and from the late 1820s onwards the horizontal method was preferred in the field, and the production of hachures became a drawing office process. No detailed account of the theory of Ordnance Survey hill-drawing exists, perhaps because it was difficult to put into words. In the early 1830s R. K. Dawson introduced the device of thickening the form-lines in five-hundred-foot bands as the height of the ground increased, but this did not become an established field procedure because of its inherent incompatibility with the scale of shade. It is certain, however, that 'zone cards', showing these bands by means of rough contours, were supplied to the drawing office.

Ordnance Survey Orthography

For its first twenty years as a map publisher, the Board of Ordnance did little to refine the system of place-name verification practised by eighteenth-century cartographers. The names of principal parishes and towns were probably checked against standard official sources such as the printed census returns, but for minor names local spoken and written forms, moderated by clergy and landowners, were adopted without too many questions being asked.

Mudge, although Superintendent of the Survey for twenty-two years, does not seem to have issued any detailed instructions on orthography. Nevertheless it was Mudge who initiated the procedure adopted for the Essex maps published in 1805:

> To make the work as perfect as possible, this survey was sent, as a mere outline, in quite an unfinished state, to different persons in the County, for the purposes of ascertaining whether or not the Spelling of Farms, Hamlets &c; was correct.[18]

The remaining maps of southern and south-west England underwent similar treatment. The proofs of two of the Essex sheets that were not returned to the Ordnance Office have survived and are now preserved in the Library of the Royal Geographical Society. A comparison with the finished maps reveals the type of place-name revision which took place. The changes were generally fairly minor, suggesting that landowners supplied only obvious omissions and were prepared to accept the majority of the Ordnance spellings once they had been engraved.

Some of those entrusted with the correction of the sheets are named in the surviving letter book. On 15 July 1820, for example, six outline sheets were despatched to 'Professor Sedgwick Trinity College Cambridge for correction' and on 4 August a similar number to 'Dr Hutton'.[19] Later in the same month 'Charles Stokes Esq. was sent an Outline of Sheets No. 7 and 13 for Correction, by order of Captain Colby' and sheet 13 went to the Rev. W. D. Conybeare of Brislington near Bristol 'to have the orthography of the names examined'.[20]

When the surveyors moved into Wales after 1810, place-names were tackled in much the same way as in England, although the problems of Welsh spelling and etymology were soon under discussion. Colby was in correspondence about the Cardiff and Swansea sheets with a number of local experts including the Rev. J. M. Traherne FRS and the antiquary and naturalist Lewis Weston Dillwyn of Penllergaer near Swansea. In December 1821 Colby wrote to the latter:

> Will you excuse my troubling you with a question which arises in definitely settling the orthography of the Glamorganshire Plate of the Ordnance Map – Penlyne Castle, Penlynn Castle, and Penlline Castle near Cowbridge: can you obtain correct information if any one of these is right.[21]

Dillwyn's reply has not survived (although in the published map Penlline was adopted) but Colby's listing of various spellings may suggest that the Survey was feeling its way towards a rule of thumb whereby the majority form among the spellings collected for a name was the one accepted.

A subsequent letter from Dillwyn to Colby, dated October 1823, provides an interesting commentary on the problem of reconciling English and Welsh spellings, especially in an area where English was widely spoken. Dillwyn discussed the Welsh forms adopted by the Survey for a number of names, and went on:

> ... you have called it Caerdiff, but both by the Corporation itself and by everybody else as well as in all legal proceedings it is now universally spelt Cardiff, and in this case I should certainly alter it to the latter for in fact yours is only a sort of hybrid word half Welsh and half English and the real old Welsh name is Caertaff.[22]

Philologically accurate or not, this comment seems to reflect two influences. First, the Survey had apparently made some effort to recognize the existence of the Welsh language. It is possible that Colby, whose family seat was near Newcastle Emlyn in Carmarthenshire, had deliberately guided his officers in this direction and, if so, there may be here an explanation of his sympathetic treatment of Irish names during the survey of that country. Secondly, it would appear that expert local opinion in South Wales was not altogether in sympathy with Colby's flirtation with Celtic place-names. Where anglicized versions were accepted and generally understood, there seemed no reason to change them and it is these forms which were engraved on the first edition of the map of South Wales.

Further west, however, the Survey encountered local differences of opinion, illustrating not only the difficulties of Welsh spelling, but also the limitations of a system of regularization based on the variable wisdom of local landowners. The disputed names lay in Pembrokeshire, the Ordnance sheets for which had been published between 1818 and 1820. In February 1821 the Master General of the Ordnance, the Duke of Wellington, had been informed that in the Ordnance Map of Part of Pembrokeshire, some of the names had been omitted, and some of them mis-spelt. In a letter to Colby, His Grace expressed his 'desire that the utmost care may be taken to avoid such errors in future, and to correct those that may have occurred if not too late'.[23]

Colby's reply is worth quoting because it throws light on the immediate issue and also on Colby's attitude to the treatment of place-names in the early 1820s just after he assumed the superintendency of the Survey:

> In regard to the erroneous Orthography of some names in the Pembrokeshire Map and the Omissions of Others, I cannot but regret that such errors should have happened and I trust on a candid examination of that Map it will appear that those errors are not more numerous than might have been expected from the General state of the orthography of the names of places in that County. On one side of it the English language is spoken, on the other the Welsh, and the orthography of the names of places is continually varying from a Conformity of the usages of the one language to that of the other according to the caprices of the successive persons who possess them. The Survey was made in 1809, and some Omissions may have arisen from the alterations that have taken place since its execution.
> Almost at the Outset of the Publication of the Ordnance Maps, General Mudge, Aware of the difficulty of obtaining the correct orthography of the names of places, because the best informed persons differ in opinion

respecting them in numerous instances, and knowing some slight inaccuracies will escape the most careful Surveyors, obtained permission to send unfinished proof sheets to Noblemen and Gentlemen in the Country who submit them to the examination of those whose local knowledge enables them readily to detect such errors. In pursuance of this system, the proofs of the Pembrokeshire Map were sent to Lord Caradon, and Mr Colby, the one residing in the Southern, the other in the Northern part of the County. Lord Caradon returned the proof sheets to General Mudge with a letter expressing his satisfaction at the accuracy of the work and with hardly any corrections. Mr Colby put the proofs into the hands of those whom he judged most likely to detect inaccuracies either in the orthography or Surveying and the map underwent a rigorous revision before it was returned.[24]

The interest of this apologia lies not so much in the reiteration of the method of proof correcting as in the demonstration of the shortcomings of early methods. Where authorities disagreed – or worse, when they had failed to make a proper examination – there was no remedy in the Ordnance map office. An undue reliance on advice from outside the Survey was a major weakness in the treatment of place-names before 1820.

The Archaeological Survey

THE WORK OF ROY

The appointment of John Leland as King's Antiquary for the period 1534–42, during which he travelled through England and Wales to collect materials for a topographical account of antiquities, marks the beginning of official concern with the subject. By the early years of the eighteenth century William Stukeley, the father of modern British field archaeology, was busy laying its foundations and men like Alexander Gordon and John Horsley were pioneering the serious study of Roman Britain. This period saw the birth of William Roy.[25]

Roy's work on the military survey of Scotland provides no evidence that he paid any special attention at first to antiquities. Obvious archaeological features were surveyed but no attempt was made to show any less evident vestiges of the past. By his own account Roy's interest in archaeology first stirred in 1752 while working on the Border where he saw remains of a Roman bath-house found in 1732 at Netherby House on the site of the CASTRA EXPLORATORVM fort.[26] At this time he was in charge of a party working over the western half of the Lowlands and his interest in Roman sites was still growing when in 1755 he met Captain Robert Melville of the 25th Foot at Edinburgh. Melville had seen Sir John Clerk of Penicuik's pioneer collection of Roman antiquities in 1751 and hoped to find surviving traces of Agricola's campaign of AD 81–4 in Scotland. After much disappointment Melville went into Strathmore in August 1754 to examine the tract between the Tay and the Mounth where the 'reason of war' taught him that this campaign must have been fought. Luckily a casual informant directed him to the remains of the marching-camp at Kirkbuddo between Forfar and Dundee which he at once recognized as Roman and plainly a campaign feature rather than a permanent fort. This supplied the first clue and the marching-camps at Keithock, Battledykes and Lintrose were also found. In a letter written in 1788, Melville says:

> Upon my return to Edinr. my first proselyte was the present General Roy, then one of the surveying engineers, but not the one who had surveyed Angus.[27]

Melville's finds changed Roy's approach to the study of antiquities in the field. Before 1755 he had only considered those 'stationary' works whose remains were still plain to be seen; after this he also looked for the less obvious traces of a Roman army on the march. He spent some time in Strathmore in the summer of 1755 and added the sites at Dalginross and Stragaeth to Melville's list, while also making careful plans of the great stationary works at Ardoch and Inchtuthil.[28] The year 1755 was truly an *annus mirabilis,* for under Roy's direction a major exercise in antiquity survey was also made along the whole line of the Antonine Wall. To quote his own words:

> In carrying out the general survey of Scotland begun in 1747, the wall of Antoninus was observed in the ordinary way, and accordingly inserted in the plan of the [Clyde–Forth] isthmus; but this, as well as every district in the country, being the allotment of work for several people, without the Wall itself becoming the principal object of the whole, or any one of them; it was therefore judged proper, in 1755, to survey accurately the line of the old intrenchment by running a suite of stations along its whole course.[29]

Since Watson had left Roy in charge there can be no doubt who was responsible for this novel exercise. Work on the map of Scotland was suddenly ended in 1755, but after the return of peace Roy was again in Scotland in 1764, 1769 and 1771, enlarging his field experience, recognizing a Roman western route into Scotland via Carlisle, Annandale and Clydesdale, identifying the Eildon Hills as Ptolemy's TRIMONTIVM and trying to follow the traces of Agricola's campaign to the Moray Firth. During his work as a military surveyor he made other observations in England and mapped various sites, notably Maiden Castle in Dorset, but his main interest was in Scotland and by 1773 he had combined the results of his work there into *The Military Antiquities of the Romans in Britain*, a book whose publication, delayed by the American War of Independence, was undertaken by the Society of Antiquaries of London in 1793 as a tribute to his memory.

The chief importance of this work lies in the series of maps and plans illustrating field discoveries which, until recently, were the only evidence for the original condition of many Roman military works which can scarcely be traced on the ground today, though aerial photography has fully endorsed the correctness of Roy's observations. A notable example, anticipating later Ordnance Survey practice, is a map engraved in 1775 on which he entered all that was then known about Roman antiquities in Scotland, the ultimate ancestor of Ordnance Survey period maps.[30] It is entitled *Mappa Britanniae Septentrionalis faciei Romanae secundum fidem monumentorum perveterum depicta*. In other words, a map of the north parts of Britain in Roman times compiled in accordance with the evidence of the ancient monuments.

It is a remarkable achievement and was not completely superseded until the publication of the second edition of the Ordnance Survey map of Roman Britain in 1928. The mode of delineating the Roman walls, roads and different types of permanent and temporary fortifications leaves little to be desired at the small scale of about one inch to twenty miles, while water features and relief were well shown also. Roy's work as an archaeologist may be summarized by saying that he was fully objective, a meticulous observer and planner, a scrupulous recorder and a pioneer both in the search for the more vestigial features of field archaeology and in the mapping of his results. At all points he was in advance of his time and foreshadowed much of later Survey practice.

ARCHAEOLOGY ON THE OLD SERIES ONE-INCH

By 1824 the Ordnance Survey had produced a series of maps on the one-inch scale covering most of England south of the Trent and much of Wales. Antiquities appeared on these maps in varying degrees, with a general tendency to increase in number as the series progressed, but for a long time there were no clear signs of marked official interest. The precedents for showing antiquities may be found in the work of the county commercial map-makers of the later eighteenth century who gave some attention to archaeological features, a practice which was acceptable to their customers who were mainly confined to the classes among whom a certain acquaintance with the subject was one of the polite accomplishments. The original detail surveyors for the one-inch series used county maps to find their way round the country and must have been influenced to some extent by their content.

General Roy had no known proselytes among those who directed the Survey after him, and any influence arising from his interest in field archaeology is more likely to have come through the Royal Society. In the beginning much reliance was placed on the support and advice of this body which normally included among its members the most competent archaeologists of the time. In a much wider context the first half-century of the Survey's work was also the period of the Romantic Movement which provided an intellectual climate favourable to an increasing supply of archaeological and historical features on the maps. The pressure of military necessity, which could have tended to exclude them, declined rapidly after 1805.

The only surviving official instruction about the mapping of antiquities belongs to the comparatively late date of 1816, and is contained in the ninth paragraph of Mudge's *Memorandum*:[31]

> That the remains of ancient Fortifications, Druidical Monuments, vitrified Forts and all Tumuli and Barrows shall be noticed in the Plans whenever they occur.

The only other source of information is the one-inch map itself and all the surviving material connected with its production. This consists of the original drawings made between 1784 and 1841 covering the whole of England and Wales south of the Trent.

The pre-1791 material at the six-inch scale contains no antiquities deliberately shown as such. In the two and three-inch drawings practice was very uneven and in many areas, particularly in the Midlands, East Anglia and Kent, very little archaeology of any kind appeared on the drawings or on the maps derived from them. By contrast the treatment of antiquities in the south-west and much of Wessex was good and reached a remarkable degree of completeness and accuracy in Wiltshire and, to a lesser extent, in Dorset, Hampshire and much of Cornwall. In Wales, where work began in 1811, the standard was also much higher than in most parts of England and it is here that the practice originated of using Gothic type in naming antiquities, with two isolated examples in 1812,[32] but this did not become common until about 1819.[33] Wales also saw the beginning of the use of Egyptian type for the original names of Roman sites, with SEGONTIVM at Caernarvon in 1816. There is little to suggest any vigorous central direction of the mapping of antiquities and in most areas this was confined to the showing of large features like hill-forts, medieval castles and the larger monastic ruins which were in any case surveyable items in their own right. On the first map published in 1801 the ancient fortresses of Dover and Richborough appeared, but the Roman Watling Street, though a continuous feature over many miles, was hardly noticed.

It seems that after 1801 the effective portrayal of antiquities must have depended less on instructions than on the personal interest of the surveyor and on his contact with well-informed local antiquaries anxious to secure the inclusion of their own work on the maps. It was still possible, a decade after a great deal of high-class work had been done, to issue an instruction like that of 1816 which, while positive that antiquities must be supplied, failed to categorize more than a few obvious examples at a time when the elaborate work on Sheet 14 was passing through the system. An examination of the hill drawings shows that at least some field staff were specially concerned with the accuracy of antiquity survey. Here and there, and particularly in Wales in the later days of the original one-inch survey, enlarged six-inch-scale versions of these features sometimes appear on the margins of the drawings in which they occur, presumably as a guide to the engravers. This again suggests that in practice much depended on the interest of the individual surveyor.

This interest and the presence of well-qualified local informants coincided with dramatic effect when the Survey began work in central Wessex in 1807. There had already been good work in Cornwall in 1804 when many antiquities were placed on the field drawings. This was not surprising because the Duchy was rich in obvious features of this kind, although there was no important Cornish field archaeologist working in 1804. William Borlase had died in 1772, but his book *Antiquities of Cornwall* was available for reference. The success of the maps of Cornwall must be credited in the main to the Survey staff, but they were, on the whole, less successful with the antiquities of Devon, though these were also numerous and obvious. On the other hand, Dorset yielded a good crop when surveyed between 1805 and 1809, particularly of ancient burial mounds, which were shown and named in large numbers. The full effect of contact with expert knowledge was felt when the surveyor Philip Crocker and his brother Edmund combined with Sir Richard Colt Hoare and William Cunnington, the antiquaries, to provide the detail for Sheet 14 covering southern Wiltshire and some adjacent parts of Hampshire. The field work for this sheet was begun in 1807 and finished four years later.[34]

Hoare was then preparing his classic publication *Ancient Wiltshire* which appeared in 1812 and 1821. Writing to Thomas Colby on 1 September 1818, William Mudge referred to a recent examination he had made of the Frome sheet on the ground and added:

> Sir Rd. Hoare, to whom I gave a proof for correction, is delighted with the work and particularly with the antiquities, to which all the persons employed on the Survey in that quarter have paid particular attention.

This evidence is reinforced by the survival of a proof of Sheet 14 in the Survey records which carries corrections in Hoare's own hand.

Both as a landowner and an archaeologist Hoare made use of the services of the Crockers of Frome who, as early as 1801, had surveyed the line of the Winchester – Old Sarum road for him.[35] Philip Crocker, who was working for the Ordnance Survey in West Sussex and East Hampshire during 1805 and 1806, was experienced with antiquities and in October 1805 got three weeks leave from the Board of Ordnance to assist Hoare in Wiltshire. In the Crocker letters preserved in Devizes museum, there is evidence of Colonel Mudge's satisfaction with Philip Crocker's work in Hampshire and of his dislike of Crocker's periods of absence while helping Hoare. By 1807 Crocker had begun drawing the illustrations and maps for Volume I of *Ancient Wiltshire* and his transference to full-time employment by Hoare, first on this work and later as his agent, followed in due course. At this time the detail surveyors were also making the original drawing of the South Wiltshire area and the virtual identity of the archaeological detail on the maps prepared by Crocker for Hoare with that on the Survey drawings shows that there must have been collaboration.

Sheet 14 covers about 670 square miles and contains one of the largest concentrations of prehistoric antiquities in Britain. Thirty-five major prehistoric monuments are shown including Stonehenge with its surrounding features in detail. In spite of the small scale, accurate accounts are given of the plans of hill-forts like Scratchbury, Yarnbury, Casterley Camp and Figsbury Ring, all of which have marked pecularities. Nineteen long barrows and 818 round barrows are shown with a great concentration of the latter round Stonehenge, 117 within a radius of one mile from the monument and 264 within a two mile radius. The Roman features of the area are also well supplied, but the detail which specially interests the modern field archaeologist is the quantity of casual ancient earthworks shown all over the map. Hoare and Cunnington were pioneers in recognizing that the chalk country of southern England was still covered by clearly recognizable field systems and settlement sites belonging to the 'Britons', by which they meant the later-prehistoric and Romano-British natives of the country. These features appeared as grass-grown systems of banks, ditches and enclosures with frequent series of more or less terraced slopes (lynchets) where the ancient fields, as well as those of medieval and much later times, had been under cultivation on hill-sides. There were also long-ranging systems of boundary ditches which presumably defined larger land divisions. Much of this was still visible at the beginning of the twentieth century but Hoare's diagnosis of its true character attracted little attention, and recognition only came when the ploughing campaigns of two world wars threatened to level most of it. Today its study in detail depends largely on air photography, and most of the barrows featured on the map of 1817 are in the same state. The information shown on sheet 14 is thus not only remarkably complete but it also anticipates modern opinion by a full century. This sheet and some of its neighbours remained unrivalled in their treatment of antiquities at the one-inch scale until after 1920. One fact lacks explanation. Original drawing 64, dated 1807–8, which covers the country west of Salisbury, the Nadder valley and a stretch of the Wiltshire-Dorset boundary, shows nothing more than five hill-forts in a tract which is full of antiquities and well within the probable orbit of Hoare's interest.

In view of the later practice of showing site antiquities (places where important finds had been made or monuments of various periods had once stood), it is of interest that as early as 1802–3 (Drawing no. 42) 'Scite [sic] of Ralegh's Cross' is noted in Devon; in 1812 (Drawing no. 221) the site of a famous find of Roman gold coins at Cleeve Prior in 1811 is shown, and in 1821 (Drawing no. 332), in the northern part of Flintshire a barrow site is indicated with the note 'levelled in 1809'. The historic sites of battles and other notable events rarely appear in the earlier work, but in 1814 (Drawing no. 259) some local enthusiast at Market Bosworth must have secured the inclusion of five traditional sites associated with various contestants in the famous battle of 1485.

Notes

1 A. Arrowsmith, 'Memoir relative to the construction of a Map of Scotland', quoted in R. A. Skelton, *The Military Survey of Scotland, 1747–1755*, Royal Scottish Geographical Society Special Publication no. 1.

2 Samuel Wylde, *The Practical Surveyor* (London 1764).

3 Charles Hutton, *The Compendious Measurer*, 3rd edition (London 1796).

4 William Leybourn, *The Compleat Surveyor* (1679).

5 John Ainslie, *Land Surveying* (London 1812).

6 OSLB ff 339–40.

7 OSLB f 267.

8 OSLB f 414.

9 OSLB f 354.

10 E. Frome, *Outline of a method of conducting a Trigonometrical Survey for the formation of Geographical and Topographical Maps and Plans*, 1st edition (London 1839), ch. IV, p. 40.

11 OSLB f 267.

12 See the two-inch to one mile sketch for *Old Series* one-inch sheet 83 (c. 1820). British Library Map Library, envelope no. 503.

13 Frome, *Method of Trig. Survey . . .*, ch. IV, p. 44.

14 *Ibid.*

15 PRO WO 55/960. Robert Dawson's 'Course of instructions in Military Surveying and Plan Drawing', 1803. See Appendix II for text.

16 PRO WO 30/115, ff 183–8. See Appendix I for text of Roy's 'General Instructions for the officers of Engineers employed in Surveying'.

17 OSLB f 267.
18 PRO WO 44/299. OSLB f 150.
19 OSLB f 54.
20 OSLB ff 101, 111.
21 OSLB f 412.
22 The letter accompanies OS two-inch hill-sketches serial 459 (one-inch sheet 36), British Library Map Library.
23 OSLB f 217.
24 OSLB ff 219–21.
25 G. Macdonald, *Archaeologia*, second series, 1917, XVIII, pp. 161–228.
26 William Roy, *The Military Antiquities of the Romans in Britain*, (1793), p. 197 and plate 46.
27 *Proceedings of the Society of Antiquaries of Scotland*, VII, p. 30.
28 Roy, *Military Antiquities . . .*, plates 10 and 18.
29 *Ibid.* p. 155 and plate 35.
30 *Ibid.* plate 1.
31 OSLB f 226.
32 Drawings no. 175 south, Runston Camp near Caerwent, and no. 176 east, Landafad.
33 Drawings, 308 and 309, dated 1819, LOVENTIVM and CANOVIVM.
34 The drawings principally concerned were nos. 61, 62, 63, 76, 77.
35 Richard Colt Hoare, *Ancient Wiltshire*, II, p. 58.

6
The Ordnance
Survey
Becomes
a Map-Publisher
1801–1820

Perhaps the most revolutionary development of the national survey was that it should have become a map-publisher with commercial ambitions, thereby outgrowing its rather narrow scientific and military origins and eventually evolving into a more truly national institution. No-one had questioned the right of the State – especially where its security was at stake – to survey and draw maps, which it had been doing continuously since the sixteenth century. But from a very early stage an ultimate goal of the Trigonometrical Survey was to produce a map of Great Britain that would be published and available to all;[1] yet for these final stages of map-making the Board of Ordnance lacked the necessary technical establishment to execute work that had hitherto been the monopoly of the London map trade. In earlier years the Board of Ordnance, the Commissioners for Trade and Plantations and the Admiralty had always relied on private engravers and geographers to undertake reproduction and publication, even when the costs of survey had been paid for out of the public purse.[2] The events which led the Board to abandon these traditional arrangements were far from straightforward and, in common with other aspects of the emerging Ordnance Survey, they have an almost accidental character rather than one resulting from any over-all plan.

The belief that the Ordnance Survey should be published in map form was certainly held by Roy.[3] Moreover, the Duke of Richmond, the most cartographically-minded of all the Masters General, was keen to emulate not only some of the map-makers of Europe (especially the Cassinis in France), but also private surveyors mapping the English counties.* By the 1790s, following from Roy's lead thirty years before, the Board was fully aware of the value of the county maps associated with the awards of the Society of Arts. These maps enjoyed considerable success in the country as a whole and the Board was not averse to furnishing materials to a commercial publisher as with the 1795 map of Sussex. Such printed county maps were useful from a military point of view, and in the 1790s there was a policy of purchasing them for the Drawing Room of the Tower through William Faden, the London map-seller.[4] But despite the revolution in county surveying, the professional military view was that these maps were inadequate for many tactical purposes, as neither their content nor their accuracy could be controlled.

The outbreak of war with France in 1793 made the requirement for adequate maps a matter of much greater urgency; it also led to the exploration of new ways of supplying them. In particular, both the Board of Ordnance and the Quartermaster-General's Department were urgently seeking maps of those coastal areas sensitive to invasion, a need which could only be imperfectly met by the handful of military surveyors employed under William Gardner. In 1792 the trigonometrical party was asked to provide points along the south coast 'for the construction of some maps which were making' for the Board of Ordnance; more explicitly, the Master General 'had found it necessary to employ Capt. Thomas V. Reynolds in carrying on the Trigonometrical Survey ... under Major Williams'.[5] No further mention is made of this addition to the trigonometric team, and the arrangement can only have been temporary, for a year later the Board was informed that 'the Master General has employed Captain Reynolds to make a Military Map of Kent, Sussex, Surrey and part of Hampshire'.[6] The

* By this date official maps had been published, not only in France, but in a number of other states including Denmark (19 sheets only, 1766), Mecklenburg – Strelitz (9 sheets, 1780) and Mecklenburg–Schwerin (16 sheets, 1788); Prussia followed in 1803 with 25 sheets and Salzburg in 1805 with 15. The beginnings of map publication by the Ordnance Survey can thus be seen as part of a European trend.

instruction to Reynolds predates the 1795 authority to fill in the triangulation , and he must have been attached to the Survey with the object of supplying trigonometrical data to stiffen his own quickly-executed surveys for the Board. This use of the Trigonometrical Survey would also explain Mudge's remark made in 1799 that it had been 'made to answer, the private purpose of the Board of Ordnance' in preparing maps of military districts.[7]

Evidently neither the Trigonometrical Survey nor the Tower draughtsmen under Gardner were capable of fulfilling the cartographic needs of the moment, and so important was Reynolds's work in supplying the maps necessary for national defence that in 1796 he was appointed, quite independently of either the Trigonometrical Survey or the Interior Survey, as

> surveyor for directing and making Military Surveys of Great Britain with an allowance of 20s per day to be paid by the Ordnance and that His Majesty has signed his Commission to that effect.[8]

The nature of this assignment was such that he was not expected to maintain the scientific precision demanded from Williams and Mudge nor the detail of Gardner's six-inch surveys. But he was expected to get results quickly, and this brought the Board of Ordnance into a much more intimate relationship with the London map trade.

A number of events combined to bring the parties together. In 1795 the Board was reviewing its defensive arrangements in eastern England, and Captain Reynolds was ordered to survey the 'Eastern Military' district.[9] During that year, the resident Engineer in eastern England, Captain Hay, had made frequent demands for a two inches to one mile map of Essex and a one-inch map of Suffolk,[10] both of which he suggested might be acquired from William Faden, Geographer to the King (in effect supplier by appointment of printed maps to the Crown),[11] who was a leading London map-engraver and publisher as well as map-seller. Faden also had a new one-inch map of Norfolk in his workshop, which had been surveyed between 1790 and 1794 by Thomas Donald and Thomas Milne. This map was vital to the Board's defensive dispositions and so, in the national interest, the Master General authorized Reynolds to

> engage Mr. Faden, of the Strand, to furnish government with a correct copy of his survey of Norfolk, for which he is to be paid one hundred guineas when the same is delivered. It may be necessary to observe that there is no map published that gives any material information of the county of Norfolk, that the engraving of Mr. Faden's survey cannot be ready for delivery before next year, and that in the meantime the copy he is to put into the hands of government within the space of three weeks will contain much of the Detail necessary for Military Operations.[12]

Faden, astute in business, did not co-operate with the Board purely for patriotic motives, or without protecting his commercial interests. It was noted that

> Mr. Faden is willing to give government a copy of his original Map of Norfolk . . . conditionally that it is not made public previous to the Engrav'd copy coming out, as he has already sunk £2000 in carrying on the survey.[13]

It was not surprising that the Board turned to Faden as the leading promoter and retailer of the type of maps it required. Like his predecessor, Thomas Jefferys, Faden had specialized in the new county cartography, and as well as commissioning surveys of his own he had systematically bought up and 'revised' many of the copper plates of other county surveys as they came on the market. The arrangement over the Norfolk map (eventually published in 1797) was to bring him into even closer contact with the Board. No doubt wishing to develop such a profitable and prestigious association he went on to forge a direct link with the Trigonometrical Survey by undertaking to publish 'at his own expence' the reports of the triangulation previously serialized in the *Philosophical Transactions*. Volume I of the *Account of the Trigonometrical Survey* appeared in 1799 with the blessing alike of the Board of Ordnance, to whom it was dedicated, and the Royal Society. Possibly as a *quid pro quo* for this, as well as for his co-operation over the Norfolk map, the Master General, some time before 1798, agreed that Faden could engrave 'under certain restrictions' the Ordnance map of Kent for public use.[14] This map, 'Done by the Surveying Draftsmen of His Majesty's Honourable Board of Ordnance, on the basis of the Trigonometrical Survey', was published by Faden in four sheets on 1 January 1801. It was dedicated by William Mudge to Lord Cornwallis 'and the rest of the Principal Officers of His Majesty's Ordnance', having been engraved by Thomas Foot, a free-lance craftsman employed by several London map-publishers,[15] who had already engraved Gream's map of Sussex. The strands were thus drawn together, but although Kent is often regarded as the first Ordnance map, it was in fact only a half-way house towards the Board becoming a map-publisher in its own right.

The Development of an Engraving Service

It seems certain that before the Kent map was published the Drawing Room lacked its own engraving facilities, but it is not known whether the engraver of the Kent map, employed under Faden's supervision, went to the Tower to work from the original material, or whether the drawings or suitable copies were allowed outside. Other plans of the Trigonometrical Survey were 'lodged in the Tower, for the use of Government, and not submitted, from obvious motives of policy, to public inspection',[16] so that the balance of probability may tilt to the engraving being done in the security of the Tower. If this was so, then it was a logical step, once Kent had been published, for Mudge to continue the arrangement by placing an engraver on the Ordnance pay-roll. Such an opportunity, perhaps, coupled with the fact that the drawings of the Essex map were ready for engraving, helped Mudge to make up his mind. On 26 February 1801 (barely two months after the official publication date of the Kent map) he wrote to the Board informing them that he had

> entered into an agreement with Mr Foot and Mr Knight to engrave the several plans at the Tower on the following terms, viz; That these Gentlemen should attend from 10 in the morning to 4 o'clock in the evening, the former to be paid at the rate of three guineas and a half per week and the latter at two guineas and a half till the work should be completed and hoped that the Board would approve of these Terms, as the Persons employed were Men of great abilities and the Terms were similar to those allowed by the Admiralty on like occasions.[17]

The Admiralty Hydrographic Service, established in 1795, had appointed its first engravers in 1800,[18] and it may be that Mudge's reference to progress in another government department helped to ensure the Board's approval of his arrangement. The annual accounts show that the amount spent on engraving in 1801 totalled £124 7s. 0d.[19]

From 1801 onwards engravers were continuously employed on the copper plates for the one-inch map of England and a small permanent establishment was gradually built up in the Tower. In the first year or so, when as well as preparing the Essex plates the engravers were already making revisions to the map of Kent,[20] Mudge sanctioned regular overtime payments for Foot and Knight to meet the increasing demands of the service. They were allowed to work four hours a day extra in winter and five in the summer, an arrangement which Mudge, in characteristic fashion, found 'highly preferable to the hiring of other Engravers to forward the business, which it would otherwise be necessary to do'.[21] Even so the engraving facilities soon became inadequate for the work demanded of them. The establishment was increased in 1802, when Mudge 'found it necessary to employ Mr Ebenezer Bourne as a writer upon 2 of the Plates containing parts of the County of Essex at 3 guineas per week';[22] and in 1804 a replacement was provided for Thomas Foot who had 'discontinued his attendance' at the Tower. His successor as principal engraver was Benjamin Baker, an experienced craftsman who was brought in from private practice in Islington.[23] By 1808 a further expansion in the permanent establishment had occurred with the appointment of Mr W. Tovey and Mr John Palmer: the circumstances, as described in a rather enigmatic Board minute, were that, in August of that year, Mudge

> requested permission to employ M.r John Palmer, as a Secondary Engraver at the Tower, in the room of M.r J. Baker, who was not capable of performing his Duty with sufficient dispatch; & that he might be authorised to employ M.r W. Tovey, who had faithfully discharged his Duty, during the time he was a Minor Engraver.[24]

The reference to J. Baker is puzzling and it could have been Joseph, the brother of Benjamin Baker, who was apparently regarded as unsatisfactory.[25] There was a tendency in this period for the Board of Ordnance to employ men in families (as with the Yeakells and the Dawsons) and W. Tovey could similarly have been a brother of Richard Tovey who by 1813 at the latest was employed as a regular engraver at the Tower.[26] The team of engravers for the early one-inch maps – although there were some changes of personnel before 1810 – thus settled down at about four permanent staff.

Until 1810 the engravers occupied accommodation in the Tower, presumably close to the Drawing Room. In that year, after an expansion of the Engineer service into offices in Pall Mall and Abingdon Street, it was noted that 'the Engravers & Printers under the direction of Lieut. Col. Mudge had removed into the Drawing Room',[27] bringing them into physical proximity with Yeakell who was engaged in reducing the plans. Such integration does not seem to have resulted in a loss of identity and Baker was allowed to develop an engraving service which reflected the wider state of the art in the early nineteenth century. There is no reason to suppose that the techniques and tools differed from those in the larger private workshops of the period, such as those of Cary and Faden. In the basic process of copper-plate engraving the details on the fair-drawings of the maps, prepared by Thomas

Yeakell, were incised into a specially prepared copper plate, using a variety of traditional tools.[28] The copper plates, relatively large for the map trade at that date, were purchased by the Board from one George Harris, a London copper-plate maker,[29] and it would then have been left to a younger engraver (such as Tovey when a 'minor engraver') to prepare these plates by planishing and then polishing to a mirror-smooth finish. After the plates had been prepared in this way, they were heated and spread evenly with a white 'virgin wax' which, once hardened, was ready to receive the design of the map. This had to be cut in reverse, after the tracing and transferring of the drawing to the waxed surface of the plate.[30]

The Ordnance engravers worked in a fixed sequence, which can be inferred from surviving proof copies of some of the early maps representing various stages in the completion of the plates.[31] Each of three distinct stages required a separate tracing, which was destroyed in the transferring process. Outline details – as of the coast, roads, building, and perimeters of woods and other vegetation categories – were usually incised first. The names were added next, then ornamental features such as rocks and woods; finally, the hills were inserted, the hachures being cut first with the burin and then deepened in places by the selective application of an etching acid.[32]*

There was also an established division of labour – long before Colby introduced it into the surveying operations – according to the specialist skills and experience of individual craftsmen. Benjamin Baker, as the senior man, presumably handled some of the more complex work, but he also acted as supervisor. During Mudge's frequent absences from the Tower the other three craftsmen were 'altogether under his controul'.[33] To Ebenezer Bourne, whose specialist skill is acknowledged in the imprint of many of the early maps, was allocated the engraving of all lettering. By 1820 Richard Tovey was becoming an expert in the hill engraving from which so much of the distinctive character of the early maps derived.

At intervals during the cutting of the copper plates, proofs were pulled to monitor the work, and in this way the absentee Mudge could periodically check on progress in the engravers' workshop. It was also normal practice to send the proofs into the counties so that the spelling of place-names could be verified; in times of military need, proofs were sometimes regarded as serviceable documents. In 1808, a year before publication, we find Mudge sending General Morse 'five Sheets of the Map of Devon, with parts of Somerset and Cornwall, the same being impressions from the Copper Plates in their present state'.[34] Corrections continued to be made on the copper plates even after the first impressions had been printed.

The sheets were printed on a roller press which had been installed in the Tower. Benjamin Baker, as principal engraver, was described as receiving 'an Allowance of one hundred pounds per annum for attending the Press'.[35] In this capacity, however, he was only supervisor, for press-work was a printing craft in its own right and the Ordnance Survey had to employ outside specialists – the firm of Cox, Son & Barnett, who were listed in the London Directories from 1799 to 1827 as copper-plate printers at 6 Breams Buildings, Chancery Lane.[36] The sporadic payments made to them by the Board suggest that, after the initial print run, most maps were printed only in very small batches, more or less on demand, and according to the level of stocks.

The links with the trade outside remained strong. The engravers, like the Ordnance surveyors a generation later during the railway mania, were conscious of the value of their skills on the open market. In 1810, they 'had represented the inadequacy of their salaries, comparatively with the Work performed', and a principal argument for an increase was that 'they had received higher offers from persons engaged in the Trade'.[37] The Board granted an increase in pay. In this, as in other matters where it came into contact with the London map trade, the Ordnance Survey was unable to operate in isolation.

The Prohibition of Publication 1811–16

One of the strangest episodes in the development of the Ordnance Survey was the ruling by the Master General of the period, the Earl of Mulgrave, that the maps should be withdrawn from sale to the

---

* OS *Methods and Processes* (1875) p. 169, describes the technique: 'The surface of the plate is first covered with a substance called 'etching ground' composed of asphaltum, Burgundy pitch and virgin wax, and the outline of the hills being traced and transferred to this ground, the features of the hills are marked through with a needle which removes the ground where it passes, exposing the surface of the copper. Aqua fortis is then applied to bite in these lines, and when the fainter lines are bit to a sufficient depth the acid is poured off and the plate is washed with pure water, and afterwards dried. The parts which are bitten in are now painted over with 'stopping varnish', and when this is dry the acid is again poured on the plate. The processes of stopping out and biting in are repeated until all the required tints from the lightest to the darkest are sufficiently corroded.'

public. The evidence for this decision is both fragmentary and difficult to interpret but the basic facts are clear enough. That the restriction was introduced in 1811 is suggested by a letter to Mudge from the Office of Ordnance dated 2 September of that year:

> The Quarter Master General's Department having made application for a few of the early Impressions of the Ordnance Map of the Isle of Wight, I am directed to express the Master General's desire that they may be supplied accordingly as soon as it shall be printed. His Lordship wishes however that in this as well as in all other cases, it may be distinctly understood, that the Map is not to be made public.[38]

As sheet 10 covering the Isle of Wight, the first sheet to be prominently labelled 'Ordnance Survey' within its top border, had been published on 1 June 1810, presumably it had already been 'made public', but the order at least confirms that a prohibition was in force by the autumn of 1811. The policy was reversed in the spring of 1816 and the decision communicated to Mudge in another letter:

> The Master General not deeming it necessary that the prohibition which exists against the publication of the Maps of the Trigonometrical Survey, should under present circumstances continue, I am directed to express His Lordship's desire that you will act in all matters connected with this publication as was permitted previous to the orders restraining it.[39]

Confirmation of these dates also occurs in a letter of 1820 referring to the 'stoppage of the publication in 1811' and the 'revival of the publication in 1816', in several comments by Mudge, and also in Colby's account of the history of the survey written in 1834.[40] In effect the prohibition was something of a compromise. Work continued on the engraving of the maps and copies were also printed for restricted military circulation, but the process of publication stopped short of sale to the public. Two groups of maps were affected: those relating to Essex (1805), Devon (1809), and the Isle of Wight and Hampshire (1810), which had already been published by 1811; and those which were completed between 1811 and 1816, including maps of Dorset and part of Hampshire (1811), Sussex and the five sheets covering Cornwall (1813).* In addition, an order was given that 'maps for correction were to be kept with the utmost privacy, and when corrected to be returned to the Tower'.[41] This was presumably a reference to proof copies circulating in the counties, although it would also have inhibited any plans Mudge may have had for revising the older published sheets.**

The most obvious reason for the withdrawal of the maps was on the grounds of security during the Napoleonic War, against a background of periodic invasion scares along the south coast. It was established practice in eighteenth-century European warfare, enshrined in the policies of Frederick the Great, to consider detailed topographical maps as 'classified' material, and to take every care to prevent them from falling into enemy hands.[42] In the England of 1811, such a precaution in relation to published sheets does not seem to have been thought out very carefully: Ordnance maps of many of the most vulnerable coasts had been circulating freely before 1811, and there were also commercial maps, such as those sold by Faden, which were easily obtainable in London. It is possible that the ban was a manifestation of military politics rather than conviction that withholding a few maps was in the national interest.

In support of this interpretation several scraps of information suggest a long-standing rivalry between the Quartermaster-General's Department (the Staff Headquarters of the Army) and the Ordnance Survey under Mudge. The former had undergone a period of revitalization, following the establishment of the Royal Military College at High Wycombe in 1799, a Royal Staff Corps in 1800, and a Depot of Military Knowledge in 1803, which included 'a Drawing Room, a Military Library, and a Depôt of Military Plans, Maps, and Memoirs',[43] designed to collect topographical and statistical information both at home and abroad. Many of the Quartermaster-General's staff had been trained at High Wycombe in field surveying and plan drawing, and also in reconnaissance techniques, and were therefore well equipped to be 'occasionally employed in the Districts of Great Britain, either for the purpose of Military Surveys, examination of Roads, marking ground for the encampment and exercise of Troops, or for the purpose of superintending and directing the progress of Works for National Defence'.[44] In short, a situation arose in which the Board of Ordnance and the Quartermaster-General's Department were both employing surveyors and draughtsmen in connection with the defence of the English coast-lands. It was the development of such activities in parallel which led to sustained rivalry between the two departments.[45] All this did not prevent the Quartermaster-General's Department from turning to Mudge for information, which was not always given willingly, about southern England in those areas where maps had been surveyed and engraved. In particular,

* As a result the 5 sheets relating to Cornwall, although their imprint includes the date 5 January 1813, were not published until the summer of 1816.

** For example, sheet 1, containing the built-up area of London, was not revised until c. 1820, despite extensive changes.

Mudge strongly deprecated the use of Ordnance material in an incomplete state and as early as 1803 he had written to Morse:

> I am afraid you will not obtain more than two out of the four sheets of the Essex map left at my office . . . Perhaps, it may not be improper to say, that I was extremely *averse* to printing any copies from unfinished plates for the Q.M.General, but the measure was forced on me by order.[46]

Such orders were still in force in 1811. Portlock refers to another letter written in November of that year which stated:

> . . . an application had been made by the Quartermaster-General to have the plans drawn from the survey sent to the Horse Guards, to be there *copied* for the use of his department. This measure was advocated by the Duke of York, and it was afterwards arranged that the plans should be sent to the Horse Guards in parcels of four, five, and eight, in succession, until the whole had been copied,* and that this arrangement should apply to the future maps as well as to those already finished.[47]

In 1819 Mudge, still suspecting some interference in the Survey's affairs, wrote to Colby (after criticism of some maps) that in his opinion the 'Quarter-Master-General's Department and Arrowsmiths are at the bottom of the whole of it'.[48]

The actions of the Quartermaster-General's Department were not the sole source of Mudge's difficulties in 1811. It was also the year of the Commission of Military Enquiry which tried to put another spoke in the Survey's wheel through the suggestion that the provision of published maps could be left to private enterprise.[49] All through the summer and autumn the whole future of the Ordnance Survey as a map-publisher was very uncertain. Not only was the sale of maps prohibited, but almost simultaneously the practice of issuing scientific reports on the trigonometrical observations was discontinued. Volume 3 of the *Account of the Trigonometrical Survey* had been published by Faden in 1811, but in October of that year Mudge informed Colby that although the 'Work is approved of and sells well' the 'publication of *future* works is stopped'.[50]

It is not surprising that Colby was later to write of the 'moral discouragement' of this period, the more so because in August 1811 Mudge had been able to make an optimistic forecast about potential income from map sales, and the Military Commissioners, in reporting on his accounts for 1800–10, noted that, against a total expenditure on the 'Local Survey' of £33 165 5s. 7d., including the cost of reducing the maps in the Tower and their engraving, he was able to offset £2 161 10s. 8d.

> received from the sale of these Maps, for they are disposed of for the benefit of the Public; and Colonel Mudge believes that not only the expense of the engraving will be altogether defrayed by the sale of them, but, in a course of time, a portion also of the original expense of the Survey.[51]**

This simple statement is one of the earliest allusions to a commercial ingredient in Ordnance Survey activities; but the Master General's decision of only a month later was a sharp setback to any aspirations Mudge might have had to make his department into an effective map-publisher.

With the resumption of publication in 1816, Mudge, with the help of Colby, took a fresh look at the Survey's publication policy. It is likely that there was a pent-up demand for both the older and the more recently completed sheets and, to try to make up for the lost opportunity in sales, Mudge began to pay systematic attention to publicity. Although the concept of publishing a series of largely self-contained county maps in 'Parts',[52] with all sheets issued on the same date, complete with their

* The maps may have been copied entirely by hand, but as the process of lithography had recently been introduced in the Quartermaster-General's Department, a copy of each map may have been traced for transfer to stone. See I. Mumford, 'Lithography, photography and photozincography in English map production before 1870', *Cartographic Journal* 1972, vol. 9, pp. 30–36.

** A further indication of the trivial cost of the Survey at this time is given in PP 1847 (171), XXXVI, in a table of expenditure for the years 1791–1820:

Year	Parliamentary Grant			Actual Expenditure		
	£	s	d	£	s	d
1791–1811	No annual vote			44 409	10	5
1812	10 000	–	–	7 604	8	2
1813	10 000	–	–	9 752	14	0
1814	10 000	–	–	8 507	14	2
1815	10 000	–	–	8 893	16	2
1816	10 000	–	–	8 986	4	3
1817	6 567	11	5	11 323	10	2
1818	8 695	10	0	8 253	12	7
1819	5 290	3	6	9 309	9	11
1820	9 000	–	–	7 620	18	1

own title-page and engraved borders, was modified after the appearance of the maps of Devon in 1809, it was still to the individual county and the loyalty of its local gentry that the Ordnance Survey hoped to direct its promotional efforts. Indeed, in this matter, there was little to distinguish its practices from those of the private county surveyors in the eighteenth century or the London map-sellers with whom the Ordnance Survey had found itself in competition after 1801. Apparently the map of Devon had been successfully advertised in that county ('where General Mudge was known personally')[53] but little had been done since. In October 1816, however, a 'printed Bill of Prices'[54] was circulated to the trade, listing the sheets which were then available, and in the spring of the following year Mudge made plans to advertise the maps in appropriate county newspapers. Even this simple matter had to go through the bureaucratic hierarchy and on 18 March, in relation to his proposal to advertise the maps 'with a view to benefit the sale of the Ordnance maps at the Drawing Room in the Tower', the Master General enquired

> whether the Maps were advertised for Sale at the Tower, or actually sold there, when they were formerly sold to the public . . . as his Lordship's approbation of, or dissent from, the measure, will be influenced by his knowledge of the past.[55]

In December of the same year, the Board officially approved:

> . . . part 6 of the Ordnance Map of Great Britain will be ready for publication at the Tower on the 1ˢᵗ of January next, and the sale of the Maps depends entirely on their Publicity . . . the Board would be pleased to direct that an Advertisement . . . may be inserted in the Public Newspapers, and that it may be continued therein for some time.[56]

The only queries were about the length of time it would be advisable to continue the advertisements, and whether there was 'any objection to Mʳ Faden's name being inserted as a Person to whom applications are to be made'.[57] Here was the beginning of a sales promotion policy for the one-inch maps.

Relationships with other Map-Sellers

One result of the growth of the Ordnance Survey as a map-publisher was that it was brought into close and sometimes uneasy contact with the world of commercial cartography; rivalry between the two sectors was caused by the common aim to provide the basic one-inch maps of the country. At first the private map-makers were largely the beneficiaries of the development of a national survey; only after 1816 when Mudge began to pursue more assertive policies on the copyright in official maps did conflicts of interest start to come out into the open. There was also interaction; the early Ordnance maps influenced both the content and design of privately-produced maps, and some of the commercial practices of the London map-sellers began to leave their mark in the Tower. But despite its international pre-eminence, the London map trade was a relatively small craft industry and only three or four businesses came into regular contact with the Board of Ordnance.

Among these cartographers and map-sellers William Faden came closest to being an integral part of the history of the Survey. By publishing the scientific reports of the Trigonometrical Survey and especially through his engraving and publication of the map of Kent, he had built up a special relationship with the Board of Ordnance. In the years between 1801 and 1820 this was being strengthened in two main directions. Faden probably held a monopoly as supplier of maps to the Board as well as for other services in colouring, mounting and repairing maps. The nature of this business can be identified in the records of the Board through the regular payments made for supplying maps and 'Articles on Account of the Trigonometrical Survey'. In February 1806, for example, Faden submitted a bill for maps supplied by him during the previous year (to the Board as a whole) amounting to £160 6s. 6d.;[58] in June there was a further bill for £47 1s. 0d. 'for maps and fixing them in the Board Room',[59] while in 1808 he was supplying maps of Spain and Portugal for Engineer officers 'ordered to proceed on Foreign Service'.[60] A full account, dated 12 June 1820, and relating to bills 'for Two Years and an Half terminating in June 1819' provides an unusually detailed record of transactions. The total came to £276 11s. 9d. with over sixty items being specified.[61] Much of the business was unconnected with the Survey, but for its direct use Faden was supplying various maps of areas in which the surveyors were due to work. J. Evans's map of North Wales was supplied for Robert Dawson's use, 'Paterson's Book of Roads' for Mudge, and maps of Scotland by Arrowsmith and 'Charts of the Orkney and Shetland Isles' for Dr MacCulloch, the newly-appointed geological surveyor of the Board of Ordnance.[62]

Faden had also acquired the right to sell Ordnance Survey maps. In view of his regular contacts with Board members and with senior officers in the Corps of Royal Engineers it was almost to be expected that he would be granted this privilege, which was in force from the time of the publication of the map of Essex. As a means of retailing the official maps it again typifies the transitional arrangements which the Board decided to make for an activity in which it had little experience. At best it can be described as a commercial compromise: the Board retained the right to retail its own maps which were available to the public from the Tower at a price of three guineas; it also granted to Faden the rights of agent for the sale of Ordnance Survey maps. The deal had been deliberated carefully and the price again fixed at three guineas, 'which price Mr Faden is to bind himself to sell them at', and he was expected to repay 'Two Guineas and a Half for each map they shall supply him with'.[63] For Faden, in competition with the Board for whom he was acting, this must have seemed a hard bargain, and in May 1805 he was arguing that the commission allowed by the 'Master General and Board for vending . . . the New Map of the County of Essex . . . was at least 10 per cent below the price usually granted'.[64] Finally, Faden was given the lucrative contract of mounting and boxing the quite large number of presentation copies which, by custom, as they appeared in Parts, were given to the Royal Family and various other nobles, to members of the Cabinet, to the Universities and to high ranking officers in the Board of Ordnance and the Quartermaster-General's Department.[65] Colby remarked in 1820 that these copies, 'fitted up', cost the Ordnance 'about 6 times as much as a Copy in Sheets',[66] so here at least the Geographer to the King made a good profit out of his official connections.

The Board's relationship with map-sellers other than Faden was not without its problems. Faden's rivals predictably objected to the exclusive nature of his appointment, and the map-seller John Cary, one of the most prolific and reputable cartographers of his day, took issue with Mudge in April 1810. He wrote complaining that William Faden

> was exclusively allowed to supply the Map of Devonshire and that he was unable to procure a Copy of it, which was a great hurt to his business; and observed that W. Faden was the sole agent on the part of The Board, but that it would be an advantage if the Maps were delivered to the regular Trade at six months Credit, and 17 p. cent Discount in the same manner as they were delivered to W. Faden.[67]

The Board approved of this suggestion and Mudge was instructed that 'it be carried into effect conformably to such arrangement as he shall think proper to adopt'.[68] But any reform of the system was deferred as a result of the restrictions placed on the sale of the maps in the following year, and not until the resumption of trading in 1816 was a move made to widen the retail arrangements.[69] Even so the grievance festered on for some years.

The new commercially-orientated era of the national survey had started on a wrong footing. Whether by design or unwittingly, Mudge and the Board had not only managed to alienate the trade at large but, through its sales at the Tower, had also damaged the prospects of Faden. Another difficulty concerned the use which a private map-maker might reasonably make of information published by the Board, which seems to have adopted a magnanimous stance towards the use of its trigonometrical data. In 1795 Williams and Mudge implied that there was a deliberate policy to allow private individuals to use the trigonometrical survey to undertake 'more correct maps of the counties over which the triangles have been carried'.[70] Little had changed by 1811 when the Military Commissioners supported the view that 'individual speculation' might 'fill up the triangles'. Against this background extensive use of the trigonometrical survey was made, notably but not solely by Christopher Greenwood, presumably without dissent from the Board.[71] Only when it was realized that Greenwood was in effect aiming at a national map was the view occasionally voiced, as by Dawson in Shropshire, that such use of the Ordnance triangles was damaging to the prospects of its own maps.[72]

After the Ordnance Survey began to publish maps, as distinct from information about the triangulation, a completely new situation developed in which some map-sellers believed they had the right to copy and reduce Ordnance maps; but this was strenuously contested by Mudge and the Board. The Ordnance Survey's first copyright dispute seems to have come to a head at the time when the Board was resuming its interrupted career as a map-publisher. In September 1816 Mudge wrote to the Board summarizing the problem:

> I beg leave to acquaint you . . . that an Idea has gone abroad among the Mapsellers of London that as a portion of the Public, at whose expence the Ordnance Survey is carried on, they have a right to reduce from and publish, Copies of the Ordnance Survey on Scales suited to their own convenience; a circumstance, whether they have that right or not, that seems likely in a greater or less degree to affect the Sale of the original Work. Under this Idea, during the prohibition laid on the vending of our Maps, Essex and Devonshire were so reduced and sold; and the great Body of the latter County had been incorporated in the general Map of England lately published by Mr. Arrowsmith; and I know for certain that the Map of Cornwall which has not

been published more than a Fortnight, is now reduced to the Scale of half an Inch to a Mile, and is about to be put into the hands of an Engraver for publication.

He went on to ask:

[that] I may be informed on legal authority whether Individuals have a right to reduce the Ordnance Survey and publish it for their own benefit, and in the event of such opinion being given in the negative . . . whether or not the Board will permit any Individual to so reduce the Work.[73]

The question was then referred to the Board's solicitors, who produced an opinion based on the Copyright Acts of 1735, 1767 and 1777. The earliest of these Acts (without specifying maps) had given protection to engraved and similar works for a term of fourteen years after publication, providing that the date of that publication and 'the name of the Proprietor' were engraved on the plate 'and printed on every such Print or Prints'; the 1767 Act extended the protection specifically to include any 'Map, Chart or Plan', and the length of the term to twenty-eight years; while the 1777 Act, as well as confirming the previous provisions, gave the right for actions to be brought, with damages to be assessed by a jury.[74]

With the Ordnance maps the legal argument hinged on the requirement for the name of the proprietor to appear on every map and on the practice which had been adopted for the maps of Essex and Devon of including an imprint, with the date: 'Published . . . by Lt. Col. Mudge Tower' on each sheet. It was this imprint, implying under the letter of the Act that Mudge rather than the Board was the proprietor of the plates, about which the map-sellers intended to 'agitate'.[75] For his part Mudge explained the wording of the imprint in a long letter dated 23 October 1816. His first point was to clear away any misunderstanding that he might have received 'the least pecuniary advantage whatever from the sale of the Ordnance Maps'. He went on to explain that by inserting his own name on the plates he was following the practice on Admiralty charts:

. . . when the first Maps were printed and published by the Ordnance, I had recourse to the Admiralty Charts, and found that the name of Captain Hurd the Hydrographer was subscribed to each plate with the period and place of its publication; and I naturally took it for granted that if I followed his example I should give equal security to the Ordnance Maps.[76]

In doing so he had believed that 'the act of the official man was the act of Government', but it was on this very point of proprietorship that the map-sellers, having taken legal advice themselves, believed that the Copyright Acts might be circumvented. It was, moreover, a question on which the Board's solicitors felt themselves unable to pronounce: they concluded that it would 'be expedient to take the Opinions of the Attorney and Solicitor General'.[77]

Mudge evidently regarded the 'magnitude of the object' to be considerable,[78] and he convinced the Board that the arguments should be laid before the law officers of the Crown. The case presented brought out two new points. First, it was noted that when proof copies of the Essex and Devon maps were circulated for correction, the imprint affording copyright protection had not been engraved; were they therefore out of copyright at the time? Secondly, while some map-makers such as Cary and Arrowsmith assumed that they were 'precluded by law from *reducing* and publishing *detached Maps* (taken from Ordnance Surveys)' they believed they had a 'right to *incorporate* all or any of the Ordnance Works' into a 'General-Map of England'.[79] On these several points the opinions expressed by the Attorney and Solicitor General were unequivocal: all reduced copies of Ordnance maps, even if part of a map of the whole country, were an infringement of the Board's legitimate copyright. They also believed that the inclusion of Mudge's name in the imprint complied with the spirit of the Acts and entitled official maps to their protection. The best mode of stopping such pirated publications, they concluded, was by a '*Bill for an Injunction* to stop the sale when they shall be published, as both Colonel Mudge, and the Board of Ordnance might be Plaintiffs in such a Bill'.[80]

The Board realized that this opinion gave it considerable muscle in its dispute with the private map-sellers. It therefore decided on a hard line, believing

that the Case appears to be of sufficient importance to justify a Prosecution against such Persons as have or may pirate or publish the Maps of the Trigonometrical Survey without the Master General & Board's authority.[81]

Mudge, however, displaying his usual cautious approach to the conduct of public affairs, argued that such court proceedings ought not to be retrospective, as they would not be in the best interests of the Ordnance Survey and could do more harm than good in his attempts to promote smooth working relationships with the map-sellers. He was afraid that the likely outcome would be 'to force the Trade into a combination among themselves to injure the sale of the Ordnance-Maps at the Tower, or at other authorised places'.[82]

A compromise was agreed on, in which a 'general Notice' was to be inserted 'in the London Gazette, and in some of the Daily Newspapers'; this would warn 'the Trade from copying, reducing or incorporating all or any of the Ordnance Maps of the Trigonometrical Survey' without permission.[83] The final wording of the notice, which was sent to the 'Offices of the Times, Morning Advertiser, Courier & London Gazette' on 28 February 1816, was:

Trigonometrical Survey
of
Great Britain

It having been represented to the Master General and Principal Officers of His Majesty's Ordnance that certain Map Sellers and others have through inadvertence or otherwise, copied, reduced, or incorporated into other Works and Published parts of the 'Trigonometrical Survey of Great Britain', a Work executed under the immediate Orders of the said Master General and Board, the said Master General and Board have thought proper to direct that Public Notice be given to all Mapsellers and others, cautioning them against copying, reducing or incorporating into other Works, and publishing all or any part of the said 'Trigonometrical Survey' or of the Ordnance Maps which have been or may be engraven therefrom; Every offender after this Notice given, will be proceeded against according to the provisions of the Act of Parliament made for the protection of Property of this kind.[84]

There was to be a curious little postscript to these events. In June 1817, evidently still following a conciliatory line, the Board gave Cary permission to produce a reduced version of the Ordnance map of Cornwall.[85] But if normal relations were quickly being restored with the map trade – the copyright issue was not to be raised again until the summer of 1820[86] – one result of the dispute may have been that the Board was made more aware of the commercial potential of small-scale maps. Indeed, at the same time that Cary made his application, Mudge came up with the suggestion that 'it might be expedient to engrave at the Tower a reduced Map of the Ordnance Survey'. A little surprisingly perhaps in view of some of their earlier policies the Master General and the Board promptly gave him their 'authority to prepare a reduced Map of the whole Trigonometrical Survey when complete'.[87] This is the earliest reference to an Ordnance involvement in a map at a scale smaller than one inch to one mile. The incomplete state of the mapping made the authorization rather academic, but it may perhaps be taken as a small symptom of a change in attitude to the Survey's role as a map-publisher.

In the four or five years following the end of the Napoleonic War the Ordnance Survey gradually extended its publications beyond southern England, yet the way in which this was done was largely unpremeditated. In a sense the Survey was becoming a victim of its own success, and as its published maps and advertisements penetrated more widely, and as it came to be regarded as a credible alternative to private cartography, so too it found itself unable to fulfil the demand for its own products. The result was that the gentry in some counties, at first abetted by Mudge, Colby and the Master General, seem to have taken a hand in fashioning the publication programme. The best-known example concerns the map of Lincolnshire. By 1817 the topographical surveyors had reached the south of this county but were progressing so slowly that the local gentry, conscious it was said of the value of good maps both in the work of agricultural improvement and in the pleasures of hunting, decided to approach the Board of Ordnance in an attempt to speed up the work. When Colby returned to the Tower of London in the autumn and was asked by Mudge for his opinion, he replied:

I really can discover no good motive for rejecting the offer of the gentlemen of that county . . . what more proper object can the survey be directed, in time of peace, than to aid the general improvement of the country: and how can that be done more effectually than in giving maps of these counties where the most beneficial changes are taking place? In the county of Lincoln, the spirit of adventurous agricultural improvement has been most eminently displayed. Individuals have improved their fortunes, and the nation acquired additional resources from their efforts. New efforts are now making in the same county, and these efforts may be rendered more efficaceous by the aid of the Ordnance map.[88]

This was a clear articulation from the future director of the Survey of its peace-time role in the tasks of national improvement. Perhaps he realized that these uses of published maps would soon outstrip the military or scientific importance of the earlier surveys but, if so, he was taking too rosy a view of the short-term advantages of extending the area of the survey in response to user demands. Such a scheme had to be financed and the Board of Ordnance was not keen to meet a request for even 'a small additional sum'. As a result, for the map of Lincolnshire to go ahead, the Ordnance Survey had to revert to the traditional expedient of the private map-seller – that of raising advance subscriptions within the county. There was a lot of correspondence about the financing of mapping and engraving along these lines, but the eventual arrangement was that the Lincolnshire map could be taken up on condition that '500 Impressions of the Map at a price not exceeding four Guineas' were subscribed for.[89]

There is no doubt that, in their eagerness to extend the peace-time scope of the Survey, Mudge and Colby were turning the clock back. They were emphasizing the local county and its needs without taking wider priorities into account in planning the larger strategy of a national map. By 1820, a number of other counties including Shropshire, Warwickshire and Worcestershire, and even a Scottish county or two,[90] had attempted to jump on the Lincolnshire band-wagon, and were petitioning the Board for similar arrangements. Subscription lists for Ordnance Survey maps were opening in a number of county towns,[91] and there was a danger that the Survey might become a free-for-all, with its services auctioned to the highest bidder. Although Colby was quick to realize the potentially disruptive effects such requests could have on the orderly progression of a national survey, the era of William Mudge ended without the Ordnance Survey laying down any clear directions for its future publication policy.

Notes

1 William Mudge and Isaac Dalby, in *An Account of the Operation Carried on For Accomplishing a Trigonometrical Survey of England and Wales . . .1784–1796* (London 1799, 1, pp. xii–xiii, wrote that, as a result of the triangulation, the 'Public' might expect to 'possess some general Map, published on the same principle with the *Carte de France*, a performance highly celebrated'.

2 J. B. Harley, 'The bankruptcy of Thomas Jefferys: an episode in the economic history of eighteenth century map-making', *Imago Mundi* 1966, vol. 20, pp. 27–48, for examples.

3 In 1766 Roy had already calculated that 'At a mile to an Inch England would make a Map of between 30 and 40 feet square'. See J. Fortescue, *The Correspondence of King George the Third from 1760 to December 1783* (London 1927), vol. I, p. 332.

4 PRO WO 55/2281, ff 32, 37 refer to the acquisition of a number of County surveys in 1796.

5 PRO WO 47/120, 13 Sept. 1792.

6 PRO WO 47/2365, 19 Dec. 1793.

7 PRO WO 47/2372, 10 April 1799.

8 PRO WO 47/2367, f 427.

9 PRO WO 47/2366.

10 See, for example, PRO WO 47/2366, f 351.

11 See Harley, *Imago Mundi* 1966, vol. 20, pp. 35–7, on this office, by which Faden was appointed a member of the Royal Household.

12 PRO WO 47/2366, f 355.

13 *Ibid.*, f 335. For further background to the map see J. C. Barringer, *An Introduction to Faden's Map of Norfolk* (Norwich, Norfolk Record Society, vol. 42, 1975).

14 Mudge and Dalby, *Account of the Trig. Survey 1784–1796, p. xiii.*

15 Foot had been employed by both Faden and Arrowsmith. See R. V. Tooley, 'A Dictionary of map-makers', part IV, *Map Collectors' series* vol. 5, no. 50 (London 1968), p. 160.

16 Mudge and Dalby, *Account of the Trig. Survey 1784–1796, p. xii.*

17 PRO WO 47/2379, 3 March 1801.

18 A. Day, *The Admiralty Hydrographic Service 1795–1919* (London 1967), p. 14.

19 *XVIIth Report of the Commissioners of Military Enquiry*; PP 1812 (5) IV, p. 246.

20 PRO WO 47/2383, 12 Jan. 1802.

21 *Ibid.*

22 PRO WO 47/2385, 26 Oct. 1802.

23 OSLB, f 137; see also Tooley, *Map Collectors' Series*, vol. 2, no. 16, p. 25.

24 PRO WO 47/2603, 17 Aug. 1808.

25 Tooley, *Map Collectors' Series*, vol. 2, no. 16, p. 25.

26 PRO WO 47/375, 9 July 1813.

27 PRO WO 47/126, 22 Jan. 1810.

28 On the technique employed by the Ordnance engravers in this early period see Coolie Verner, 'Copperplate printing' in David Woodward (ed.), *Five Centuries of map printing* (Chicago 1975), pp. 51–75.

29 PRO WO 47/262, 16 Dec. 1811. George Harris does not appear to be listed in the London Directories for this period.

30 Verner, *Five Centuries . . .*, p. 53.

31 Proof copies in outline only have survived in the collection of the RGS for two of the Essex sheets (2 and 48); that they were completed in outline by 1803 is confirmed by PRO WO 55/960.

32 PRO WO 55/960 refers to the copperplates of the Essex map being 'bitten-in' in August 1803.

33 *XVIIth Report . . .* : PP 1812 (5) IV, p. 168.

34 Mudge to Handfield, 8 Sept. 1808: PRO WO 55/960.
35 *XVIIth Report . . .* : PP 1812 (5) IV, p. 167; the quarterly accounts submitted by Mudge for the payment of the engravers contain also various claims for Baker 'attending the printer': OSLB, *passim*.
36 Ian Maxted, *The London book trades, 1775–1800* (Folkestone 1977).
37 PRO WO 47/137, 19 March 1810.
38 Phipps to Mudge, 2 Sept. 1811, OSLB f 131.
39 Chapman to Mudge, 17 April 1816, OSLB f 125.
40 Colby to Crew, 23 Oct. 1820, OSLB f 150; PRO T 1/4060.
41 Stamford Raffles Flint (ed.), *Mudge Memoirs . . .* (Truro 1883), p. 143.
42 Harley, *Mapping the American Revolutionary War* (Chicago 1977), ch. 3.
43 *Eleventh Report of the Commissioners of Military Enquiry*, pp. 13–41: PP 1810 (79) IX, for a full description of the activities of the Department in this period.
44 *Ibid.* p. 14.
45 Richard Glover, *Britain at Bay. Defence against Bonaparte, 1803–14* (London 1973), pp. 103–24, for much of the background to this.
46 Mudge to Morse, 6 Aug. 1803, PRO WO 55/960.
47 Portlock, *Memoir of Colby*, p. 40.
48 Mudge to Colby, 21 Feb. 1819, quoted in Close, *Early Years*, p. 70.
49 *XVIIth Report . . .* : PP 1812 (5) IV, pp. 168–9.
50 Mudge to Colby, 1 Oct. 1811, quoted in Close, *Early Years*, p. 59.
51 *XVIIth Report*: PP 1812 (5) IV, p. 168.
52 For a contemporary list of the 'Parts' of the *Old Series* maps, excluding the last (Part 10, Lincolnshire), finally published in 1824, see W. Faden, *Catalogue of the Geographical Works, Maps, Plans etc., published by W. Faden 5 Charing Cross, Geographer to His Majesty* (London 1822, reprinted 1963).
53 Colby to Crew, 27 July 1820, OSLB f 86.
54 A copy is stuck inside a bound volume of Sir Joseph Banks's set of the maps of Cornwall: British Library, Map Library.
55 Crew to Mudge, 18 March 1817, OSLB ff 4–5.
56 Crew to Mudge, 24 Dec. 1817, OSLB f 15.
57 *Ibid.*
58 PRO WO 47/2588, 5 Feb. 1806.
59 PRO WO 47/2590, 25 June 1806.
60 PRO WO 47/2452, 28 Dec. 1808.
61 Attached to a letter from Colby to Crew, 12 June 1820, OSLB ff 56–60.
62 *Ibid.*
63 PRO WO 47/2409, 22 May 1805.
64 *Ibid.*
65 Colby to Crew, 23 Oct. 1820, reviewing the development of the practice which went back to the beginnings of map publication by the OS: OSLB ff 149–51.
66 Colby to Crew, 23 Oct. 1820, OSLB ff 149–51.
67 PRO WO 47/142, 11 April 1810.
68 *Ibid.*
69 'Bill of Prices' of OS Maps, British Library, Map Library, Maps 148.e.27. indicates that by 1816 all map-sellers were allowed roughly 16% discount.
70 Edward Williams and William Mudge, 'An Account of the Trigonometrical Survey carried on in 1791, 1792, 1793, and 1794', *Phil. Trans*. 1795, LXXXV, p. 474.
71 Crew to Mudge, 7 April 1817: the Greenwoods seem to have obtained permission to use the published trigonometrical data after 1817, OSLB f 129.
72 Robert Dawson to Colby, 6 Aug. 1820, making an explicit reference to Greenwood's use of the triangulation, OSLB ff 108–9.
73 Mudge to Crew, 28 Sept. 1816. PRO WO 44/299.
74, 75 Memorandum from Smith and Son, Assistants to the Ordnance Solicitors, 4 Oct. 1816, PRO WO 44/299.
76 Mudge to Crew, 23 Oct. 1816, PRO WO 44/299.
77 Smith and Son to the Board, 29 Oct. 1816, PRO WO 44/299.
78 Mudge to Crew, 23 Oct. 1816, PRO WO 44/299.
79 Smith and Son to the Attorney General, 8 Jan. 1817, PRO WO 44/299, f 3.
80 Smith and Son to the Board, 21 Feb. 1817, where the 'Opinion' was set out: PRO WO 44/299.
81 Smith and Son to the Board, 9 Jan. 1817, annotation by a secretary to the Board: PRO WO 44/299.
82 Smith and Son to the Board, 27 Jan. 1817, summarizing Mudge's views: PRO WO 44/299.
83 *Ibid.*
84 PRO WO 44/299, 24 Feb. 1817.
85 PRO WO 47/661, 27 June 1817.
86 Crew to Colby, 3 Aug. 1820, OSLB ff 91–2.
87 PRO WO 47/661, 27 June 1817.
88 Portlock, *Memoir of Colby*, p. 93.
89 Mudge to Chapman, 7 Feb. 1818, OSLB f 157. OSLB ff 419, 424–6, for lists of subscribers.
90 OSLB, *passim*.
91 See, for example, *Aris's Birmingham Gazette*, 2 Aug., 27 Sept., and 18 Oct. 1819, where subscribers were invited for the proposed Ordnance Map of Warwickshire.

7
The Survey
of Ireland
to 1847*

The Spring Rice Committee and its Antecedents

Although the Irish Government retained a measure of autonomy after the union with Britain in 1801, none of its departments was directly concerned with map-making and there seems to have been a general assumption that Mudge's Trigonometrical Survey would eventually produce both a triangulation and a military map of Ireland to match its work in England. But as long as the Survey was restricted by lack of funds to a painfully slow progress across the south of England, this prospect remained too distant to be worth considering in detail. Irishmen soon realized that in spite of the union they themselves would have to meet their country's rapidly expanding cartographic needs for some time to come. The Government itself made this clear in 1809 by commissioning a special survey of the principal bogs,[1] and the counties continued to supply themselves with the 'Grand Jury' maps that had been authorized by the Dublin Parliament in the eighteenth century.[2] A number of able engineers were brought into prominence by these surveys; some were Irish residents of long standing, like William Edgeworth, others newly imported, like Richard Griffith, William Bald and Alexander Nimmo. Encouraged by the achievements of these men, the Irish map-using public seems rather to have lost sight of the Ordnance, and there were hopes that the country's own surveyors, native and adopted, would be able to connect their separate triangulations into a single national network. It was another London department, the Admiralty, which remained most sceptical on this point and which continued to press the claims of Irish cartography in Pall Mall. Their lordships began at the end of the Napoleonic wars by proposing that the Board of Ordnance should at least supply the trigonometrical skeleton for a new hydrographic survey; they repeated the suggestion in 1822 after one of their sloops had been wrecked on an uncharted sandbank off the Wexford coast, and again in the following year when a naval officer discovered errors in a chart made by Nimmo for the Irish Fishery Board.[3]

In naval circles, then, the issue of an Irish Ordnance Survey was kept alive. But in Ireland itself attention had been shifting to problems of larger scale cartography.[4] The cause of anxiety here was the county cess, a tax which paid for many of the country's roads and bridges and much of its local government machinery. The cess was traditionally apportioned among small territorial units, averaging about three hundred statute acres in size, which were known in most parts of the country as 'townlands'. In some counties the origins of the assessment were lost in antiquity; in others it was based on out-dated admeasurements of which the Strafford Survey (1636–40) was the oldest and William Petty's Down Survey (1654–9) the best known. Even if they had been wholly accurate in the first place, these surveys would have long since been made obsolete by changes in townland boundaries and by the progress of agricultural improvement; by the 1800s it had become common for Irish estate surveyors, mapping individual properties at new standards of accuracy, to expose gross inequalities in the burden of the cess. The English rating system was open to similar objections, but in Ireland, not for the last time, efficiency seemed to demand a more active participation by the central government in the affairs of the counties, with the result that a country generally regarded as backward became instead a source of administrative innovation. In this case, opinion may have been influenced by the fate of the Irish population census of 1813, which had been entrusted to the Grand Juries of the counties with a striking lack of success. At any rate there was a shift of emphasis between 1816, when a select committee recommended that each county should survey itself,[5] and 1819, when it was proposed in Parliament to place the whole operation under the Lord Lieutenant.[6]

Whoever made it, a survey intended as a prelude to land valuation would have to be laid down on a larger scale (eight inches to one mile was suggested in 1819) and executed by other methods than those in which Mudge and Colby were most experienced; it would also cost more, £300 000 being a common estimate for the whole of Ireland.[7] At this stage many people seem to have visualized a

---

* For a fuller treatment of the Irish survey, see J. H. Andrews, *A Paper Landscape* (Oxford 1975).

Down-Survey-type map showing not the whole landscape but only the acreages and boundaries of the townlands. But there were some far-sighted commentators who remembered how Petty, acting as a private individual, had tried to give a wider significance to his official task by including topographical along with cadastral information. And it was in this spirit that William Shaw Mason, the editor of a series of Irish parochial memoirs modelled on Sinclair's *Statistical Survey* of Scotland, expressed the hope that by showing houses and enclosures as well as townland boundaries the new maps would be more generally useful as 'the common-place book of the statesman'.[8]

In a Commons debate of 1819 these currents of thought were brought together by the Admiralty secretary, J. W. Croker, who not only recommended that the Ordnance should direct the Irish survey, but urged that it should be hydrographical and 'statistical' in character as well as geographical.[9] In February the Duke of Wellington, as Master General of the Ordnance, agreed to conduct the Survey of Ireland, and prepared for it by selecting twenty cadets for instruction and by arranging for a small sum of money to be included in the Ordnance estimates to cover initial expenses. A month afterwards, the Government gave the cess-payers a slightly belated voice by appointing a select committee, composed mainly of Irish Members of Parliament under the chairmanship of Thomas Spring Rice, to 'consider the best mode of apportioning more equally the local burthens collected in Ireland and to provide for a more general survey and valuation'. Wellington had been moved to action by his brother Lord Wellesley, Lord Lieutenant of Ireland, who was determined to keep the survey out of Irish hands. 'Neither science', he told the Duke, 'nor skill, nor diligence, nor discipline, nor integrity sufficient for such a work can be found in Ireland'.[10] Whether Irish surveyors deserved such summary dismissal was a question soon to be made irrelevant by the course of events. What gave Wellesley's statement a special interest was that, whereas the Ordnance Survey had hitherto been associated mainly with geodesy and military map-making, it was at the cadastral level that the question of 'integrity' was most likely to arise, for it was here that pressure might be put on local surveyors by occupiers seeking to evade their fair share of the cess. For his part Wellington seems to have felt 'rather indisposed' to enter so new and unmilitary a field,[11] and an estimate drawn up for him at about this time was confined to the trigonometrical and topographical portions of the survey, leaving the townland boundaries to be dealt with by some other department.[12]

Spring Rice's team thought better of the Irish surveying fraternity than did Wellesley; well enough, at any rate, to summon a number of professional witnesses from Dublin and to hear them with respect. But in the end it too accepted the idea of an all-Ordnance operation. Partly, perhaps, it was influenced by the sheer difficulty of drawing sharp technical and administrative boundaries between major triangulation, minor triangulation and detail survey: as the Committee's minutes show, its attack on this problem, though determined, was not very successful. And it must also have been impressed by the confidence with which Mudge's successor, Colby, undertook to survey the townlands in a matter of seven or eight years, provided that their boundaries were pointed out to him by the Irish Government. The next step, which Spring Rice took on the last day of the hearing, was to counter Wellington's opposition by getting eight members of the Committee to testify individually in favour of an Ordnance townland map. The Duke was won over, but some senior army officers continued to distinguish in their own minds between the military part of the forthcoming survey and the unfamiliar new task which the Dublin Government had contrived to impose on them.

Maps and surveys cannot easily be considered apart, and although Spring Rice's terms of reference made no mention of cartography as such, it is nevertheless surprising that the Committee did not say more about the contents and character of the proposed map. Its timidity almost gives the impression of an understanding whereby Wellington agreed to measure the townlands provided that the Irish members agreed not to meddle too deeply in any other aspect of the matter. There was certainly no 'battle of the scales' in 1824. Colby's cadets were already drawing practice maps at six inches to one mile (a scale that the Ordnance had previously made use of in several parts of England), and this was the scale he recommended for Ireland. As it happened, the closely similar ratio of one inch to forty plantation perches (1:10 080) had long been favoured for Irish official surveys and property maps, but this near-coincidence seems to have arisen by chance and in any case six inches would probably have been regarded as too small for general estate use by a majority of early-nineteenth-century surveyors; too small for valuation purposes as well, according to more than one of the Committee's Irish witnesses. The Committee sided with Colby, however, though it added that he might need to double his scale in mapping urban areas.

It also shared Colby's opinion that field boundaries should be omitted as an extravagance. Shaw Mason with his 'common-place book' was evidently in a minority: the Spring Rice report made some token references to the value of a six-inch map for statistical and estate purposes, but both inside and outside the committee room the map was commonly envisaged either as a content (i.e. boundary) plot for townland areas, in which case the fields were irrelevant, or as a model for one-inch draughtsmen and engravers, in which case there would be no room for them. The only other concrete suggestions proposed in the report (that the edge of cultivation and the heights of the principal mountains should be shown on the maps) were as applicable to the small scale as to the large, and it was the small scale that the Committee proposed to have engraved. As a map in its own right, then, the six-inch had failed to capture the official imagination. However, the report left Colby plenty of scope by urging that the survey should not only achieve its specific military and civil aims but also do credit to the 'scientific acquirements of the present age'.

The Committee had been quick to reach its decision and the Board of Ordnance was even quicker. On 22 June 1824, the day after the Spring Rice report was signed, the Board's secretary gave Colby the following order:

> The report of the Committee of the House of Commons on the survey of Ireland having been made to the House, and the Master General having consented that such survey shall be made by this department, I am directed to acquaint you, that the Board think it right to make the earliest communication to you and to desire that you will immediately take the necessary steps by providing instruments and making the proper additions to the persons employed under your direction so that the work may be proceeded with without a moment's delay. And I am to add that the Master General and Board are prepared to receive from you any proposition you may be desirous of submitting to them for proceeding upon the survey.

Though worth quoting as the foundation for all that was to follow, this order conveyed little except a sense of urgency. Its opening clause could be, and was, interpreted as an endorsement of the Select Committee's report in minor matters as well as in principle, but the report itself had been vague at many points, especially as regards the allocation of detail between the large-scale valuation map and the small-scale military map that was to be derived from it. The last word on this subject was Wellington's. 'The map must be drawn and filled up on the scale of six inches to a mile', he announced on 29 October. 'It can be reduced afterwards to any scale that may be thought expedient, and may be engraved on such scale, or on the original scale of six inches. But the record must be complete on that scale'.[13]

So far as the Board of Ordnance was concerned, Colby was now free to go ahead. Unlike the survey in Britain, operations in Ireland were governed by specific Acts of Parliament as well as by the decisions of the executive, but these Acts, like the directions he received from the Board, did little to restrict the Superintendent's freedom. It had been generally agreed throughout that measurement and valuation were two distinct processes and that the latter, like the demarcation of the townlands, should be directed by the authorities in Dublin. Accordingly there was one Act (6 Geo IV, c. 99) providing that the boundaries of counties, baronies, parishes and townlands should be delimited separately but in association with the Ordnance Survey; and another (7 Geo IV, c. 62) directing that the Lord Lieutenant's valuators should be supplied with the necessary Ordnance maps. The boundary survey and valuation were both entrusted to Richard Griffith, a civil engineer and geologist who had made his name in the bog surveys of 1810–14. From his position at the head of these twin departments, which he was to occupy for forty-three years, Griffith exerted more influence on the Irish survey than any other civilian.

The Military System 1825–8

Colby's first needs were men and materials. He was given the power to appoint and dismiss his own staff and in the course of 1825 and 1826 Wellington's initial force of twenty cadets was enlarged, and to some extent replaced, by successive intakes from the Royal Engineers together with a few officers from the Royal Artillery.[14] Several of them had already worked on the British survey (notably Lieutenants T. Drummond, R. K. Dawson and J. E. Portlock) but the majority were freshly commissioned and although they had undergone a course in surveying as part of their military education it was recognized that the early proceedings in Ireland would be to some degree instructional and probationary. Even Colby's second-in-command, Major William Reid, though distinguished both in battle and in administration, lacked previous experience of the department.

In his evidence to the Spring Rice Committee Colby had proposed that each officer should be supported by a subordinate staff. It was not until later in the year, however, that he decided (apparently at Reid's suggestion[15]) to use the Corps of Royal Sappers and Miners for this purpose. Draughtsmen and engravers, when the time came to employ them, would have to be recruited from the commercial map and print trades, but in the case of field-work it was hoped that soldiers would prove not only cheaper than civilian practitioners but also easier to instruct in a new and uniform system. The sappers were given some preliminary training at Chatham and the first detachments were sent to Ireland in the course of 1825.* To secure the goodwill of the local population, it was agreed with the Irish Government that the sappers would not be used as a police force in cases of civil disturbance.[16] The same conciliatory motive, coupled with the low wage-level prevailing in Ireland, induced the Ordnance to engage a number of country labourers to assist the military surveyors. From these various sources the Survey was built up, in a matter of months, to a strength unheard of in Mudge's day.

NUMBERS EMPLOYED IN THE SURVEY OF IRELAND

	Officers and cadets	Other ranks	Civilian assistants	Labourers
31 December 1825	35	87	0	53
31 December 1826	36	132	43	133
31 December 1827	39	224	98	303

In equipping himself with instruments, also, Colby was more fortunate than might have been expected. On learning of his new appointment, he had at once made enquiries among all the principal instrument-makers in London without finding a single theodolite in a finished state. And although the leading manufacturer, William Simms, turned over his whole establishment to supplying the wants of the Irish survey, it took some time to relieve the shortage and this may have been one factor that led Colby to a method of content surveying which depended as much as possible on the chain. By 1829, however, he was in possession of 164 theodolites (5 twelve-inch, 5 eight-inch, 17 seven-inch and 137 five-inch) together with no less than 576 sets of chains and arrows.[17]

Having grappled with the problems of organization and logistics, Colby had to divide his own attention between the mathematical groundwork of the survey and the detail. At this point an awkward dilemma presented itself. The trigonometrical operations obviously called for close supervision, for everything else depended on them, but it was in the new and unaccustomed business of content surveying that the worst growing-pains could be expected. What tilted the balance was that in this case the geodetic foundations were to be laid partly by new methods and mostly (as it happened) by new personnel. For the first three years, then, the management of the detail parties had to be left to Reid, and Colby spent relatively little time at the Survey's new headquarters at Mountjoy House in Phoenix Park just outside Dublin.

It was in the north of Ireland, in any case, that both triangulation and detail survey were inaugurated, for it was there that the former could most easily be carried across from Britain. A number of Ulster hill-tops had already been observed from stations in Scotland, so that it was possible to begin computing all-Irish trigonometrical distances without waiting to measure a new base line. The Irish observations began with Ramsden's three-foot 'Board of Ordnance' theodolite on Divis mountain, county Antrim, in July 1825. Methodologically, as well as geometrically, they were a continuation of what had been done in Britain, but there were new officers to be instructed, and much time was also lost through poor visibility. It was in solving the latter problem that Drummond made history on 9 and 10 November by effecting the 66-mile connection from Divis to Slieve Snaght, county Donegal, first with his newly-invented limelight, and then with his improved solar reflector or heliostat.[18] By that time, no less than two hundred objects had been observed from Divis and although only one Irish station had been visited with the great instrument, a trigonometrical skeleton was now available for one-seventh of the island. The next summer followed a similar course with Colby and his party encamped on the slopes of Slieve Donard in the Mourne Mountains, but this second season brought the instructional phase of the triangulation to an end and the rest of it was now entrusted to Portlock, who visited seven more mountain tops in the course of 1827 and completed the primary network at Feaghmaan, county Kerry, in August 1832.[19] Though physically arduous, his task had presented less difficulty than might have been feared. Mountains are well distributed through Ireland, and although some of the rays across the midlands were very long (too long by later standards) the limelight and heliostat were not, as it turned out, very often required. The main problem was persuading the local people not to remove the trigonometrical poles before they had been observed.

Although there was not time to adjust the primary triangulation before issuing distances to the

* The 13th and 14th Companies of the Royal Sappers and Miners, followed by the 16th Company in 1826.

detail parties, Colby was determined to conduct the whole operation on the highest scientific plane and already in 1824 he had chosen the site for an Irish base of verification.[20] The line selected, on the plain of Magilligan near Lough Foyle in county Londonderry, lay conveniently close to the sea, both vertically and horizontally, and far enough north to be quickly tied into the Hiberno-Scottish triangulation. Progress was held up, however, by the need to make a preliminary survey of the ground and even more by the problems of designing a suitable measuring apparatus. Colby hoped to avoid some of the uncertainties, arising from variations in the temperature and tension of chains, to which base measurement had been subject in the past. In the close seasons of 1825–6 and 1826–7 he had several officers working on a series of experiments at Drummond's London quarters in Furnivalls Inn and at the Tower.[21] One possibility was to measure the base with strips of mica, a non-expanding medium but not easy to keep rigid; another (not investigated in detail on this occasion) was to use parallel bars of different metals connected at one end so that the distance between the other ends would record the temperature of the apparatus – to measure the base with a large thermometer in fact. Both these ideas were suggested by Drummond, but it was Colby himself who hit on the notion of compensation, as used in the manufacture of balances and pendulums, whereby different rates of expansion could be made to cancel each other out. His apparatus consisted of two bars, one of brass and one of iron, joined rigidly in the middle and connected across the ends by steel tongues which were free to move to and fro as the iron and brass responded to changes in temperature.[22] Six sets of bars were made under Drummond's direction by Troughton and Simms (Plate 9).

The Lough Foyle Base was measured in a total of sixty working days in September and October 1827 and between July and November in the following year. As a check, certain doubtful sections (notably the crossing of the River Roe) were repeated, and there was also a side triangulation in which each part of the line could be used to test the remainder. To round off the work permanent marks were set up at each terminal on land purchased by the Government. In 1828–9 these points were connected with the primary triangulation and thenceforth Lough Foyle was the source of every trigonometrical distance in Ireland. When Lough Foyle was remeasured by Tellurometer in 1960 the result was only one inch different from the length recorded by the bars.[23] The events of 1827–8 may therefore be regarded as one of Colby's greatest triumphs.

While the base party was at work, the main force of the survey had been dispersed across the north of Ireland in five districts (reduced to four in 1829 and to three in 1832) which were scheduled to advance steadily southwards in line abreast until the whole country had been mapped. The first of Colby's annual reports described how each district captain was supplied with the results of the great triangulation which were then incorporated into a secondary network averaging two or three points in every parish. A district was composed of a number of divisions, each under a subaltern who made his own 'parish' observations (the word 'tertiary' was not used at this time) to fix points at a density of one or two per townland. The problem of co-ordinating these networks was not fully solved until 1832, when Portlock was able to transfer his attention from the primary triangulation to the secondary.[24]

To guide his officers through the novelties of the detail survey, in 1825 Colby worked out a special code of instructions that came to be known as 'the colonel's blue book'.[25] These were intended not as a comprehensive survey manual, but only as a guide to the differences between the new Irish operation and the routine military surveys in which his readers had already been instructed. The most important innovation was the content survey of the townlands. And the most original feature of Colby's system was the method by which, to avoid the distorting effects of expansion and contraction in the paper, parish and townland areas were to be computed as far as possible from ground distances reduced to the horizontal plane. This meant that the chained lines used in area measurement had to be arranged in triangles (fitting into the theodolite triangles against whose trigonometrical distances the longer chain lines could be checked), with paper computation* limited to small offset spaces. The term 'chain triangulation' was often applied by contemporaries to this method of surveying, although some of the smallest cells in the network were quadrilaterals rather than triangles. Since the chain was to be laid along the slope instead of being held level, it followed that vertical angles would have to be observed at intervals along the lines, an operation which, as Colby pointed out, would incidentally make it possible to provide the maps with spot heights.

The field books of content surveying and theodolite 'levelling', together with the 'registers' in which the results were calculated, formed the central components in an elaborate document-complex through which each part of the survey could be traced back to the man and the instrument responsible,[26] a system which, by means of detailed boundary records, Colby did his best to extend to

---

* Measurement on the map of the area plotted.

Griffith's department as well as his own. Much of the rest of the 'blue book' was devoted to points of scientific or utilitarian interest which might otherwise have been ignored as irrelevant to military surveying. Variant spellings of place-names were to be collected, along with 'a short description of the place and any remarkable circumstances relating to it', and each officer was to keep a journal of 'all the local information he can obtain relative to communications by land and water, manufactories, geology, antiquities or other matters connected with the survey'. Another sign of Colby's interest in transport facilities was his order that spot heights should include hill-tops, cols, lakes (bed as well as surface), rivers, canal locks, the summit levels of roads, and key points on possible future lines of communication.

Except where the measurement of area was involved, the blue book had little to say about actual surveying techniques. There was a clause providing that lines were to be related to trigonometrical points in such a manner as to prevent 'sensible' error, but it was not clear whether this should be read as an insistence on chain triangulation or merely as a prohibition of unadjusted traversing. Certainly an incidental reference to 'bearings' in an earlier clause had seemed to be compatible with the use of traverse surveys, and it is clear from the early records of the Mountjoy office that the surveying of 'contents' (the townland boundaries) and of 'roads' (the rest of the landscape) were treated in practice as two distinct operations, performed to a large extent by different men, noted down in different books and carried to different standards of accuracy.[27] However, Colby seemed to have made sufficient provision against looseness by demanding plans 'drawn with all the accuracy and minuteness of detail which [the six-inch] scale admits'; and against incompleteness by requiring the surveyors to show everything (except fences) 'attached to the ground'. The form of the ground itself was to be omitted until enough detail had been surveyed for specialist hill-sketchers to be put to work.

Printing these instructions gave them an air of completeness that was misleading. In fact they were issued in instalments over a period of several months and supplemented, in the course of the next two years by a number of important *addenda*. The use of the compass was forbidden in June 1825; offsets were ordered to be kept short in June 1827; boundaries common to two parish surveys were to be superimposed and assimilated from July 1827;[28] and at an early stage it was arranged for content registers to be calculated independently by two individuals, a task which was sometimes performed by country schoolmasters and others not regularly employed on the survey.[29] Another principle on which Colby laid great stress but which was not mentioned in the instructions was the division of labour. Valued at first as a means of training men more rapidly, it was seen soon afterwards to be important as a check on accuracy and by the third year of the survey there was a clear understanding that no content surveyor should be allowed to plot his own work.[30]

Colby in Trouble 1826–33

At first the progress of the detail survey seemed disappointingly slow. Some of the delay could be traced to the boundary department, for Griffith's team was not complete until early in 1826 and even then the Ordnance officers continued to complain about instances of unpunctuality and incompetence on the part of the boundary surveyors and the local residents who acted as meresmen. For his part, Griffith was impeded by contradictory information about townland geography and by the absence of recognized boundaries in many tracts of bog and mountain: like other surveyors before him, he found himself becoming a creator of new boundaries as well as a recorder of old ones.[31] But although his department was in good order by the second half of 1826, there was little sign of a proportionate improvement in the progress of the Ordnance parties.

Colby's confidence remained unshaken. Visiting the districts in October 1826 he remarked that since some plans were now nearly complete it was time to start looking out for civilian draughtsmen and engravers. He also arranged with Griffith and the Irish Chief Secretary that the maps should be engraved at full size from funds supplied by the Irish Government. This division of responsibility between Pall Mall and Dublin Castle arose from the fact that while a number of copies would be required for valuation and other local government purposes, the Ordnance would need no more than the single copy that its draughtsmen would be reducing to the military scale. The agreement was not without its inauspicious overtones, but in the long run the interests of cartography were well served by giving the Irish administration a direct voice in the fortunes of the six-inch map.

For Colby's critics, of whom his own deputy was beginning to emerge as the chief, the decision to recruit civilians had a different and more immediate significance. Having begun as an advocate of the military system, Reid now wished to save time by drawing on ready-trained personnel for field work as well as for office work. As soon as the need for draughtsmen had been mentioned he seized the opportunity of advertising for surveyors too,[32] and by the end of the year Colby was surprised to find that he had forty-three civilian assistants on the Survey's books. But although the measure was contrary to his intentions and was taken without his knowledge he agreed to retain the newcomers provided that their work was supervised as strictly as possible. Thus originated the combination of sappers and civilians that was to characterize the Ordnance Survey's staff structure for many years to come. By the late 1830s civilian assistants, many of them recruited in Ireland, were to outnumber the sappers by more than four to one.

Reid was still not satisfied. Two years had gone by with only one per cent of the country on the map, and there were complaints, from inside the department as well as outside, that at the current rate the survey would last another ninety-nine years. Such calculations were patently misleading, for some causes of delay, such as inexperience, could be expected soon to disappear. Nevertheless many of the Survey's own officers, including Drummond, had come to regard the methods of the blue book as by their nature unnecessarily slow and cumbersome.[33] The arithmetic involved in the content register, particularly, was so laborious that errors were almost unavoidable. Assembling evidence to this effect, Reid appealed over Colby's head to the Irish Government and by March 1828 his views had acquired enough momentum to reach the ears of Wellington, who had recently become Prime Minister. Colby defended himself with vigour and, for the time being, with success.[34] The most he would admit was that the system of a Dublin deputy had been a failure, and accordingly in May he arranged for Reid to be returned to the general duties of the Corps and prepared to manage the Irish survey himself.[35] Reid's successor at Mountjoy was not a major but a lieutenant, Thomas Larcom, and instead of deputizing for Colby he was confined to the relatively minor and peripheral task (as it must have seemed) of supervising the work of the engravers.

The Board of Ordnance was not prepared to leave the matter there, however, and in the summer of 1828 a senior Engineer officer, Major-General Sir James Carmichael-Smyth, was sent to enquire into the rumours that Colby's system was causing undue delay and expense.[36] His other commission, which was to assess the relative value of the work done by sappers and civilians, suggests that the six-inch map was still an object of suspicion in military circles; as Wellington's cartographer at Waterloo, Carmichael-Smyth could certainly be expected to see matters in a military light. After several weeks spent interviewing officers, inspecting documents and visiting field parties, he brought back a verdict that was unfavourable both to chain triangulation and to the content register. The former was unnecessarily laborious and should give way, by degrees and at the discretion of the district officers, to traversing. The register was nearly three times as expensive as paper computing and took nearly four times as long, and although he was willing for the registering of large triangles to continue as a check on parish areas, Carmichael-Smyth endorsed Reid's statement that the system had not succeeded in preventing errors, some of them distressingly large. He also recommended that the six-inch plans be lithographed instead of engraved, that a start should be made with the hill-sketching of Ireland, and that the proportion of sappers on the detail survey should be reduced. In short, Carmichael-Smyth was anxious to diminish his department's concern with those aspects of the survey that seemed to be of purely local and civil application. One such aspect, evidently, was the style and content of the six-inch maps themselves: it was a subject touched on only once in the forty-one pages of his report with the dismissive phrase, 'merely skeleton maps'.

As a sequel to the enquiry, Colby found himself for the first time receiving orders and counter-orders on matters of technical detail. To begin with, he was directed to compute townland areas from paper instead of by registry, but he opposed this practice so vigorously that a new departmental committee, under Sir Alexander Bryce, was appointed in May 1829 to reconsider this and other outstanding questions connected with the Irish survey. The Committee recommended that the Superintendent of the Survey should submit quarterly reports to, and take his orders from, the Inspector-General of Fortifications; that he should work to an accuracy of 1 in 150 (1 in 300 for more valuable ground); that he was to begin sketching the hills; and that he was to spend at least nine months of each year in Ireland. But at least the Committee gave Colby his own way in the matter of area measurement, and as his officers gained more experience of laying out lines, complaints of slowness and inaccuracy rapidly diminished.

The threat to engraving was also beaten off. And it is in the earliest engravings, of county Londonderry, that an otherwise unrecorded by-product of the Carmichael-Smyth investigation can be seen. The north of the county, completed in the early part of 1828, was laid out in parishes or groups of townlands with no regular arrangement of sheet-lines; the southern and later half is laid out in non-overlapping rectangles filled up to the margins in the familiar modern fashion.[37] As Colby pointed out, the latter system was a way of saving copper;[38] it would also provide future hill-sketchers with base maps that depicted continuous blocks of country. Whichever reason was the more important, the six-inch had been promoted from a parish map to a county map.

The parishes were combined by choosing a centrally-placed trigonometrical point (not necessarily a primary or even a secondary station) as county origin* and by arranging the sheet-lines parallel and perpendicular to the meridian of this origin in rectangles equivalent to 32 000 feet by 21 000 feet – these being the ground distances, in round numbers of feet, that allowed the closest approximation to a sheet size of 36 inches by 24 inches. From the county origin the remaining trigonometrical points were recalculated as plane rectangular co-ordinates and their sheet-line distances laid off on the copper by a special measuring device, after which the detail could be fitted onto the plates one triangle at a time. This method of actually constructing a map on the engraver's platform instead of simply giving him a finished manuscript model is said to have been Colby's own invention.[40] No latitudes and longitudes were engraved in the margins of the maps, and the geographical co-ordinates of the sheet corners were not published. There is no contemporary record to show whether the separate county meridians were adopted to reduce distortion or whether they were simply a way of detaching the urgent matter of publication from the more leisurely business of perfecting the triangulation.

By the spring of 1830 the department seemed to have recovered from the Carmichael-Smyth crisis and to be advancing more rapidly than ever before. Nearly six million acres (out of about twenty million) had been surveyed and one whole county engraved. It was time for Griffith's valuators to take the field. Their orders were to define small soil regions by digging up samples and to sketch the boundaries of these regions by interpolation from the printed detail of the Ordnance map. The results were disquieting. While the townland boundaries and acreages were comparatively good, many buildings, road and streams proved to have been omitted or misplaced.[41] Whether, without prior notice of Griffith's system, the maps could have been expected to satisfy him in matters other than townland boundaries was to become a hotly disputed question. But one thing was beyond dispute: the Londonderry maps must be withheld from the public and the bulk of the field force brought back from the midlands to the north of Ireland to bring these and other not-yet-published maps up to standard. The blue book was amended by an order that the edge of cultivation should be surveyed (a point on which Griffith laid special emphasis) but the other criticisms, as Colby indicated, could be met by proper attention to his original orders. Some of the plans were revised, others resurveyed. In the course of the latter process it became customary to use the same network of chained lines for road and content surveys and to enter them in the same book. Here was an important step in the integration of the six-inch map, and an element in the Survey's nineteenth-century methods and processes that was at least as important as the instructions of 1825: yet it never seems to have been the subject of an explicit order.[42] At about the same time, in June 1831, the role of traversing was redefined: it could be used 'within proper limits and under proper instructions . . . where it is most advantageous to apply it and in particular cases'.[43] No doubt improvements in the technique of field exam-ination were introduced at the same time, but this aspect of the survey's history appears to be undocumented.

The years 1830–33 were the blackest in the history of the Irish survey. They revealed a failure of communication not only between Colby and Griffith, but between Colby and his own officers, and they exposed a certain vagueness in the concept of accuracy, the accuracy of the military surveyor being evidently different from that of the estate surveyor and land valuer. Whoever was to blame, there was no escaping the fact that the Survey was entering its ninth year in Ireland with not a single finished map to show for the £290 000 already laid out. Before the original estimate of £300 000 was exceeded, the Treasury insisted on a new investigation and another Ordnance committee (of which Colby himself was a member) was appointed in the summer of 1833.[44] Griffith's requirements were now defined in full, apparently for the first time. They included the edge of cultivation with the positions of buildings and carriage roads on the six-inch scale, together with plans of principal towns at five feet to one mile instead of the twelve-inch and twenty-four-inch scales that the Survey had previously been supplying for urban areas. The committee could find no fault with these demands. On the question of delay and expense, it refused to blame the Survey for not anticipating the number and intricacy of the boundaries to be mapped, or the amount of interior detail needed for pur-poses of valuation. Colby thus escaped censure. His technical knowledge, his organizing ability, and now his unique (if bitter) experience of surveying townlands in the mass, had made him in-dispensable.

---

* Only 5 of the 32 county origins were points of the primary triangulation.[39]

Colby Triumphant 1833 – 46

By 1833, in any case, the Survey had turned the corner. Londonderry was published in May of that year, two more counties in 1834 and another two in 1835 – a considerably faster rate of progress than the recent committee had ventured to predict. Four years later the Irish branch reached its all-time maximum strength of more than two thousand persons,[45] of whom only twenty-two were officers: Colby had rightly forecast that his parties would eventually need less supervision. Later, both staff and progress diminished as men were attracted away by the high wages paid in English tithe surveys or were withdrawn by the Ordnance Survey itself to take up the new six-inch map of northern England.[46] But by 1846, and at a total cost of about £820 000,[47] all thirty-two counties were in print and more than one hundred and twenty towns had been drawn in manuscript.[48]

This time nothing had gone wrong. Roads, houses, acreages, and boundaries passed the scrutiny of the valuators; and on the coast, triangulation and detail alike proved generally acceptable to the Admiralty surveyors who were active in Irish waters throughout the period of the survey and for some years afterwards. The methods followed by the detail parties seem to have remained basically the same from 1833 to 1846: it is not until the 1850s that the Irish records begin to mention such later features of the Ordnance Survey system as the practice of horizontal chaining, the insistence on a linear accuracy of 1 in 500, and the limiting of offsets to 100 links. But there were a number of changes on the face of the maps themselves as they evolved from the skeleton survey of Carmichael-Smyth's day to what Larcom described as a 'full-face portrait of the land'.

Besides the names, acreages and boundaries of townlands, parishes and baronies, the early maps showed water, houses, roads, several forms of land cover (notably bog, moorland, marsh and wood), and a variety of small names and descriptions. Among the first additional items were the demesnes adjoining gentlemen's country houses. To begin with, these had been ignored unless they happened to coincide with townlands, but in April 1834 it was decided to include them as 'matters of topographical information,[49] their boundaries being defined on the authority of the owner or his agent. The history of ordinary enclosures was more complex. Many of the manuscript parish plans of 1833 and 1834 are peppered with short pen strokes showing where unmapped fences crossed the line of the chain or joined the roads, streams and townland boundaries. These intersections were later said to have been shown at the request of the valuators, but since they were not all engraved it seems more likely that they were intended as an aid to the Survey's own examiners in identifying detail.[50] The next step, the representation of entire fields, appears to have been taken in county Monaghan by Lieutenant John Chaytor. On 27 October 1835 Chaytor's district officer sought positive instructions in view of the fact that the maps drawn in his district were now showing field boundaries while those of the neighbouring district were leaving them off. (The boundary of the two districts can be clearly seen in sheet 19 of county Monaghan.) (Plate 6.) Colby agreed that the 'leading fences' should be mapped, but it took some time before this order was understood to include the whole fieldscape, and the northern maps – where fences were generally omitted – are separated from the southern – where all were shown – by a transitional area in the north midlands where the record was incomplete.[51] In this episode, increased confidence was carrying the Survey ahead of the valuation department: six months after Colby's 'leading fences' order, Griffith was telling a Parliamentary committee that fields were of no use to him.[52] It was only after 1838, when the Irish Government decided to arrange the new poor-law valuation by tenements instead of by townlands, that he was led to alter his opinion on this point.[53] In some of the midland and southern maps the fences appear to have been added by the examiners;[54] in others the junctions were fixed by offsets. In neither case did they add appreciably to the cost of the work, despite the forebodings expressed in 1824. There was some criticism of their accuracy from the Survey's private competitors, but this was more applicable to enlarged versions of the Ordnance map than to the six-inch scale itself.[55]

Similar advances took place in the representation of relief and altitude. The great majority of the early heights were fixed by vertical angles, and discrepancies of up to 12 feet had to be dealt with when the trigonometrical department began in 1832 to compare the different values given by neighbouring districts to the same point.[56] Portlock's solution was to connect and stiffen the district networks by selecting a line of trigonometrical stations running all the way across the country from east to west, linking them by vertical angles observed with the large theodolite, connecting them with the sea at either end, and distributing the apparent difference of sea-level through the line. He began to run a series of such lines across the country and from this skeleton to carry the heights down to the corners of the smallest theodolite triangles. But before this programme was finished, the feasibility and superior accuracy of long-distance spirit-levelling had been brought to the notice of surveyors by the British

Association's Axmouth–Portishead experiment of 1837–8. It was accordingly decided to adopt the same system for Ireland and in 1839–43 more than 2000 miles of altitudes were levelled along main roads under the direction first of Lieutenant G. B. Downes and later of Lieutenant John Cameron. The levelling lines were chained and the level set up half-way between the forward and back staves. Each line was levelled in both directions, the greatest difference between the forward and back levelling being 1.629 feet on the 158-mile line from Dublin to Cashla Bay. The adjustment of the levelling was primarily aimed at achieving internal consistency; on each of the twenty-six lines the mean of the forward and back levellings was taken and the results on four lines (Dublin–Cashla Bay, Dublin–Kilbaha Bay, Dublin–Belfast, Ballinasloe–Old Head-Clew Bay) were accepted. The heights of thirteen junction points along these four lines were obtained and the remaining lines were then adjusted to these heights so that all were brought into sympathy. In Clare, Limerick, Tipperary, Cork, Kerry and Waterford, the heights published on the maps were those of the new levelling. Elsewhere Downes and Cameron had come too late, though the altitudes and descriptions of their bench-marks* were subsequently added to the plates.[57]

Besides the inherent uncertainty of vertical angles, one weakness in the original system of altitudes was the use of a number of different datum points. Removing the first of these sources of error made it desirable to tackle the second. The obvious solution was to define or redefine all Irish heights in terms of the datum adopted for Dublin, namely low-water of spring-tides as observed at Poolbeg Lighthouse on 8 April 1837. But the scientific interest now attaching to tidal phenomena made Colby dissatisfied with this expedient, and in 1842 he collaborated with the Astronomer Royal, G. B. Airy, in connecting the Irish levels with a three-months series of tidal observations at twenty-two points around the coast.[58] Low spring-tide levels were found to vary by as much as 9 feet from one station to another; mean sea-level (which Airy's researches placed about 8 feet above the Dublin datum) by some $2\frac{1}{2}$ feet. Hitherto, low water had been favoured as the most useful base level for engineering purposes; but mean sea-level, it now appeared, would keep local anomalies to a minimum as well as being a more logical interpretation of the term 'sea-level'. Against the advice of more than one of his officers Colby decided to put principle before expediency and alter the Irish datum,[59] though he did not attempt to change the thousands of low-water-based altitudes already engraved.

Except for a few small areas of special interest, like the sites of major antiquities, there was no hachuring on the published six-inch maps. The sketching of the hills, begun in 1829 under the direction of Lieutenant R. K. Dawson (son of the Survey's leading instructor in this art), was intended for the military map and carried out on manuscript one-inch reductions by a staff of civil assistants working independently of the six-inch survey districts.[60] Dawson's men sketched by horizontal lines in the manner of rough contours, and contours were also implicit in his practice of shading higher ground, irrespective of slope, with thicker lines than lower ground. But the idea of adding numbered contours to the six-inch map seems to have originated with Larcom, and to have been inspired by the efforts of a Parliamentary commission in 1836–7 to use the maps for planning an Irish railway system.[61] It would have been difficult to change the practice of the hill department at this time for Dawson had been detached, in 1835, for special duty in England (he was in any case opposed to the use of contours unsupported by hill-sketching) and active experimentation with instrumental methods of contouring did not begin until he had relinquished the department to another officer in 1838. The first contours,[62] surveyed in the Inishowen peninsula of Donegal in 1839–40, were well received both by Colby and by the Ordnance, and specimens were sent to Chatham for use in instructing engineer cadets.[63] The next problem was to fit contouring into the routine of the survey. The hill force was moved from Inishowen first to Louth and then to Kilkenny (where it was hoped that contours would throw light on the geological structure of the Castlecomer coalfield) but it proved impossible to publish a contoured first edition of any Irish county.[64]

Two main functions were envisaged for contours at this period. They would provide the hill-sketcher with useful guidelines and from the start it was customary to begin the sketching process by interpolating non-instrumental contours between the measured altitudes. But the contour line itself was intended for engineering purposes rather than as a substitute for shading and it was in this utilitarian spirit that vertical intervals were made smaller on lower and more valuable ground, though Colby recognized that the chance of mineral discoveries at high altitudes made it undesirable to be too rigid about vertical intervals.[65]

* Bench marks are permanent marks provided at intervals of one-third of a mile or less along a line of levelling. They are cut on vertical surfaces at about knee height usually in durable material such as stone. An incised horizontal bar defines the level to which the height is referred and a broad arrow is positioned immediately below the bar; the whole mark occupies a space of about 4 inches square. The name derives from the angle iron which is fitted into the horizontal cut to give a 'bench' or support for a levelling staff.

Toponymy was another subject on which Larcom made a considerable impact. The townland names of Ireland were settled by Griffith's boundary department, but the Survey was free to choose its own orthography and Colby had begun by adopting whatever spelling appeared to be the most generally accepted. This method had its disadvantages in the case of a Celtic nomenclature that had been corrupted by English-speaking settlers over a period of several centuries, and when in 1830 orthography was transferred from the districts to headquarters, Larcom introduced a new system which, although rational and well-intentioned, has been bitterly criticized (and completely misunderstood) by a number of later Irish writers. In the first place it was not Larcom's policy to invent a new nomenclature for Ireland: his names are similar in general character, and often in exact spelling, to those found in most Anglo-Irish maps of the eighteenth and early nineteenth centuries. It is true that by adding a number of Irish scholars, including the talented John O'Donovan, to the Survey's Dublin staff, he made a serious attempt to recover the original Irish descriptive terms and personal names from which the modern place-names had evolved; but there was never any question of publishing these on the Survey's maps. Before the Gaelic revival of the later nineteenth century an Irish-language Ordnance Survey map would have been unwelcome and incomprehensible to most of the Department's clientele, as well as diminishing the utility of the maps for legal and administrative purposes. And latter-day Irish place-name scholars, however gratified by any such endeavour to anticipate the cultural preferences of their own age, would probably disagree with many of the interpretations of individual names put forward in the 1830s.

What Larcom sought to do, with the help of O'Donovan,[66] was to collect existing versions of each name from a wide range of authorities and then to publish the one that seemed to come nearest to the presumed original Irish form.[67] Though successfully pursued in a large number of cases this principle had to be modified in two important ways. Firstly, it seemed advisable to standardize the spellings of a number of recurrent prefixes and suffixes such as Drum, Drim or Drom (a ridge: now generally Drum) and Derry or Dirry (an oakwood: now generally Derry). Secondly and more controversially, where there was no current spelling that brought out the true meaning, Larcom often felt obliged to adopt a new one. In any nation with a more compliant attitude to authority than the Irish, a government might well expect the orthography published on its official maps to become generally accepted. But where the spellings of the Ordnance Survey of Ireland differed from common early-nineteenth-century usage, they have often failed to win the favour of the twentieth-century public or even of other government departments like the Post Office. Among the resulting anomalies are Ballynacorra, Cahir, Monasterevin and Skull (Ordnance Survey spellings) as compared with Ballinacurra, Caher, Monasterevan and Schull (normal Irish usage). Because of the special status of townlands under the Boundary Act of 1826 the Survey was unable to change the names of these divisions, and it remained unwilling to do so even when such changes had been authorized, under certain conditions, by another Act of Parliament (22, 23 Vic., c. 8).

Demesne names presented less difficulty, for the landowner's decision was accepted as final even where he differed from all the Survey's other authorities as to the spelling of a name which was common to his own demesne and one of the local townlands. Theoretically, physical and topographical nomenclature was treated in the same way as townlands, but the gathering speed of the detail survey after 1833 set strict limits to the amount of research that could be devoted to inessential names and there are considerable variations in density from one sheet to another. The same is true of descriptive captions, though public buildings, industrial premises and antiquities were usually well served in this respect and any local resident advocating the inclusion of some special feature would find his opinions treated with respect. Early in the progress of the survey a number of conventional signs were introduced – more successfully, perhaps, for types of land cover (e.g. bleach-greens and brick-fields) than for small objects like limekilns and forges, where their purpose was less to save space than to avoid the labour of writing.

The parish plans were drawn in the district offices and included certain features, like the attempt to distinguish between stone houses (carmine) and mud cabins (black), which do not appear on the engravings. When they arrived at Mountjoy, Larcom became responsible for a measure of editorial supervision of their contents, for transferring them to the plates, and for the processes of engraving, printing and publication.[68] By extending Colby's division of labour from field to office he made it possible for maps to be, in his own words, 'manufactured in large numbers rather than made as individual constructions', so that although each sheet took two or three months to pass through his hands, he was eventually able to issue them at the rate of two in three days. His engraving staff, which at one point numbered nearly sixty artists, was divided into separate branches for outline, writing and ornament. Its superintendent, James Duncan, must be credited with the remarkable balance between these three branches and with the qualities of lightness and delicacy that distinguished the Mountjoy work from his arrival in 1827 to his retirement thirty-nine years later. Although the maps continued to be described as the 'townland survey' of Ireland, the townlands were kept in subordination by using fine dots for their boundaries and open capitals – reduced in size after the first few sheets – for their names. At the same time some features of military interest such as woods and marshes, which are rather harshly emphasized on some of the earlier sheets, were toned down to match the bland and unaggressive ambience of the mature six-inch map. In the engraving room, as elsewhere, disparate strands were being woven into a single topographic concept.

As always, engraving was one of the slowest and most expensive stages in the map-making process. But Larcom's industrial revolution included mechanical aids as well as the division of labour and it is a tribute to Duncan and his staff that these novelties did nothing to impair the craftsmanlike appearance of their work. One of them was a waterlining device employed in 1835 to cope with the tortuous pattern of lakes and islands in county Fermanagh.[69] Other early innovations were a roller for impressing the bog characteristic on the plates, a spring punch for engraving hedgerow trees and a similar appliance for punching altitude figures. Most important, perhaps, was a ruling machine that showed demesnes and foreshores by fine dots and buildings by solid lines.[70] This device came into its own in 1840 when Larcom, apparently without pausing to get written authority from either the Ordnance or the Irish Government, took the opportunity to publish a heavily built-up specimen sheet of the Dublin five-foot plan.[71]

The punches and ruling machine were designed and constructed by the engraver William Dalgleish who followed them up in 1837–40 by perfecting a new method for duplicating the engraved copper plates from which the Survey's maps were printed.[72] Its principle was to deposit a layer of copper electrolytically onto an engraved plate. On this layer, known as the matrix, the incised detail of the original would stand out in relief, and a duplicate plate could then be formed by depositing another layer onto the matrix and so converting its raised lines into depressions. By this method, known as electrotyping, it became possible to reproduce for £5 a plate that might have cost as much as £100 to re-engrave, an important factor in prolonging the life of the copper-plate press into an era of cheaper reproductive techniques. One use of duplicate plates was as a base on which further information could be engraved without preventing the continued production of the maps in their unaltered form, as when the Inishowen contours were inserted on specially made duplicates of the six-inch map of Donegal. Electrotypes also offered a means of making corrections. The maps of county Dublin, engraved in 1837–8, had to be left unpublished for several years pending the alteration by Parliament of certain administrative boundaries, by which time the townscape had been altered too much for the Dublin city plates to be corrected by the normal method of 'hammering out'. The solution was to take a matrix, scrape off the unwanted detail, and make a new plate on which each scraped portion would present a blank surface ready for the engraver's additions. Here was a powerful new weapon in the map reviser's armoury.

After some costly experience of paying a contract printer at piece-work rates, Larcom brought the division of labour into another area by employing different workers for the inking and cleaning of the plate, the dampening of the paper, and the working of the press. He also arranged for superfluous ink to be removed from the plate by light wiping with an alkaline solution instead of by hard rubbing as in the past. Besides being quicker, this process helped the plates to withstand the printing of a large edition.

Editions were certainly larger than had been expected. By 1846 an average of sixty-one copies of each sheet (there were 1907 sheets for the whole of Ireland) had already been sold, a far cry from the eight copies thought to be sufficient twenty years earlier.[73] There were also sheet-line indexes, one for each county, generally on the half-inch scale, which had some claim to rank as topographical maps in their own right. Publication was entrusted to the Dublin bookselling partnership of John Hodges and George Smith at a retail price of five shillings per sheet with agent's allowance of thirty-three and one-third per cent. Through their advertisements and the efforts of their travelling representative, who claimed to have conducted a house-to-house canvas of all Ireland over a period of fifteen years, Hodges and Smith made a major contribution to the popularity of the maps.[74] Another factor was the generosity of the Irish Government, which by 1845 was presenting sets to seventy-seven libraries and government departments in Britain and Ireland.[75] Fortunately all the counties had been published before the authorities in London (having taken over the publication of the maps in 1846) made a drastic reduction in the number of complimentary copies.[76]

Although it ended tragically in famine, the period 1833–46 was marked by a closer and more constructive interest by both Parliament and executive in Ireland's social and economic problems.

The Ordnance maps reflected this trend and contributed to it, and as they improved in topographic coverage so their use went further beyond the need of valuation. New roads and, later, railways were laid out on them and they were extensively used in the drainage operations which were supported from public funds under an Act of 1842. They served as base maps for the Irish geological survey as well as for the abortive soil survey begun by the agricultural chemist Robert Kane.[77] The survey also played its part in the reform of Ireland's administrative geography. In addition to Griffith's pre-publication review of the boundaries of townlands, parishes and baronies, there were special maps of parliamentary borough boundaries in 1831–2 and of municipal boundaries in 1836 and again in 1841–3.[78] The maps also provided an opportunity for delimiting petty sessions districts and for a rational arrangement of the unions and electoral divisions created under the Irish Poor Relief Act of 1838.

Both before and after his departure from the Survey in 1846, Larcom took a prominent role in seeking new uses for the maps.[79] As one of the commissioners for taking the Irish census of 1841, he hoped to plot the population of each settlement on the six-inch scale. Given charge, six years later, of Ireland's first agricultural statistics, he began by proposing to collect his data in the form of a field-to-field land-use survey, and when in 1849 he was employed in the reform of poor-law divisions he caused the boundaries of every estate in Ireland to be added to a set of six-inch maps. Some of his ideas were premature, anticipating by almost a century what might be described as the essentially six-inch spirit of modern Irish geography as developed by twentieth-century scholars such as E. Estyn Evans and T. W. Freeman. But one thing was clear in 1846. Having begun with a narrower purpose than its English counterpart, the Irish survey had ended by being more widely known and more widely used. Ultimately, the credit for this achievement belongs to Colby. His liberal, open-ended interpretation of his task had led him into a new world of all-purpose cartography, and thanks to his good judgment of men and his willingness to delegate authority, that world had finally been conquered.

Geology and Statistics 1826–45

Maps were only part of the output of Mountjoy. In the first of his annual reports, Colby had written:

> In addition to the maps and plans themselves, a great variety of materials towards the formation of statistical and other reports will be collected whilst the work is in progress. The roads and the nature of the materials of which they are composed will be noted, as well as the bridges, fords, ferries and other circumstances which relate to that species of internal communication. The rivers, canals, aqueducts, wharfs, harbours, shipping places and other conveniences for the transport of goods will also be noted in the remark books. These books will also contain a great deal of information respecting the means of conveyance, state of agriculture and manufacture, and in short of almost everything that relates to the resources of the country. The general disposition of the minerals of the country is so important in every branch of political and domestic economy connected with its improvement that I have thought it right to direct a very particular attention to this subject. The outline plans of Ireland are the best bases ever given in any country for a geological and mineral survey and the Ordnance will, I hope, be able to accompany their map of Ireland with the most minute and accurate geological survey ever published.

It is not clear whether at this stage Colby intended to publish any of this non-cartographical information other than the geology, but he may already have thought of accompanying the maps with some kind of printed topographical dictionary or gazetteer. The earliest means of implementing these policies were the officers' journals and, more successfully, the name books. Next came a scheme devised by Captain J. Pringle in 1827 for collecting rock specimens, observing the dip of the strata and making a geological plan of each parish.[80] The necessary field-work was to be done by the divisional officers but the plan was vetoed by Carmichael-Smyth on the ground that they were insufficiently qualified in geology. It was revived during the brief period of optimism that preceded the valuation crisis[81] but real progress had to wait until 1833, when Portlock, a gifted geologist in his own right, was allowed to organize a department specially devoted to the subject.[82]

Meanwhile the field parties had been asked to compile 'statistical remarks' for every parish as it was surveyed, including its name, boundaries, extent, divisions, surface, soil, produce, turbaries, notable rocks and minerals, towns and villages, markets and manufactures, roads, rivers, bogs, woods, population and antiquities. It was not long before this framework was further elaborated by Larcom. On the one hand he grouped the subjects into broad categories such as 'natural state', 'ancient and modern topography', 'social economy' and 'productive economy'. At the same time he expanded each heading with a formidable list of suggestions that ran to thirty-seven pages. Colby's approach to 'statistics', which had been governed mainly by military and economic considerations, had now been widened to embrace a broad vista of scientific and scholarly enquiry, with an emphasis on social and administrative questions (illustrated by the following extract) which befitted his deputy's future career as Under-Secretary of Ireland, but which was not always very closely related to the business of topographical map-making.

> How many magistrates? stipendiary or otherwise? their residences? are they within convenient distances, firm, and respected by the people? the usual force of police, (revenue and constabulary;) if a military station, what is the general number of troops, and number of coast guards, if on the coast? are there any peculiar jurisdictions, as manor courts, courts leet, etc.? when and where are petty sessions held? what number of magistrates are generally in attendance? Note the number of outrages that have been committed with a recent date? have they increased? or are they decreasing? have the perpetrators been properly punished? have the outrages been committed with reference to agriculture? commerce? or manufactures? have they been resorted to by misguided persons to repress inventions, the use of machinery, or to keep others out of work? do any combinations exist to deprive workmen of the liberty of working as they please, and at any price? Is illicit distilling carried on? is it diminishing? any smuggling? what nature of goods? Are insurances of houses, furniture, manufactories, farm produce, etc. common? can they be easily effected? what insurance offices have insured the property generally? have the insurance offices paid the losses readily in cases of accident? or have they litigated cases, and protracted payment, so as to create distrust, and deter persons from insuring?

The collection of statistical remarks was never made compulsory, and the answers submitted by the Survey officers to Larcom's questionnaire varied in quantity and merit. One problem was that, as the detail survey became faster and more self-regulating after 1833, the time spent by each officer in any one parish was reduced. To fill the gap, Dawson's hill department began to devote part of its time to compiling a new series of parish memoirs. Their early efforts were poor, but by concentrating the work in the hands of the most able members of the team the standard was gradually raised until by the late thirties the hill men's essays were longer, more comprehensive, better illustrated (and, in general, more sympathetic towards Irish *mores*) than most of what had been produced by the Royal Engineers. This made it unnecessary for the latter to persist in memoir writing, and their statistical remarks are mainly confined to the counties of Antrim, Armagh, Donegal, Down, Fermanagh, Londonderry, Monaghan and Tyrone.[83]

Larcom seems to have made it his policy to draw every department of the Survey into the realm of science and statistics. The computing staff at Mountjoy conducted a series of meteorological observations (published in 1856), beginning with barometric pressure in 1829 and later extended to rainfall, temperature and relative humidity, which he saw as the forerunner of Irish weather stations.[84] Meanwhile, in pursuance of his plan for authenticating place-names, obsolete spellings had to be culled from historical documents and early literature, and in 1835 a new department was set up for this purpose at the Dublin home of its superintendent, the artist and antiquarian George Petrie.[85] This body, which included among others the Irish scholar Eugene O'Curry and the poet James Clarence Margan, was generally known as the Topographical Department. While Petrie's assistants were copying and abstracting documents, O'Donovan was in the country listening to the local pronunciations of the names and on the look-out for topographical and archaeological indications of their meanings. With Larcom's encouragement, his journeys evolved into what was virtually a one-man survey of Irish local history.[86] From field and bookshelf alike, then, orthography brought in a richer harvest of scholarship than could ever be displayed on the face of the maps themselves.

In 1833 Colby asked the Treasury to authorize the publication of this non-cartographic material at the rate of one moderately sized volume for each county, and the Chancellor (who happened to be Spring Rice) agreed to the printing of a single county as an experiment. This was the beginning of what was always described in Irish Ordnance Survey circles as 'the memoir'.[87] In the first volume, which was devoted to the parish of Templemore in county Londonderry, Larcom acted as editor and there were contributions by Dawson on natural features, topography and social economy, by Portlock on geology, natural history and productive economy, and by O'Donovan on place-names. But since the main feature of the parish was the large and abundantly documented city of Londonderry, it was Petrie's historical material that dominated the book to the point of imbalance. The Templemore memoir was printed in 1835 for distribution at the Dublin meeting of the British Association and published in an enlarged form two years later by Hodges and Smith.[88] The choice of location had not been calculated to quieten opposition on financial grounds: instead of £400–£500 for a whole county, as proposed in 1833, a single parish had cost no less than £1700. No-one questioned the accuracy and scholarship of the results, but many readers were startled to find them running to 350 pages. Among the latter was Spring Rice. Literary endeavours of this magnitude, the Chancellor sharply observed in April 1838, would not only divert the Survey officers from their proper duty of map-making but also bring the Government into competition with private scholars and involve its officials in the kind of party strife that seemed inseparable from Irish historical studies.[89] He ended his broadside by offering to consider a revised estimate for future memoirs, but his tone was so discouraging that Colby judged it better to wait until public opinion could be mobilized in favour of the scheme. The impression in Dublin was that the Chancellor had crushed the whole memoir, but one reason for Colby's hesitancy was a lack of enthusiasm on the part of the Irish Government, and particularly of his former subordinate Thomas Drummond, who was now serving as Under-Secretary.[90] For the time being, however, only the question of publication was involved; the hill and topographical departments continued their researches and Portlock his geological survey.

Up to now, the Survey, the Irish Government and the Treasury had been the chief participants in the memoir controversy. But whoever paid for printing and publication, it was the army who carried the responsibility for how its officers were employed and in 1840 the Inspector-General, Sir Frederick Mulcaster, complained that Colby's staff had been led into 'indefinite research of curiosity'. After much correspondence, the Survey was ordered in July to 'revert immediately to its original object under the valuation Acts': existing memoir material could be arranged, but no more collected or published. This prohibition was not taken to apply to Petrie, for his team was contributing directly to the place-names on the maps, but the hill department's memoirs were now brought to a halt with only the counties of Antrim, Armagh, Down, Londonderry, Monaghan and Tyrone at all adequately covered. Geology had some claims to recognition as a special case, more closely related to topographical surveying than were any of the other memoir subjects. This at any rate was Colby's own view, and he was backed by a private deputation which persuaded the Ordnance to publish as much of Portlock's work as had been finished. This appeared in 1843 under the title *Report on the geology of the county of Londonderry and of parts of Tyrone and Fermanagh*. It included a half-inch geological map, a review of the county's rock formations and a long descriptive list of its fossils, while the essentially geographical spirit of the memoir idea was conveyed in a section on soils, drainage and agriculture. Unfortunately its 784 pages had taken so long to write that Colby lost confidence in Portlock and on the eve of publication secured his removal from the Department. Like the Templemore memoir, the *Report* was in a sense too successful, for such massive volumes were hard to visualize as routine by-products of a topographical survey.[91]

Outside the name books (which survived to the end as a useful repository of local information) active statistical work had now officially ceased, though the Survey records include a certain amount of later material for the south of Ireland of whose history nothing appears to be known. Backed by the Royal Irish Academy, Larcom and his supporters fought hard to revive the original memoir concept, and finally induced Peel's Government to appoint a commission of enquiry on the subject.[92] With Larcom's ally, Lord Adare, taking a prominent part, this body recommended a modified memoir scheme, and its report provoked a remarkable display of enthusiasm from Dublin newspapers of every shade of political opinion.[93] In proposing to suppress the study of place-names, antiquities and local history, it was widely felt that Peel was making a deliberate assault on Irish national feeling. It was a reaction that brought the Department more publicity than perhaps it has ever received (or desired) on any other issue, British or Irish, and over a century later there were many Irishmen who saw the Survey's history in a wholly literary or antiquarian light, with O'Donovan (who left at about the time that the topographical department was broken up in 1842) taking the principal role as hero and victim. The picture of the Survey as a 'peripatetic university' painted in Mrs A. S. Green's book *Irish nationality* (1911) affords a stirring expression of this distorted view.

Peel turned the tables by offering to publish the memoirs if private individuals would also contribute to the cost.[94] One of his maxims about Ireland – to which the history of the Survey had itself borne testimony – was that 'everybody looks for everything to be done at the cost of the public in this country', so he was probably not surprised when no-one took up his offer. In the end, all that the Treasury agreed to was the continuation of the Ordnance geological survey, and even that was not for long.[95] Supported by the Master General, Peel decided that the geology of Ireland was a matter for full-time specialists, and in 1845 it was handed over to the Office of Woods and Forests to be conducted by Sir Henry De la Beche and a staff of civilians on the same footing as the geological survey of Great Britain.[96] The memoir material was transferred in due course to the Royal Irish Academy, where it became a major source for Irish local history; the geological and natural history collection went to the National Museum. All that remained to Mountjoy were the meteorological observations and the responsibility for engraving and printing the geological maps supplied by De la Beche. There was not even a topographical dictionary or published index of place-names, for the failure of the great memoir had made it seem impracticable to proceed with a smaller one. But the subject should not be dismissed without remembering how much subsequent research in Irish history, statistics and literature, whether by the Government or private individuals, can be traced to the inspiration of the Ordnance Survey.

The Aftermath 1842–7

As one county map followed another, control of the publication process began to emerge as the key position in the Irish Survey. After 1838, in particular, when the Ordnance relaxed its rule that Colby must spend three-quarters of his time in Ireland,[97] Larcom found himself acting as master of Mountjoy and especially of its relations with the Irish Government and public. The memoir was only one example of his efforts to draw the Survey out of the framework laid down in 1824, and to channel its growth to fit the cartographic needs of his adopted country. As long as these needs were changing and expanding (a process which was unlikely to be terminated by the publication of the six-inch or any other single map), he believed that Irishmen should have their own map-making service. For Larcom, English competence was the best cure for Irish indigence and he had no wish, except as a desperate last resort, to break the links between Mountjoy and Pall Mall. But with men supplied by the Ordnance and money by the Treasury, he felt well qualified to put the Irish Survey on its feet and keep it there.

Apart from instances already quoted, it was perhaps the 'Railway map' that best illustrated and justified this point of view. The Irish railway commission of 1836–8 was a fertile source of cartographical ideas, as might be expected from a body that included both Drummond and Griffith. Its seminal role in the adoption of contours and its contributions to statistical cartography (which, however, there is no direct evidence to link with the Survey or with Larcom) are well known.[98] It also provided the occasion for a masterpiece of eclecticism in the form of a quarter-inch hill map of Ireland in six sheets, with the triangulation and part of the detail supplied from the Ordnance Survey, the geology provided by Griffith, and the detail for the southern counties (not yet surveyed by the Ordnance) pieced together from earlier maps. The result, though compiled in some haste, displayed a staying power that was remarkable. The first edition of 1839 was followed in 1847 by an administrative edition printed from electrotypes, showing unions and electoral divisions, and in 1855 by a revised geological edition. There was also a special version overprinted with fishery districts and coastguard stations in 1863 and another supplied to a commission on Irish parliamentary boundaries in 1885. In an attempt to estimate the cost of contouring Ireland, Larcom caused the map to be roughly layer-coloured in manuscript; a copy of this relief map was printed at one inch to ten miles in the Devon report on the occupation of the land in Ireland (1845) and later placed on sale as a separate publication. All this was done at Mountjoy before the Survey had published a single map of England on the quarter-inch scale. But there was another and less happy touch of independence about the Railway map. It was signed by Larcom and Griffith with no mention of the Board of Ordnance or of the Survey and its Superintendent: since the map was partly derived from outside sources, Colby preferred not to give it the imprint of his Department.[99]

Here was the hint of a larger difference between master and pupil. Both Colby and Larcom saw the Irish survey as a work that went far beyond its military beginnings in the direction of science, scholarship and general utility. In one sense it was Colby who took the larger view, for in the forties he faced the task of restoring Britain to its proper place in the cartography of the United Kingdom while Larcom remained prone to interpret 'justice for Ireland' in the manner of his adopted countrymen. Within these limits, however, Larcom's was the broader approach – more creative and outward looking, if also less economical of government funds. But because the two men differed in age, health, and temperament, their divergencies of principle came to seem wider than they need have done.

For the time being, however, they were united in opposing the negative attitude to Mountjoy which prevailed in the office of the Inspector-General. Mulcaster's simplistic view was that the Survey had been sent to Ireland to measure the townlands and that when this task had been finished the Dublin office should be closed.[100] The first line of defence against this threat in the 1840s was to deny that the townland survey had been finished. It was true that the detail parties were completing their allotments in 1841–2 and that by the end of the latter year there was but one officer left in the districts. But only two county maps had been fully contoured and at least eight were inadequately provided with fences. Having welcomed contours when they were introduced, Mulcaster turned cooler in 1843 when they seemed to be promising to extend the life of the Irish survey, and his coolness was shared by the Treasury. Larcom's counter-attack was planned with care. He induced the Donegal Grand Jury to memorialize the Government on the value of contours in planning new roads;[101] he recommended them to the Cork meeting of the British Association, which duly passed on his recommendation to the

Government;[102] and he persuaded Peel's memoir commission to come out in favour of contouring, in spite of the fact that the subject had no obvious connection with its terms of reference. This was the kind of politicking that made Larcom unpopular with the military authorities, but he got his way in July 1844. A month earlier, thanks to representations from the Grand Juries of Londonderry and Antrim, the Government sanctioned the 'completion' of those northern maps that were without fences. Both contouring and revision were assigned to a new division under Lieutenant G. A. Leach.

With these concessions in their pockets, Colby and Larcom were in a strong position to oppose the threatened closure of Mountjoy. But there was more than one way of keeping Mountjoy open, and the two men finally parted company over a Treasury Minute of February 1846 which transferred the publication of the maps from the Irish Government to the Ordnance (in itself a reverse for Larcom) and ruled that the Dublin establishment should be 'carefully revised with reference to the duties which may for the future be expected from it and that every practicable reduction may be made in the expense.' As a basis for these economies, Colby directed that the greater part of the Mountjoy records should be sent to his new office at Southampton. It was an order that struck hard at Larcom's cherished autonomy. Supported by the Chief Secretary of Ireland, he declined to obey it, and on 4 May Colby relieved him of his appointment.[103] For the second time the affairs of the Irish survey were referred to the Prime Minister of the day, complicated this time by the fact that the Dublin superintendent was currently assisting the Irish administration with its famine relief programme. Peel condemned Colby's action,[104] and is said to have been on the point of transferring Mountjoy from the Ordnance to the Irish Board of Works when his Government was overthrown by the corn-law crisis.[105]

A large quantity of Irish records duly went to Southampton, where all trace of them was lost. Within a year Colby himself had retired. Under his successors the Dublin office continued to print and publish most of its own maps, and to look after its own records. Larcom, like Drummond, took high office in the Irish Government. The role of Mountjoy thereafter was more submissive but not so interesting.

Notes

1 *Reports of the commissioners appointed to enquire into the nature and extent of the several bogs in Ireland, and the practicability of draining and cultivating them.* PP 1810 (365) X, 389; 1810–11 (96) VI, 579; 1813–14 (130, 131) VI, 1, 167.

2 E. M. Rodger, *The Large Scale County Maps of the British Isles, 1596–1850*, second edition (1972), pp. 40–5.

3 *Report from the Select Committee appointed to consider the best mode of apportioning more equally the local burthens collected in Ireland, and to provide for a general survey and valuation of that part of the United Kingdom.* PP 1824 (445) VIII, pp. 35–7: J. W. Croker's evidence. Original sources in PRO IND 4964 and Adm. 1/634 (1822), IND 4970 (1823).

4 The chief source for this section is the *Report*, minutes and appendices of the Select Committee on the survey and valuation of Ireland, 1824.

5 *Second Report from the Select Committee [on] regulating the Grand Jury presentments of Ireland*, PP 1816 (435) IX, p. 2.

6 *Hansard* XL 1st Series, cols. 804–6.

7 Brown to H. Goulburn, 26 June 1822: Surrey County Record Office, Goulburn papers. *Hansard* XL 1st Series, col. 805.

8 W. S. Mason, *A statistical Account or Parochial Survey of Ireland*, II, 1816, pp. lxxxv–lxxxvi.

9 *Hansard* XL 1st Series, cols. 805–6.

10 *Despatches, correspondence and memoranda of Field Marshal Arthur, Duke of Wellington*, II, 1867, pp. 218–19. *Hansard* X 2nd Series, col. 541. *Gentleman's Magazine*, March 1824, XCIV, p. 268.

11 *Report from the Select Committee appointed to inquire into and report on the present state of the Ordnance Survey of Ireland, and on the works which will be required for its completion*; PP 1846 (664) XV, q. 277 (evidence of Lord Monteagle, formerly Mr T. Spring Rice).

12 No contemporary copy traced. Copy of 1828 in PRO WO 44/115.

13 Both quotations in this paragraph from copies of 1828 in WO 44/115.

14 Unless otherwise stated, Colby's annual reports for 1825, 1826 and 1827 are the sources for this period. Copies of the first two are in WO 44/115 and of all three in the OSO Dublin.

15 *Second Report from the Select Committee on Army and Ordnance Expenditure*, PP 1849 (277) IX, q. 9053 (W. Reid's evidence).

16 OSO Dublin: Index of tables of contents to such orders as are to be considered standing orders, 1826, No. 12 (5 Sept. 1825).

17 George Everest's report on the Irish survey, 1829: British Library Add. MS 14380, f 83.

18 J. F. McLennan, *Memoir of Thomas Drummond* (1867), pp. 66–78.

19 A. R. Clarke, *Account of the Observations and Calculations of the Principal Triangulation* (1858).

20 Unless otherwise stated, the following account of the base is derived from W. Yolland, *An Account of the Measurement of the Lough Foyle Base in Ireland with its Verification and Extension by Triangulation*, 1847.

21 The recollections of Lieutenant T. A. Larcom and other documents relating to the base measuring experiments are in vol. 7511 of Larcom's papers, cited henceforth (as here) by their reference number in the National Library, Dublin.

22 See p. 140.

23 W. R. Taylor, 'The remeasurement of the Lough Foyle base', *Empire Survey Review* 1962, XVI, pp. 339–47.

24 Mountjoy registers 3507 (8 Feb. 1832). This title is applied henceforth to the volumes in which the external correspondence of the Irish headquarter office was summarized from 1824 onwards. From 1832 onwards there is a single consecutive series; before that year there are separate registers for in-letters and out-letters. The registers are cited only when the original registered correspondence (referred to below as 'Mountjoy letters') is wanting, as is usually the case in the period 1824–46. Some correspondence failed to pass through the chief clerk's office, and is cited below as 'Unregistered letters'. The name 'Mountjoy', used here in a nineteenth-century context for the sake of brevity, has now fallen out of use.

25 *Instructions for the Interior Survey of Ireland*, lithographed at the OS Office, Phoenix Park, Dublin, 1825. See Appendix III.

26 The documents of the 1825–30 surveys do not appear to have survived. Those of 1830 and later are preserved at the OSO Dublin. The most important are the field books, content plots, content registers, line diagrams, levelling books, levelling registers, field name books, examination traces and plans. (The finished six-inch drawings were known as parish plans, or simply as plans, and are now generally called 'fair plans', the word 'map' being reserved in this context for the printed sheets).

27 Statements of the progress of the parish surveys, with staff classification lists, are to be found in the monthly district reports which survive discontinuously from 1826 onwards in the OSO Dublin.

28 Mountjoy registers 188 (out, 1825), 5029 (in, 1827), 1340 (out, 1827).

29 Colby to Sir J. Carmichael-Smyth, 29 July 1828: WO 44/115.

30 The report for 'B' district, December 1826, contains an early example of Colby's insistence on the division of labour.

31 Statement of the progress in the perambulation of baronies, parishes and townlands in Ireland ... by Richard Griffith ... 28 May 1828: *Second report from the Select Committee on the Public Income and Expenditure of the United Kingdom*. PP 1828 (420) V, App. 23.

32 *Dublin Evening Post*, 25 Nov.–30 Dec. 1826.

33 C. W. Pasley's diary for December 1826 to April 1827 summarizes letters from Reid on this subject: Add. MSS 41984–5.

34 *Wellington's despatches, IV*, pp. 331–3. Correspondence between Colby, the Ordnance and the Irish Government in PRONI Anglesey papers, X, 74–80.

35 WO 46/31 (27 May 1828).

36 Carmichael-Smyth's instructions, WO 44/519. There are copies of his report in PRO P.R.O. 30/35/75 and (with associated correspondence) WO 44/115, and copies of further correspondence on the same subject in the office of the Geological Survey of Ireland, Dublin.

37 PRO MPHH 296 includes all 56 sheets of the 1827–30 Londonderry printings except sheets 5 and 48. Copies of sheets 35, 38, 39 and 40 are in the OSO Dublin.

38 Colby to Ordnance, 14 Dec. 1832: PRO T1/4060 (1834–5).

39 See J. H. Andrews, *A Paper Landscape*, p. 98.

40 J. E. Portlock, *Memoir of the Life of Major General Colby* (1869), p. 232.

41 Valuators' letters and Griffith-Colby correspondence, 1830; PROI Valuation office letter books.

42 There are references to this (otherwise almost undocumented) change, and to the 1830–33 'revision' in general, in the recollections of a civil assistant A. McLachlan (dating from 1843) in the 'Early Life' volume of John Tyndall's papers at the Royal Institution.

43 Mountjoy registers 3025 (out, 1831).

44 Report of Ordnance committee on the survey of Ireland, 24 Sept. 1833: copies in State Paper Office, Dublin (official papers 1834/484) and in PRO T1/4060 (1834–5), the latter with preliminary correspondence between the Ordnance and the Treasury.

45 *Return of officers of the Corps of Royal Engineers and others, who have been employed on the Ordnance Survey of Ireland on the 31st of March of each year, from 1838 to 1846*, PP 1846 (423 II) XXVI, 626.

46 *A statement of the progress which has been made in the Ordnance Survey and townland valuation of Ireland, respectively, since their commencement*, PP 1840 (74, 489) XLVIII.

47 This round figure is based on the two slightly different figures given in *Statement of the receipt and expenditure on account of the survey of Ireland*, PP 1846 (423) XXVI and Abstract of the aggregate amount paid in each year on account of the survey of counties up to January 1847, PP 1847 (171) XXXVI.

48 The five-foot plans are listed in *Return of the towns of the United Kingdom surveyed by the Ordnance*

Department on the sixty inch scale, PP 1847–8 (320) LX 391. The smaller scale town plans are listed in OSR 1868.

49 Index to general orders and circulars issued for the regulation of the Ordnance Survey of Ireland, n.d. [c. 1842], c. 5288.

50 The reference to the valuators is in Colby to Inspector General of Fortifications, 16 May 1844: WO 44/703. For a contemporary reference supporting the second interpretation see Mountjoy registers 4246 (1833).

51 Mountjoy registers 6425, 6462 (1835). Report on the mapping of fences by Capt. J. Cameron, 22 Feb. 1849: Mountjoy letters 533.

52 *Report from the Select Committee appointed to inquire into the duties, salaries and fees of the officers paid by counties in Ireland*, PP 1836 (527) XII, q. 682.

53 *Report from the Select Committee on townland valuation of Ireland*, PP 1844 (513) VII, q. 210.

54 'Fingal', 'Some passages from the life of an architect', *Irish Builder*, 1882, XXIV, p. 101 (reminiscences of a former civil assistant).

55 For an example, see Sir D. Norreys in *Correspondence respecting the scale for the Ordnance Survey, and upon contouring and hill delineation*, PP 1854 [1831] XLI, p. 70.

56 J. Cameron, *Abstracts of Principal Lines of Spirit Levelling in Ireland, carried on during the years 1839 to 1843* (1855), pp. vii–ix.

57 Quarterly reports for 1847–54 at the OSO Dublin.

58 G. B. Airy, 'On the laws of the tides on the coast of Ireland, as inferred from an extensive series of observations made in connection with the Ordnance Survey of Ireland', *Phil. Trans.* 1845, I, pp. 1–125. F. E. Dixon, 'Irish mean sea level', *Royal Dublin Society Scientific Proceedings* XXV (1949), pp. 1–8.

59 No official order for changing the datum has been traced. The matter is referred to in Colby to Larcom, 12 March 1844: copy in Mountjoy letters 465.

60 WO 46/31 (4 April 1829). *Report of the Select Committee on the Ordnance Survey of Ireland*, qq. 295–315 (Dawson's evidence): PP 1846 (664) XV.

61 Portlock, *Memoir of Colby*, pp. 216–17.

62 The earliest first-hand description of the methods of contouring used on the Irish survey appears to be that given in 1854 by Capt. G. A. Leach, who had taken over the hill department in 1843: Mountjoy letters 1043, 1171.

63 Mountjoy registers 9205 (1840).

64 Larcom's notes on the Irish contouring (originals lost) quoted in C. F. Close, *The Early Years of the Ordnance Survey*, p. 142. *Report of the Commissioners appointed to inquire into the facts relating to the Ordnance memoir of Ireland*, PP 1844 [527] XXX, q. 554 (Larcom's evidence).

65 Larcom's memorandum on contouring in *Report from Her Majesty's Commissioners of inquiry into the state of the law and practice in respect to the occupation of the land in Ireland*, PP 1845 (672) XXII, Appendix 44.

66 OSO Dublin: O'Donovan's notes on the orthography of Irish place-names.

67 *Report on the Ordnance memoir of Ireland*, 1844, q. 24 (Larcom's evidence).

68 Portlock, *Memoir of Colby*, pp. 231–9: description of office methods in the production of the six-inch maps. There is a slightly different, MS, version of this memorandum in Larcom papers 7574.

69 Mountjoy letters 1037 (1853).

70 Larcom papers 7559. Mountjoy letters 1157 (1854), 1278 (1854), 1740 (1856).

71 'No special authority was considered necessary for Dublin': Larcom to Colby, 21 March 1846: Mountjoy registers 11396.

72 Larcom papers 7549, 7559. T. A. Larcom, 'Electrotype' in *Aide-mémoire to the military sciences, framed from contributions of officers of the different services, and edited by a committee of the Corps of Royal Engineers*, Vol. I, by G. G. Lewis, H. D. Jones and R. J. Nelson, 1846.

73 *Abstract of the amount paid on account of the survey of counties*, 1847.

74 Mountjoy letters 566 (1849). Larcom papers 7523, 7552.

75 Mountjoy letters 29 (1846).

76 Mountjoy registers 91 (1846) and letters 641 (1850).

77 R. C. Simington and T. S. Wheeler, 'Sir Robert Kane's soil survey of Ireland', *Studies* (Dublin), 1945, XXXIV, pp. 539–51.

78 *Copy of instructions . . . with reference to the cities and boroughs in Ireland sending representatives to Parliament*, PP 1831–2 (519), XLIII. *Copy of instructions . . . with reference to the boundaries and division into wards of the several cities, boroughs and towns corporate in Ireland*: PP 1837 (301) XXIX, Larcom papers 7459, 7462–3, 7521.

79 Larcom papers 7525, 7743. *First report of the Commissioners for inquiring into the number and boundaries of poor law unions and electoral divisions in Ireland*: PP 1849 [1015] XXIII, 369. There is a volume of Larcom's papers on this last subject in the Central Statistics Office, Dublin.

80 Mountjoy registers 1031 (out, 1826). Colby-Pringle correspondence in the office of the Geological Survey of Ireland, Dublin.

81 WO 46/31 (9 Jan. 1830). Mountjoy registers 2528 (out, 1830).

82 Portlock, *Report on the geology of the county of Londonderry and of parts of Tyrone and Fermanagh* (1843), pp. iii–v.

83 No date is printed in the *Heads of Inquiry*. Larcom's own copy (Larcom papers 7550) carries the MS date 1832, but there is a reference to the circulation of headings in March 1834 (Orders and circulars, c. 5287) and it is not until after that time that the new system appears in the officers' memoirs. Most of the latter are now in the Royal Irish Academy, Dublin. For a general account of the contents, see B. Trainor (ed.) *Ordnance Survey memoir for the parish of Antrim* (Northern Ireland Public Record Office, 1969) pp. ix–xlii.

84 Larcom papers 7548. J. Cameron, *Meteorological observations taken during the years 1829 to 1852 at the Ordnance Survey Office, Phoenix Park, Dublin* (1856).

85 W. Stokes, *The Life and Labours in Art and Archaeology of George Petrie*, 1868, Ch. 4. For the materials collected by Petrie's department, see R. Dudley Edwards, 'Ordnance Survey manuscripts; preliminary report', *Analecta Hibernica*, 1966, XXIII, pp. 277–96.

86 Letters on Irish antiquities from O'Donovan and his colleagues to Larcom (covering all counties except Antrim, Cork and Tyrone) are in the Royal Irish Academy. There are typescript copies in the leading Irish libraries.

87 Larcom papers 7551. Hodges and Smith, *Prospectus of the Ordnance Survey of Ireland* (1836).

88 T. F. Colby, *Ordnance Survey of the county of Londonderry. Volume the first: memoir of the city and north western liberties of Londonderry: parish of Templemore* (1837).

89 Larcom papers 7553.

90 Colby to Larcom, 18 Feb. 1840: Larcom papers 7555. Larcom to Petrie, 21 Jan. 1839: Larcom papers 7566.

91 The foregoing paragraph is based on WO 44/703, a selection of Board of Ordnance correspondence relating to the Irish survey in 1840–6 and especially concerned with geology, hill sketching, contouring, the one-inch map, the memoir, the future of Mountjoy, the six-inch revision, and the dismissal of Larcom.

92 *Report on the Ordnance memoir of Ireland*, 1844. The Peel papers (Add. MS 40480) include a copy of the Academy's memorial. Larcom's letters to T. R. Robinson in the period 1843–5 (Larcom papers 7545) give a detailed account of the attempt to revive the memoir.

93 *A collection of documents expressive of public opinion on the utility and importance of the Ordnance memoir of Ireland*, Dublin, 1844.

94 Peel's suggestion, omitted from the Hansard account, was reported in the *Freeman's Journal* (Dublin), 25 July 1844.

95 Larcom papers 7556.

96 Papers relating to the transfer to the Office of Woods and Forests were later printed in *Report from the Select Committee on Scientific Institutions* (Dublin). PP 1864 (495) XIII, Appendices 6–7.

97 Correspondence on Colby's claim for arrears of salary, 1847: WO 44/614.

98 A. H. Robinson, 'The 1837 maps of Henry Drury Harness', *Geographical Journal*, 1955, CXXI, pp. 440–50.

99 Portlock, *Memoir of Colby*, pp. 216–17. Colby to [H. D.] Jones, 17 May 1837: Larcom papers 7459.

100 Mulcaster's Minute of 14 April 1840: WO 44/703.

101 *Report on the occupation of the land in Ireland*, 1845, Appendix 44.

102 British Association: *Report of 13th meeting*, p. xx; *Transactions of sections*, p. 18.

103 WO 44/703. Larcom papers 7520.

104 Peel to Sir George Murray, 17 May 1846: WO 80/3.

105 Larcom's preface to volume 7520 of his papers seems to be the only authority for this statement.

8
Colby's
Reforms
in
Great Britain
1820–1840

Publication and Marketing

At the time Colby was put in charge of the Ordnance Survey, thirty-two plates forming eight parts of the general survey of Great Britain had been finished and were on sale, completing the map of the coast from Orfordness in Suffolk to Land's End in Cornwall. Part IX, covering Pembrokeshire and parts of Cardiganshire and Carmarthenshire, was about to be published and other sheets were in hand.[1] The initial print run of each sheet was small, partly because Colby had not enough room to store large numbers of printed maps,[2] but also because sales were poor.

Within a few weeks of his appointment as Superintendent, Colby wrote to the Board:

> Since I have been honoured with the superintendence of the Survey I have been using my best endeavours to discover and remove the causes which tend to diminish the sale of Ordnance Maps. Among these I have ascertained the want of sufficient publicity and the active opposition of some of the London mapsellers as principal causes. The latter, namely the opposition of persons in the trade, arises from the Ordnance Map being so accurate and so beautifully engraved that the taste and expectation of the public are not so easily satisfied with their imperfect productions. Besides, the allowances granted to persons selling the maps, being much less than the ordinary percentage of the Trade, affords a rate of profit too small to make their sale an object to them; . . .[3]

He had already done something, with the approval of the Board, to publicize the products of the Survey. An advertisement had been issued in June 1820 listing the plates available and those in preparation,[4] and on 1 July copies of the Eighth Part were sent out to the surveyors in the field, with instructions that the maps should be shown to 'any Gentleman who may appear interested in the progress of the survey'.[5] A further advertisement was authorized on 31 July, in which the number of plates shown as published was increased to thirty-seven; future parts were to 'follow as fast as the nature of such a work will admit without increasing its annual expense'.[6] Although it consented to advertisement, the Board could not bring itself to adopt other commercial practices. When Mr Jackson, a bookseller of Louth, claimed to have obtained thirty subscribers for the Lincolnshire map and asked for 'an allowance', Colby curtly replied that 'the Ordnance have never employed any agents to solicit subscribers to any of their maps'.[7]

Colby recalled later how he and the Board had attempted to resolve some of the early difficulties of the map-sellers:

> When I had the honour of receiving from the Duke of Wellington the appointment of Superintendent of the Survey in 1820, I found the sale of the maps carried on in two ways, the one by the principal engraver at the Office in the Tower, the other by Mr Faden, the mapseller, at Charing Cross. A trade price and a selling price were established, but all those who came to the Tower received maps at the trade price, whilst those who purchased of Mr Faden paid the selling price. The sale of the maps at the trade price to the public at the Tower irritated all the mapsellers against the Ordnance . . . and they most strenuously opposed the sale of the maps by every means in their power . . . On the 30th August 1820 the Master General and Board were pleased to grant Mr Faden an allowance of 10 per cent to enable him to supply the rest of the trade . . . He received maps from the Tower on sale or return. Mr Faden was not bound by any agreement to sell the Ordnance maps in preference to others.[8]

As a result of these measures map sales began to increase. From 17 April to 31 December 1821, 1025 sheets were sold at the Tower[9] and from 31 August 1820 to 31 December 1821, 756 by William Faden;[10] out of this total of 1781 only 319 were individual sheets, the remainder being in county sets.

However, the financial arrangement with Faden was not a complete success, mainly because the discount was too low, and on his retirement a change was made. On 26 February 1823 the Board of Ordnance

> Ordered that the Proposition of Maj. Colby for Mr Gardner to be employed on the Sale of the Ordnance Maps be adopted upon condition that Mr Gardner completes the computations he is upon. And afterwards that he shall be discontinued on the establishment of the Survey.[11]

Colby gave further details of Gardner's appointment in a minute written shortly afterwards:

> When Mr Faden retired from business, the Honourable Board entered into an agreement with Mr James Gardner, who was well qualified as a geographer, to act as their agent. And he, on the faith of his agreement, purchased a house in Regent Street to carry on the sale of their maps, and bound himself down not to sell any other maps which would supersede them.[12]

James Gardner was the Board's sole agent for the distribution of maps to the trade from this time until 1840. On 24 January in that year the Board

> Ordered in reference to the wish of Mr James Gardner of Regent Street to resign the Agency for the sale of the Ordnance Maps on the 20th March next when he quits his present residence, that the following arrangement proposed by him and Colonel Colby and approved by the Master General be made, viz. That Mr John Arrowsmith of Soho Square be allowed to hold the Agency until the 30th June next, Mr Gardner being held responsible for such sale for the period between these dates (which will give time for the Board to select an eligible Agent as Mr Gardner's successor), the Maps ordered and received being paid for Quarterly as they are at present.[13]

On 7 August the Board appointed two agents:

> Mr John Arrowsmith of 10 Soho Square for sale of Ordnance Maps at 35 per cent for the West End of London, and . . . Messrs Grattan & Gilbert of 51 Paternoster Row for such sale at 30 per cent for the City.[14]

The agents were at first appointed on the basis of their tenders for the discount rates, but in December 1845 the Board, with the concurrence of the Treasury, put an end to this by standardizing the discount at twenty-five per cent of the gross price.[15] The sale-or-return system was abolished at the same time and thereafter agents were required to pay for all the maps they received. Seven new agents were appointed in 1846 and the number continued to increase until, in 1856, there were sixty-one retailers in forty-seven cities and towns who obtained maps directly from the Ordnance Survey at a discount of twenty-five per cent. But these arrangements did not win general approval:

> . . . the agent always had to buy his goods outright and no facilities in the way of exchange and extension of credit were ever afforded him. The rule of the Ordnance Survey, . . . was . . . the rule of a rod of iron.[16]

Perhaps the best known of the agents listed in the *Report* for 1855–6 was the firm of Edward Stanford of 6 Charing Cross, whose association with the Ordnance Survey was to be long and sometimes stormy. The Stanford agency was established in 1852, for the first year in partnership with Trelawney Saunders.[17] In 1854 Stanford added 7 and 8 Charing Cross to his premises and the firm remained at this address until 1873 when the site and buildings were acquired by the Metropolitan Board of Works for the construction of Northumberland Avenue.[18]

The Reform of the Topographical Survey

Not all those who bought the new official maps were pleased with their purchases. Criticism had been levelled at their accuracy before Colby became Superintendent and the critics included no less a person than the Master General of the Board of Ordnance, the Duke of Wellington himself.[19] From Colby's reference in his *Précis of the Progress of the Ordnance Survey* (1834) to the 'bad quality of the surveying work discovered about the year 1820 which had rendered necessary not only a very extensive revision of unfinished work, but also of some plates already before the public', it would appear that he was not only aware of the main causes that led to the criticism, but that he had resolved to take steps to remove them. He turned his attention at first to the field surveys then in hand. In 1820 there were eight experienced draughtsmen/surveyors employed on the topographical survey: Stanley, Stevens, Metcalf, Budgen, Field, Yeakell (responsible for the reduction of the two-inch sheets), Dawson (responsible for training) and James Gardner (the same Gardner who on his retirement became the map agent); all were former members of the Corps of Royal Military Surveyors and Draftsmen. The first five of these carried out the detail survey under Captain Richard Mudge whose main responsibility was to supervise their work. James Gardner provided more control points for the topographers when this proved to be necessary, but Colby was not prepared to squander Gardner's services. When Stevens, working on the two-inch survey in the neighbourhood of Newark in 1820, asked for Mr Gardner to fix more points, Colby replied sharply that, as an experienced surveyor, he ought to be able to deal with the matter himself.[20]

A good deal of the field-work left much to be desired and Richard Mudge was instructed by Colby to take a firm line about poor work. 'You must not be backward in ordering resurveys when errors appear', he wrote on 8 August 1820,[21] and later the same month he wrote again saying:

> Notions of inaccuracy have got among some of our surveyors which cannot too speedily be eradicated, and I shall be much obliged by your making them correct their work at their own expense whenever you find it erroneous. Experience will soon teach them that the cheapest way is to do their work well at first.[22]

Colby himself took every opportunity to check the surveyors' work and in September 1820, when visiting Norfolk and Lincolnshire, he took with him the unpublished plans of the regions through which he would travel. The result was another letter to Mudge:

> . . . the Lynn plan of Mr Yeakell, jr, is, with the exception of the main roads, done in a most slovenly inaccurate manner; one wood was fully double its real size and more than twice its breadth out of its place. In short there was too much sketching and that of a very bad quality.[23]

The continued employment of unauthorized assistants, engaged and paid for by the surveyor, was a reason for some of the errors, although this practice had been expressly forbidden in the circular from Colonel Mudge. If this circular were disobeyed, said Colby:

> I will most assuredly reject the plan and not forward any bill for the work until it has been redone by the authorised person.[24]

He must indeed have been taken aback when, in answer to his complaint that the Oxford district map had been poorly executed, Stevens, one of the Board's surveyors, replied that 'in that district there were not less than thirty young men employed in different parts of it, at different times, and of various abilities'.[25]

In the light of his experience in these first few years, Colby formed decided views on how the surveyors should be rewarded. He thought they depended too much on that element of their pay which was received for each square mile surveyed (thirty-two shillings and sixpence), and concluded:

> . . . it would be better to have a less dependence on quantity, and a higher salary. I would propose that the plans should be examined before any payment is made to the surveyor, and that the payment should be regulated by the quality and quantity of the work.[26]

Writing in 1834, Colby referred back to his early days as Superintendent, and mentioned that he had obtained an order that those who had 'performed grossly inaccurate plans' should be charged for their correction. 'It was not my intention', he added, 'to carry this order to a pitch of severity for the punishment of the old surveyors, but merely to use it sufficiently to act as a strong moral check on future surveys.'

To correct errors, field books had to be re-examined and the ground revisited. When he found that some of the field books and preliminary sketches had been destroyed and in consequence a good deal of time had been lost, Colby issued orders to all draughtsmen and surveyors to preserve the field books, sketches and other documents from which the plans were laid down.[27] Of the inaccurate maps made by surveyors who had since left the service, some had to be done over again and others required so much revision that this work became a delaying factor in the progress of the survey.[28] Sometimes, when errors in the published maps were pointed out, one of Colby's officers was sent to 'wait upon' the complainant.[29] If the errors were serious, revision and the issue of a corrected sheet were considered; this was done when the Admiralty complained in September 1820, after the operations by the *Hasty* surveying vessel off Lundy Island, that 'the direction of this island as given by the Ordnance Survey is quite inaccurate'.[30] It transpired that the original survey of Lundy, which had been made by a young Mr Compton as instructed by Colonel Mudge, had not been tied into the general triangulation.[31] Colby at first blamed Budgen for these errors but, rather surprisingly, accepted the somewhat sketchy excuse that 'Mr Compton was with me but not under my superintendence'.

The question of revision was brought to the notice of the Master General in 1821 when a vague general approval was given without the implications being fully appreciated. But from this time Colby considered himself free not only to correct existing errors, but to insert on reprinted sheets the new lines of canals and roads and other improvements which were constantly taking place. This naturally placed extra burdens on the engravers, of whom there were only six, including Benjamin Baker, the superintendent. The general practice, after the plate had been engraved, was for proofs to be run off on the presses and submitted for inspection to either Mudge, Gardner or Colby himself. Copies were also sent to the Lord Lieutenant of the county and to the Member of Parliament, for their comments. This preliminary circulation was enlarged when desirable to include knowledgeable persons and, in coastal areas, the Admiralty; for instance, sheet 69 (The Wash) was sent to the Hydrographic Office in May 1820 to have 'mud banks' added.[32] The corrections made on the proofs were transferred to the copper plate by the engravers and the printing put in hand. Sometimes several proofs were made before the plate was passed for final printing, presumably because of the need to incorporate further corrections and revision.

The discovery that the surveys of Lincolnshire were poorly executed, 'even worse than I had been led to expect', as Colby said in March 1822, led to Lieutenants Dawson and Robe being sent there to go over the survey sheet by sheet.[33] The production of the Lincolnshire map marked a turning point in the development of the topographical survey for the one-inch; higher standards were thereafter demanded of the surveyors and the checking of the work was much more thorough. From this time there were few complaints of 'imperfect work', although one-inch methods continued to be improved.

After 1825 Colby kept a small group of surveyors on the English survey, but it was very weak because replacements were still awaited from the trainees who were with Dawson. Colby himself reported that between 1825 and 1830 progress was 'fearfully slow . . . there were hardly any assistants qualified, and the work lingered very heavily'.[34] Nevertheless, several important reforms were carried out in Great Britain during this period and in the five years which followed.

In 1831 quarter-plates were introduced for engraving. This meant, as Colby explained to the Board of Ordnance in 1834, that

> the work was placed on the copper successively as it arrived from the Country: and completed and placed in the hands of the public before new roads or other local improvements in the country rendered further revision expedient. Thus, instead of publication every third or fourth year, there are now three or four publications every year.[35]

After 1834 the surveyors' pay was no longer partly dependent upon payment by the square mile. The two tasks of outline-surveying and hill-sketching which had hitherto been done by the same surveyor at the two-inch scale were separated, the outline being surveyed at the two-inch scale, while the hill work was added on one-inch reductions by specialists in hill-sketching.[36] The new system was put into operation at the beginning of 1835 when, under Lieutenant C. Bailey RE, a group of five surveyors trained in Ireland began work on the resurvey of sheet 48 and on the survey of parts of sheets 49, 50, 66 and 67, all in East Anglia.* The irregular field sheets were superseded by plans in rectangular form with edges parallel to the sheet-lines of the published maps; these plans were one-quarter of a published sheet in north to south extent and one-sixth in east to west, making twenty-four plans to the whole sheet. In a letter to the Board of Ordnance Colby explained that the outline-surveyors were now instructed to 'lay down roads, rivers, buildings and other matters which required to be laid down, from actual measurement'.[37] The East Anglian survey was evidently a pilot scheme; subsequently the same system of producing rectangular two-inch plans with separate hill sketches was continued into the north Midlands, terminating approximately on the Hull-Preston line in 1841.

On the backs of the rectangular two-inch plans and of the corresponding hill sketches there was normally a record of the various surveying stages, with each item dated and signed by the responsible surveyor. The sequence was usually as follows: plotting from the field books, filling in and drawing (which would appear to refer to the addition of detail by the hill-sketcher and completion with the pen in conventional colours), examination of the ground and correction. When compared with modern one-inch maps, these Bailey two-inch field documents, from both East Anglia and the north Midlands, show a remarkably high standard and consistency in planimetric accuracy, demonstrating the effectiveness with which Colby's instruction that detail 'should be fixed by actual measurement' was carried out.

Richard Mudge remained in general charge of the English work,** but Colby's suggestion that he should be placed in independent command was not adopted, perhaps wisely, since Mudge was not a particularly strong or effective officer. Between 1828 and Colby's return to England in 1838, thirty full sheets and ten quarter-sheets were published. These completed the coverage of Wales, except for

---

* Colby was able to report this reinforcement to the Board of Ordnance in 1835 when the latter was faced with replying to a Memorial from the British Association in which the 'languid condition' of the Survey in Great Britain was contrasted with the rapid publication of the Irish map.

** By 1834 the field staff in England and Wales had been increased to 22 surveyors and assistant surveyors, controlled by 4 RE officers; 10 engravers were employed in the map office.

the north coast and Anglesey, where the survey had already been finished, and also covered the eastern counties of Norfolk, Suffolk, Cambridge and Lincolnshire and the Midland counties south of a line from Snowdon to the Wash.

THE ONE-INCH SURVEY OF SOUTHERN SCOTLAND

The topographical survey of southern Scotland, for a map at the one-inch scale, had been authorized on 20 May 1819:

> His Grace the Master General, having signified his pleasure that the survey of Scotland should be commenced with all proper speed, and be executed like that of England . . . it will be necessary that six engineers should be selected for that service, of whom two should be attached to Capt. Colby, and the other four for the purpose of surveying within the area triangulated.[38]

The engineers appointed later that year were all officers in the Corps of Royal Engineers, an unprecedented use of such man-power for a topographical survey. The whole episode has the character of an arrangement entered into privately by Wellington, probably as a result of lobbying by some of his noble friends.[39]

Captain Hobbs and three subalterns, Lieutenants Victor, Battersbee and Renny, went to southern Scotland in June 1819 and worked together in the field as a party,[40] a very different procedure from that on the English survey, where the ex-warrant-officers of the Corps of Military Surveyors and Draftsmen operated on a loose rein as individuals. The officers seem to have been responsible for fixing their own control within the main triangulation, for in February 1821 Hobbs was sent a 'point-fixing theodolite' as a replacement for a defective instrument.[41] Hobbs was obviously careful to avoid the surveying errors that had embarrassed Colby in the south. In 1821, referring to methods of survey, he wrote: 'With regard to accuracy I know but one system.'[42] Not surprisingly his progress on the two-inch topographical survey was considerably slower than that of the experienced but less scrupulous surveyors in England. On 21 July Colby wrote to Hobbs:

> As we have had no particular orders from His Grace . . . to proceed with the interior survey along the western coast of Scotland, it will be necessary that we should proceed with it according to the most advantageous and natural course – completing the southern part and advancing gradually northwards.[43]

In the same month the gentlemen of Ayrshire appear to have made a request to Hobbs that their county should be given preference,[44] but this was not further pressed when, the cost of the survey having been worked out at between £3612 and £4300, a subscription of $3\frac{1}{2}$ guineas and a guaranteed number of subscribers were asked for.[45] The survey finally terminated in 1828 on the death of Hobbs,[46] by which time the whole of Wigtownshire and one-half of the counties of Ayr and Kirkcudbright had been mapped at the two-inch scale. As far as can be ascertained no part of the map was ever engraved and it was certainly never published. No drawings or field books have survived.

REVISION AND THE GEOLOGICAL SURVEY[47]

The correction of imperfect work covering 18 000 square miles had been completed by 1834 when Colby reported on the progress of the survey to the Board of Ordnance, but he estimated that a further 6000 square miles remained to be done. He drew attention to the corrections that had been made to the old Devonshire map, the insertion of many roads in Middlesex, and the re-engraving of the northern and eastern parts of Essex, as well as many other alterations that had been made to the published plates to prevent the maps from becoming obsolete. The Board of Ordnance promptly reproved him for completing such a large programme of revision without authority, and ordered that no financial provision should be made for revision in the new estimates. Fortunately, in some localities at least, Colby was able to find a way round this crippling restriction by exploiting the needs of the geological survey.

Between 1826 and 1845 officially-sponsored geological mapping in Great Britain was directed from within the Ordnance Survey; from 1832 onwards its progress depended largely on the state and quality of the one-inch. In 1826 the Treasury had sanctioned the employment of Dr John McCulloch on the systematic mapping of the geology of Scotland, but he had had to use Arrowsmith's map as a base. In England Colby encouraged his one-inch surveyors to keep a 'register of the mineral changes accompanying variations in the outline of the land', but he also saw fit to warn the surveyor J. R.

Wright, working in Herefordshire in 1832, that this work should not delay 'the Map'. In the same year Henry De la Beche, a qualified geologist, sought the support of the Ordnance for recording the geology of Devon on eight of the official one-inch sheets; this he offered to do for £300 in the space of two years. The suggestion was supported by Colby, and within a few weeks was agreed to by the Board. The maps, when completed, were acclaimed by the President of the Geological Society of London, who expressed the hope 'that a work so admirably begun may not be suffered to terminate here'. The recommendations of the Geological Society and Colby's estimate of the cost of putting the geological survey on a permanent basis – £1000 a year exclusive of De la Beche's salary – were accepted by the Board and the Treasury, although the latter made a reservation about ascertaining the total expenditure.

Unfortunately the early Ordnance Survey maps of Devon and Cornwall, particularly of the coastal features, fell well short of the standard required for geological mapping, so that Colby still had to provide for revision to support De la Beche's work. Undeterred by the cutting off of funds for this purpose, he wrote to the Master General in January 1835:

> When the Geological Survey of Cornwall shall be directed to be carried into effect I propose to attach to Mr De la Beche a practical surveyor who has already some knowledge of Geology and who will correct the Geographical details of the Ordnance Map of Cornwall . . . at the same time that he is proceeding with the Geological enquiries.

This subtle approach, implying that the geographical corrections would be paid for out of the geological grant, seems to have caused no objections. The 'practical surveyor' was Henry McLauchlan who was also a Fellow of the Geological Society of London; in July he was instructed to join De la Beche in Cornwall. The Board of Ordnance must have been persuaded of the necessity of the 'geographical corrections,' probably by De la Beche himself, for at this time a 'geographical correction account' appears in the records of the Survey, and there is evidence that the cost of the revision was shared between this account and the geological grant. The geological survey thus became the means of establishing the necessity for revision and of instituting formal provision for it, although the Board continued to keep a sharp eye on revision generally.

The field staff of the geological survey was transferred to the Office of Woods and Forests in 1845,[48] but the Ordnance Survey still engraved and printed the geological maps. While they formed a branch within the Ordnance Survey, the geological surveyors wore a dark blue Ordnance uniform which included a tight-fitting buttoned frock coat, but these inconvenient accoutrements were at once discarded when control passed to the Office of Woods and Forests. However, in the early days the uniform may have helped to establish the official character of the investigations, the English countryman being apt to regard unusual activities with great suspicion and even active hostility.

CARTOGRAPHY – THE OLD SERIES ONE-INCH

Portlock put the Lincolnshire survey into perspective when he said:

> The British Survey [had] just passed into the transition state between a collection of detached and not very harmonious works, and a work executed on uniform principles as one whole; the maps had assumed . . . that purity of style and just gradation of shade, which have raised them to the first rank amongst the most beautiful specimens of topography of the present age.[49]

The beauty of the maps depended not only upon the work of the field surveyors but also upon the draughtsmen and engravers. Although the one-inch was at this time a basic scale, it generated a lot of genuine cartographic work in the Drawing Room at the Tower, notably the reduction of the field sheets and the preparation of the hachured hill drawing, so that the published map was not merely a reproduction of the surveyor's work. Soon the drawing office began to exercise an influence on the quality of the plans received from the field. In July 1821 Richard Mudge wrote to Budgen:

> I enclose a tracing of the Canal . . . the engravers cannot understand what is meant by the double lines, or indeed any part of the work on both sides of it. Is it intended for the double lines to go through to the towing path? Are the enclosures woods or brakes, or is there a cut in the side of the hill with precipitous sides down to the Canal? I have marked the most unintelligible with a red Cross . . . Pray do not put anything in your Past Work except the points that are to be engraved.[50]

The content of the map and the conventions used must have been brought to a better state of uniformity by 'office remarks' such as this. Another problem which troubled the Drawing Room (and all its drawing office successors) was the reconciliation of edges on the field sheets. This difficulty was aggravated because Colby did not permit the surveyors to compare edges: in accordance with his principles, if the work was right, there would be no discontinuities. The drawing office, on the other hand, would have been quite content with a survey a little short of perfection providing the edges fitted.

Compared with later sheets, the early one-inch maps look somewhat coarse because of the rather large writing, the comparative thickness and irregularity of the line-work, and the hills which have not altogether lost the wooden formalized appearance characterizing eighteenth-century hachured maps. The Lincolnshire map represented a step forward in cartography as well as in field surveying. There was a discernible improvement in the quality of the line-work, and the woods and parks were treated in detail with great care – perhaps understandably in a map that had been underwritten by the local gentry. The soft Lincolnshire relief encouraged delicate shading, and in the Wolds the slope-changes were realistically shown by variations in the weight of hachuring giving an effect not achieved before.

By the middle 1830s the engraving executed by Benjamin Baker and his assistants – whom Colby regarded as the best topographical engravers in Europe[51] – had reached a state of near-perfection; the refinement of the line-work, writing and ornament is perhaps unexcelled. Tighter control in the field had led to greater uniformity and to a significant increase in the density of detail, particularly evident in the depiction of small towns and villages where the fine detail was shown with great clarity; only in the larger towns were the built-up areas blocked in and even then this treatment was usually confined to the centres. The most successful sheets were in areas of gentle relief, such as sheet 52 (Huntingdon) which was sent twenty years later to Ireland as a model (Plate 7). However, in the hilly but densely populated areas of the Pennine fringes and in South Wales, the engraved map began to fail, especially where names coincided with woods and steep slopes.[52]

ADVANCES IN THE TREATMENT OF PLACE-NAMES

The Lincolnshire survey also marked a new approach to the treatment of place-names. There was no immediate question of the traditional checking of proofs by the gentry being scrapped, and most of the eight Lincolnshire sheets were farmed out to different landowners. Colby's simple improvement, introduced in the early 1820s, was to push much of the task of place-name verification directly onto the field surveyor. In Lincolnshire, surveyors were expected to make systematic local enquiries, two aspects of which were novel. Rather than confining themselves merely to establishing the current form of the name, the surveyors were encouraged to be curious about the meaning of names. Richard Mudge, for example, wrote to Charles Budgen in September 1821:

> In the neighbourhood of Wainfleet, you have written a name frequently that we do not understand the meaning of, and as it recurs so often it is desirable to know that we are quite right, Wainfleet Tofts, Wrangle Tofts &c are they rightly spelled, and what is the meaning of the word Toft?[53]

A second aspect of the place-name work in Lincolnshire was a trend to refer to 'authorities' – written sources as well as people – which could be cited in support of a particular spelling. On several of the manuscript drawings covering areas within Old Series sheet 86 (Hull), the surveyors have annotated the plans with lists of place-names set out in columns headed 'Added', 'Erased' and 'Altered', with an extra column to show the authorities.[54] Here, in embryo, was the method later developed in the place-name books of the Survey.

The weight given to printed authorities can be judged from a letter to Earl Brownlow from Richard Mudge, dated July 1822. On his proof copy of the Boston sheet, the Earl had altered the spelling of Freiston – about three miles east of Boston – to Frieston, and the copper plate had been amended accordingly. During the revision of the field plans, however, the surveyor concluded that it ought to revert to its original state. Mudge explained:

> He infers [this] from old documents, awards and acts of Parliament and which we have further supported by Carlisle in his Topographical Dictionary and the population abstract authorities which we are accustomed to respect in cases of doubt.[55]

Apart from the range of sources it consulted – including inclosure awards, Acts of Parliament and census returns – the Survey was clearly familiar with recent place-name studies, in particular with the work of the worthy secretary of the Society of Antiquaries, Nicholas Carlisle (1771–1847). In *A Topographical Dictionary of England* (2 vols 1808) Carlisle informed his readers:

> Neither the spelling of the [Parliamentary] Returning Officer, nor that of more ancient date has been implicitly adhered to: and that all due correctness in this particular might be acquired, the Orthography of each name has

been collated with the spelling in every County History, or other Topographical Work, and a uniformity attempted as exact as the modern pronunciation and the etymology seemed to admit.[56]

This paragraph shows an attitude to place-names similar to that accepted by the Ordnance surveyors in England for the remainder of the nineteenth century.

In Wales, too, Carlisle's treatment of place-names may have influenced Colby. Here, as well as consulting the Parliamentary Returns, Carlisle sent a questionnaire to the 'Officiating Minister' of each parish, which asked:

> In what manner is the name of your parish most usually spelled; and, if the name is derived from the Welsh language, what is the meaning of it in English?[57]

A later comment of Carlisle's echoes Colby's difficulties in South Wales and Pembrokeshire:

> To illustrate the tottering fragments of an expiring language, or to adjust the orthography which time has unsettled, is difficult and dangerous.[58]

Nevertheless, Carlisle felt the effort worthwhile if only to 'preserve from further corruption a language' which he believed to be derived from 'Hebrew . . . that Mother Language of Mankind'! The Survey's later attempts to standardize Welsh orthography were in the spirit, if not in the letter, of Carlisle's researches.

Study of the treatment of place-names during the course of the Lincolnshire survey makes it possible to revise the accepted view of the contribution of the Irish Survey to the development of Ordnance Survey techniques in this respect. There can be little doubt that Colby transplanted to Ireland the system which was evolving, albeit in a rather inchoate form, in Lincolnshire. This is made clear by his well-known Irish instructions of 1825 which stipulated:

> The persons employed on the Survey are to endeavour to obtain the correct orthography of the names of places by diligently consulting the best authorities within their reach.[59]

What seems to have happened in the late 1820s and 30s is that, within their respective terms of reference, the Irish survey and the Survey of England and Wales developed a treatment of place-names along parallel lines. Although geographically separate and certainly different, they were part of one organization and were subject to common decisions of policy and to the single-minded direction of Colby. There was every opportunity for a pooling of ideas and it would have been surprising if this had not taken place.

The earliest surviving English or Welsh example of a place-name sheet (c. 1835) is 'A list of Names of Buildings, Rivers & Hills &c in the neighbourhood of Llanbrynmair' which accompanies the hill sketches for sheet 60 (Montgomery).[60] This consists of two manuscript sheets, with four columns ruled and headed 'Names, Situate, Correction, Authorities & Remarks' and although little was entered in the two final columns, the layout, as well as reflecting Colby's Irish instructions, probably exemplified the form of the English place-name sheet from the mid 1820s onwards. By the late 1830s printed name sheets were being issued which could be sewn together to make a book. The earliest surviving example (c. 1839) is associated with Old Series sheet 87 (Doncaster);[61] the printed headings of the four columns were 'Adopted Name', 'Different modes of Spelling the same Name', 'Authorities for the different modes of Spelling' and 'Remarks'.

In the spelling of farms and smaller places the proprietor had a definite say. Richard Mudge, writing to Sir Henry Verney in February 1833 'respecting the correction of Names in the SE of the Banbury Sheets', turned to the subject of the alteration of the word Claydon:

> . . . as you have a perfect right to spell your own place as you may think proper Cleydon shall be substituted Claydon if you wish it to be so; but I find all the authorities modern and ancient prefer the *a* to the *e* for example in Domesday Book it is *Clainone*, in Speeds Atlas published in 1614, all the Claydons in Buckinghamshire are also Claidone, Vol 1, Page 150 spelt Claydon, also in the Index Villaris published in 1680, likewise Claydon in Carlisle's topographical Dictionary 1808, Claydon, and in Lewis' Topographical Dictionary not long published Claydon. Population abstracts ditto. There is a Claydon 6½ miles at E of Banbury in Oxfordshire – Botolph Claydon shall be spelt. I hope the map will be advanced sufficiently in the course of a few days to allow me to send you a proof, and to request you will have the goodness to examine it and see if we have made any more blunders.[62]

This impressive parade of learning, if not of syntax, appears to have convinced Sir Henry, and Claydon was the spelling adopted in the map.

In one other important respect – the treatment of Celtic names in Wales – the English survey in the 1830s was at least partly in step with events in Ireland. Welsh orthography had, in the main, been regularized by local gentry with varying degrees of success or by antiquarian clergymen such as the

Reverend Mr Davies of Bangor,* of whom Robert Dawson tells us that the survey of North Wales was 'much indebted' to his 'trouble of thoroughly examining the names . . . and supplying a great number of corrections.[63] However, in 1831 Captain Mudge, replying to a letter from Mr Alfred Thomas who had offered his assistance in correcting the spellings of Welsh names, wrote:

> . . . in order to further insure accuracy as far as means and foresight can extend, the Welsh work is consigned to the care and superintendence of natives of Wales who[se] labours are almost entirely confined to that country.[64]

So, by 1831 at the latest, the practice of employing surveyors who were at least Welsh speakers, if not linguistic scholars of the calibre of O'Donovan, had begun.

The Completion of the Primary Triangulation of Scotland

On 14 July 1837 the House of Commons published a memorandum from Colby in which he reported that the survey of sixteen Irish counties was finished and that, if sufficient funds were granted, the remainder would be completed within three or four years.[65] Also published on the same day were 'Copies of memorials addressed to the Government from different Bodies in Scotland on the subject of the state of the Trigonometrical Survey of that country',[66] drawing attention to the fact that the triangulation of Scotland had been almost completed nearly twenty years before and that it could be finished at no great expense. These memorials, written two months earlier, had already been referred by the Board to Colby who proposed, if funds could be raised, to resume the triangulation in the north-west of Scotland the following summer, 'but for that purpose I shall require timely notice, that I may train one or two officers this year'. In a further letter, Colby said that no delay whatever would arise in either the English or the Irish surveys if the trigonometrical survey of Scotland were continued in 1838. Writing to his wife at the end of May, Colby's private comments were:

> The Scotch are coming forward for their survey in good earnest. The Societies have petitioned, and some influential men see the Chancellor of the Exchequer tomorrow about it. A more powerful mass of noblemen and gentlemen are coming forward on that point . . . There is nobody that I could trust to put in charge of the Scotch Survey, and I suppose I must make it part of my business. All the leading movers of the matter are my personal friends.[67]

The Treasury made the necessary funds available so that the preparation for the resumption of the Scottish triangulation could be put in hand, and the work started the next year. In the early summer of 1838 Colby returned to Scotland to continue the field-work on the north coast of Sutherland, and small parties of sappers were detached from the main body in Ireland to assist. Lieutenant Robinson and a party of twelve went to the north of Scotland and Captain Henderson, with six rank and file, was employed in the Firth of Clyde. The northern party 'endured much fatigue in carrying out this service' and for this reason was made up of men 'selected on account of their physical strength'.[68] For the first two years the military detachments returned to Ireland at the end of each observing season, but from 1840 onwards parties of sappers moved permanently into Great Britain, completing the triangulation of Scotland in 1841.

* The 'Rev. Mr Davies of Bangor' was probably Hugh Davies (1739–1821).

Notes

1 OSLB f 56.
2 OSLB f 231.
3 OSLB f 97.
4 OSLB f 56.
5 OSLB f 65.

6 OSLB ff 86, 87.
7 OSLB f 414.
8 Quoted in C. F. Close, *The Early Years of the Ordnance Survey* (reprinted Newton Abbot 1969), p. 79.
9 OSLB f 264.
10 OSLB ff 347, 459.
11 Board of Ordnance Minutes, PRO WO 47/2678.
12 Quoted in Close, *Early Years*, p. 79.
13 Board of Ordnance Minutes, PRO WO 47/2681.
14 *Ibid.*
15 Board of Ordnance Minutes PRO WO 47/2062.
16 Edward Stanford, *The Ordnance Survey from a Business Point of View* (1891), p. 8.
17 J. K. Stanford and E. G. Godfrey, *The House of Edward Stanford Ltd.* (1952). Trelawney Saunders was the first man in London to issue a classified catalogue of the best foreign and English maps.
18 J. Aylward, 'Retail Distribution of Ordnance Survey maps', *Cartographic Journal*, June 1971, p. 58.
19 Close, *Early Years*, p. 70.
20 OSLB ff 37, 38.
21 OSLB f 96.
22 OSLB f 102.
23 OSLB ff 122, 123.
24 OSLB f 94.
25 OSLB f 165.
26 OSLB f 16.
27 OSLB f 90.
28 OSLB f 393.
29 OSLB f 311.
30 OSLB f 112.
31 OSLB f 182.
32 OSLB f 40.
33 J. E. Portlock, *Memoir of the Life of Major-General Colby . . .* (London 1869), p. 95.
34 Thomas Colby, 'Precis relating to the Survey of England and Wales', 1834, PRO WO 44/614.
35 *Ibid.*
36 J. B. Harley, 'Error and revision in early Ordnance Survey maps', *Cartographic Journal*, December 1968, *passim.*
37 *Trig. Survey of Britain*, p. 4: PP 1836 (106) XLVII.
38 Mudge to Mann, 20 May 1819: OSLB f 8.
39 OSLB f 224.
40 OSLB, End papers: bills for Plans numbered 1 and 2; and f 235.
41 OSLB f 192.
42 OSLB f 235.
43 OSLB ff 82, 83.
44 OSLB f 89.
45 OSLB ff 208, 209, 213.
46 PRO T 1/4060, 7 Jan. 1834.
47 The source for this section, unless otherwise stated, is J. B. Harley, *The Ordnance Survey and the Origins of Official Geological Mapping in Devon and Cornwall*, Exeter essays in Geography, 1971.
48 Close, *Early Years*, p. 63.
49 Portlock, *Memoir of Colby*, p. 162.
50 OSLB f 349.
51 OSLB f 71.
52 See, for example, *Old Series* sheet 87.
53 OSLB f 373.
54 Two-inch hill-sketches, serial 505 (sheet 86), British Library Map Library.
55 OSLB ff 534–5.
56 N. Carlisle, *A Topographical Dictionary of England*, (1808), I, p. xi.
57 Carlisle, *A Topographical Dictionary of the Dominion of Wales* (1811), p. xiii.
58 *Ibid.* p. xvi.
59 Instructions for the Interior Survey of Ireland, (OSO Dublin 1825). See Appendix III.
60 Two-inch hill-sketches, serial 481 (sheet 60), British Library Map Library.
61 Two-inch hill-sketches, serial 506 (sheet 87), British Library Map Library.
62 'Letters copied from a book in the possession of the Ordnance Survey . . . 1830–1841', De la Beche papers, p. 92, National Museum of Wales, Dept. of Geology.
63 Two-inch drawing no. 303, British Library Map Library.
64 De la Beche papers, pp. 36–7.
65 PP 1837 (522) XXXIX, p. 281.
66 PP 1837 (525) XXXIX, p. 507.
67 Quoted in Close, *Early Years*, p. 92.
68 T. W. J. Connolly, *History of the Royal Sappers and Miners* (London 1855), I, p. 302.

9
Changing
Needs in
Great Britain

The Introduction of the Six-Inch Scale

The mapping activities of the Ordnance in Ireland, in particular the production of the six-inch map, eventually claimed the attention of the citizens of Great Britain. In March 1839 the Treasury received from the Directors of the Highland and Agricultural Society of Scotland a memorial calling for more information to be shown on the Ordnance maps and suggesting that, while there should be a general map at the one-inch scale, there ought to be a special survey of the manufacturing and mining districts and of the highly cultivated agricultural areas at the six-inch scale.[1] The Treasury passed the memorial to the Board of Ordnance, asking for its views and an indication of the cost.

It was, however, not only the scale for the map of Scotland which had to be decided, but also that for the unsurveyed districts in the north of England. The longer this question was unresolved, the greater would be the delay to the survey, and the expense to the nation. In April 1840, in a letter to the Inspector-General of Fortifications, Lieutenant-General Sir Frederick Mulcaster, Colby pointed out that some of the surveying parties would be ready to leave Ireland by the beginning of 1841 and it was therefore highly desirable that the scale of the survey of Scotland should be decided as soon as possible.[2] A month later he confirmed that the triangulation was adequate to form the basis of a survey on any scale and suggested that two maps should be prepared for Scotland: a general shaded map at one inch to three miles and a larger one at six inches to one mile, 'having the boundaries, roads, rivers, canals and buildings, with altitudes etc.' He drew the attention of the Inspector-General to the fact that the survey of the manufacturing and mining districts of the north of England was then in progress on a scale 'which does not admit of the minuteness of detail which will be hereafter required, and if any alteration of scale was contemplated, that alteration should be immediately considered and decided upon'. In a further letter to the Inspector-General, Colby proposed that the survey of England and Wales should be carried northwards at a scale of six inches to one mile and that from it a reduced map at one inch to one mile should be made for the sake of uniformity over the remainder of England. These arguments did not go unheeded and in a Minute dated 1 October 1840 the Treasury conceded that 'if the nation incurs the cost of a survey, that survey ought to be of the kind which is admitted to be the most generally useful', and therefore gave consent to the survey of the remainder of England and the whole of Scotland at six inches to one mile.[3]

On the question of maps at the reduced scales of one inch to one mile, or one inch to three miles, the Treasury Minute agreed with the Duke of Wellington: 'a map upon a smaller scale . . . I should prefer to leave to the trade', but there was opposition from the Master General, Lord Vivian, and the Board of Ordnance. On 23 December the Board wrote to the Treasury asking that the matter might be further considered since, if the decision of 1 October were acted upon, there could well be 'an inundation of imperfect, incomplete, and badly reduced copies of the Ordnance Survey'.[4] It proposed that Colby should be instructed to continue the survey of England and Scotland at six inches to one mile and at the same time go on with the publication of the one-inch map of England, since subscribers had a claim to the continuance of the English map at this scale. The reduced map of Scotland should be at one inch to three miles. In reply the Treasury expressed its willingness to reconsider the question as soon as the survey of Scotland was sufficiently advanced and an estimate of cost could be submitted.[5]

It was not until two years later that authority was given for the one-inch map of England to be continued. On 24 January 1843 a Treasury Minute read:

My Lords . . . think it advisable that the Ordnance maps of the remaining part of England should also be engraved on the same scale as those which have already been published, so that the public may be put in possession of a complete map of the whole of England.[6]

A certain amount of surveying had been carried out in the southern part of Lancashire and

Yorkshire at a scale of two inches to one mile but, because of these decisions, this area was subsequently resurveyed at the six-inch scale, starting in Lancashire in 1842. In Scotland the new surveys at the six-inch scale were put in hand in the three counties of Wigtown (1846), Kirkcudbright (1848) and Edinburgh (1852), and the work already done at the two-inch scale was thrown away. By June 1842, 217 of the sappers of the survey companies had been transferred to Great Britain, leaving less than 50 in Ireland.[7]

An unplanned diversion of effort occurred in Scotland before the end of the decade. Sir James Matheson, the owner of the Isle of Lewis, applied to the Ordnance Office for a survey of the island to be made, offering to pay £1200 towards the cost and to take one hundred copies of the maps. The offer was accepted by the Treasury in July 1846 and the triangulation of the island was begun in the same year, with the detail survey at the six-inch scale and the instrumental contouring following shortly afterwards.[8] This side-tracking of scanty resources to a remote area did not escape criticism, in spite of the financial inducement.

THE SURVEY ACT 1841

The change to the six-inch scale in Great Britain meant that, if the work was to proceed expeditiously, legislation was needed both to ensure the provision of essential information for the maps and to protect the surveyors working on the more intensive survey required for the new scale. Hitherto they had proceeded under the authority of the Board of Ordnance, unsupported by any specific Parliamentary sanction, although certainly from 1820 onwards 'March Routes' signed by the Master General had been issued 'for the protection of the Surveyors and other Persons employed on the Ordnance Survey'.[9]

On 9 February 1841 the Master General 'desired that the Solicitor to the Ordnance should confer with Colonel Colby, and prepare such a Bill as would be necessary in order to give the Officers engaged in the Survey of England and Scotland the means of acquiring the information necessary to complete it on a Scale of Six Inches to the Mile', and ordered that 'instructions be given to the Solicitor to the effect desired . . . and that the Inspector General of Fortifications be requested to make the requisite communications to Colonel Colby'.[10]

The preamble to the Bill to 'authorise and facilitate the Completion of a Survey of Great Britain and the Isle of Man', published in February 1841, was not very informative about the purposes of the measure or the reasons for its introduction at that particular time:

> Whereas several Counties in that part of the United Kingdom called England have been surveyed by Officers appointed by the Master General and Board of Ordnance, and it is expedient that General Surveys and Maps of England, Scotland, Berwick-upon-Tweed and of the Isle of Man, should be made and completed by Officers in like manner appointed, and that the boundaries of the several Counties in England, Scotland, Berwick-upon-Tweed and the Isle of Man should be ascertained and marked out.

In the debate on the motion for going into Committee, Sir Robert Peel put forward his view that the six-inch survey should start in all the counties simultaneously, showing a remarkable lack of understanding on how far the resources of the Survey could be spread.

One of the main objects of the proposed legislation was to provide persons authorized to point out the boundaries of the various administrative divisions to the surveyors; many of the amendments to the Bill reflected differences of opinion on how this should be done. It had been proposed in the Bill that the Lord Lieutenant should be given authority to appoint the person holding the rank of County Surveyor, but Lord Granville Somerset strongly objected to both the Lord Lieutenant and the County Surveyor. The latter, he said, was 'a man of little or no education . . . who would not understand the business that was to be delegated to him'. In the Act, the Lord Lieutenant and the County Surveyor were eliminated and the duty was placed upon the justices at quarter sessions 'to appoint one or more fit and proper persons'.[11]

The Act of 1841 (4 and 5 Vict. c. 30) was, in fact, based on the Irish Survey Act of 1825 (6 Geo IV c. 99) amended to conform with the administrative terminology current in Great Britain. As was done in the Irish Act it listed the boundaries to be shown:

> . . . of each county, city, borough, town, parish, burghs royal, parliamentary burghs, burghs of regality and barony, extra-parochial and other places, districts and divisions, in England, Scotland, Berwick-upon-Tweed and the Isle of Man.

It also provided legal authority for the persons appointed by the justices and for the surveyors to enter into and upon any land, ground or heritages of any person or persons whomsoever, for the purpose of making and carrying out any survey . . . and for the purpose of fixing any mark or object to be used in the survey or any post, stone or boundary mark whatsoever.

Notice of intention to enter had to be given in writing but if a mark had to be fixed, three days notice was obligatory. The provisions included penalties against those nominated to indicate the boundaries for failure to attend and for refusal or neglect, and against any person for removing marks or obstructing the survey. The Board of Ordnance was to pay for any damage done in the course of the work.

An interesting section of the Act affirmed that the operations which it authorized could not be deemed or construed to alter or in any way to affect any boundary, whether of an administrative area or of private property. The effect of this was that territorial claims could not be based solely on the evidence, whether correct or incorrect, of features shown on the map. In the words of the Act:

. . . all right and title of any owner or claimant of any land or property whatever . . . shall remain to all intents and purposes in like state and condition as if this Act had not been passed; any description of any such land, with reference to any such hundred, parish, or other division or place whatever, or otherwise, or anything in this Act contained, or any law, custom, or usage, to the contrary in anywise notwithstanding.

The Fire in the Tower

An event which must have caused a good deal of disruption both in office routine and in Colby's private life was the removal of the Headquarters of the Survey from London to Southampton.

On 30 September 1841 fire broke out in the Tower and the Armoury was gutted. The Map Office, which was close by, was damaged, but all the instruments, maps and records were moved to safety, except Ramsden's zenith sector which was destroyed. The Map Office was transferred to Southampton in 1842, as this was the only place where accommodation could be found at the time.[12] The new headquarters were eighteenth-century barracks which from 1816 had housed a branch of the Duke of York's Royal Military School, until in 1840 the reduced number of pupils had led to its closure. The separation from London must have been very hard for Colby to bear, and the lack of continuous contact with the Board, government departments and the scientific societies may well have had an effect upon the appointment of a successor when Colby eventually retired. But to compensate for the loss of touch, the Survey gained a certain degree of independence as well as a good deal of extra space.

One aspect of the move to Southampton remains a mystery. A contemporary description of the fire published in *The Times* mentions a meeting of the Board of Ordnance on 6 November 1841 at which it was recorded that 'it had long been the wish of the Officers of the Survey Department to remove their headquarters to Southampton'. But a few years later, in 1849, Major-General Charles R. Fox, Surveyor-General of the Ordnance, when giving evidence before the Select Committee on Army and Ordnance Expenditure, spoke of the desirability of the Survey's returning to the Tower, and on further questioning seemed a little uncertain about the reasons for the choice of Southampton.[13] The 'wish of the Officers . . . to remove to Southampton' has never been authenticated or explained.

When the Ordnance Survey celebrated its Jubilee after fifty years in Southampton, apparently only one member of the original party which took possession of the 'Duke of York's Asylum' had survived. His account of the event was printed in a local newspaper:

On the last day of the year 1841, early in the afternoon, the first arrivals asked for admission at the entrance gates – which was refused by the old barrack-sergeant then in charge of the buildings. This party was from Dublin with a quantity of stores. In a few minutes Lieutenant Yolland arrived from London, and he was not a person to hold a long parley with. Admission was soon obtained, and then the minor Trigonometrical Department arrived from Cork, and in about an hour Lieutenant Pipon and his party from Cumberland followed. Everything at first was confusion. At half-past nine Lieutenants Robinson and Hornby, with a large party from Scotland, finished the arrivals on the last day of the year . . . Next morning a large load of furniture, bedding, and other requisites arrived from Winchester Barracks, which was soon put in order, and by night all was prepared, and, being Saturday evening, matters were ready for a fair start. Carpenters, bricklayers, smiths, masons, painters and every kind of workman which the corps could produce were set to work. Civilians were also engaged, and in a very short time the establishment was got into working order. The officers who formed the head-quarters at Southampton at the first were Lieuts Yolland, Robinson, Pipon, Cameron, da Costa and Gosset who joined from Chatham. The engravers from London were a very small number, and the map printers were the late Mr Ramshaw and his assistant.[14]

New Uses for Maps

TITHES, INCLOSURES AND RAILWAYS

The era of Colby's superintendency was marked by a steady extension of the purposes for which maps were needed. In England, after the passing of the Tithe Commutation Act (1836), Commissioners were appointed to administer the Act and in February 1837 they wrote to the Chancellor of the Exchequer stating that they must insist on the production of maps of undoubted accuracy before they could confirm any apportionment under the Act; and that, in order to obtain maps for this purpose, it would be necessary to have them specially constructed according to principles recommended by their Assistant Commissioner, Lieutenant Dawson RE.* They further pointed out that, since the existing parochial and estate maps were so inaccurate, many new surveys would have to be made. 'It seems therefore', the letter ran,

> to be a point at least of the very grave consideration of the . . . Government . . . whether the large sum of money, which must now be expended on the maps . . . supplied for the purposes of the Tithe Act, instead of being wasted for all other public purposes, shall be so expended as to be the means . . . of supplying all the wants of the Nation as connected with surveys.[15]

The Commissioners urged the acceptance of the idea of a national survey, but submitted alternative proposals prepared by Dawson in September and November 1836 respectively. The first was for a national survey by parishes at a scale of 26⅔ inches to one mile (or one inch to three chains). This scale was the one in most common use throughout the country for estate surveys and one which the Commissioners approved 'as the smallest which can faithfully show all the detail required'. The surveys were to be made by the Ordnance surveyors on 'Trigonometrical Principles' at an estimated cost of £1 502 800. Dawson listed the advantages of such a map and concluded:

> . . . such are some of the benefits to be derived from the work, and it is a subject for astonishment and regret that nothing of the nature of a general Content Survey has hitherto been undertaken in Great Britain.[16]

On the question of engraving the maps he requested time 'for consideration of the matter with my friend Colonel Colby'.

The second proposal related 'rigidly and exclusively' to surveys made for the purposes of the Tithe Act alone and set out in detail how they should be done. The recommended scale was again one inch to three chains and the survey was to be based on a simple system of triangulation clearly described by Dawson. These 'Instructions to Surveyors' were, in the future, to be adopted generally by private surveyors working on estates in England.[17]

A Select Committee was appointed in March 1837 'to consider the best mode of effecting the Surveys of Parishes' relating to the Tithe Act. After taking evidence from the Commissioners and from Dawson, it came to the conclusion that no general survey was necessary for carrying out the provisions of the Tithe Act.[18] It did, however, state that where new maps were required, these should conform to Dawson's recommendations. With regard to the making of a large-scale national survey, it regarded itself as precluded by the terms of its appointment from discussing the expediency of such an operation.[19]

The Report of the Select Committee was published on 8 May and there was disappointment that no large-scale survey had been recommended. Colby, writing to his wife on the 26th, said:

> My having been in London is most fortunate, for poor Dawson's complete failure in the tithe commutation business would have cast a sad damp upon all our work if I had not been there to avert the evil.[20]

The Select Committee's decision burdened the parishes

> with an expense of 9d. an acre, while the Survey executed by the Ordnance cost but little more than half the sum. The higher price thus paid to the contractors enabled them to attract to their employment civil assistants trained by the Ordnance, to do their work. Many resignations of superior surveyors and draughtsmen were therefore the result.[21]

To compensate for these losses Colby managed to obtain an increase of 48 men in the establishment of the survey companies, bringing the total in 1839 to 315. But the sappers also were becoming restless because of the high rewards from the tithe surveys. Again Colby acted, this time procuring an extra 'working pay' allowance for his sappers, to a maximum of three shillings a day.[22]

With the passing of the Inclosure Act of 1845, the Inclosure Commissioners were empowered to use the Tithe Commissioners' maps for their own work. Unfortunately, only about one-sixth of these

---

* Lieutenant Dawson had been seconded from the Ordnance Survey in 1836.

were of sufficient accuracy for the purpose of Inclosure and many areas had to be resurveyed. In 1856 the cost of this extra survey work was estimated to be £45 077. The preparation of the maps for the Inclosure Commissioners added, indirectly, another obstacle to the progress of the Ordnance Survey because, once more, a number of surveyors left to take up the new work, which carried a higher rate of pay.

There was yet another development which had even graver consequences for the Survey: the demand for railway surveys which reached its peak in 1845. This year, described as 'the great railway year',[23] was one in which an immense demand arose for maps for use in plotting and constructing railway routes. When the existing one-inch proved inadequate, recourse was made to the larger-scale maps of the Tithe Commissioners, but since only a small fraction of these were 'first class', new surveys were often necessary.* To attract surveyors, the railway companies were willing to pay three or four guineas a day and in consequence surveyors left the Tithe Commission and the Ordnance Survey. Not only did this lead to delays but it focused attention on the inadequacy of the existing official surveys. The lack of large-scale maps for railway planning caused the Duke of Wellington to make a remark which had its echo just over a century later.** On 5 October 1840 he had written:

> It cannot be doubted that much expense would have been avoided . . . as well as much inconvenience if the Government could, ten years ago, have had information to enable them to consider the construction of railroads as a whole, and to consent to their extension to all parts of the country, if such accurate information should have shown that they were required, or to prevent their extension when not required excepting for the purpose of promoting the schemes of jobbers in shares.[24]

Two hundred civil assistants, sixty labourers and twenty-seven of all ranks from the survey companies were discharged during the railway boom at their own request, and Colby was again faced with a shortage of man-power. He countered by proposing the formation of a fourth surveying company, but it was not until 1848 that the 19th Survey Company, Royal Sappers and Miners, was created.[25]

SANITARY REFORM

During the 1830s there was growing anxiety about sanitary conditions and public health generally, particularly in large towns. One of the concerns of the Poor Law Commission, established in 1834, was the relationship between poverty and disease, and under the influence of its pioneering secretary, Edwin Chadwick, it proclaimed that the prevention of disease was one of the first duties of the state. But the prevention of disease depended upon improved sanitation, and for this large-scale maps were essential.

When it was decided to survey the northern counties at six inches to one mile, it was agreed that towns should be mapped, as the six-inch work proceeded, on the scale of five feet to one mile, which was the same as that adopted for the larger Irish towns. The survey of several towns in the northern counties was therefore put in hand, but the reports of the Commissioners on the state of public health in large towns and populous districts led to demands for these to be given priority. The first report, issued in 1844, gave an account of the Commission's enquiries. Of fifty towns investigated:

> . . . in scarcely one place can the drainage or sewerage be pronounced to be complete and good, while in seven it is indifferent, and in 42 decidedly bad as regards the districts inhabited by the poorer classes.[26]

Captains Dawson and Vetch gave evidence before the Commissioners and Colby submitted estimates for producing town surveys 'upon the scale adopted for the towns now in progress under the direction of the Board of Ordnance':

> The cost of surveying . . . and laying down contour lines, with the sewer, gas and water pipes, would not amount to more than 8s. per acre, but . . . if such additions were made while a survey for the Ordnance map was in progress, the extra cost would be reduced to 1s.4d. per acre, or to 6d. only, if the levels merely were taken and bench marks inserted.[27]

A year later the Commissioners issued their second report, in which a firm recommendation was made that 'before the adoption of any general measure for drainage a plan and survey upon a proper scale, including all necessary details, be obtained, and submitted for approval to a competent authority'.[28] Moreover, they gave a direction to their recommendation when they said:

---

* As classified by the Tithe Commissioners on the basis of accuracy, only 20% were 'first class'.

** The streamlining of the railways by Lord Beeching in the 1960s.

The facilities that we have shown to exist for obtaining complete surveys for drainage and other sanitary purposes, at a very small charge upon the inhabitants of the district, through the medium of the Ordnance department, where the surveys are in progress, will, we trust, induce the local authorities in these districts to take the proper steps to procure them without further delay.

As the movement for sanitary reform gathered momentum, so more town plans were called for. In 1845 only four plans were being made – Fleetwood, Clitheroe, Manchester and Lancaster. In 1846 and 1847 eleven more were put in hand and in the following two years a further twenty-four were begun. At first the five-foot scale was accepted, but in practice this was found to be too small for the necessary amount of detail to be shown. Between 1848 and 1852, after the Board of Health was formed, plans of twenty-eight towns at the ten-foot scale (1:528) were made at the instigation of the Board, partly paid for by the towns concerned. This group of town plans showed sanitary features in very great detail, including the positions of drains, privies, and cesspits (Plate 8). Their preparation not only threw extra burdens on the surveyors – something that had been realized by the Commissioners[29] – but also upon the engravers, so that the town plans had to be given priority over the engraving of the one-inch map of northern England with a consequent delay in its publication.[30]

The Beginning of the Scales Controversy

The increasing demands on the Survey led to an extended controversy on the general question of the scales of official maps, which lasted for over twenty years. The pattern of this lengthy argument was established in 1842. On 18 April the Tithe Commissioners, in a letter to the Home Office, wrote:

> We now have reason to suppose that the Ordnance survey of the four northern counties is now carrying-on, on a plan which is meant to make it available for civil purposes. We think it right to report to you that on the scale at present contemplated, . . . the proposed survey will be useless for such purposes as the maps supplied to us are meant to answer; and also useless, as we have reason to believe, for almost all other civil purposes.[31]

The reasons given for the survey to be made at a larger scale were considered by the Home Office to be strong. The letter was therefore forwarded to the Treasury and thence to the Master General and the Board of Ordnance for a report on the estimated expense of increasing the scale of the survey of the six northern counties from six inches to one mile to $26\frac{2}{3}$ inches to one mile, the scale recommended by the Tithe Commissioners. The increased expense which would be incurred in adopting the larger scale was estimated by the Ordnance Survey to be £68 500, based on an extra twopence per acre.

Upon receiving this figure the Treasury again wrote to the Board of Ordnance, asking whether

> . . . taking into consideration all the engineering and other civil objects in every part of this island which are likely to be facilitated by a work of this description, the enlarged scale which has been already resolved upon is sufficient for the purpose, or whether decisive reasons exist for incurring the additional expense which would attend the completion of the map on a still larger scale.[32]

In reply the Board sent a report from Colonel Colby, which contained a very decided opinion in favour of the larger scale 'supported by very statesmanlike reasons'. The question was referred to the Duke of Wellington who, without denying the advantages of the larger scale, recognized that if it were agreed to, it would have to be extended to the whole country. He called for more estimates from the Ordnance and these were quickly produced. The figure for the resurvey of England and Wales south of the Hull–Preston line was £1 309 000, which, together with the estimate for the northern counties, gave a total of £1 377 500 for the whole country. This was less than the £2 million which had eventually to be spent on the much less perfect tithe maps,[33] which could not be converted to general national purposes.

The Treasury consulted James Walker, a civil engineer, who expressed himself in favour of the six-inch scale for the northern counties:[34]

> I consider the six-inch scale to be sufficiently large, and likely to be on the whole more useful than a larger scale . . . It may be expected that . . . owners of estates . . . may be desirous of taking advantage of the opportunity afforded by the ordnance surveyors, for having maps of their property to a large scale, and may make application for this, offering to pay the additional expense . . . I see no objection . . . on the contrary, the map might be useful for public purposes, as for those of the Tithe Commissioners.

The Treasury accepted Walker's advice over that of Colby and the Board of Ordnance. In a Minute dated 24 January 1843 it expressed its determination to adhere to the six-inch scale, mainly on the grounds that, if a larger-scale survey were adopted, it would be demanded for the whole of the country. The Assistant Secretary to the Treasury, Sir Charles Trevelyan, when giving evidence before the Select Committee on the Ordnance Survey of Scotland in April 1856, said that the decision was in fact arrived at by the Treasury on strict financial considerations.[35]

The Staff

The roles of the non-commissioned officers of Royal Sappers and Miners and the officers of Royal Engineers employed on the Survey underwent a change in the early 1840s, brought about partly by the large reduction in the number of officers which had reached a maximum of forty-five during the Irish Survey but was, in the succeeding decade, reduced to nine.[36] Yolland wrote of this change:

> It is perhaps right to mention that whereas formerly it was deemed necessary to employ general officers and scientific individuals to make the required observations with the theodolite to carry forward the principal triangulation, the whole is now being done by non-commissioned officers of sappers, the only difference being that in the one case the general officer worked out his own results and in the other the non-commissioned officer simply forwards his observations to Southampton for computation.[37]

These remarks also applied to the observations for latitude with Airy's zenith sector. From 1845 onwards these were made by Sergeant James Steel at all of the seventeen remaining sector stations. One day when travelling from Cornwall to Exeter by coach, Steel (then a corporal) found himself sitting next to a fellow-passenger who showed great interest in the survey and eventually asked:

> 'What instrument have you been using?'
> 'Professor Airy's zenith sector', Steel replied.
> 'Indeed! I am Professor Airy.'

Steel, surprised and pleased, was able to obtain some first-hand advice on the most efficient ways of using the instrument, as well as on other astronomical matters.[38] Steel was no doubt exceptional, but his ability to converse at length with the Astronomer Royal on a highly technical subject is nevertheless remarkable. Airy was himself very much interested in the practical side of his profession and was closely involved in the work of the Survey throughout his long period of office (1835–81), particularly with the zenith sector observations for determining the Figure of the Earth, the determination of the longitude of Valentia in 1844 and the discussions on the sea-level datum. He occupied 'the position of official scientific adviser to Colby and his successors';[39] he is known to have had a high regard for the sappers whom he commended on several occasions.

The reduction in officer strength and the emergence of the non-commissioned officers of the Royal Sappers and Miners enabled the sappers to establish an unbreakable hold on the superintendence of the day-to-day work of the Survey, and this was to become a protracted source of grievance among the civilian staff. The 'assistance of civilians', according to Connolly, the historian of the Royal Sappers and Miners, was 'simply to serve as the muscles for the military skeleton'. He goes on:

> The officers of royal engineers have the chief direction. Their number, however, is by no means constant, but is regulated by the extent of the ground under survey, and by the degree of proficiency of the non-commissioned officers.[40]

Here is a clear hint of the growing influence of the senior non-commissioned military staff which came to have a strongly stabilizing effect on Ordnance Survey affairs, at the same time perpetuating its own high standards and *esprit de corps*.

The End of the Colby Era

Colby was promoted to the rank of Major-General in November 1846, and in accordance with service custom, retired from his position as head of the Survey in April the following year. He had been in the service of the Ordnance Survey for forty-five years and its Superintendent for twenty-six years, and each year had been filled with twelve months' hard work. The primary triangulation was almost finished. The survey of England and Wales at the one-inch scale had been published up to the Hull-Preston line, and the northern counties and Scotland were being surveyed at six inches to one mile. The question of the right basic scale had still to be settled, but Colby had already expressed the view that the six-inch was not large enough. His major work, the six-inch survey of Ireland, was complete, the last sheet being published in the year of his retirement.

In June 1846 the House of Commons printed the financial accounts of the Survey from 1791; these showed that, for England and Wales, Votes had totalled £550 012 and expenditure £574 439.[41]

Receipts from various sources, including sale of maps, were £4259. The figures for Scotland were £46 095 voted, and £28 375 spent. There was, therefore, a rough balance between actual and authorized expenditure for Great Britain; for the future it was estimated that £316 492 would be required to complete the survey of England on the six-inch and one-inch scales. For the financial year 1846–7 it was proposed to employ 9 officers, 156 Royal Sappers and Miners, 265 civilian assistants and 147 labourers on the English survey; the numbers for Scotland were 1, 71, 56 and 64 respectively.

One of Colby's last acts as Superintendent was to prepare a paper for the Board of Ordnance on the finances of the Survey. This was by order of the House of Commons and the paper was published on 11 March 1847.[42] The main figures were the same as those printed in June 1846, but arranged to show more clearly the breakdown of costs between survey and engraving. The total sum spent on surveys in the British Isles since 1791 was £1 462 522. A record of map sales since 1825 was given, the highest occurring in 1845 when over 28 000 copies were sold of the 90 English one-inch sheets published. It was also recorded that since 1825 there had been three major price changes for the maps, down in 1829, up in 1831, and down again in 1837. In 1847, 59 of the sheets cost seven or eight shillings each, and the rest between three and six shillings.

AN APPRECIATION OF COLBY

Colby was rather short in stature and was not the most dignified of men, yet, says Portlock, 'there was about him an air of will and determination which secured for him the obedience and respect of his subordinates'.[43] When on duty, he was reported by Larcom as being immovable when he had once decided on a course of action, but kind and considerate when dealing with officers and men. He would lend a hand raising cairns for observation or building shelters for soldiers, and would also join in games and end-of-season activities. Off duty, during his bachelor days in London, he played the father to his young officers.

> All who served under him at that time . . . will remember to have, on some occasion, met him running rather than walking (for such was his custom) along the street on his return from the Ordnance Office to the Tower, and to have been greeted by the hearty invitation: 'Come back, my boy, and take a beef-steak with me' . . . or 'Come to the lecture at the London Institution, and let us take a chop by the way'.[44]

Colby had a wide circle of friends 'to whom he was endeared by his ability, zeal and simpleness of heart'.[45] Sir George Airy had been a particularly close friend and wrote of 'the happiness of enjoying the hospitality of Knockmaroon Lodge' (Colby's Dublin residence) and that Colby's 'appearance was always a source of friendly pleasure'.[46] He was a man of moderate private means, and was always ready to help others. Lieutenant-Colonel James recounted to Portlock the story of Colby's generous offer of a loan to Lieutenant Thomas RN who had command of the ship in which Colby had sailed during his work in the Orkneys, and who was engaged in a lawsuit. When Parliamentary Votes for the Survey were exceeded, Colby, to keep down current expenditure, did not draw his salary for at least five years before he left the Survey. This pay was never refunded, although he did apply for it during the first year of his retirement.[47]

As a general rule Colby's judgment was sound, yet upon occasion it did not prevent prejudice or enthusiasm from influencing him, and this led to a certain hostility and harshness in some of his relationships. Biot, the French scientist, did not see eye to eye with him during the latitude observation in the Orkneys, and Lieutenant Portlock and Major Reid found life difficult under him in Ireland. Portlock, who had ample opportunity to weigh Colby's merits and demerits, says:

> I learnt to appreciate his accurate knowledge, his sound judgment, his untiring energy and consummate skill, and above all, his unbounded liberality in imparting to me and others the stores of his own knowledge.[48]

Portlock puts forward three reasons why the Survey prospered and was greatly improved under Colby. These were that he gave a new character to its scientific branch by the invention or application of new instruments; that he took the highest view of the objects of the Survey, looking upon it as the basis for national improvement and consequently as the groundwork for historical, antiquarian, geological, statistical and natural history surveys; and that he endeavoured in every way to improve the artistic character of the maps.[49] Colby's keen interest in advancing geodetic science led him to belong to a number of scientific institutions in London. Not only did he attend their public meetings but he dined out at their clubs three or four nights a week. He was a Fellow of the Royal Society and of the Astronomical, Geological, Geographical and Statistical Societies, and an honorary member of the Institution of Civil Engineers. He was therefore in touch with scientific thought not only in this country, but also abroad, and he counted among his friends some of the best scientists of his day. His officers, too, were of a high calibre: Drummond, who became Under-Secretary for Ireland; Dawson, who became Assistant Commissioner on the Tithe and Inclosure Commissions; Larcom, who supervised the Irish survey after Colby's return to England and who also became Under-Secretary for Ireland, being knighted for his services; Robe, who did similar work for the Scottish survey; Murphy, who later took charge of the scientific operations of the Euphrates expedition; and Portlock, the author of the *Memoir* of Colby and the *Report on the Geology of the county of Londonderry etc.* – to name but a few. His failures with some of his subordinates are attributable partly to the effect of his inflexible perfectionism on men of very high ability who were already chafing at the bit.

Although he was a perfectionist with strong views on the way the survey should be executed and controlled, Colby was no bureaucrat, and on other subjects was surprisingly liberal in his attitude. In 1822 the question was raised whether private surveyors could obtain from the Ordnance Office a certificate vouching for the accuracy of a privately-prepared county survey. A certain Mr Baker had produced such a survey of Cambridgeshire and brought it to Colby, offering to sell it to him for republication as an Ordnance survey. When it was pointed out that the county had already been surveyed and was awaiting publication, Baker asked for 'a certificate'. In recording his refusal Colby added:

> As Mr Baker has no doubt been at considerable expense in making his map, the Ordnance may probably be disposed to defer their publication of the plans of Cambridgeshire until some of the Midland counties are completed, which will give him time to remunerate himself by a greater sale of impressions.[50]

Another example was provided by Colby's response to an alleged infringement of the Ordnance Office's copyright by Mr Cary, the private map publisher. It was suggested that the best way of stopping further publication would be by a bill of injunction,[51] but when Colby's opinion was sought, he replied that the extent of the piracy was difficult to determine and suggested that Cary should be warned about the consequence of publishing the second part of his work if it were based on Ordnance maps without authority. He recalled that Colonel Mudge had given Cary permission to use Ordnance maps of Cornwall and that certainly Faden had Mudge's permission to copy the Ordnance map of Devon on a reduced scale.[52] Colby's advice was accepted and no further action was taken, except to 'keep the subject in view'.[53]

Colby married Elizabeth, daughter of Mr Boyd of Londonderry, in 1828. They lived together in Dublin near Phoenix Park, the headquarters of the Irish Survey, until Colby came to London in 1838 to direct the work in England and Scotland. After some little delay, they set up house in London, moving to Southampton when the Ordnance Survey was transferred there in 1842. They were very happy together as a family. Larcom describes how:

> . . . at home, the steady calm reasoner of one moment became the next, almost the giddy boy, when playing joyously and without restraint with his children[54]

and Portlock says that 'his greatest happiness was found in the quiet of his own home' and that 'unruffled calm . . . pervaded his domestic establishment'.[55] On Colby's leaving the Survey, the family moved to Bonn, but eventually returned to England and settled in New Brighton near Liverpool. He died unexpectedly on 2 October 1852, when sixty-nine years of age, leaving a widow and seven children. His widow was awarded a life pension by the Government.

Notes

1 *Report from the Select Committee on the Ordnance Survey of Scotland*, App. 1, p. 116: PP 1856 (198) XIV.
2 *Correspondence respecting the Scale for the Ordnance Survey . . .*, p. 1: PP 1854 [1831] XLI.
3 *Ibid.*, p. 15.
4 *Select Committee on Ordnance Survey (Ireland)*, p. 2: PP 1846 (664) XV.
5 *Ibid.* p. 3.
6 *Ibid.* p. 5.
7 T. W. J. Connolly, *History of the Royal Sappers and Miners* (London 1855), II, p. 11.
8 *Second Report from the Select Committee on Army and Ordnance Expenditure*, pp. 463–5: PP 1849 (499) IX.
9 OSLB f 124.
10 Board of Ordnance Minutes, PRO WO 47/1887.
11 *Hansard* LVII, 3rd Series, cols. 510–22, 772–3.
12 *Second Report . . . Army and Ordnance Expenditure*, p. 556.
13 C. F. Close, *The Early Years of the Ordnance Survey* (reprinted Newton Abbot 1969), pp. 144–8.
14 From a newspaper cutting, undated, in the possession of Mr H. C. Baker; copy in OS Library, Southampton.
15 *Survey of Lands (Tithe Act)*, p. 4: PP 1837 (103) XLI.
16 *Ibid.* p. 8.
17 *First Report of the Commission for Enquiry into the State of Large Towns*, q. 5815, p. 377: PP 1844 [572] XVII.
18 *Select Committee on Survey of Parishes*, p. 3: PP 1837 (285) VI.
19 *Ibid.* p. 7.
20 Close, *Early Years*, p. 92.
21 Connolly, *History of the Royal Sappers and Miners*, I, p. 320.
22 *Ibid.* p. 321.
23 *Report . . . on the Ordnance Survey of Scotland*, p. 32: PP 1856 (198) XIV.
24 *Correspondence respecting Scale . . .* p. 17.
25 Connolly, *History of the Royal Sappers and Miners*, II, p. 42.
26 *First Report . . . into the State of Large Towns*, p. x.
27 *Second Report . . . into the State of Large Towns*, p. 15: PP 1845 [602] XVIII.
28 *Ibid.* p. 16.
29 *Ibid.* p. 15.
30 *Report from the Select Committee on the Ordnance Survey (Scotland)*, p. 182: PP 1851 (519) X.
31 *Report . . . on the Ordnance Survey of Scotland*, p. 3: PP 1856 (198) XIV.
32, 33 *Ibid.* p. 4.
34 *Correspondence respecting Scale . . .*, pp. 337–9.
35 *Report on . . . the Ordnance Survey of Scotland*, p. 4: PP 1856 (198) XIV.
36 Connolly, *History of the Royal Sappers and Miners*, II, p. 262.
37 *Ibid.* p. 266.
38 *Ibid.* pp. 120–21.
39 Close, *Early Years*, pp. 148–50.
40 Connolly, *History of the Royal Sappers and Miners*, II, p. 261.
41 PP 1846 (423) XXVI, p. 607.
42 PP 1847 (171) XXXVI, p. 467.
43 J. E. Portlock. *Memoir of the life of Major-General Colby . . .* (London 1869), p. 6.
44 *Ibid.* p. 5.
45 Obituary notice: *Journal of the Royal Geographical Society*, 1852.
46 Portlock, *Memoir of Colby*, p. x.
47 Close, *Early Years*, p. 96.
48 Portlock, *Memoir of Colby*, p. 314.
49 *Ibid.* p. 303.
50 OSLB ff 452, 453.
51 OSLB f 92.
52 OSLB ff 114, 115.
53 OSLB f 142.
54 Portlock, *Memoir of Colby*, p. 311.
55 *Ibid.* p. 6.

10
The
Superintendency
of
Lewis Alexander Hall

Colby's Successor

Before Colby retired, he had written to Sir John Burgoyne, the Inspector-General of Fortifications, recommending that Captain William Yolland should succeed him. Yolland had joined the Survey in 1838 at the age of twenty-eight and had been promoted Second Captain in 1843. He was an able an popular officer, greatly trusted by Colby, and in 1842 was placed in charge of the general work at the Southampton office. In his letter of recommendation Colby wrote:

> ... an objection may arise to the appointment of so young an officer as Captain Yolland; the continuance of peace has made promotion slow, but he is about the same age (37 years) and has about the same length of service (19 years) which I had, when I succeeded the late Major-General Mudge ... in 1820[1]

But the Inspector-General, in spite of Colby's protests, recommended that another officer, Lieutenant-Colonel L. A. Hall RE, should be appointed the next Superintendent of the Survey. The appointment was announced in March 1847 and it was thought by some that justice had not been done so far as Yolland was concerned. Douglas Galton, writing to him on 19 March, said:

> ... everyone who knew anything about the Survey knew that all the improvements of late years had been introduced at your suggestion, and that although it is quite fair that General Colby should have praise due to these improvements, because he placed you in that situation, yet it is not fair that on his retirement a fresh person knowing nothing of the subject should be brought in to gain credit from your brains.[2]

Colby's comment was that the appointment

> will show most distinctly that neither Sir John Burgoyne nor Lord Anglesey [the Master General] have any notion that the charge of a great national survey requires any experience of the nature of such a duty.

Lieutenant-Colonel Lewis Alexander Hall took up his appointment in April 1847 at the age of fifty-three. He was only nine years younger than Colby, and had been first commissioned as Lieutenant on 21 July 1810. He had served overseas at Gibraltar, in the West Indies, the Netherlands and France, and for five years in Ireland. His last appointment before joining the Survey, of which he had no previous experience, was as Chief Engineer of the London District.

The Scales Dispute

HALL AND YOLLAND IN CONCERT

It was obvious that the new Superintendent would have to rely on Yolland for a good deal of help and guidance in both the administrative and technical fields. There was much for him to learn from published official papers on the development of the Survey and he had to come to grips with the greatest current problem, that of the basic scales, which had yet to be settled. The Report of the Select Committee on the Ordnance Survey (Ireland) had been published on 20 August 1846; its last paragraph probably gave the new Superintendent food for thought:

> In so great and so valuable a work as a National Survey ... there should have been more attention paid to uniformity of result ... there should have been a fuller consideration of all the purposes to which the Maps of such a Survey would be applicable.[3]

For the next seven years Hall was to hear this said in a variety of ways, by a bewildering succession of committees and commissions, the conclusions of one being frequently nullified by those of another.

The machine left behind by Colby was, within its limits, running smoothly and Hall was not called upon until May 1848 for his first special report. This was on the town plans which were being produced both in Ireland and in Great Britain at the scale of five feet to one mile.[4] A return was requested of the names of the towns, the dates of survey, area and cost, and which of them had been undertaken specially for sanitary purposes. Hall gave as much information as he could, but he pointed out that, since the data required for the town plans also served for the six-inch maps, no separate costing of the plans had been made. The engraving of the plans had only recently been authorized and in consequence only eleven were in hand; for these the cost had been 'carefully kept in view'. He reported that only two plans had been specially prepared for sanitary purposes: those of Southampton and Windsor. Southampton had been completed in January 1847 and Windsor in March 1844, but neither of these had been engraved. He added an interesting comment:

> Southampton is the headquarters of the Survey; advantage was therefore taken . . . to make the execution of this survey serve as a school of instruction in surveying etc. for the recruits posted to the Survey Companies.

The making of further large-scale town plans had been mooted a few months previously, in November 1847, when both Hall and Yolland had been called to give evidence before the Metropolitan Sanitary Commissioners. Hall said that there was no order at that time indicating the Government's intention to resurvey the south of England, but he thought that if an order were given for the Metropolis to be surveyed, a large-scale map, similar to those being prepared in the north of England, could be completed in six to eight months. Yolland concurred and added that it would need about nine hundred sheets to cover the area required.[5] Colby had estimated some years before that the survey would cost about £104 000 and it had been turned down on this account, but Yolland made it clear that the cost would be much higher if the survey were carried out by private surveyors, who were paid 'from 500 to 1000 per cent above the rates of the Ordnance Survey'.[6] The Commissioners accepted Yolland's evidence and in their report recommended an official survey:

> We beg leave to represent the expediency of concentrating early the largest practical force of the Ordnance Survey upon the Metropolis.

The survey was started in 1848 on the five-foot scale and was completed in 1850, rather less expeditiously than had been suggested by Hall although it did not include as much detail as was normal at this scale. A strong detachment of sappers under Yolland had to be moved from the north of Great Britain, and their presence in London attracted some hostility from surveyors in private practice as well as a good deal of public attention. Particular objects of interest were the observing platforms on the north-west tower of Westminster Abbey and above the cross of St Paul's. The latter, which consisted of a timber structure 92 feet high, was designed by Sergeant James Steel of the Royal Sappers and Miners, and erected by Sergeant Beaton, assisted by two sappers and some labourers. Between eight and ten thousand observations were made from the cross, mostly by Steel, over a period of four months, using the eighteen-inch Ramsden theodolite, and the whole operation was completed without accident to life or limb, although two substantial pieces of wood were dropped; one plank struck the pavement near the Cathedral with a report 'like the booming of a piece of Ordnance'.[7]

In June 1849 both Hall and Yolland appeared before the Select Committee on Army and Ordnance Expenditure.[8] They were examined together which would seem to indicate that in some quarters it was felt that the Superintendent, even after two years in office, was not familiar with all branches of the Survey. The two officers had no doubts about certain future developments. On the extension of the six-inch survey to the south of England, Yolland said:

> When the survey of the six northern counties is completed, they will have a very enormous advantage over the whole of the south of England . . . which must be done over again, with the exception of the primary triangulation.[9]

Hall believed that future needs could only be met by a large-scale national survey, and cited the example of the tithe maps; had a national survey been authorized instead, it would now be available for planning routes for railways and for other purposes. Yolland thought that in all probability a survey 'would be connected, before any great lapse of time, with a complete registration of property',[10] and he suggested that all alterations to property boundaries etc. should be notified to some central department, so that a surveyor could be sent periodically into each county and parish to obtain the data from which the maps could be kept up to date. The questions asked about the need for large-scale plans of towns provoked a long discussion, since this topic was being considered by national and local authorities. Yolland said that nearly every town in the southern part of the kingdom would require surveys on a large scale, and that it would be very much more costly to call in the aid of civil surveyors.[11] He pointed out once more the difference between surveyors in civil practice and those employed by the Ordnance. The former, if qualified, were expected to be capable of undertaking all aspects of survey work, but the latter were employed upon particular branches of duty only:

> We have in point of fact a distribution and division of labour in the Ordnance Survey which no civil surveyor dreams of carrying out in his own profession.

In its report the Committee ventured an opinion on a subject seemingly remote from any military concern, which may, even at this early date, have raised doubts in some minds about the appropriateness of providing for the Survey under a military Vote:

> It appears advisable that the survey of the large towns should be preferred before the general survey of the counties . . . Such a proceeding will . . . increase the cost of the survey; but, on the other hand, it will relieve municipal bodies from the necessity of undertaking local surveys, and moreover, it will hasten the adoption of sanitary measures throughout densely-peopled districts, where such improvements are most needed.[12]

Another matter which apparently had little direct military relevance, was the subject of a Commission set up in February 1850.[13] Its task was to consider the system of registration of deeds and the forms of conveyancing, and once again Ordnance officers were called upon. In their evidence they held that the provision and use of public maps would lessen the expense of investigation of title and introduce conciseness in conveyancing. Captain Dawson thought that the six-inch maps then being produced for the northern counties of England would not be of sufficiently large a scale for registration purposes. He called attention to the fact that the tithe maps, at a scale of one inch to three chains, were now being used for the planning of railways, the sale of properties and for rating purposes. But Yolland, whilst believing that even the three-chain scale might prove too small in some cases, thought that six-inch maps, with additional data, could be 'made to answer for the rural districts'. This additional data – ownership of boundary fences and hedges etc. – he planned to put on the maps by using the electrotype method which he described in detail.[14] He believed that six-inch maps would be extended to the southern part of the country eventually, and that since so much survey work on this scale had been done, it should be accepted and made to answer in all practical cases. The maps should be periodically revised on the same principles as he had laid down before the Select Committee the year before. He would have preferred a scale of twelve inches to one mile, but he thought the scale of one inch to three chains 'altogether too large for a general map of the Kingdom'. In his final words to the Committee, Yolland insisted on the importance of an immediate decision:

> If, on the one hand, a survey on the present scale of 6 inches for the general map, and 60 inches for the towns of the northern counties and Scotland be insufficient, it would be better that it should, before more public money is expended on it, be changed to a sufficient scale. On the other hand, if it be sufficient, which I believe it is, then the sooner larger funds are devoted to the more rapid progress of the work, and for its progress southwards, as well as to the north, the greater will be the ultimate saving to the community.[15]

In April 1851 a Select Committee of the House of Commons, chaired by the Honourable Francis Charteris (who later became Lord Elcho), was appointed to enquire into and report on the present state of the Ordnance Survey of Scotland. Evidence was taken during May, June and July, and again both Hall and Yolland were called. The whole history of the Scottish survey was gone into and the reasons for the delay in the publication of the general map on the one-inch scale were discussed. Both officers were closely questioned on the merits of showing relief by contours against other methods, and both agreed that reduced contours, from which hill-shading could be produced, represented the best method.[16] Hall reported that the triangulation of Scotland was now finished, and Yolland that survey operations had moved from Wigtown and Kirkcudbright to Dumfries and Edinburgh, the latter county to be finished by the coming October. The town plans of Wigtown and Stranraer at five feet to one mile had been completed. In the course of the hearing it was reported that sheets of the six-inch survey of Lancashire and Yorkshire were then being published; the first sheet had appeared in April 1847, seven followed in 1848, twelve in 1849 and four in 1850. The publication of the one-inch map was held up because all the available engravers were engaged on the town plans and on the six-inch maps.

The Select Committee reported in July 1851. It recommended:

1 that the six-inch scale be abandoned;
2 that the system of contouring be abandoned;
3 that the survey and plotting on the two-inch scale be proceeded with as rapidly as was consistent with accuracy, with a view to the publication within ten years of a one-inch map, shaded and

engraved in a manner similar to the Ordnance one-inch map of England, with as many elevations as possible given in figures;

4 that the survey be proceeded with steadily from south to north, as was the original intention;

5 that the suggestions made by Mr Brunel* be adopted (the showing on future Ordnance maps of lines of latitude and longitude at every half degree or 15 minutes).

The decision in favour of the one-inch map was taken on the grounds that 'it was better adapted to geographical purposes and that the six-inch map alone was not of sufficient public utility to justify the large expenditure of public money that was required'. These extraordinary recommendations were a new delaying factor in the progress of the Ordnance Survey. When it received the Select Committee's report, the Treasury wrote to the Master General and Board of Ordnance, saying that it was 'disposed to concur in the opinion of the Committee' and asked if there were any objections to the adoption of the recommendations.

Hall's reply was sharp and cogent.[17] He said that the decision to survey the northern counties of England and Scotland at the six-inch scale had been reached, after much consideration and representation, by the Government in 1840 and that this was in accordance with the views expressed by the Highland and Agricultural Society of Scotland. Since this Society had not made further representations, the views of its Secretary, who gave evidence against the six-inch scale, 'should be received with caution'. Hall pointed out that the Committee's recommendations had been based on the evidence of three civil engineers, who had little experience of using six-inch maps and that

the opinions relied on are exceedingly contradictory of each other, and opposed to the opinions entertained by civil engineers generally, and in some instances the facts alleged are so erroneous as to admit of explicit denial.

He suggested that, if the final decision went against a general six-inch map, at least that scale should be retained for the 'mineral, manufacturing, and improvable districts'. As for contours, if the expense was too great, perhaps contouring could be limited to land below 1000 or 1500 feet. But he added:

I venture further to point out the want of economy that frequently attends a compliance with an ill-judged recommendation, though ostensibly pointed towards an apparent saving at the outset . . . I would venture also with great deference to observe, that the Committee was almost entirely composed of non-professional men; that the question, that of a proper scale for a national survey, is of a professional nature.

Together with his own letter he submitted others from civil engineers and scientists, among them one from the Astronomer Royal in Scotland, who regarded the recommendations to abandon the six-inch scale and contouring as 'an intense absurdity . . . a decided case of retrogression to the dark ages' and thought that the Committee were 'altogether erroneous in their foundations, and untoward in their conclusions'. The Superintendent's opinion was upheld by Sir John Burgoyne who wrote in a covering letter that

there is little doubt but that the advocates for the small scale have, on a partial or imperfect view, greatly undervalued the utility of the larger map.

After receiving these letters, and pending a decision by Parliament, the Treasury issued a Minute dated 16 December 1851[18] in which it agreed to the six-inch survey being continued in those counties at present being surveyed at that scale:

. . . and according to the same arrangements in other respects as are now in force; but that no expense should be incurred for the survey of other counties until this important subject shall have received more full consideration.

This concession at least gave the Ordnance Survey the prospect of continuing with its existing programme, but it was obvious that, unless firm decisions were taken shortly, a good deal of time and money would be wasted. But some fifteen months were to pass before the chairman of the Select Committee of 1851, Francis Charteris, replied to the letters of Hall and Burgoyne. During this time the six-inch surveys, within the limited counties, and the town surveys were continued, and the engraving of these and of the one-inch maps went ahead, but the survey of Haddingtonshire was started on the one-inch scale.

THE QUARREL BETWEEN HALL AND YOLLAND[19]

While the arguments about the basic scale exercised Parliamentary committees, a smaller dispute was taking place between Hall and Yolland, which ended with the latter being transferred to Ireland and

* I. K. Brunel, the engineer.

his place taken by Captain John Cameron of the Irish office. This dispute started in July 1852, when it came to Hall's notice that the volume entitled *Astronomical Observations made with Airy's Zenith Sector 1842–1850* had been printed. The work on this volume had been done by Yolland and the title-page as then printed made no mention of the Superintendent. Hall felt that, as head of the Survey, the proofs should have been passed to him for approval before being sent to the printer, and told Yolland so. This led to charge and counter-charge between the two officers and eventually the matter was referred to the Inspector-General, who supported the Superintendent. In his letter to Yolland of 22 August 1852 conveying this information, Hall wrote:

> ... alteration to be made in any officer's work does not *necessarily* imply a censure, although in this case it certainly does in some degree, and under the Inspector-General's apprehension, deservedly so.

On 26 August Hall issued an order removing Yolland from executive control of the headquarters at Southampton and limiting his duties to the charge of those employed in the field and office in connection with the triangulation. Yolland wrote to the Inspector-General, through Hall, asking for an enquiry to be held into the circumstances connected with the publication of the zenith sector operations:

> ... which have led to my removal ... from ... executive duties ... with which I have been entrusted for upwards of twelve years, without ... complaint.

He went on to say that the charges levied against him were due not only to the disagreement with Hall about the publication of the *Astronomical Observations*, but also to

> my respectful remonstrances made to him from time to time ... against changes in the arrangements and mode of carrying on the survey duty, such changes being in opposition to those under which the Ordnance Survey has attained its present position in the Public estimation.

He also said that he had been kept in ignorance of certain changes and alterations respecting the survey, but that these had been discussed by Hall with other officers. Hall's marginal comments on this letter show the deepness of the rift between the two men:

> I have a right to apportion work or men as I please.
> I command this Survey, not Captain Yolland.
> The practice in a military department is to adhere to military etiquette.
> I protest against officers under my command giving opinions on my orders unless called to do so.

Hall sent Yolland's letter with his own comments to the Inspector-General, with a further letter setting out his position and containing a severe criticism of Yolland's attitude:

> [This] has been forced upon me by Captain Yolland's overbearing tone. Difficulty or demur during my whole period of service in the Corps I have never before experienced from any other officer under me and I had hoped to continue to rule by kindness. But an attempt to render me a cypher I must oppose with firmness.

Burgoyne wrote to the Master General informing him that there was no cause for an investigation and that the alteration to the title page of the Zenith Sector publication was of 'trifling importance' and ought not to be regarded by Yolland as a censure. The Master General, in reply, said that both officers should be informed that it was Lieutenant-Colonel Hall's duty to reorganize the Survey as he thought fit and also amend publications if required, but in the specific actions referred to it could not be 'justly considered that any censure upon Captain Yolland was implied'. He concluded that he hoped there would be 'no more differences or obstacles to the cordial performance of all the duties of this important branch of the service'. There the matter might have ended, but on 2 October Hall wrote two letters: one was to Yolland saying that he had received information that he had used '*private* means ... to oppose the official course of a late correspondence from this office'; the other was to the Inspector-General, stating that Captain Yolland was available for general duties of the Corps from 1 November. Yolland denied the charge, but added:

> ... it has been a subject of regret to me, that the Master General of the Ordnance should have removed that censure, without having permitted me to shew in detail, that it was entirely unmerited.

Hall was asked by the Inspector-General to reconsider his decision about Yolland and this he did, and on 7 October offered to retain him in the Survey, but in Ireland. Yolland hedged and asked if he could continue to work on the publication of the triangulation, but Hall became impatient, and on Monday morning, 11 October, sent a curt note:

> I cannot ... further alter my arrangements to suit your private convenience. To my offer of the 7th I must request a reply this evening.

Yolland accepted and left for Ireland on 18 November, taking over from Cameron, who reported for duty at Southampton.

The seeds of this discontent were probably sown in 1847 when Hall was appointed Superintendent, although Yolland had been preferred by Colby and others. Yolland had for long been accustomed to Colby's tolerant ways so far as he was concerned, and changes, especially when made by a man who had no previous experience in survey, must have been hard for him to bear. Hall, on the other hand, was sixteen years older and a stickler for military etiquette and he clearly felt the weakness of his position at Southampton. Once he had found his feet, with the help of Yolland, Gosset and Tucker, he wished to rule. A clash was inevitable, but the departure of Yolland was a tragic loss to the Trigonometrical Branch.

THE SCALES DISPUTE RESUMED

On 10 February 1853 Charteris issued a memorandum in reply to Hall's review of his Committee's recommendations and the subsequent Treasury Minute of 16 December 1851. On the question of scale he said that his own view had not changed: he still thought that six inches to one mile was too large for general purposes and too small for most civil purposes. But no less than thirty-four memorials had been received from various Scottish local authorities and institutions since May 1852 for the six-inch scale to be continued and, in spite of the Treasury Minute of 16 December limiting the six-inch scale to the counties where it was in operation at that date, sanction had been given for it to be extended to the counties of Haddington and Fife in Scotland and to Durham in England. He had also found out from the Ordnance Map Department that surveys at the same scale had been begun and subsequently stopped in the counties of Dumfries, Ayr and Linlithgow. In view of all this permitted activity at the large scale, Charteris realized that it would be difficult to refuse further requests and he agreed with Hall's suggestion that the six-inch scale should be extended over the whole of the cultivated districts, and that a one-inch map should also be published. However, he urged that, before a final decision was taken, it might well be advisable to consider surveying the cultivated districts upon a much larger scale than six inches to one mile. He suggested twenty-four inches to one mile for the survey scale and twelve inches for that of the published maps. There was a strong case for further enquiry into the question of the basic scale for the general survey of towns, since the present scale of five feet to one mile was proving too small. On contouring, Charteris merely stated that his Committee had 'entered fully into the subject, and unanimously recommended its abandonment, as being of no real practical use'.

The memorandum set in motion a whole series of correspondence about the basic scale and the showing of relief, which was to last for the next eighteen months, and led eventually to the scale of 1:2500 (approximately twenty-five inches to one mile) being partially accepted, together with the system of contouring supplemented by hill shading.[20]

The surveys of Haddington, Fife and Durham, and later of Dumfries and Ayr, referred to by Charteris, were the results of letters to the Treasury from Hall. In February 1853 he wrote again:

> The time has now come when it is absolutely necessary that I should receive immediate instructions as to the scale on which the counties of Dumfries and Ayr are to be executed, and until I am favoured with a decision to enable me to proceed with some counties in the south-west of Scotland, I shall be unable to allocate a new district to the surveyors' force which is now completing other parts.[21]

No reply had been received by 13 April so he wrote once more:

> . . . officers and men are at the present moment awaiting the allocation of new districts and . . . a continuance of delay in receiving orders will cause considerable loss to the public service both of time and money.[22]

This produced a response from the Treasury, giving authority for the surveys to be carried out 'with that degree of accuracy which would admit of the plans of the cultivated districts being hereafter drawn to the scale of 24 inches to a mile, if desired'. The survey of County Durham at the 1:2500 scale, the first English county to be so treated, was considered to be authorized by this ruling.

Charteris's memorandum, the correspondence which passed between the Treasury and the Ordnance in 1840 before the six-inch scale was adopted, and a letter from Dawson advocating a basic scale of twenty-four inches to one mile for rural areas and a ten-foot scale for towns, were sent in April 1853 by the Treasury to many private persons, authorities and institutions. The documents were accompanied by a Treasury circular which simply asked what increase, if any, should be made in the present six-inch scale for rural surveys and in the five-foot for the towns, it being understood that, in any circumstances, a separate map at one inch to one mile would be published. Of the one hundred and fifty-two replies received by November, only thirty-two were in favour of retaining the six-inch scale; the rest were in favour of a larger scale. The majority of the latter preferred a survey scale of between 24 and 26 inches, and a published scale of between six and twelve inches, although a few expressed a wish to see the published scale the same as the survey scale. For the survey of towns, the majority thought the ten-foot scale should be adopted and the engraving made at the five-foot. One of this majority was Mr Farr, who had been appointed by the Registrar General to attend the Statistical Conference at Brussels in September 1853. He reported that at the Conference, which discussed the scales of national maps, opinion was unanimous in favour of scales of 1:500 and 1:2500, and of a reduction to 1:10 000. The 1:2500 and 1:500 scales were also recommended by the Statistical Society of London.

The Treasury circular of April 1853 and the accompanying documents had been sent to the Master General of the Ordnance and thence via the Inspector-General of Fortifications to Hall, who replied that, although he had spoken for the retention of the six-inch before the 1851 Committee and now attached letters from civil engineers supporting this view, he had never contended that the six-inch scale provided the answer for all purposes. He was

decidedly of the opinion that the 12-inch is the best scale to be adopted for a general map of all the arable rural districts of the Kingdom; villages and towns to be on exceptional scales of two feet, five feet and ten feet to a mile, according to the nature of the place . . . Whatever be the scale of the published plans, those are the plans the public generally will use, not the manuscript tracings.[23]

On the showing of relief, Hall could not 'understand that doubts should exist as to the superiority of contouring over any other system for physical relief on the large scale, and as a basis for any kind of expression of relief on the one-inch map'.[24] He was very outspoken about Dawson's unfavourable attitude to contouring and critical of the man himself:

Lt-Col Dawson . . . seems to forget that while he has been absent from his corps duties for the unusually long period of 17 years, his brother officers have been studying their profession, and . . . the various systems of hill-delineation on all scales in vogue, and that the Ordnance Survey, since Lt-Col Dawson's connection with it, has acquired an accumulated amount of experience and information that should render its opinions on these subjects worthy of respect and confidence.

Lieutenant-Colonel Tucker and Captain Gosset, who had been sent to Paris in 1852 to study French methods of map design and printing, wrote agreeing with the Superintendent, as regards both scale and relief. The Inspector-General and the Master General added their own letters to Hall's report on its way to the Treasury: both thought that the six-inch and one-inch scales should be retained, and that contouring should not be abandoned without further consideration.[25]

Within a few days Hall and Gosset were called before another Select Committee, under the chairmanship of Sir Denham Norreys, which had been appointed in July 1853 to consider the reduced map of Ireland and, in particular, how relief should be shown.[26] Hall restated his opinion that the hill shading used on the English maps was objectionable on account of its intensity, and necessitated the omission of other detail. As a method of showing relief, contouring was superior to all others:

As an engineer, I should prefer on the one-inch map . . . simple contours. . . . But as Superintendent of the Ordnance Survey, it is not for me to advance my own opinions, but to attempt to meet the requirements of all classes; the man of science, the engineer, and the less instructed, though perhaps more numerous, public; and I have . . . strongly advocated the reduced contours on one plate . . . and hill sketching . . . on a duplicate plate . . . the hill shading being based on contours . . . Contours compel the truth to be given as nearly as hill shading can give it.[27]

He added that experiments were being made in printing contours in colour. Gosset agreed with all that Hall said and stated that the experiments being conducted at Southampton on the use of colour would be completed in about a month.

The Select Committee issued its report on 12 August, recommending that on the Irish one-inch map the relief should be shown by contours, supplemented by hill shading 'of a character as transparent as possible'.

In January 1854 the Treasury sent our a further circular listing three groups of scales and asking each recipient which group he would recommend for adoption, bearing in mind that the scale should be sufficiently large 'to comprehend all the objects for which Surveys and Maps are usually made'. The scale groups were:

1. 24 inches to one mile for rural areas and ten feet to one mile for towns;
2. 26⅔ inches to one mile for rural areas and ten feet to one mile for towns;
3. 1:2500 for rural areas and 1:500 for towns.

The Treasury also asked whether the adoption of decimal scales 'would be productive of any practical inconvenience'.

All replies were passed to a Committee composed of Sir John Burgoyne, Mr W. Blamire and Mr James Rendel, which had been appointed by the Treasury in June, to consider and assess the opinions given. It reported in July that one hundred and ninety-one replies had been received: thirty-nine in favour of the first group, sixty-two in favour of the second and seventy-nine in favour of the third. Eleven proposed alternative scales. On the question of inconvenience, fifty-two thought there would be some, ninety-one thought there would not

The Treasury thereupon issued a Minute dated 15 July which authorized the survey of Ayrshire and Dumfriesshire at 1:2500 and stated that 'until a final determination shall be arrived at, as to the scale upon which the Ordnance Survey shall be conducted and engraved, the course which has been authorised in reference to Ayrshire and Dumfriesshire should be applied to the Survey of other districts'. It also stated that, before sanctioning the adoption of the large scale 'as a general measure', comparative costs must be obtained and that in the rural surveys 'trial be made of the system of piecework within the Department, and of that of independent contracts with other Surveyors supervised and approved by the Officers of the Survey'. A report on the expenses of the new large-scale survey and a comparison with the six-inch survey was requested at an early date.

As the enquiry about scale was proceeding, a similar one was being conducted on the question of showing relief. Sir Charles Trevelyan wrote on 20 October 1853 to Major Larcom, whom he called the 'Father of contouring in this country', and who was still in Ireland, asking for his views. In his reply Larcom outlined the history of the use of contours and stressed the advantage of showing them:*

> But I think all the Treasury need do is affirm or approve the principle; all else may best be left to the Surveying Department.[28]

Lieutenant-Colonel Dawson wrote to Trevelyan in December and agreed that contouring could be useful for works but 'only when carried out with a degree of precision . . . which would render its adoption for a National Survey perfectly unjustifiable. But the superiority of the pictorial mode of expression has been exemplified and admitted in the Welsh maps'. So far as engineering works were concerned, 'levels applying to the natural lines of ground should be equally effective for these purposes'. Charles Vignoles, the eminent civil engineer, who also had been approached by Trevelyan, suggested that a combination of contouring and a system of surface levels would be the best solution, saying that he would be 'very sorry indeed that the system of Contours should be wholly abandoned'.

To complete his dossier Trevelyan obtained from the elder Robert Dawson a paper on the representation of the physical forms of ground in topographical maps. This concluded with a remark which, perhaps, summarizes Dawson's attitude to mapping:

> The draftsman's art is to do justice to nature and the engraver's to do justice to the draftsman; on neither should rules and methods be imposed, except by superior artistic judgment . . .[29]

A Treasury Minute was issued on 23 May 1854, appointing a Committee on Contouring composed of nine members, including the Earl of Ellesmere as Chairman.[30] The terms of reference were amplified in another Minute dated 6 June:

1 the maps to be considered for contouring were the one-inch, six-inch and 'a scale not less than 24 inches and not more than $26\frac{2}{3}$ inches';
2 the Committee should 'ascertain what mode of conducting the Survey would be attended with the greatest public advantage'.

The Committee held several meetings at the Ordnance Office which Lieutenant-Colonel Dawson and Captain Gosset attended; it issued a report on 20 July. It recommended that a map founded on a national survey should have recorded on it numerous surface levels laid down with great accuracy, and that these levels should be taken on certain principal lines and shown in feet to two places of decimals. They should be given upon roads, highways, railways, canals, bridges, churches etc. On the six-inch map 'contour lines to a certain extent' should be added. They should be instrumentally traced with

---

* The first applications of contours in the United Kingdom appears to have been in 1777 when Charles Hutton and Nevil Maskelyne attempted to derive the mean density of the Earth by determining the attraction of the Scottish mountain Schiehallion on the plumb-bob. Hutton connected together 'by a faint line all the points of the same relative altitude' in order to calculate the figure and dimensions of the mountain. Larcom was certainly largely responsible for the introduction of contours on Ordnance Survey maps, although military engineers had been familiar with their use since the end of the eighteenth century. He attributed the term 'contouring' to the elder Dawson who probably brought it into use when he was instructing young officers at the Royal Military College.

accuracy (the cost: five shillings a mile), and the system of interpolating contours abandoned. Contour lines, if in a different colour, would be useful on a one-inch map, but inexpedient on a 24-inch or 26⅔-inch map. Where a 24-inch or a 26⅔-inch map existed, it would be desirable that a reduction to a six-inch should be made and published. And in the preparation of the one-inch map, 'the most improved system of representing the features of the Country should be employed'. In its final paragraph the report stressed the importance of completing the one-inch map as soon as possible.

The recommendation about the one-inch map was further clarified as meaning 'hill-sketching on the ground, and hill-drawing on artistic principles, to which . . . should be added selected contours from those that might be authorised for the larger surveys, if they could be laid on the maps of a different colour'. Treasury Minutes of 28 July and 4 August 1854 approved the report and instructed that it was to 'be acted upon in future, in the conduct of the Ordnance Survey'.[31] The effect of the recommendations on contouring was a considerable reduction in the number of contours being surveyed or sketched for the six-inch map, but the new system did not conform with any simple rule.[32]

In the midst of all this activity the immediate direction of the Survey passed into different hands.

Hall's Successor

Hall, who had been promoted Brevet Colonel in June, left the Survey in August 1854 to take up a command in Corfu. He had held the post of Superintendent for seven years, which were possibly some of the most difficult in the history of the Survey. In almost every one of them he was summoned to appear before some committee or other to give evidence, or was asked to pronounce at length on various aspects of the survey, both past and present. And during the whole of this period no final decisions were reached on the question of scale, or the method of showing relief; instead decisions were made and then changed so that work started at one scale had to be continued at another. It was impossible to plan ahead and Hall's cry to the Treasury in February 1853: 'It is absolutely necessary that I should receive immediate instructions' would seem to echo across the years of his appointment. In addition he had staff troubles. Yet, as is evident from his statements before the various committees, he soon mastered the intricacies of the Survey's administration. The technical side he was bound to leave largely to others. He was a strict disciplinarian who did not hide his opinions as his comments about Dawson in his report of July 1853 and his treatment of Yolland demonstrate. He did not, however, try to push his own ideas on the Survey, but preferred that the needs of map users should be carefully considered. Hall was promoted Colonel in September 1854, Major-General in May 1859, and Lieutenant-General and a Colonel Commandant RE in August 1863. He died at Southampton on 16 March 1868 at the age of seventy-four.[33]

The question of a successor had to be settled. Yolland, who had been passed over in 1847 and who was the best qualified scientifically, had been sent to Dublin in 1852 and the following year had been moved to Enniskillen, 'the remotest survey office in the British Isles'.[34] The most obvious candidate was Major Henry Tucker, who had seen service on the Irish survey, had commanded a survey divisional office in northern England, and had been at headquarters in Southampton before being sent to Dublin in 1854. There was, however, another contender, Major Henry James, who had worked under Tucker in the field and who was well thought of by Hall. Tucker was turned down on account of his deafness – a disqualification put forward by Colonel Matson, the Adjutant of the Corps of Royal Engineers and James's father-in-law[35] – and Major James was appointed to the vacant post on 11 August 1854, at the age of fifty-one.

He had joined the Survey in 1827 and for fifteen years had served under Colby on the Irish survey and at one time had his eyes on the post at its head then occupied by Larcom who, he thought, might succeed Colby at Southampton.[36] For four years, 1846–50, he was employed on general Corps duties and became Chief Engineer at Portsmouth Dockyard. On his return to the Survey in 1850 he took charge of the divisional office at Edinburgh, a position which he was holding at the time of his appointment to the superintendency. The immediate reactions to his appointment were the resignations of Tucker and Yolland. The former died a few years later in the West Indies;[37] the latter was appointed an Inspector of Railways under the Board of Trade, and became Chief Inspector in 1877.*

---

* Yolland was one of the most distinguished officers of the Board of Trade Railway Inspectorate and had a profound influence on the introduction of safety measures, largely through his ruthless criticism of dilatory railway managements.

Notes

1 C. F. Close, *The Early Years of the Ordnance Survey* (reprinted Newton Abbot 1969), p. 152.
2 *Ibid.* p. 153.
3 *Report from Select Committee on Ordnance Survey Ireland*, p. v: PP 1846 (664) XV.
4 PP 1847–8 (320) LX, p. 391.
5 *Metropolitan Sanitary Commission, Minutes of Evidence* No. 32: PP 1847–8 [895] XXXII.
6 *Ibid.* No. 33.
7 T. W. J. Connolly, *History of the Royal Sappers and Miners* (London 1855), II, pp. 77–82.
8 *Minutes of Evidence taken before the Select Committee on Army and Ordnance Expenditure*, p. 456: PP 1849 (499) IX.
9 *Ibid.* p. 496.
10 *Ibid.* p. 461.
11 *Ibid.* p. 500.
12 *Ibid.* p. lxiv.
13 *First Report . . . Registration and Conveyance Commission* p. 1: PP 1850 [1261] XXXII.
14 *Ibid. Minutes of Evidence*, p. 563.
15 *Ibid.* p. 569.
16 *Report from Select Committee on Ordnance Survey (Scotland)*, p. 214–16: PP 1851 (519) X.
17 *Correspondence . . . in reference to Ordnance Survey (Scotland)*, p. 2: PP 1852 (506) LIII.
18 *Ibid.* p. 14.
19 See OS Library, 4690, for Hall's correspondence on this subject.
20 *Correspondence respecting the Scale for the Ordnance Survey*, p. 19: PP 1854 [1831] XLI.
21 *Report of the Select Committee Ordnance Survey of Scotland, Minutes of Evidence*, p. 9: PP 1856 (198) XIV.
22 *Ibid.*
23 *Correspondence respecting Scale . . .*, p. 202: PP 1854 [1831] XLI.
24 *Ibid.* p. 214.
25 *Ibid.* p. 195.
26 *Select Committee on the Map of Ireland*: PP 1852–3 (921) XXXIX, p. 393.
27 *Ibid.* p. 2.
28 *Correspondence respecting Scale . . .*, p. 348: PP 1854 [1831] XLI.
29 *Ibid.* p. 363.
30 *Ibid.* p. 364.
31 *Ibid.* p. 367.
32 See the table, Appendix IV.
33 *The Times*, 21 and 24 March 1868.
34 J. H. Andrews, *A Paper Landscape* (Oxford 1975), p. 212.
35 *Ibid.* p. 246.
36 *Ibid.* p. 245.
37 *Ibid.* p. 246.

11
The Scales
Dispute –
Henry James
1854–1863

The Conclusion of the Scales Dispute

James had shown himself to be a man of marked ability and ambition with an eye to the main chance and a willingness to quarrel with persons putting forward views differing from his own.[1] Once in authority he began to give the positive and determined leadership the Survey needed. There is no doubt that he had kept himself informed of the changes proposed by the various Parliamentary Committees over the previous few years and, within two weeks of taking office, he was writing to the Inspector-General of Fortifications making proposals and suggesting policies. On 26 August 1854 he wrote stating that he was carrying on the survey on the 1:2500 scale in accordance with the Treasury Minute of 15 July, but pointed out that no instructions had yet been received on the scale of the town surveys. He suggested 1:500, which would bring 'the plans of the towns in harmony . . . with the plans of the rural districts, and be a further step towards introducing the decimal system into our topography'.[2] He wrote a second letter on the same day, requesting orders to start the survey of Glasgow at 1:500 without calling for a contribution from the local authority, and proposing that in future no contribution should be asked for from towns in areas undergoing survey. These letters were passed to the Treasury and on 19 October the Secretary, Sir Charles Trevelyan, drew up a memorandum listing the points to be decided and giving possible solutions.[3] This memorandum went to Lord Elcho who, in February the next year, produced one of his own. Both memoranda drew attention to the fact that the public had shown that they wished to have a second engraved map at a scale larger than one inch to one mile, but expressed doubts about the necessity for making and publishing a large-scale survey of the whole of Scotland. Both agreed that the town surveys should be made at the 1:500 scale.

On 22 March 1855 James, now Lieutenant-Colonel, submitted a memorandum in which he commented on the recent debate in the House of Commons, when Lord Seymour had at first opposed the introduction of the 1:2500 scale, but had withdrawn his opposition when Lord Palmerston agreed that 'nothing should be done upon the large scale except in Ayrshire and Dumfriesshire until the experiments on relative costs were concluded'. James strongly advised that the large-scale survey should continue, since 'whatever is done for the large-scale is always available for any smaller'. Any other course would cost time and money. The debate in the House had also been noticed by Lieutenant-Colonel Dawson, who wrote to the Treasury urging that 'the prosecution of a Property survey as a national work, must be undertaken at no distant date.'[4]

Six weeks later, in answer to questions from the Treasury, James restated his conviction that the six-inch scale was the least which should be adopted for the whole of Scotland, and that the 1:2500 should be applied in the cultivated areas. A one-inch map should also be published for the whole country. He ridiculed the idea that the one-inch would be a sufficiently large scale for the uncultivated areas, remarking that 640 acres would be shown by a square inch:

> We might draw the plan of an estate of 500 acres on the proprietor's thumb nail.[5]

He estimated that this programme would cost £677 000 and that, with grants of £70 000 a year, it could be completed within ten years.[6]

The Treasury considered the various points set out in this latest correspondence and issued an important Minute dated 18 May 1855, granting authority for the 'populous, cultivated, and mineral districts of Scotland' to be surveyed at 1:2500, and giving the Superintendent of the Survey discretion to choose these districts. The uncultivated areas were to be surveyed on the six-inch scale, but these and the 1:2500 surveys were not to be published, although copies could be made on request from the originals by the anastatic process.* The one-inch map was to be proceeded with as rapidly as possible and town surveys were to be made at the 1:500 scale. A final paragraph stated that local contributions were no longer required, except in the case of special surveys made in districts in which the general survey was not in progress.

James's point that the 1:2500 survey could be reduced to six inches to one mile, so that a complete map at this scale would be available over the whole of Scotland, was not taken up, and on 30 June he wrote to the Inspector-General of Fortifications, asking that this should be considered. He pointed out the necessity for having all the information that was portrayed on the 1:2500 plans

> condensed for all general purposes into a smaller and more convenient size, even to the smallest size upon which everything can be properly represented to scale; and this we know from experience is the scale of 6 inches to a mile.[7]

He also asked that, in future, the boundaries of properties should be shown on the Ordnance plans. This letter was passed to the Treasury on 1 August by Lord Panmure, the Secretary of State for War,** 'for favourable consideration' and with a recommendation that although no 1:2500 plans should be engraved or lithographed until Parliament had given approval for surveys at this scale to be extended beyond the present experimental limits, the reduction at six inches to one mile could be engraved and published.

By his perseverance James was successfully obtaining more room to manoeuvre and also gradually placing the Survey on a secure foundation. By February 1856 he had completed his investigations into comparative costs between surveying at 1:2500 and at six-inch scale, the system of piece-work within the Department, and contracts with independent private surveyors. He submitted his conclusions to the Inspector-General, who forwarded them without comment to the Treasury the following day. The cost per acre of surveying at the 1:2500 scale was one shilling and, at the six-inch, ninepence farthing. James was confident that the former would soon be reduced to elevenpence. Piece-work was a success:

> I have tried the experiment on almost every branch of the work, and in all the counties in progress, and the result is highly favourable to the system.[8]

On the other hand, the trial of independent contracts proved unsatisfactory. The contract surveys had to form an integral part of the general survey and therefore had to be based on the general triangulation. Diagrams were supplied to the contractors and, for a small payment, sheets could be obtained by them with the marginal lines and scale already plotted; a survey officer prepared a boundary sketch from boundary traverses and these were given to the contractors; levels were also supplied. Yet, 'with all this, the system failed';[9] plans received under it were badly and inaccurately drawn; the county of Peebles was incomplete for want of the plans contracted for.

Five years after the disastrous Select Committee of 1851 the scales for the survey of Scotland still remained to be formally settled. By this time the secondary triangulation was proceeding in Lanarkshire, Selkirkshire and Roxburghshire, so that the topographical survey could continue in this part of Scotland, and the counties of Wigtown, Kirkcudbright, Edinburgh, Haddington, Fife and Kinross, Linlithgow and the Isle of Lewis had all been surveyed and engraved on the six-inch scale. The Isle of Lewis had also been contoured 'to an enormous extent . . . perfectly unjustifiable in that island'[10] and engraved at the one-inch scale. The counties of Ayr, Dumfries, Renfrew, Linlithgow, Peebles and half of Berwick had been surveyed and partly published at 1:2500. James had issued instructions that, as the large-scale work was finished, it was immediately to be reduced to the one-inch and engraved, and in consequence a large number of sheets at this scale were in preparation.[11] As the large scale in each county proceeded, so did the 1:500 of the towns with over 4000 inhabitants; some important smaller towns were also surveyed. By April 1856 the towns completed were Berwick, Cupar, Dalkeith, Dumfries, Dunfermline, Edinburgh, Haddington, Kircaldy, Kirkcudbright, Musselburgh, St Andrews, Stranraer and Wigtown.

Another Select Committee was appointed on 3 March to consider the scales for Scotland. It was composed of ten members and sat from 8–11 April under the chairmanship of Viscount Duncan. Ten witnesses were called to give evidence; these included James and Dawson, and the Lord Advocate.

The Lord Advocate spoke in favour of a 1:2500 map and gave it as his opinion that in ten to twenty years the deposit of maps of property in mortgage and transfer deals would completely supersede the

---

* A method of direct transfer from an original to a specially prepared zinc plate. The original had to be soaked in dilute nitric acid before the transfer could be made. The process was not invented by Rudolf Appel, an assistant in the Ordnance Survey Office, as claimed in *Methods and Processes* (1875) but by C. F. C. Baldamus in about 1840.

** Control of the Ordnance Survey passed to the War Office in August 1855. See p. 135.

writing of detailed descriptions by lawyers.[12] Charles Vignoles, the civil engineer, also spoke on this theme and drew attention to the similarity between the proposed 1:2500 plans of Scotland and the 1:2500 Bavarian survey. He pointed out the advantages that would accrue in Scotland, where every conveyance and transfer of property was already registered, if the same officers who registered the deeds were also to register the plans.

James, who gave evidence on three of the four days of the enquiry, referred to the opinions he had received from assessors in various parts of Scotland who were particularly concerned with the registration of property. They had, he said, all agreed that twenty-five-inch plans could be of immense service and infinitely more useful than small-scale maps. The revaluation of Scotland was proceeding under the Valuation Act of 1855 and James gave it as his opinion that this work could not possibly be carried out without a survey upon which all the properties could be shown.[13] When questioned about present policy, he repeated that when he took over from Colonel Hall in August 1854 he had the Treasury order of 15 July upon which to act. He continued:

> . . . and on the very same day I issued orders to all the people engaged upon the survey to commence upon that large scale; I did not look right or left, but went straight forward with that order before me; . . . we had now got six counties engraved upon the six-inch scale, and I considered that to apply that large 25-inch scale to the Highlands would be absurd; I had to consider that the six-inch survey was eminently suitable for all hydrographical purposes . . . that it was absolutely essential for the long seaboard of the country and that it was absolutely necessary for geological purposes; and taking all these subjects into consideration . . . I had no hesitation . . . in coming to the conclusion that the proper and safe course was to have the whole of the uncultivated districts upon the six-inch scale, and then to reduce the cultivated portion also to the six-inch scale, so as to make the whole survey complete and consistent within itself.[14]

Asked about the difficulties of distinguishing between cultivated and uncultivated land, James said that no instructions were needed:

> I can, without confusion or difficulty, trace through all the sinuosities of a glen or strath those portions necessary to be put on a large scale.[15]

In addition to the 1:2500 map of cultivated areas and the general six-inch map, he advocated a one-inch to be engraved of the whole of Scotland, which would be a reduction from the large-scale surveys.

In answer to questions on the estimated cost of the survey of Scotland, James said that the estimate had been based on the assumption that the 1:2500 survey could be made at one shilling an acre, but accounts kept over a year and a half had proved the cost to be a fraction less. The figure he gave was £917 000, which included the survey of the cultivated areas at 1:2500, the uncultivated areas at six-inch, the engraving and printing of maps on these scales and their reduction and engraving and printing at one-inch. It also included the cost of contouring. About one quarter of the survey had been completed at a cost of £284 000[16] and a further ten years' work was envisaged,[17] which would cost £633 000. An annual Vote of £63 000 would therefore be required over this period. James estimated that, because of Government indecision as to the scale of the survey, £5000 had been lost on surveying Haddingtonshire, Peeblesshire and Berwickshire at the one-inch scale after work on the six-inch had been suspended; the one-inch work was subsequently thrown away. Because he was without orders as to publication scale for fifteen months, surveys covering 867 000 acres had accumulated while the draughtsmen and computers had to remain idle. The estimated cost of this enforced idleness was £25 000.[18] Indirectly other losses had been incurred by other departments, as John Washington, the Hydrographer, revealed in a letter dated 1856:

> . . . within the last fortnight it has been my duty . . . to report to Parliament that the delay in completing the hydrographical survey of the lochs and sounds on the north-west coast of Scotland arises from not having any Ordnance map to work upon; consequently the marine surveyors have had to execute the whole of the topography, thus consuming ten years in a survey that ought to have been finished in half that time, and would have been so finished had we had the advantage of a six-inch Ordnance map.[19]

The Committee's report was published on 6 May 1856. On the cost of the survey it concluded:

> whatever the first outlay may be, it may hereafter be found . . . that it is more economical in the first place to produce a large cadastral map, from which other maps on smaller scales can be reduced at trifling expense, than to re-survey the ground, as had been the case, both in England and Scotland, owing to the insufficiency of the parent survey . . . the time has now arrived when it is absolutely necessary for Parliament to consider, and finally determine the comprehensive question, what is the nature of the survey they are prepared to sanction as the one which will most conduce to the general interest of the nation at large.[20]

The majority report faithfully reproduced James's recommendations, and was adopted by Parliament on 19 June 1856, but not before a motion objecting to the 1:2500 scale and proposing a reduction in the Vote for the Survey had been defeated.[21] A Treasury Minute, issued on 25 November, directed that the 1:2500 plans should be reduced to the six-inch scale, and published as recommended by the Committee. But alas for James's hopes! In a footnote added to his Report for 1855–6 he records:

> The decision of the House of Commons, on the 18th instant, [June 1857] has rendered nugatory all the arrangements we have made for making the plans on the 25-inch scale, and the reductions from them; and, after a seven years' discussion, we revert to precisely the same position we were in when the Treasury Minute of 1st October 1840 was issued.

The decision referred to was taken after a debate in which, on the motion of Sir Denham Norreys, the House decided by a majority of ten that the parish plans on the 1:2500 scale should be discontinued, and that the original survey should be plotted on the six-inch scale only, as was done in Ireland, in Yorkshire and Lancashire, and in several counties in Scotland.

The resources of the Survey were immediately reduced. The grant for 1857 was cut by £27 000 and James had to discharge eight hundred and fifty civilians. The strength of the survey companies was lowered from one hundred and twenty to one hundred per company, a further loss of eighty men.

To a less determined man this would have been a crushing blow, but James immediately resumed the fight, firmly repeating the recommendations he had made to the Committee of 1856. James has sometimes been accused of suppressing initiative and enterprise by his policy of standardization, but it was his consistent and confident adherence to this policy which steered the Survey through the final years of the scales dispute. Neither Colby, Yolland, nor Hall had spoken with such unvarying conviction.

On 24 December 1857 a Royal Commission was appointed to enquire into the Survey and to report on:

1 the principal purposes of the survey;
2 its progress and the scales upon which it had been drawn;
3 the changes in scale and detail to be made, if any;
4 estimated cost of completion of the survey in the manner recommended.

The Commission, under the chairmanship of Lord Wrottesley, President of the Royal Society, met on 10 March 1858 to receive evidence. James was one of the five called on. He produced the details of cost of the large- and small-scale alternatives, and a potted manual of surveying and printing for the commissioners to study, together with a memorandum on the advantages of having four map series: Towns 1:500, Parishes 1:2500, Counties six-inch and Kingdom one-inch. His evidence covered seven pages out of the thirty-five of the final report, in which he was referred to as 'the present able Superintendent'.

The Report was published on 20 May 1858 and it recommended that:

1 the one-inch map of the United Kingdom be forthwith completed, engraved and published;
2 the survey of the northern counties of England and the counties of Scotland should be completed and published, the cultivated districts at 1:2500 and the whole at six-inches and one-inch except the Highlands of Scotland, which were to be surveyed for the one-inch scale only. The sheets which included the coastline of all Scotland should be drawn at the six-inch scale for the hydrographic survey then in progress;
3 the revision of the six-inch map of Ireland should be completed;
4 the final determination of the question as to the expediency of extending the survey on the 1:2500 scale to the whole of the United Kingdom . . . 'to be left to the decision of the Legislature when the contemplated measures, with which it is more immediately connected, may have been adopted'.[22]

No action on the Report had been taken by 14 August, when the Secretary of State for War wrote to the Treasury, drawing attention to the fact that

> great delay and expense will be incurred if the Ordnance plans are drawn on the six-inch scale, as now directed, and should have again to be drawn on the 1:2500 scale as recommended by the Commissioners.

On 11 September the Treasury replied that the earliest opportunity would be taken of submitting this subject to Parliament, and authorized the continuation of the arrangements for publishing the results of the survey directed by the Treasury Minutes of 18 May 1855 and 25 November 1856.

James therefore continued the survey in accordance with the instructions issued prior to the Commons debate of 18 June 1857 – on the 1:2500 scale.[23] A great effort was obviously being made to complete the survey of the six northern counties of England, with the object of showing such progress to Parliament as to amount almost to a *fait accompli*. Yorkshire and Lancashire were complete and published on the six-inch scale; Durham was being engraved at the same scale and it was hoped the 1:2500 of this county also would be published by 31 March 1859. The completion of the survey of Westmorland was planned for the same date and surveying parties had been moved down from Scotland into Cumberland and Northumberland to help speed up the work in these two counties. The survey of towns continued and those of South Shields and Gateshead were published during the year, and since there were scarcely any more large towns to take-up in the north, it was expected that the 1:2500 survey would proceed more rapidly. In Scotland the survey of the Lowlands was almost complete at 1:2500 and at the six-inch, and a number of sheets had been published at both scales; the survey of the major towns was virtually completed and this, as in the north of England, meant that the 1:2500 would 'no longer be impeded by this difficult and expensive part of the work'.[24]

In his *Report* for 1859 James forecast the completion of the 1:2500 survey of the northern counties of England and of the one-inch map in 1860. He went on:

> The time has arrived for taking into consideration the expediency of proceeding with the detail survey of the remainder of England . . . I therefore strongly recommend that the subject of proceeding with the survey of England on the 25 inch scale should be taken into consideration by government and by Parliament, this year, that I may be enabled to make the preliminary arrangements . . . for proceeding without any costly delays with the survey of the remaining three-fourths of England and Wales.[25]

These high hopes suffered a severe set-back because of 'very numerous and extensive surveys' which were ordered 'for purposes connected with the Defences of the Country'. After the cession of Nice and Savoy to France in 1860, Palmerston's suspicions about the intentions of Napoleon III led him to the conclusion that war with France was a possibility that had to be provided for. He persuaded the House of Commons to vote £9m for the fortification of British ports and arsenals; the planning of this work was the cause of the demands made on the Ordnance Survey. The military surveys were of the London area, Chatham and Sheerness; Portsmouth and the Isle of Wight; Plymouth and environs; Pembroke and environs; Dover, Harwich, Torbay, East Hampton, Shoreham, Newhaven, and Cannock Chase. James was instructed on 22 August to postpone extending the six-inch and 1:2500 survey into new districts.[26] He withdrew one entire survey division from Northumberland and formed two new divisions by drawing a number of men from each of the other divisions. These three groups were placed under Major Burnaby, Captain Carey and Lieutenant Le Poer Trench for work on the defence projects. The number of acres to be surveyed was about 400 000 – later increased to 672 500[27] – and James proposed to deal with most of the areas at the 1:2500 scale and the rest at 1:500, making the work an integral part of the national survey. He was doing this, he said in his reply to the War Office on 27 August, because he anticipated that the cadastral survey would be extended to the whole of the United Kingdom.[28]

James's insistence was rewarded on 17 June 1861 by the appointment of a Select Committee to enquire into the possible extension of the 1:2500 scale into the south of England. The Committee, consisting of fifteen members under Viscount Bury as chairman, called seven witnesses, including Sir Henry James (knighted in 1860 for his services to science). The hearing lasted for four days and James gave evidence every day: the first day he was the sole witness. Of the Report's fifty-eight pages, his evidence occupies twenty-eight.[29]

At the end of July, having regard to the approaching end of the session, the Committee agreed to report the evidence taken so far, and proposed that it should be reappointed in the next session of Parliament. However, it made one recommendation on James's suggestion: that the 1:2500 map of the Isle of Wight, part of which had been surveyed at this scale for the National Defence Commissioners, should be completed.[30]

The Select Committee was reappointed in March 1862. The evidence already collected was carefully reconsidered and on 10 April the Committee issued its Report for consideration by Parliament. It recommended that the cadastral survey on the scales directed by the Treasury Minutes of 18 May 1855 and 11 September 1858 should be extended to those portions of the United Kingdom which had been surveyed on the scale of one inch to one mile only and that the work should be carried out as speedily as possible. The cost was estimated at £90 000 a year for twenty-one years, or £150 000 a year for twelve years.[31]

James had completely convinced the Committee of the rightness of his proposals and at last secure foundations were laid for the continuance of the work. Early in 1863 his success was confirmed. A Treasury Minute dated 18 March was issued, ordering the prosecution of the survey in the south of England on the 1:2500 and other scales mentioned in the Minute of 11 September 1858.

That the scales dispute ended at this time was partly a consequence of another development which established beyond question a need for accurate large-scale maps. A Royal Commission appointed in

1857 reported in favour of a system of registration of title to property and, on the subject of maps, concluded:

> . . . the use of a Government map, properly authenticated, for each individual property, together with the customary verbal description, would probably furnish the best means of describing and identifying the land and indexing it correctly.[32]

In 1862 the Land Registry Act introduced registration of title into England, and H.M. Land Registry was formed. However, the system authorized by the Act was not a success, partly because registration was voluntary, and partly because the Act required property boundaries to be precisely defined, which led to many disputes. Another reason was the lack of suitable maps over a large part of the country. In spite of this hesitant start, the requirement for official cadastral maps was never withdrawn and it remained the primary justification for the large-scale survey.

Looking back over the period of the scales dispute Matthew Arnold cynically wrote in 1862:

> The English government could not well shirk the duty of providing a map of England; but in discharging this duty, it has been hampered as only an English government is hampered, and it has shown an irresolution such as only an English executive can display. The history of our Ordnance Survey and of the Select Committees which have kindly undertaken to be its nursing fathers, is the satire of administration under a Parliamentary Government.[33]

The truth was that the industrial progress of the country and its social development resulted in a complex of new, sometimes overlapping, needs and in a clash of new and old interests. To some, the large-scale survey represented another extension of state intrusion, and to others an unwarranted incursion into the field of private enterprise. In determining the eventual pattern of the national survey, the personality of James and the consistency and force of his recommendations were undoubtedly of major importance. On this issue, he must be regarded as one of the key figures in its history.

The One-Inch Map in Disgrace

The year 1862 brought public criticism of the state of the one-inch maps of southern England. In a letter to *The Times* which was printed in the issue of 17 September, a correspondent calling himself 'Surveyor' complained bitterly of the out-of-dateness of one-inch maps which he had recently purchased in London. Railways were not shown and towns were portrayed as they had existed half a century earlier. There were especial criticisms of sheet 17, Dorchester and Weymouth area, which was dated 1811; sheet 24, Plymouth and South Devon, dated 1809; and sheet 7, London, dated 1822 and 'full of errors'. 'Surveyor' was of the opinion that 'the very numerous defects' were 'a disgrace to the national undertaking'. *The Times* published a leading article on 22 September, critical of the Ordnance Survey, and including the comment:

> if . . . English topography is left to private enterprise, we have no doubt the want [of up-to-date maps] would be shortly supplied, [but] private enterprise will not venture on a field which Parliament has seized.

On the same day James's reply to 'Surveyor' was printed. He admitted that the one-inch maps of southern England were out of date, but not as badly as stated. He offered 'Surveyor' revised editions of sheets 17 and 24 and explained that the London sheet was at that moment undergoing revision. But, in general, as regards the one-inch coverage of southern England, he thought that half a loaf was better than no bread. If the public of southern England wanted only a one-inch map, the revision of the existing sheets was a simple matter but he reminded his readers that there were demands for a cadastral survey at 1:2500 over this part of the country and that a decision on this by Parliament was awaited. Such surveys would not only be of great benefit, but would at the same time provide the material from which the present one-inch could be revised. This, however, would take time.

Edward Stanford, the map-seller who had supplied 'Surveyor' with his maps, took up a point from *The Times*'s leading article. In a letter published on the 23rd, he offered to undertake the publication of up-to-date maps if he could be free of government competition.

The charge that the one-inch maps had become obsolete had a good deal of truth in it; moreover, many people complained that the quality of the maps had suffered by their being reprinted so many times: that the plates had become worn and the impressions faint, and the beauty of their hill shading had disappeared. Matthew Arnold wrote in the *London Review* in December 1862:

> To amend their effaced shading thay have done nothing. They have . . . attempted a little detestable patching here and there; but the remedy is worse than the disease . . . Where is the Cumnor hill country on the right

bank of the Thames, as the original map gave it? Where is Bredon Hill, with all its beautiful staging from the plain to its summit?

He poured scorn on the suggestion of *The Times* that a cure would be to leave the work of map-making to private enterprise, but thought that the real culprit was Mr Joseph Hume from Montrose, a radical member of Parliament, who, by procuring a reduction in the price of a full sheet to two shillings, and of a quarter-sheet to sixpence, had created a demand for maps which had worn out the plates. 'It will be long,' he said, 'before electrotyped maps equal for beauty and clearness the best engraved ones: still the preservation of the new plates has been rendered possible. But, meanwhile, the old plates are spoilt.' Arnold argued that it was the Government's duty to provide a good map of its country, not a cheap one. 'Sir Henry James,' he said, 'reproached with the imperfections of his maps, talks to us about new means of multiplying impressions of them. Let him clearly understand what is expected of him.'

The complaints about the lack of revision and the deteriorating quality of the one-inch map were to continue for the next thirty years, as the varying resources of the Ordnance Survey became almost entirely absorbed in the cadastral survey.

The End of the Board of Ordnance

While the scales dispute was in progress two important changes occurred, one in the control of the Ordnance Survey and the other in the functions of its Superintendent. In 1855 the Board of Ordnance was abolished in the military reorganization that took place at the time of the Crimean War. Its powers were transferred to the War Office under the Ordnance Board Transfer Act of August 1855, and the direction of the Ordnance Survey passed to the Secretary of State for War. On 17 October 1856, the Royal Engineer Officers and the Royal Sappers and Miners were combined in the Corps of Royal Engineers under the Commander-in-Chief. The effect of these changes on the conduct of the survey of Great Britain was not very great but, as a direct result, the Superintendent of the Ordnance Survey acquired an additional responsibility.

The collection of topographical data for military intelligence[34] was first undertaken by a branch of the Quartermaster-General's Department in 1803, but this never became an effective organization and was virtually moribund at the time of the Crimean War. The so-called 'Depot of Military Knowledge' did nothing to provide the Army with maps of the Crimea, and these were eventually prepared by Major T. B. Jervis, a retired officer of the Survey of India, at his own expense; he was subsequently invited by the Secretary of State for War to form and take charge of a Statistical and Topographical Office within the War Department. When Jervis died in 1857 a committee was appointed to consider the future of the new Office. It recommended that the three military organizations with responsibilities for mapping – the Depot of Military Knowledge, the Topographical Office and the Ordnance Survey – should be placed under one Head of Department. Lord Panmure accepted this recommendation and appointed Lieutenant-Colonel James to be Director of the Topographical and Statistical Department of the War Office, which was to include the Ordnance Survey and the Quartermaster-General's Depot.

As it turned out, absorbing the Ordnance Survey was no easy matter; the sources of its vitality already lay outside the military field, and the result was that the Topographical and Statistical Office became virtually an appendage of the Ordnance Survey. When the surveys of Jerusalem and Sinai were made under the general supervision of James, it is significant that these were done by the Ordnance Survey, and not by the Topographical Office as might have been expected.

One of Lord Panmure's instructions was to influence the work of the Ordnance Survey for many years even after the connection with the Topographical Office was broken:

> Lord Panmure is desirous that you direct an early attention to the subject of Colonial Surveys, ascertaining as far as possible what works are in progress at the expense of Colonial Legislatures, and reporting whether it may not be possible to establish a system under which your department, with the concurrence of the Secretary of State for the Colonies, may assist in their systematic prosecution.

During 1858 several officers from the Survey were detached for work overseas: Captain R. M. Parsons with a party of twenty non-commissioned officers and men to survey British Columbia; Lieutenant-Colonel J. S. Hawkins and a party of six to survey the 49th parallel between British Columbia and the United States; Lieutenant W. Bailey and a party of six to survey the Cape of Good Hope. James also reported an application to survey the Colony of Victoria in Australia.[35]

The Staff — the Clash of Military and Civilian Interests

The system of military control which had developed in the 1840s had certain advantages which the officers of the Survey never failed to point out whenever it was brought into question. In the field the surveyors, military and civilian, were dispersed in small numbers throughout the United Kingdom; in 1855 there were no fewer than thirty-six detached levelling parties.[36] Each party, however small, on the triangulation, detail and contouring duties was under the charge of either a non-commissioned officer or a sapper who was responsible, in the strict military sense, for the work being carried out 'according to orders'. In this way a small number of Royal Engineer officers exercised, through the disciplinary hierarchy of the military organization, a remote but effective control over the operations of the Survey. Colby, at the time of his retirement, wrote:

> The Royal Sappers and Miners in the Survey are entrusted with the charge of difficult and important works without the advantage which other soldiers have, of being under the control of officers . . . to direct them in all cases requiring knowledge and consideration.[37]

Hall, on his departure from the Ordnance Survey, referred to the enhanced opportunities for promotion recently conferred through the addition of a Quartermaster, a Sergeant-Major and a Quartermaster-Sergeant to the sapper establishment.[38] The first to be commissioned as Quartermaster was William Young, who had worked directly under Yolland in the preparation of the zenith sector observations, and later under Clarke.[39] In the mid nineteenth century the opportunities for advancement were almost entirely with the sappers.

The dominant position of the sappers at the lower management and supervisory levels seems to have been accepted by the civilian staff for some years. The career prospects for the civilians were very uncertain; their number was increased for the town surveys in 1851 but this was followed by the drastic reductions of 1857, a further increase in 1859 and another severe reduction in 1861. Pay was low, and James's piece-work system introduced in 1854 could hardly have been popular with the staff. The work was classified into five groups – very open, open, medium, close, and very close – and each was paid for at a different rate; deductions were made for work below standard.[40]

Towards the end of the fifties, the grievances of the civilian staff began to be voiced. In December 1859 Mr Digby Seymour MP wrote to the Under Secretary for War, saying that the civil employees on the Ordnance Survey ought, in his 'humble judgment, to have an increase of pay, a better mode of advancement and test of proficiency, shorter hours of labour, and an extended leave of absence'.[41] The average daily pay was much lower than in other government departments; for promotion they depended upon the recommendation of the officer in charge, who, in some cases, was only a sergeant or corporal; they worked from 9 am to 5.30 pm, whereas other government employees worked from 10 am to 4 pm, or 9 am to 3 pm; and finally, they had fourteen days' leave a year, against the month of other employees. It was argued that £5000 a year would cover the wage increases and this could be found by lopping off some of the military staff. In his reply on 23 May 1860, after he had received a report from James, the Under Secretary spoke of the advantages of working for the Survey and of the improvements which had recently taken place with regard to pensions,[42] and ended by saying that he saw

> no reason for making the changes suggested . . ., believing that such changes would only lead to the disorganisation of a department which produces results which give general satisfaction to the public.

Agitation on behalf of the civilian assistants led to reactions from the military side and, in *The Times* of 13 August 1860, a letter was printed calling attention to service conditions. It was signed 'A Sapper, Royal Engineers' and pointed out that, whilst the civilian assistants had some cause for complaint, their lot was better than that of their military colleagues. 'There is no branch of the Ordnance Survey in which a Sapper of the Royal Engineers does not perform the duty as effectually as any of the civil force', yet while the civil force had fourteen days paid leave per annum and also Christmas, Good Friday, and all general feast days, the Royal Engineers were not allowed one half-day throughout the whole service without losing pay. The military worked under an existing order 'that no military man shall be allowed working pay save only for the time certified as actually at work by his commanding officer'. 'A Sapper' bemoaned the fact that the Saturday half-holiday movement had not yet been extended to the government offices in the War Department. He ended: 'It is sufficient that the government has acknowledged its utility and necessity and it is most certainly a piece of carelessness, if not of injustice, that it has not been extended to us'. Bold words for a serving Sapper!

In only one branch of the Ordnance Survey was the staff entirely civilian in 1855; this was the engraving department, where the rates of pay were higher than anywhere else. The Superintendent of

Engraving Hills was, as a rule, the most highly paid individual in the Department,[43] apart from the more senior officers. On the other hand, the civilian surveyors were at the bottom of the pay list. In 1863 surveyors with over ten years' service averaged only three shillings and tenpence a day compared with eleven shillings for the engravers of hills.[44] Among the field staff, the hill-sketchers received the highest reward – an average of six shillings a day.

In the early sixties the complaints of the civilian staff became focused on the lack of any standard system for regulating increases of pay. Increments were awarded at no stated times and by no fixed scale, but only on the special recommendations of the individuals charged with the superintendence. The claim of Hall in 1849 that the pay of the civilians at ten shillings a day compared favourably with military pay was false, because in practice it very rarely reached this figure, particularly in the field where the standards of the superintendence seem to have been very severe. Another extraordinary anomaly was that the Civil Assistants employed in the Topographical Office were paid at nearly double the rates applying in the Ordnance Survey, although both groups worked in the same office, sometimes under the same superintendent, on broadly similar duties.[45]

Whatever its other merits, and it had many, the prolonged military domination of the Ordnance Survey sustained itself on the arguments of effective control and cheapness. For the civilians the uphill road to equality was to be a long one.

James and Technical Developments

In accordance with instructions given by the Secretary of State for War in November 1855, James produced the first published *Report on the Progress of the Ordnance Survey* 'up to the present time and during the past year' (1855–6). No report was produced in 1857, but thereafter it became an annual affair which James, unlike some of his successors, used to full effect as a vehicle for publicity; at the same time it provided an invaluable record. In James's *Reports*, much of the descriptive text was written in the first person singular: this particularly applied to the technical and scientific aspects of the work. He was never one to hide his light under a bushel or to fail to publicize his successes, and he usually ascribed to himself the credit for the achievements of his Department.

In 1856 he wrote a short account of his investigations into improved methods of production and the use of photography for reducing the large-scale drawings to the smaller scales. He recounted how he had visited Paris in 1855 to test the practicability of accurately reducing plans by photography, and 'having satisfied myself that it was practicable to do so, I had two of the sappers who were with me instructed in the art of photography'. This method was thereafter employed and James gave an example of time saved:

> . . . during the last week one man, with the assistance of a printer and a labourer, reduced 32 000 acres from the 1:2500 to the six-inch scale, and . . . he produced three copies of 45 sheets, or 135 impressions in six days, besides some other work. One hundred draughtsmen could not have produced so much work.[46]

In this connection he recorded two years later an extraordinary intrusion by Parliament and the War Office into what would appear to have been a purely technical matter within the competence of the Ordnance Survey. Doubts had been expressed in Parliament about the accuracy of the photographic method of reduction; this led the Secretary of State to appoint a committee under the chairmanship of Sir Roderick Murchison, the Director of the Geological Survey, to investigate and report. This must have been a galling experience for James; however, the Committee reported that it was satisfied about both the accuracy of the photographic method and its financial advantages.

James's claim in later years to have discovered photozincography[47] appears in a rather different light in the *Report* for 1859, where the credit for introducing chromo-carbon photographic prints (which could then be transferred to waxed copper or to zinc) is given to Captain A. de C. Scott and Lance-Corporal Rider. In 1859 James seems to have restricted his personal claim to the invention of the name given to the process.[48]

Notes

1 J. H. Andrews, *A Paper Landscape* (Oxford 1975), pp. 246–7.
2 *Treasury Minute and Papers relating to the Ordnance Survey*, p. 19: PP 1854–5 [1933] XXXII.
3 *Ibid.* pp. 2–6.
4 *Ibid.* p. 16.
5 James's Minute to the Treasury of 7 May 1855.
6 *Treasury Minute* . . ., p. 17: PP 1854–5 [1933] XXXII.
7 *Report from Select Committee on Ordnance Survey of Scotland*, p. 118 (App. 2): PP 1856 (198) XIV.
8 *Ibid.* p. 120 (App. 2).
9 *Report . . . on Ordnance Survey of Scotland, Minutes of Evidence*, p. 48: PP 1856 (198) XIV.
10 *Ibid.* p. 71.
11 *Ibid.* p. 111.
12 *Ibid.* p. 82.
13 *Ibid.* p. 49.
14 *Ibid.* p. 59.
15 *Ibid.* p. 66.
16 *Ibid.* p. 53.
17 *Report . . . on Ordnance Survey of Scotland*, p. vii.
18 *Report . . . on Ordnance Survey of Scotland, Minutes of Evidence*, p. 114.
19 *Ibid.* p. 70.
20 *Report . . . on Ordnance Survey of Scotland*, p. vii.
21 OSR 1855–6, p. 6: PP 1857 [147] XXVII.
22 *Report of the Ordnance Survey Commission*, p. 11: PP 1857–8 [2396] XIX.
23 OSR 1858, p. 4: PP 1859 [2482] VIII.
24 *Ibid.*, p. 17.
25 OSR 1859, p. 4: PP 1860 [2629] XXIII.
26 *Correspondence relating to the Topographical Survey of Scotland*, p. 1: PP 1862 (104) XXXII.
27 *Ibid.* p. 2; *Report of the Select Committee on the Cadastral Survey*, p. 7: PP 1862 (161) VI.
28 *Correspondence . . . Topographical Survey of Scotland*, p. 2: PP 1862 (104) XXXII.
29 *Report . . . on the Cadastral Survey, Minutes of Evidence*: PP 1861 (475), XIV, p. 102.
30 *Ibid.* p. 95.
31 *Report of the Select Committee on the Cadastral Survey*, p. iii: PP 1862 (161) VI.
32 *Ibid.* p. 13 of App.
33 Matthew Arnold, *Prose Works*, ed. R. H. Super (1962), vol. 2, p. 255.
34 G. R. Frith, *The Topographical Section of the General Staff* (Chatham 1906), pp. 3–15.
35 OSR 1858, p. 11: PP 1859 [2482] VIII.
36 T. W. J. Connolly, *History of the Royal Sappers and Miners* (London 1855), II, p. 261.
37 *Ibid.* p. 286.
38 *Ibid.* p. 287.
39 *Ibid.* pp. 283–6.
40 OSR 1855–6, pp. 23–4: PP 1857 [147] XXVII.
41 PP 1860 (397) XL, p. 201.
42 Haydn Williams, *A Statement . . . on a System of Classification of Pay and Promotion* (London 1866), p. 24.
43 *Ibid.* p. 34.
44 *Ibid.* p. 32.
45 *Ibid.* pp. 25–6.
46 OSR 1855–6, p. 21: PP 1857 [147] XXVII.
47 OSR 1874, p. 5: PP 1875, C. 1204, LX.
48 OSR 1859, pp. 5–6: PP 1860 [2629] XXIII.

12
Clarke
and the
Principal
Triangulation

Alexander Ross Clarke

Although by 1841 the primary triangulation of Roy, Mudge and Colby together covered the whole of the United Kingdom, the resulting network was not of a uniform standard, neither had it been adjusted, with the measured lengths of the bases, to form a homogeneous whole by removing the effects of the many diverse errors and discrepancies that inevitably occur during such extensive and protracted operations. The work of adjusting the primary triangulation, taking into account the related problems of local attraction and of the size and shape of the Earth, demanded a level of mathematical ability which the Survey did not always command. Yolland had many of the qualities needed and while he was at Southampton, between 1842 and 1852, did much of the essential preliminary work. Not only did he remodel the procedure for observing and abstracting the angles but he also studied ways of calculating the triangles in order to establish over-all internal consistency, a subject on which he had extensive correspondence with Airy.[1]

Yolland's dispute with Hall put an end to any possibility of his completing the work of creating a national geodetic network but, by great good fortune, the Survey soon acquired the services of another officer of exceptional mathematical talent – Alexander Ross Clarke. Clarke had been commissioned as a second lieutenant in the Royal Engineers on 1 October 1847, passing out first in his batch, and seems to have made up his mind from an early stage that the Ordnance Survey would provide scope for his mathematical interests. On being approached in 1850, Hall, the Superintendent, said that his funds did not then admit of an increase in the number of officers on the Survey but that, from the following April, he was to have a separate Vote of £2000 per annum for the preparation and publication of an account of the Trigonometrical Survey. Clarke was in fact posted to the Ordnance Survey in April 1850, but in 1851 he was ordered to Canada where he remained until 1854 when he returned to the Survey. Two years later he was placed in charge of the Trigonometrical and Levelling Branch.

Clarke completed the work begun by Yolland, perfecting the methods that were used and directing the computations. The adjusted geodetic network was known as the Principal Triangulation, a term taken from Clarke's eight-hundred-page quarto volume entitled *Account of the Observations and Calculations of the Principal Triangulation, and the Figure Dimensions and Mean Specific Gravity of the Earth as derived therefrom*, which was published in 1858.

Instruments and Observations

ANGULAR MEASUREMENTS

The primary triangulation did not satisfy geodetic requirements everywhere and most of the observations made before 1824 had to be repeated in order to bring the triangulation to an acceptable standard before the work of adjustment could begin. At some of the earlier stations not all the angles needed to complete the primary network had been measured and at others the number of observations of each angle was too few. The work of improving and strengthening the primary triangulation continued under Yolland during the 1840s and was eventually completed in 1852.

The two three-foot and the eighteen-inch Ramsden theodolites were used throughout and in 1826 a fourth instrument, made by Troughton and Simms, was added. In this theodolite the two-foot horizontal circle was fixed and the telescope and micrometers revolved as a unit, unlike the Ramsden instruments in which the circle revolved with the telescope, and the micrometers were fixed. There were five evenly-spaced micrometers with a sixth bisecting one of the spaces between them. The two vertical circles were of 15 inches diameter, one on each side of the telescope; all three circles were divided to 5 minutes of arc and read to one second. The theodolite was made with a repeating table to permit observations by 'repetition', but this method was little used.*

After 1824 it gradually became the standard procedure to include several stations in each round of angles, starting and finishing with a 'referring object' which was generally an artificial mark near the observing station, likely to be visible at all times. Observations were made to poles, heliostats** and lamps, and a reward was given to anyone spotting a light from a distant station, rising from sixpence for under 10 miles to a guinea for over 100 miles.[2] The limelight invented by Drummond was apparently used only once, at Slieve Snaght, for the ray to Divis. Readings were made with the theodolites face right and face left, on a number of different zeros, which entailed lifting and turning the Ramsden instruments.

IMPROVEMENTS IN BASE MEASUREMENT

Between 1791 and the start of the Irish survey, all the bases had been measured with the steel chains under tension, a method not altogether satisfactory because of wear in the links and the difficulty of determining precisely the temperature of the chain at the time of measurement.[3] To remove these uncertainties. Colby had devised his compensation bars[4] (Plate 9).

When the base on the shores of Lough Foyle was measured in 1827–8 with the compensation bars, its length was found to be 41 640.8873 feet in terms of the Ordnance bar O_1[5] at 62 °F. As a test of the primary triangulation, the length of the Salisbury Plain Base was computed through the triangulation from the Lough Foyle Base, giving a length about one foot longer than as measured in 1794. It was therefore remeasured with the compensation bars in 1849 and found to be 36 577.8581 feet of O_1 at 62 °F which was 1.028 feet longer than the original measurement and in very close agreement with the calculated length. The trial calculation not only confirmed the high standard of measurement attainable with the compensation bars but also that of the connecting triangulation.

LATITUDE AND LONGITUDE

After 1823 Ramsden's zenith sector was used only once – at Greenwich in 1835 – before it was destroyed in 1841. To replace it Airy designed and superintended the construction of the zenith sector named after him. It was made of cast-iron and could be fixed to a wooden framework or direct to rock;[6] its main advantage was that observations face right and face left could be made at the same transit; in addition, the telescope could be raised from the trunnion bearings and turned over, so that observations in four different positions of the telescope were possible. The instrument was set vertically by a system of levels instead of by a plumb-line as in Ramsden's sector; as far as possible each of the parts of the sector was cast in one piece to give it rigidity (Plate 10).

Latitudes were measured at twenty-seven stations with Airy's sector. Including all the observations made with Ramsden's sector, latitudes were observed at thirty-seven stations of which Greenwich, Balta, Cowhythe, Dunnose and South Berule were visited twice. At those stations where observations had been made by both sectors, the figures for the seconds of arc of the latitudes measured by the two sectors showed a high level of agreement:[7]

	Ramsden	Airy
Dunnose	07.07	06.98
Balta	01.55	01.68
Cowhythe	09.30	09.58

---

* The angles of a triangulation may be measured either by the direction system or by repetition. In the direction system each angle is measured several times – either singly or in conjunction with others – and the mean of all the measurements is taken as the final value. In the repetition system the angle is measured from a reference station; the theodolite is then swung back by means of the repeating table to the reference station without altering the theodolite reading, and the angle is then measured a second time. The theodolite reading will now be twice the value of the angle. This procedure is repeated, say, ten times, and the accepted value for the angle will be a tenth of the final reading of the theodolite. In theory this lessens the effect of any graduation errors of the circles, but it may introduce errors due to the movement of the circle clamps.

** Three sizes were used: the largest was rectangular, 20 inches by 16 inches; the other two were circular, of 12 inches and 5 inches diameter.

Before the invention of the electric telegraph, it was difficult to make accurate determinations of longitude because this requires an exact comparison between local time observed astronomically and Greenwich time. But in 1844, after the extension of the triangulation to the south-west of Ireland, Airy measured the difference of longitude between Greenwich Observatory and Feaghmaan by the transport of chronometers.[8] Thirty chronometers, packed fifteen to a padded box, were carried by a variety of transport from Greenwich via Liverpool and Kingstown to Feaghmaan. Observatories equipped with transit instruments were built at Kingstown and Feaghmaan which, together with the observatories at Greenwich and Liverpool, made it possible to measure the chronometer errors on local time at each of the four observatories and so deduce the difference of longitude between them. All the observatories were connected to the Principal Triangulation.

The difference of longitude between Greenwich and Feaghmaan was also calculated through a number of triangles, some very large, deduced from the unadjusted observations of the primary triangulation by Delambre's* method on Airy's spheroid.[9] The differences of longitude obtained by the various methods were:

by transport of chronometers and astronomical observation for local time at Feaghmaan	$10°20'\ 43''.45$
by unadjusted triangulation using Delambre's method	$10°20'\ 46''.05$
by the adjusted Principal Triangulation	$10°20'\ 45''.31$

In addition to the observations for latitude and longitude, astronomical azimuths were measured at sixty-one stations, although the *Account of the Principal Triangulation* gives details for only thirty.

Calculation and Adjustment of the Principal Triangulation

STANDARDS OF LENGTH

An essential but sometimes confusing aspect of geodetic measurement is the need to define the standard to which the measured lengths and the dimensions of the reference spheroid are related. The latitudes and longitudes of the stations of the Principal Triangulation were computed on Airy's spheroid, published in 1830, having the constants:

   major semi-axis (a) 20 923 713 feet
   minor semi-axis (b) 20 853 810 feet.[10]

The foot used by Airy was derived from Sir George Shuckburgh's five-foot brass scale made by Troughton in 1796.[11] However, another standard was used in calculating the side lengths of the Principal Triangulation.

In 1826–7 Troughton and Simms had constructed two ten-foot wrought-iron bars designated O_1 and O_2 but it is not known from what source the bars were laid off. They were compared at different times between 1827 and 1846 with other standards including the prismatic bar and Roy's brass scale, with the following results:

bar O_2	9.999 997 2 feet of O_1 at 43° F	
prismatic bar	20.000 765 6 feet of O_1 at 62° F	
Roy's scale, 0–40 inches	3.333 336 8 feet of O_1	temperature not
Roy's scale, 0–36 inches	3.000 028 1 feet of O_1	recorded

These comparisons enabled all lengths of the triangulation prior to 1823 to be converted to terms of bar O_1 which became the standard used for the later triangulation.'** In the calculation of the spheroidal latitudes and longitudes, Airy's spheroid was used as if it had been in terms of O_1, but this did not have any significant effect on the results.

---

* Jean-Baptiste Joseph Delambre, 1749–1822. Astronomer.
** It is not easy to avoid confusion. For example, the length of the Hounslow Heath Base is given in various publications as:

1784	27 404.7219 feet	in terms of the Royal Society's brass scale, reduced to mean sea-level.
1784	27 404.0137 feet	in terms of the Royal Society's brass scale, reduced to mean sea-level, with error in temperature correction removed.
1784	27 404.0843 feet	the previous value, but not reduced to mean sea-level.
1791	27 404.3155 feet	in terms of the Royal Society's brass scale, not reduced to mean sea-level.
	27 404.2 feet	the mean value of the two previous measures; used by Mudge for all calculations between 1791 and 1820.
	27 405.14 feet	in terms of the prismatic bar.
	27 406.19 feet	in terms of O_1

The last two values are converted from one of the earlier values but it is not certain which one was used.

ADJUSTMENT

For each station an abstract of angles was made by the somewhat complicated rules given by Clarke.[12] The bearing of each ray obtained from the abstracts is recorded in the *Account of the Principal Triangulation* for 289 stations, together with the number of pointings and the reciprocal of the weight.[13] The 'weight' of an observation is a measure of its relative trustworthiness; e.g. the mean of two independent and equally reliable measurements has twice the weight of a single one.

The methods of adjustment used by Clarke later came to be known collectively as 'adjustment by condition equations'. The purpose was to determine the best corrections to apply to all the observed quantities, and specially to the observed angles, so that maximum theoretical accuracy was attained in the final calculation of the network and, at the same time, all the necessary geometrical conditions were satisfied; for example: all angles of a triangle to add up to 180° plus spherical excess, all angles at a station to add up to 360°, all side lengths to agree irrespective of the route by which computed. By the theory of errors the 'best' corrections are those which, when squared and added together, have the minimum total – the method known as 'least squares'.

Out of the 289 stations for which abstracts were given, 202 were selected to form the vertices of the figures to be adjusted, together with sixteen up-stations. A further fifty-three stations were required for fixing minor points such as base terminals and sector stations; the remaining thirty-four stations were not used for reasons which were not given. The sum of all the sides totalled about 40 000 miles, with an average length of 35; the longest, 111 miles, was from Slieve Donard to Sca Fell.

If the reductions had been carried out in one figure there would have been 920 condition equations to be solved simultaneously – a number which was quite unmanageable in those days. A satisfactory approximation, however, could be made by dividing the triangulation into a number of smaller figures, each with a reasonably small number of equations for solution; the corrections obtained from one such figure could then be substituted in the equations for the next figure, and so on. Accordingly, Clarke divided the triangulation into twenty-one figures, of which four, figures 1, 7, 12 and 14, were adjusted independently. The remaining seventeen figures were all dependent in some way on these four (Plate 11). The derivation of the thirty-nine equations of condition for Figure 1 is set out in detail in the *Account of the Principal Triangulation*; for the remaining figures the condition equations are given with tables of the calculated corrections.

The following bases, sector stations etc. were not incorporated in the adjustment of the relevant figures, but were connected to them by means of additional triangulation adjusted by least squares:

Bases: Hounslow Heath, Misterton Carr, Rhuddlan Marsh, Belhelvie, Salisbury Plain (as measured with the compensation bars).
Zenith Sector Stations: Southampton, Isle of Wight, Feaghmaan, Delamere, Tawnaghmore, Great Stirling, Gerth of Scaw, Kellie Law, Burleigh Moor.
Observatories: Greenwich, Edinburgh, Cambridge, Dublin, Durham.
Azimuth Stations: Mordington, Burnswark.

All six bases would normally have been included, with their appropriate weights, in the determination of the side lengths of the adjusted triangulation. However, the Lough Foyle and Salisbury Plain Bases were measured with the compensation bars, whereas steel chains were used between inadequately marked terminals for the others. The triangulation was therefore made to depend on the Lough Foyle and Salisbury Plain Bases only. After the twenty-one figures had been adjusted, the Salisbury Plain Base was calculated from Lough Foyle and found to be 0.4 foot shorter than its measured length, and this discrepancy was divided between the two bases in proportion to the square root of their lengths. With these corrected values the whole triangulation was computed to give for each triangle the spheroidal lengths of the sides in feet to two, and sometimes three, decimal places.

The following table shows the date when each of the bases was measured, its length in terms of the prismatic bar, in terms of O_1, and as calculated from the Principal Triangulation. It will be seen that, except for Rhuddlan Marsh and Salisbury Plain (1794), there is reasonable agreement between the lengths as measured and as calculated:

| Date measured | Base | Length in feet | | |
		Prismatic bar	O_1	as calculated
1791	Hounslow Heath	27 405.14	27 406.190	27 406.363
1794	Salisbury Plain	36 575.43	36 576.830	36 577.656
1801	Misterton Carr	26 343.05	26 344.060	26 343.869
1806	Rhuddlan Marsh	24 514.06	24 516.000	24 517.596

Date measured	Base	Length in feet		
		Prismatic bar	O_1	as calculated
1817	Belhelvie Sands	26 516.52	26 517.530	26 517.770
1827–8	Lough Foyle		41 640.887	41 641.103*
1849	Salisbury Plain		36 577.858	36 577.656*

* corrected values as described above.

The method of adjustment of the Principal Triangulation only satisfied the geometrical conditions of the triangulation. It included neither the astronomical observations for azimuth and latitude nor the measured lengths of four of the bases.

Clarke had deduced formulae for obtaining the latitude, longitude and reverse azimuth of a station fixed by azimuth and distance from a known station.[14] By these formulae the latitudes and longitudes on Airy's spheroid of about one hundred of the stations of the Principal Triangulation were calculated and published.[15] Later in the *Account* a table for all the stations is given but the values were computed on a different spheroid.[16] In 1919 a complete list on Airy's spheroid was published but the exact method of derivation is unknown:[17]

> The latitudes and longitudes of most of the primary stations . . . have been obtained by Clarke's method, or by converting the known rectangular coordinates into differences of latitude and longitude.

But any points so fixed from County rectangular co-ordinates must be suspect.[18]

The lists of co-ordinates upon Airy's spheroid of the stations of the Principal Triangulation represented the final stage of the primary triangulation from the domestic point of view of the Ordnance Survey. The speed of the work was amazing, for the calculation of the triangulation, the applications of least squares to its adjustment, the effect of local attraction, and the computations for several figures of the Earth were all published only four years after the return of Clarke. With the triangulation divided into twenty-one figures, there would have been an average of over forty equations of condition for each figure. To solve these with logarithms must have required very skilled computers and first-class direction and supervision. The credit for much of this must go to Sergeant-Major William Young of the Royal Sappers and Miners, who was principal assistant to both Yolland and Clarke.

The Principal Triangulation stood until the retriangulation, begun in 1935, but it was not used as a framework for the mapping of the United Kingdom, most of which depended on separate minor triangulations for each county or group of counties.* The minor triangulation included stations of the Principal Triangulation but any consistent relation between the two was virtually non-existent. Nevertheless, the Principal Triangulation was a fine scientific achievement which brought the Ordnance Survey great international credit.

The Figure of the Earth

A large part of Clarke's volume deals with work which was of the greatest international importance in geodesy: observations and calculations to derive better values for the dimensions of the reference spheroid used for geodetic calculations or, as both Airy and Clarke called it, the Figure of the Earth, a term which in modern usage is usually applied to the geoid.[19]

An important consideration was that of local attraction – that is, the deflection of the true vertical (a line normal to the geoid) from the spheroidal normal. Mudge had thought that there was no deflection at Dunnose but that there might be as much as 8 seconds at Clifton and Arbury Hill. Yolland had some doubts about Dunnose and selected stations near by, at which latitudes were measured with Airy's

---

* A. R. Clarke describes the method of projection used for the county maps in *Methods and Processes of the Ordnance Survey (1875)* p. 14:

> The method of projection adopted for . . . the . . . maps of counties is this:— A, B, C . . . are stations of the Principal and Secondary Triangulation in the county to be projected. A central meridian having been determined on, perpendiculars are drawn to this meridian from the stations A, B, C . . .; let these perpendiculars intersect the meridian in a, b, c . . ., and let O be any fixed point on the meridian. The latitudes and longitudes of A, B, C . . . having been computed, the lengths of the arcs Aa, Oa; Bb, Ob; Cc, Oc; . . . are readily obtained. These computed lengths are then used as rectangular co-ordinates, by which the points A B C . . . are actually laid down on the map.

This projection is generally known as Cassini's projection.

sector. The differences between the astronomical and geodetic latitudes were later found by Clarke to be:

Dunnose	− 2.01 seconds*
Boniface Down	+ 0.47 seconds
Week Down	+ 0.25 seconds
Highport Cliff	+ 1.28 seconds

These results show that the deflection changes by 3.29 seconds in the 1.5 miles from Dunnose to Highport Cliff. It became evident that it was unsafe to calculate the curvature of an arc from latitudes at its ends only, and that it was necessary to have a number of latitude stations along the line of the arc and to calculate the effect of local attraction at these points.

It is possible to estimate the effect of local attraction due to surface topography from a contoured large-scale plan divided into compartments by a series of radiating lines and concentric circles. The volume of each compartment and its assumed density will give the attraction of that compartment and hence the attraction of the whole area. By this method Clarke obtained the deflections at sixteen of the thirty-two latitude stations, calculating the effect of the topography out to limits of from 8 to 50 miles.[21] Thence, by considering the latitudes at the thirty-two stations, the azimuths at thirty-five stations and the longitudes of Feaghmaan and of the observatories at Cambridge, Durham and Calton Hill, he deduced the spheroid most nearly representing the surface of Great Britain and Ireland, having dimensions:

$$a \quad 20\,927\,005 \pm 295 \text{ feet}^{22}$$
$$c \quad 282.94 \qquad \text{where } c = \frac{a}{a-b}$$

for which geodetic tables from latitude 49° to 61° were computed. But the latitudes and longitudes of all the Principal Triangulation stations given on pp. 723–7 of the *Account* were calculated, not on this spheroid, but on another with dimensions:

$$a \quad 20\,926\,330 \text{ feet}$$
$$b \quad 20\,856\,337 \text{ feet.}^{23}$$

Because of the irregular shape of the Earth's surface, no one spheroid fits all parts of it equally well. By incorporating the results of the measurement of arcs further afield, Clarke was able to deduce a series of spheroids each of which has been used to good effect in some part of the world. He compared the results of the Principal Triangulation with arcs measured in France, Russia, India, Peru, Prussia, Hanover and Denmark and therefrom deduced his 1858 spheroid:

$$a \quad 20\,926\,348 \pm 186 \text{ feet}$$
$$b \quad 20\,855\,233 \pm 239 \text{ feet.}^{24}$$

This spheroid was immediately put to practical use following an unprecedented international venture in the field of geodesy, which took place in the early 1860s when Russia invited Prussia, France, Belgium and the United Kingdom to collaborate in the measurement of an arc along the 52° parallel, from the Urals to the west of Ireland, covering over 75° of longitude. The project, which was instigated by Struve, the Director of the Pulkowa Observatory,** required first of all that the triangulations of the participating countries should be connected together. In 1861, as its share of the project, the Ordnance Survey remeasured the cross-Channel connection from stations at St Peter's Church near Ramsgate, Coldham and Fairlight, including observations at eight stations in France and Belgium. As part of the same project the Astronomer Royal decided to remeasure the longitude between Valentia and Greenwich Observatory, this time using the electric telegraph. The Ordnance Survey connected the telegraph terminal at Knightstown with the Principal Triangulation, strengthened the fixation of Feaghmaan and made the necessary transit and azimuth observations at Kilbeg, near Knightstown.

Since the results of the new work were calculated on Clarke's 1858 spheroid,[25] they were not directly related to those from the Principal Triangulation which were on Airy's spheroid; there is also some doubt about the standard of length used,[26] but the new fixation for Feaghmaan made it 3.44 feet east and 3.15 feet north of its old co-ordinates. The longitude of Knightstown was found to be:

by astronomical observation and the electric telegraph 10°17′ 27″.15 west
by triangulation, on Clarke's 1858 spheroid   10°17′ 16″.11 west

---

* Bessel adjusted the latitudes of a number of European stations by least squares and obtained a deflection of −1.816 seconds at Dunnose.[20]

** Friedrich Georg Wilhelm von Struve, 1793–1864. Became Director in 1839 of the newly-built observatory at Pulkowa in Russia. He was an indefatigable observer of double stars of which he listed many thousands.

The difference of 11″.04 was due to the local deviation of the vertical referred to Clarke's spheroid. Allowing for the difference between Clarke's and Airy's spheroids, the result obtained by telegraph was within about 2″.16 of that obtained by the transport of chronometers or, expressed in time, 0.14 second.

The Ordnance Survey also undertook to compare the standards of length of the countries taking part in the measurement of the arc of latitude, and for this purpose a room was specially prepared in the Ordnance Survey Office, Southampton. Separate and independent foundations were provided for the observers, the bars under comparison and the micrometer microscopes, and the walls and roof were made double to prevent any sudden changes in temperature. Here were compared several copies of the national standard yard (the original standard was destroyed in the fire at the Houses of Parliament in 1834), the Ordnance Survey ten-foot standard bar O_1, the intermediate standard $O1_1$,* the Ordnance toise, metre and foot, the Russian double-toise, the Prussian standard toise, the Belgian toise, the Royal Society's platinum metre which had been compared with the French metre by Arago, and the Indian and Australian ten-foot standard bars.[27]

Using the results of the comparison of standards, Clarke then deduced his 1866 spheroid from the Formentera–Saxavord arc and arcs in India, Russia, South Africa and Peru.[28] He noted that the Equator was not truly circular, its radius being greatest in longitude 15°34′E and least in 105°34′E, a difference of 6378 feet. His 1866 spheroid had the constants:

> a   20 926 062 imperial feet
>
> b   20 855 121 imperial feet,[29]

and was used in the surveys of the United States, Canada and Mexico.

Several years later Clarke produced his 1880 spheroid, from a study of arcs in Western Europe, Russia, India, South Africa and South America. The dimensions of this spheroid were:

> a   20 926 202 feet
>
> b   20 854 895 feet.[30]

The 1880 spheroid was adopted for mapping in several countries, notably France and South Africa. Clarke's celebrated book *Geodesy*, which remained for many years the most authoritative work in English on the subject, was published in 1880.

The Initial Levelling of Great Britain

The initial levelling of England and Wales was begun in 1841 on a datum 100 feet below a mark on St John's Church, Old Haymarket, Liverpool, but the results of Airy's work on the Irish tides showed that a datum at or near mean sea-level was desirable. Accordingly a tide pole was fixed in 1844 at the entrance to the Victoria Dock by which the height of mean sea-level was found to be 43.14 feet above the St John's Church datum. However, the observations had only been made over a short period, so this value was rounded down to 43 feet, which became the datum for the initial levelling; it was found to be 4.670 feet above the zero of the tide gauge at George's Ferry Basin, near George's Docks.

The levelling was extended over Scotland and the whole was completed in 1859. It is fully described in Clarke and James's *Abstract of Principal Lines of Spirit Levelling in England* and *Abstract of Principal Lines of Spirit Levelling in Scotland*, both dated 1861. No details, however, are given of the instruments used or of any change in methods from those adopted in Ireland, but all lines were double-levelled, their lengths totalling 10 000 miles. The levelling was adjusted in two parts: from the Channel coast northwards to the line Longtown – Hawick – Edinburgh – Berwick-on-Tweed, and from this line northwards to cover the rest of Scotland. The adjustment was by least squares involving ninety-one and seventy-seven condition equations respectively for the southern and northern parts.

The Resignation of Colonel Clarke 1881

In his note on *The Life and Work of Colonel Clarke*, Colonel Sir Charles Close wrote:

> It was a very fortunate thing for the Ordnance Survey that Clarke came when he did and stayed so long. The older men of science had disappeared. Colby had left a few years before his arrival and was succeeded by an officer of no scientific ability. Drummond was dead and Portlock had gone in 1843 and there was no officer left who was capable of undertaking the difficult and laborious task of reducing the triangulation. It is only right to say that during the greater part of Clarke's time on the Survey that Department was commanded by an officer, Sir Henry James who, though no mathematician himself, did thoroughly appreciate the necessity for a sound

---

* Bar $O1_1$ was originally made as an intermediate for comparisons between O_1 and the national yard.

mathematical foundation for the Survey and in every way supported Clarke officially in his labours; though it might be suggested by some that Sir Henry James himself absorbed some of the credit which was due to Clarke, on the whole James as Director and Clarke as geodesist worked well together. Clarke might reasonably have expected to have succeeded to the next vacancy as Director of the Survey and to have served until he was retired for age. But in 1881 when he was not quite 53 an official 'of a familiar type' woke up to the fact that Clarke had been at home station for 27 years and he was ordered abroad to a tropical station as Commander Royal Engineers. Clarke was a man of somewhat hasty temper and on receipt of his order he at once sent in his papers. His retirement was approved and he was at once gazetted out. Immediately a storm of indignation rose in the scientific world and representations from influential quarters were made to the War Office. Of no avail. His retirement had been approved and must stand. A lesson must be taught to those who cherished the illusion that any officer was indispensable.

But Close went on to say:

Clarke was indispensable. He was the one man fitted for the post that he had occupied with so much distinction for so many years. His successor in this post was a well-known officer of charming personality universally popular, but, alas, without mathematical ability. From that time for a long period the history of the Ordnance Survey is from a scientific point of view but a melancholy recital of mediocrity. For the remaining thirty years of his life Clarke published no more scientific work.[31]

Notes

1 A. R. Clarke, *Account of the Observations and Calculations of the Principal Triangulation, and the figure dimensions and mean specific gravity of the Earth as derived therefrom.* (Ordnance Survey 1858), p. 271.

2 *Ibid.* p. 52.

3 William Yolland, *Account of the Measurement of the Lough Foyle Base in Ireland etc.* (1847).

4 See p. 83.

5 See p. 141.

6 *Account of the Methods and Processes adopted for the production of the Maps of the Ordnance Survey of the United Kingdom,* (HMSO 1875), p. 10.

7 Yolland, *Astronomical Observations made with Airy's Zenith Sector etc.* (1852), p. xxxviii. Clarke, *Principal Triangulation*, p. 669.

8 Airy, *Determination of the Longitude of Valentia in Ireland*, (1845).

9 *Ibid.* p. ccxxvii.

10 Airy, *Encyclopaedia Metropolitana* 1848, vol. V.

11 Ordnance Survey, *History of the Retriangulation of Great Britain 1935–1962*, p. 42.

12 Clarke, *Principal Triangulation*, p. 64 *et seq.*

13 *Ibid.* pp. 72–166.

14 *Ibid.* p. 249 *et seq.*

15 *Ibid.* pp. 677–84.

16 *Ibid.* pp. 723–7.

17 A. J. Wolff, *The Mathematical Basis of the Ordnance Maps of the United Kingdom*, (1919), pp. 19–27.

18 *Ibid.* p. 7.

19 See p. 347.

20 F. W. Bessel, *Astronomische Nachrichten* no. 438, p. 115.

21 Clarke, *Principal Triangulation*, p. 625 *et seq.*

22 *Ibid.* p. 712.

23 *Ibid.* p. 728.

24 *Ibid.* p. 772.

25 In the United Kingdom, France & Belgium: See H. James, *Extension of the Ordnance Survey into France and Belgium* etc., 1863 and Clarke, *Determination of the position of Feaghmain and Haverfordwest* etc. 1867.

26 H. St J. L. Winterbotham, *An Investigation into the Accuracy of the Principal Triangulation of the United Kingdom*, Ordnance Survey Professional Papers, New Series no. 2 (HMSO 1913), p. 5.

27 Clarke, *Comparisons of the Standards of Length of England, France, Belgium, Prussia, Russia, India and Australia etc.*, (1866).

28 *Ibid.* pp. 281–7.

29 Clarke, *Geodesy* (Oxford, The Clarendon Press, 1880).

30 *Ibid.*

31 C. F. Close, *The Life and Work of Colonel Clarke,* RE Journal, XXXIX (1925) pp. 658–65.

13
The
Irish Survey
Under
Hall and James

Devolution – The Irish Survey Under Hall 1847–54

With Colby and Larcom gone, the main preoccupations of the Irish Survey were to be cartographical rather than political. The new Superintendent, Lieutenant-Colonel L. A. Hall, believed as a general principle that the Irish maps should match the style of their English counterparts,[1] but he was not qualified to enter into technical *minutiae*. Within the framework of financial allowances and scale specifications laid down by the Government, Larcom's successors – Captain J. Cameron (1846–52), Captain W. Yolland (1852–3) and Lieutenant-Colonel H. Tucker (1853–4) – enjoyed a fair measure of independence; so did the revision party based at Londonderry under Leach.

In Britain Hall's superintendency was marked by a new interest in cadastral maps and town plans. In Ireland controversy was focused on the smaller scales. For many years the one-inch map had been the Survey's best-known product; so well entrenched, Colby and Larcom evidently considered, that in an Irish context they could leave it almost undefended while fighting the battle of the six-inch scale. In 1843 it looked as if their victory was about to recoil on them. Since the Irish maps were so detailed and exact, the new argument ran, their reduction to a smaller scale was a task within the powers of any competent publisher, an official one-inch map being not only unnecessary but an 'improper interference with private trade'. It was an opinion that came naturally to its principal exponent, the tight-fisted Treasury Secretary, Charles Trevelyan. But with the whole question of scales in the melting-pot, Trevelyan's parsimony also obtained a degree of support in military circles which earlier generations would have found surprising. The Duke of Wellington, the Board of Ordnance, and even, briefly, Colby himself, all united in rejecting the notion of an Irish one-inch, and the Government felt justified in ignoring a select committee of 1846 that reported in its favour.[2] The six-inch had placed Ireland so far ahead of Britain that this reaction was understandable. All the same, there was a certain appearance of conflict between centralizing the Ordnance and geological surveys and at the same time refusing to provide all parts of the kingdom with the same maps. The most vigorous proponent of this view was De la Beche who, given the task of assimilating the Irish geology to the British, found that he was expected to publish the former on small-scale county indexes.[3] In 1851–2 his repeated protests finally convinced the Treasury of the necessity for an Irish one-inch map, but even then the Survey was ordered in the interests of economy to omit the hill features. Here was another break with the traditions of military map-making. And although the decision was reversed three years later, when another select committee had reported in favour of the hills, the episode played an important part in introducing the familiar late-nineteenth-century distinction between outline and relief maps.[4]

Like most of the Survey's more advanced mathematics at this time, the computations for the Irish one-inch map were supervised by Yolland, and it was presumably he who recommended plotting the new map on Bonne's projection, with an origin near Athlone at 8° W and 53½° N. The sheet-lines of the large-scale maps were fitted into the one-inch network by calculating the latitudes and longitudes of four points enclosing each county as a rectangle. This involved bringing the Irish triangulation beyond the state in which it had been left in the thirties. The county adjustments had been made before any latitudes and longitudes had been astronomically fixed to the highest order of accuracy (hence the absence of geographical co-ordinates from the Irish six-inch maps) and Portlock had made no use of the latest techniques for giving equal weight to every theodolite reading. Yolland had the advantage of a series of latitude observations made in 1843–4 with Airy's sector – at Forth Mountain, Hungry Hill, Feaghmaan, Tawnaghmore and Lough Foyle – and also of Airy's determination of the longitude of Valentia in 1844. The positions of the county origins were now calculated, and their meridians were recalculated, with results that were a little different from those used in the six-inch maps. Some of Yolland's positions were later to be slightly modified in turn as a result of Clarke's final adjustment published in 1858.[5] In some of the counties of central Ireland the Clarke values were available in time for the construction of the one-inch maps; in the remaining counties the map was based on the earlier figures, with the result, for example, that the values assigned to the Antrim origin (Knocklayd) were 0.89 second south of, and 0.54 second west of, what eventually came to be regarded as its correct position.

Once the six-inch sheet corners were fixed in position, the detail was reduced by pantograph for the earlier sheets and by photography for the later.[6] The first instalments of the one-inch map were issued in quarter-sheets measuring 18 inches by 12 inches, an arrangement which was made permanent (except for a few combined 'district' sheets) when the sheets were renumbered in 1858 as a single consecutive series from 1 to 205.

The new map afforded a good opportunity to reaffirm the independence of Mountjoy at least in matters of design. English models were disregarded and at first nobody interfered with the Irish draughtsman's natural tendency (already evinced in the one-inch illustration to the Templemore memoir) to produce a miniature six-inch map. But these first results were soon condemned as overcrowded with townland names, townland boundaries, detached buildings and small patches of uncultivated land; it was only as a stop-gap that some of them were issued, with townland boundaries erased, to the now impatient Geological Survey and so found their way into print.[7] In recasting the map, two principles appear to have been adopted: there was to be no detail that could not be easily identified on the ground, and there were to be no small names that did not refer to visible features – hence the disappearance of most of the townland names seen on the earliest (geological) sheets. The orders of Leach, who took over from Tucker at Mountjoy in 1854, were recorded in the letter register:

> Captain Leach holds it as a principle that, with few exceptions, all detail should be connected with some feature of greater importance, a building with a road, a minor road with a principal road, a stream with a river . . . proposing therefore in future to omit all houses which interfere with the clearness of the map, and to insert only those which from position or connection with some other feature could be undoubtingly identified on the ground.[8]

Parishes and baronies remained, but the final version showed some progress from an 'administrative' towards a more strictly topographical or traveller's map. It was a development not wholly dissimilar to the earlier history of the six-inch map, but since it involved removing detail instead of adding it, the change could be made more quickly and with less publicity.

Seeds of further evolution along the same lines were contained in the researches on relief depiction, originally started under Larcom, which with Hall's encouragement were now continued by the Mountjoy engravers James Duncan and William Dalgleish. Their object was to produce an effect that was more transparent and more continuous than hachuring and easier to keep uniform than aquatint. One way of imitating the latter process, explored by Dalgleish, was by a differential etching of closely-spaced parallel lines. Another, invented by Duncan and said to be cheaper than hachuring once the technique had been mastered, was named by its creator 'triotinto' (subsequent writers abandoned the final 'o') because its effect resembled those of the three processes of aquatint, mezzotint and hand stippling.[9] These experiments may be seen as a recognition that even at the one-inch level Mountjoy had something to teach the Survey's British branch.

In Ireland the problem of one-inch revision is as old as the one-inch map itself, for engraving began in a county (Wicklow) where the most recent field information – that of Colby's six-inch surveys – was now too old to be used without making some attempt to bring it up to date. The worst anachronisms in this and other southern counties were avoided by sending a surveyor over the ground at a rate of about three six-inch sheets a week to insert new roads and the more important new buildings.[10] In part of Ulster, however, (Antrim, Donegal, Fermanagh, Londonderry and Tyrone), the new one-inch detail could be taken from the 'completion' of the six-inch maps authorized in 1844.[11]

This latter task had inevitably involved much more than adding what had been left out in the thirties. Apart from the need to take account of new roads and buildings, many townland boundaries had been physically altered by give-and-take fences or by the straightening of streams, and it became a question whether the old administrative boundaries should be preserved as legal fictions or whether, as Griffith proposed, they should be adapted to the new physical and tenurial realities.[12] The second course was authorized by Parliament in 1854 (17 Vic., c. 17) and 1857 (20 and 21 Vic., c. 45) and thenceforth the Ordnance revision was accompanied by the Boundary Commissioner's review of townland geography. There were no precedents, or at any rate no happy ones, to govern the actual technique of six-inch revision, and a conflict of views had appeared when in 1845 Leach began in Donegal by plotting new detail onto the old impressions, surveying each piece of work by running short chain lines from mapped detail to the new features, and having the processes of survey, plotting and drawing all done by a single reviser. Colby, acting on his principle that revision must be 'entirely performed in the same way the original was done', had promptly forbidden the practice, insisting that the booking and plotting of both contours and detail must be done independently by separate parties.[13] In practice, the most appropriate revision method depended on the merit of the original survey. When the revisers moved from Donegal to Londonderry they had in any case to sweep everything from the map except townland boundaries and major physical features, building entirely new surveys on the trigonometrical points. In Tyrone, the new measurements were based on houses and fence junctions as near as possible to the original main lines. In Fermanagh there was much discussion of a scheme for replotting the original field books after obsolete entries had been cancelled and new ones added, but eventually this county, together with Antrim and Down, was surveyed afresh. Certainly the old work needed correcting as well as completing, and there were many minor alterations in permanent detail: in Londonderry, for example, 1654 instances were found of townland boundaries slightly in error.[14] The differences were seldom gross: they could always be fitted into the old sheet-lines.

It had been hoped to engrave the revision on the original plates, but even in the midlands and south the changes proved too numerous for this to be possible and the work had to be done by means of scraped matrices and duplicates. This set a limit to further mechanization, for punching was less successful on electrolytic copper than on commercial copper.[15] But it did mean that the original plates were preserved for posterity (except those of Donegal, Londonderry, Tyrone and Antrim, which were thoughtlessly sold as old copper), modified only by the addition of railways and a few other details.

On the six-inch as well as the one-inch scale, Hall took a particular interest in the third dimension. In 1848 he restored the low water datum at Poolbeg Lighthouse, though not before the greater part of Donegal had been contoured on Colby's orders to mean sea-level. He also restored sketched contours, which had been implicitly prohibited by Colby's order about field books in 1845, and then abolished them again in 1853. And in the latter year he replaced Leach's octonal intervals (in which the eight-hundred-foot contour had been given prominence because of its close relationship with the limit of cultivation) by the English decimal system.[16] As the following table shows, the resulting picture is somewhat confused, but Hall had made creditable progress in bringing contours out of their experimental phase, and they were now widely accepted as preferable to the old spot heights, most of which (to avoid clashes) were removed from the revised plates.

THE CONTOURING OF IRELAND 1839–57

(Heights in feet above low water spring tides)

	Inishowen	Louth	Kilkenny	Rest of Donegal	London-derry	Tyrone	Antrim	Dublin
				SKETCHED CONTOURS				
S	1839–40	1840–41	1841–3	1848–51	1853–4			
E	1853			1853–4	1853–5			
VI	10*	10 or 20	10	25	25			
				INSTRUMENTAL CONTOURS				
S	1839–40	1840–41	1841–2	1845–51	1851–2	1853–7	1854–7	1855–7
E	1853	1855–6x	1846–9x	1848–54	1853–5	1856–8	1858–9	1856–7
VI	200 ** / 1000 / 100 / 400 / 50	100 / 500 / 50 / 50 / 25	100 ** / 800 / 50 / 300 / 30 / 50	400 ** / 1607 / 200 / 507 / 100 / 407 / 50	100 ** / 400 / 50 / 100 / 25		250 / 1000 / 100 / 500 / 50 / 100 / 25	

S = Date of survey or sketching
E = Date of engraving on electrotypes
VI = Vertical interval (Limits shown by right hand figure in lower table)

* { Sketched VI = 10 feet
    { Engraved VI = 25 feet
x Engraved on original plates
** Excluding local variations

Assimilation – Sir Henry James and After

Unlike Hall, Major Henry James took office at Southampton with many years of Ordnance Survey experience behind him and since most of those years had been spent in Ireland he naturally kept a close eye on Mountjoy. James made no deliberate attempt to downgrade the Irish branch, neither did he go out of his way to maintain its self-sufficiency, as witness his refusal to equip it with a camera.[17] His policy for Ireland, though not always successfully carried out, was in essence simple and inflexible: scales, styles and methods of production were to conform to those of England, Scotland and Wales. In so far as he achieved this aim, Irishmen got their share of the remarkably wide and full range of maps that James and his supporters regarded as essential to State cartography. But there was no longer any prospect of keeping the activities of Mountjoy in constant and sensitive adjustment with the special needs of Ireland.

James's most striking innovations were in the field of very-large-scale plans. Under Hall, the Irish survey had done little in this direction except to finish publishing the Dublin five-foot, but his successor had to deal with a number of applications for plans under the Towns' Improvement Clauses Act of 1854. Where a town was due for six-inch revision, James offered a new plan for the price of making the extra copy. Elsewhere he proposed to charge the full cost of the necessary special survey, a cost which, as it turned out, no Irish town was willing to pay.[18] In these circumstances, the initiative for urban cartography remained with the Survey itself and with the Valuation Office.

The policy announced for Britain in 1855 was to map all towns of more than 4000 people at the unprecedentedly large scale of 1:500. Griffith was opposed to this on two counts: he wanted to bring in more Irish towns by dropping the population limit to 1000, while remaining satisfied with the five-foot scale as agreed between himself and Colby in 1832–3. It was characteristic of James that he gave way, in 1857, on the first point but not the second, except in so far as he agreed to retain the five-foot for a number of northern towns where arrangements for using it were already in hand.[19] Since most Irish towns were now declining in population, his 1:500 programme was less burdensome than might have been feared, but the larger centres at least were undergoing considerable topographical change and in 1866 the Treasury authorized town surveys of Cork, Limerick, Waterford and Galway in advance of the normal county sequence.[20] To cope with the extra work, these towns were mapped at five feet instead of 1:500. Elsewhere the latter scale was retained until 1879.[21] Though valued in England as an aid to sanitary progress it had made little appeal to Irish map-users, official or private.

Special town triangulations were observed by the officer in charge of the six-inch revision and computed at Southampton without being rigorously fitted into the surrounding county networks.[22] Except for a few cases where arrears of work had to be sent to England, the maps were prepared and printed in Dublin. To begin with, it had been intended to engrave towns of more than 4000 people and zincograph those of 1000–4000, but the first part of this programme proved too heavy and except for the revising and extending of earlier maps there was virtually no town engraving after the completion of Cork and Limerick in 1872. In fact, with the grand design of 1857 reduced from two directions, the only town to be engraved at 1:500 was Armagh.

James was equally enthusiastic about the second largest of his scales, the cadastral map of cultivated areas at 1:2500. As long as Irish map coverage was far ahead of British the replacement of the six-inch of 1833–46 by a larger scale could hardly be treated as a matter of urgency. For the time being, even James admitted that an Irish 1:2500 would be 'the height of extravagance', notwithstanding his belief that such a map could easily be made by replotting the six-inch field books.[23] Accordingly Ireland was not mentioned in the Treasury minutes of 1855–63 which inaugurated the British 1:2500. Behind the scenes, however, James was anxious to prepare for the country's cadastral future. His first opportunity came in 1858 with a request for maps from the Landed Estates Court in Dublin. This body had been created ten years earlier to handle the flood of land transactions that had followed the famine. Finding that the published six-inch maps were in many cases too small, the judges authorized the making of special *ad hoc* surveys at what they described as the 'ordinary estate scale' of sixteen inches to one mile. They were so dissatisfied with the results produced by private surveyors, however, that at Larcom's suggestion they asked the Ordnance Survey to supply the necessary maps instead. James agreed on condition that the scale for field-work and plotting was increased to 1:2500 and that the surveys were paid for out of the proceeds of the land sales. From now on, in spite of opposition from the Survey's would-be competitors, Landed Estates Court work formed an important part of the Irish branch's duties. The usual procedure was to replot the six-inch field books, revise and examine on the ground, and compute the areas from large-scale plots, though in most cases the maps were reduced again to six inches before being zincographed or lithographed for the Court.[24] After 1869 similar surveys of glebe lands were undertaken for the Church Temporalities Commission[25] and eventually about one-seventh of Ireland was covered by special large-scale surveys of one kind or another.[26]

The experience of the Landed Estates Court was a useful weapon in the British battle of the scales. James was also eager to win over the Irish Valuation Department. But although Griffith admitted that 1:2500 might have been a better choice in 1824, it was now too late for him to think of altering a system that had been successfully adapted to the six-inch; and he preferred making his own special surveys of small tenements, where necessary, to the prospect of being burdened with a large-scale Ordnance Survey plan of every parish.[27] His department had been surprisingly successful in scaling tenement areas from the printed impressions; but then hair-splitting accuracy was not required when Griffith's valuation had to combine area-measurement with other kinds of assessment – of soil quality, locational advantage and the like – which by their nature could never be more than approximate. When the Government began to publish his acreages and values, Griffith's opposition to the 1:2500 was strengthened, for awkward discrepancies would arise if his areas, derived from the six-inch map, were to be compared with Ordnance Survey 'area books' computed from the large scale.

The rigidity of James's ideas and his determination to put them into practice are well illustrated by what happened in county Dublin in the sixties.[28] As a preliminary to his own revision of the city in 1863, Griffith asked for the five-foot plan to be extended into certain expanding suburbs on the south side. Since some of the areas wanted were mainly superior residential neighbourhoods in which the detail was rather open, the question arose of using the rural (1:2500) scale instead of the urban, whereupon the Survey managed to persuade Griffith to have the whole county of Dublin (much of it open farmland) revised at 1:2500. To avoid confusion it was agreed not to publish parcel areas but this promise was later forgotten and the usual area books, complete with land classification, were issued in 1868–72. Griffith was not the only one to be misled in the course of this episode; James somehow got the impression that the Dublin 1:2500 was produced by replotting the old measurements, but although the triangulation had been treated in this way the detail had been rechained. Later, small areas on the outskirts of Bray and Londonderry were published at 1:2500, but when Griffith's successor rejected the offer of a large-scale map of county Cavan the Survey finally decided, in 1873, to drop the pressure for an Irish 1:2500.[29]

In the case of the six-inch map the two departments were in closer accord. James's main contribution here was to help ensure that the authority for the northern revision, obtained in 1844, should be extended first, in 1859, to the counties of Louth, Cavan and Leitrim, and later, in 1868, to the whole of Ireland.[30] Although resisted by the Treasury, this was no more than a logical consequence of the need to keep the valuation up to date. And while it was true that not many parts of Ireland were being transformed at this time by industrialism or population growth, the landscape was changing rapidly enough in detail, especially through the kind of alteration in field boundaries that had been predicted by the Spring Rice Committee. The six-inch revision, like the original survey, advanced from north to south with some irregularities to meet the special needs of the Valuation Office. In 1863 it was decided that resurveys, where necessary, were to be plotted at 1:2500 before being fair-drawn for publication at six inches.[31] By this time, however, resurveying had almost ceased to be necessary; once the revision reached the north midlands, where the original maps had been fairly well supplied with fences, it proved possible to revert to 'card revision', based on Leach's Donegal method, in which the alterations were plotted directly onto a specially printed copy of the original map.[32] It thus became possible either to increase the speed of the work or to reduce its cost. Evidently the latter alternative was chosen for in the seventies it was still taking two years to revise a single county – a short time by later standards, perhaps, but considerably longer than the gestation period achieved in Colby's day.

James's other method of economizing on the six-inch maps was less fortunate. He soon discovered that the cost of contouring, especially when closely-spaced town contours were included, ran substantially higher than the estimate he had given to a Parliamentary committee in 1856.[33] The gap was bridged partly by widening Hall's vertical interval and then in 1857 by bringing the Irish contouring to an abrupt halt.[34] The published explanation for this change, that the six-inch map was already well studded with levels, did not come very convincingly from one who was on other occasions a strong advocate of contouring as of everything modern.

Though no one-inch sheets had been published for Ireland when James took office in 1854, much of the necessary groundwork had been laid. His main concern at this scale was to assimilate the map to English standards.[35] Triotint was abandoned before the public had been given a chance to see it – except at exhibitions – to make way for a threefold sequence of hachured sheets, uncontoured outline sheets, and contoured outline sheets, the last numbering only seventeen because of the abolition of contours. The outline edition was issued between 1858 and 1862.

The hachured edition took much longer, for the hill-sketching of Ireland had been postponed in favour of contouring in the early 1840s with less than half the country completed. The first of James's hill-sketches was done on the six-inch scale but in 1863 he reverted to a one-inch base, partly to avoid confusingly intricate hill work (even when reduced and engraved the six-inch sketching remained clearly distinguishable in this respect from the one-inch) and partly for the sake of more rapid progress.[36] But even in this scaled-down form, the field work was not finished until 1875 and, because of the shortage of hill-engravers, the last of the hachured sheets was not completed until 1895: it was then, and not in 1870 as sometimes stated, that the Survey finished the military map of the United Kingdom that it had started a century earlier.

After a hundred years black hachured maps were passing out of favour, mainly because of the difficulty of reading names and outline in heavily shaded mountain country, a difficulty that was not much mitigated by the use of a side light in the Mountjoy hachures. The Irish hill map enjoyed a certain advantage in that there were no contoured maps to compete with it in most parts of the country. On the other hand, it could not be fully revised for fear of damaging the hachures, whereas a good deal had been done between the 1860s and the 1890s to keep the outline plates up to date. The fact is, however, that neither version of the one-inch was as popular in Ireland as the English one-inch in England. In a country where objects of interest are (at this scale) rather thin on the ground, the small sheet size must have been an important factor militating against its success.

The quarter-inch, by contrast, showed James responding to a local need, for it was an enquiry from the Irish Government about a new map of poor-law divisions that led him in 1864 to embark on a successor to the Railway map.[37] The history of this new quarter-inch map extends far into the period following James's retirement. Its four sheets were divided for latitude and longitude at Southampton, the rest of the map being produced after many interruptions at Mountjoy. When finally published in 1887, it showed some decline from the good taste that had characterized the earlier products of the Irish survey: names and roads were too numerous and major features failed to stand out with sufficient clarity. In fact it was too closely modelled on the one-inch, just as the one-inch had itself begun by being too closely modelled on the six-inch. Another point of similarity with the one-inch was the proposal to issue the new map in three versions – in outline, with hill-shading, and with (partly interpolated) contours. The contoured edition was soon abandoned, but the hills were engraved on duplicate plates by George Duncan in the triotint process which he had learned from his father. By the time he had finished in 1898, the outline he was working on became too dated to be publishable, and the last creative flame of Mountjoy flickered out unnoticed at the turn of the century.[38]

Notes

1 Mountjoy letters 1416 (1854).
2 PRO WO 44/703. *Report on the present state of the Ordnance Survey in Ireland*, 1846. The quotation is from Trevelyan's evidence (q. 34).
3 Correspondence between De La Beche, T. Oldham (local director of the Irish Geological Survey) and the Treasury, 1849–51, in Geological Survey Office, London.
4 *Report from the Select Committee on the Map of Ireland*, PP 1852–3 (921) XXXIX, 393. Mountjoy registers 1577 (1855).
5 T. Murphy, *The Latitudes and Longitudes of the six-inch sheet maps of Ireland*, Dublin Institute for Advanced Studies: School of Cosmic Physics: Geophysical Bulletin, No. 13 (1956).
6 Mountjoy letters 2709 (1861). OSR 1897–8: PP 1899, C. 9079, LXXVIII.
7 Mountjoy registers 1013, 1063, 1091 (1853), 1360, 1380, 1418 (1854). The original correspondence relating to the one-inch map is almost all missing. Some details are given in the monthly reports for 1854.
8 Mountjoy registers 1428 (1854).
9 Larcom papers 7559 and (for triotint) 7523. *Report from the Select Committee on Ordnance Survey (Scotland)*, PP 1851 (519), X, qq. 176–9, 252–3.
10 Unregistered letters, 19 Jan. 1853. Mountjoy letters 805 (1851–6). At the OSO Dublin there are six-inch impressions of county Wicklow with the MS additions made for the one-inch map.

11 Mountjoy letters 3424 (1896).

12 Mountjoy letters 1090 (1853–4). Larcom papers 7521.

13 Mountjoy letters 10988 (1845). Correspondence from Leach on the revision of county Donegal, 1844–5: Larcom papers 7521.

14 Mountjoy letters 771 (1851), 788 (1851–3), 1006 (1853), 1090 (1854), 1170 (1854). Unregistered letters, Leach to Cameron, 29 July 1850.

15 Mountjoy letters 3910 (1877).

16 Mountjoy letters 465 (1848), 1625 (1853).

17 Mountjoy letters 2166 (1859).

18 Mountjoy letters 1496 (1855). Larcom papers 7521.

19 Mountjoy letters 1422 (1854–7), 1790 (1856), 1632 (1857).

20 Mountjoy letters 3385 (1866).

21 Mountjoy letters 4015 (1879).

22 Mountjoy letters 8206 (1890) and 14130 (1911), the latter now at the OSO Belfast. K. M. Papworth, 'The Ordnance Survey of Northern Ireland', *Chartered Surveyor* 1958, XCI, p. 347.

23 *Report of the Ordnance Survey Commission*, PP 1857–8 [2396] XIX, q. 423.

24 Mountjoy letters 2777 (1862). Larcom papers 7790. OSR 1858 and 1859.

25 Mountjoy letters 3664 (1872).

26 *Report of the Royal Commission on the Land Law (Ireland) Act, 1881, and the Purchase of Land (Ireland) Act, 1885*; PP 1887, C. 4969, XXVI, F 1.

27 Mountjoy letters 1790 (1856).

28 Mountjoy letters 2912 (1863–4), 3064 (1864–5), 3372 (1867). OSR 1863: PP 1864 [3278] XXXV; OSR 1866: PP 1867 [3834] XLI.

29 Mountjoy letters 3236 (1866), 3314 (1867), 3716 (1873).

30 OSR 1859, p. 10: PP 1860 (2629) XXIII; OSR 1868, p. 11: PP 1868–9 [4124] XXXVI.

31 Mountjoy letters 2982 (1863).

32 Mountjoy letters 1797 (1856–8), 3424 (1868). Division orders for the revision of Ireland, in the OSO Dublin, 1868–71.

33 *Report from the Select Committee on Ordnance Survey of Scotland*: PP 1856 (198) XIV, q. 570.

34 Mountjoy letters 1777 (1856), 1972 (1857). OSR 1858.

35 Mountjoy registers 1429 (1854).

36 Mountjoy letters 2958 (1863).

37 Mountjoy letters 3072–73 (1864–5), 5035 (1885–9), 3293 (1896).

38 Mountjoy letters 3936 (1898), 4543 (1898). 'Officers' memos' in the OSO Dublin, 18 June 1898.

14
The Surveys
of Jerusalem
and Sinai*

The responsibility conferred upon the Ordnance Survey by the Survey (Ireland) Acts, and the Ordnance Survey Act of 1841, did not extend beyond Great Britain, Ireland and the Isle of Man. Yet at various times members of its staff were employed in many parts of the world either on secondment to other authorities or on special tasks not provided for in the Survey Acts but which were nevertheless directed to some extent from its Headquarters in Southampton. Surveying and mapping operations in the latter category may be regarded as part of the official work of the Ordnance Survey, although each had to be individually sanctioned and sometimes independently financed. Perhaps the most interesting of these surveys, and certainly the most publicized, were those in the Middle East carried out between 1864 and 1870 under the general surveillance of Sir Henry James.

The Survey of Jerusalem 1864–5

The survey of Jerusalem was promoted by a petition from Dean Stanley of Westminster, representing a committee which included the Bishop of London, to Lord de Grey and Ripon, the Secretary of State for War. Its object was to set on foot a survey which it was hoped would lead to improvements in the water supply and sanitation in Jerusalem, a city which was visited by thousands of pilgrims every year. The Ordnance Survey had recently made a major contribution to the health of London by a special 1:1056 survey, and the new main sewerage system there was on the verge of completion. Its help was now sought in a more distant field, but one which was of great interest to mid-Victorian Britain. The diplomatic background for such a survey was propitious because the relations between Great Britain and Turkey were in a cordial phase after the countries had been allies against Russia in the Crimean War; until relations worsened some thirty years later owing to developments in Egypt, Turkey raised no objections to British survey parties in her Palestinian territory. Moreover, at this time the War Office was ready to give its approval – it may be surmised that it was very willing to take advantage of the opportunity to obtain accurate maps of at least a part of an area which was strategically sensitive at a time when the Suez Canal project was going forward.

Sir Henry James, when asked for an estimate, considered that the work could be carried out for £500, and this was provided, anonymously at the time, by Miss Burdett-Coutts.[1]** The War Office raised no objection to the use of military personnel, but was not at first prepared to pay the engineer officer who would be in charge. His pay could not be found out of the £500 but, as a compromise, Lieutenant C. W. Wilson was permitted to go on the basis that two months in any year would be regarded as ordinary leave on full pay, with the rest of the year on regimental pay only. The men's pay and any engraving or other work were to be charged to the Committee's fund. Wilson was a good choice for leader of the party as he was qualified by years of work on the American Boundary Commission as well as by his own interest in antiquity; he might also hope for financial assistance from his own family.

James's insistence on having full financial and administrative control of the expedition was clear from the beginning, and provoked some friction with James Fergusson, a member of the Committee,

---

* This account of the Ordnance Survey's involvement in surveys in Jerusalem, Palestine and Sinai between 1864 and 1872 is mainly condensed from a more extensive treatment of the subject which was compiled in 1932 by Lt.-Col. H. E. M. Newman RE at the instance of the Director General, Brigadier H. St J. L. Winterbotham. This was fortunate because the material on which the compilation was based came from Ordnance Survey files which were destroyed in the bombing of Southampton in 1940. The full version is in the OS Library, Southampton, entitled *The Work of the Ordnance Survey outside Great Britain and Ireland*.

** Angela Burdett–Coutts (later Baroness), the wealthy philanthropist described by Edward VII, when Prince of Wales, as 'after my mother the most remarkable woman in the Kingdom'.

but Sir Henry handled this opposition with characteristic vigour and remained a central figure in all that followed. Preliminary arrangements included the collection of earlier surveys, among them that done by Lieutenant J. F. A. Symonds in 1841; the Turkish Government was induced to promise protection and assistance at Jerusalem, and the British consuls at Jaffa and Jerusalem were instructed to hire local labour.

The party, consisting of Wilson, now promoted to Captain, a sergeant, two lance-corporals and two sappers, left Southampton on 12 September 1864, with instructions that were very wide in scope. Two maps were to be produced, one at 1:2500 scale, contoured at ten-foot intervals, covering an area one and a half miles from north to south and one mile from east to west, including the city; the second was to be at 1:10 000 scale and to extend three miles north to south and two and a half miles east to west with levels along principal valleys and high ground. A town plan of the city itself at 1:500 was also to be made and public buildings, as far as permission could be obtained, were to be surveyed inside and out with as much detail as possible. Photographs were to be taken of all public buildings. Triangulation was to cover the whole area, and a base line of from one-half to three-quarters of a mile was to be measured on the north side of the city. Levelling was to proceed from a datum established near the fountain of Nehemiah, and bench-marks were to be cut at various points on the city walls, gates, churches and buildings, where permitted. All summit heights in the city and its neighbourhood were to be accurately determined. If time allowed, the whole area surveyed was to be covered by contours at twenty-five or fifty-foot intervals. A careful examination was to be made of the local geology with measurements and descriptions of the various strata; these were to be plotted on the 1:10 000 scale along with two geological sections across the city. A collection of specimens and fossils was to be made. It was also suggested that the comparative heights of the Mediterranean (at Jaffa, Jerusalem and the Dead Sea) should be estimated from a series of barometric readings at the three points, and that further funds might be available for the running of a line of levels between them.

For archaeological purposes the ground north of the city was to be examined for ruins of ancient walls and, in the city, buildings examined for possible remains of pre-existing buildings. It is surprising that no more detailed emphasis was put on investigation into archaeological remains in view of the fact that in mid-nineteenth-century England there was great interest in Biblical problems, and many controversies had emerged, in which James Fergusson had been prominent, over the exact where-abouts of Biblical sites. But it was evidently considered politic in Victorian England to place cleanliness before godliness when courting official benediction. Finally, the detachment was to return to Southampton not later than February 1865.

The party travelled via Alexandria and Jaffa and reached Jerusalem on 3 October where they were able to hire accommodation on easy terms at the Prussian Hospice. The work proved to be far more arduous than expected because of the heat, the rough nature of the terrain and the filthy state of the city. The Turkish Governor, Izzet Pasha, was helpful, but in an area with such diversities of religion and population it was necessary to proceed with caution in a task which required constant trespass on private property. After a false start at the north of the city, a base 3875 feet long was finally measured on the Plain of Rephaim to the south-west. The triangulation proceeded steadily, and surprisingly little trouble was met with in working among the population, even in the more fanatically disposed parts of the city and in the sacred Haram area (the part of the Old City containing the Dome of the Rock).

At the end of October Fergusson arrived, after what appears to have been some altercation with James as to who was in control of the survey. The chief significance of his visit lies in the fact that he inspired in Wilson a much more immediate interest in the topographical archaeology of the place, which led to many investigations by Wilson after Fergusson had returned to England. These discoveries, however, in the end supplied abundant evidence in support of the authenticity of tradition rather than of the views of such controversialists as Fergusson.

By the beginning of 1865 time was running out and Wilson was doubtful if the difficult work of contouring the terrain, which ranged through a vertical height of nearly 700 feet in a small compass, could be completed before the February deadline. In any case the deadline became meaningless when two more tasks were laid on the party. The first was the running of a line of levels between Jaffa and the Dead Sea, which had been adumbrated in the original instruction, and had been brought forward by the Royal Society in November 1864. It was also desired to add pendulum observations to this to provide data for a determination of the mean density of the Earth. James regarded the latter proposal as impracticable, but he supported an approach to the Treasury for a grant to carry through the levelling project at this favourable moment. At first Wilson thought that another £100 would cover the cost, but when he worked out the details, which would have to include extra equipment, extra staff, and 'a small train of mules to carry our luggage and water, of which there is little on the way', he had to double this figure. James was already trying to raise £100 from the Royal Society, but when he received the increased estimate, he not only endeavoured to enlist the support of the Treasury, but also wrote a letter to *The Times*, in the guise of a progress report on the survey 'for the information of those who have contributed to the fund' (one person), introducing the levelling project, the cost of which would be about £200, adding that he was 'not without hope that it may be obtained from some source'. As a result of this letter an offer of the whole sum was received from a firm of publishers who were anxious to publish Wilson's history of the explorations, but this does not seem to have been accepted. There were other lesser contributions towards expenses, but eventually the Royal Geographical Society and the Government Grant Committee of the Royal Society each subscribed £100. Wilson himself was given £150 by his father.

Wilson's instructions laid down that he should run his line of levels from Jerusalem by the valley of the Kedron down its course by Mar Saba to the Dead Sea and later, on the homeward journey, from Jerusalem to Jaffa. A double line of levels was to be run which was to close from time to time on common points to provide checks. Bench-marks were to be cut, a sketch plan of the route made and maximum and minimum levels of the Dead Sea recorded. A start was made on 7 March after Wilson had made a risky reconnaissance of the Kedron route and found it to be impracticable, so that the line finally adopted was the Wady el Hodh, the course of the ancient and modern route to Jericho and the Dead Sea. The expense of this part of the work proved more than expected but Wilson hoped to compensate for this with a less costly operation between Jerusalem and Jaffa; in the event the £200 estimate was only exceeded by the sum of £14 15s 6d. The level of the Dead Sea below the mean level of the Mediterranean was established at 1298 feet, with some seasonal variations.

The second task also involved levelling. At the end of 1864 Sir Moses Montefiore, one of the contributors who had responded to the appeal in *The Times*, had approached James about a possible 'examination of the country round Jerusalem for the purpose of ascertaining what supplies of water are available and could be brought into the city'. The sponsoring body was the Syrian Improvement Committee which was prepared to make a grant of £100 for the project. The work would be done after the return from the Dead Sea, and, wrote James:

> I certainly think it would be well to have a line of levels run through Bethlehem to Solomon's Pools and connect it with the levels of Jerusalem . . . Under Solomon [and] Herod they had the will and the power to make the cisterns for storing the water of winter available for the whole year and to collect it from every source . . .

After a few modifications James's instructions finally were that a line of levels was to be run from Jerusalem to the Pools of Solomon; that Herod's Conduit was, so far as discernible, to be traced back to its source; and lastly:

> I wish you to make a traverse survey from Jerusalem along Herod's conduit to the Pool fixing as many objects as possible by observations on either side.

The small staff was under considerable pressure to complete their main task, made more difficult by the onset of the hot weather, and there is no clear evidence that all of this second assignment was fully performed. Something was certainly done in the middle of May but, writing from Alexandria on 18 June when on his way home, Wilson said:

> I am very glad to get out of Jerusalem as the health of all was suffering, and I was not able to do as much as I could have wished towards the work at Solomon's Pools in consequence. To have done the thing thoroughly would have been another week's work which I do not think the men would have stood.

The party arrived home on 10 July and a fortnight afterwards Sir Henry announced the result of the Dead Sea levelling in a letter to *The Times*. The work of compiling the results of the whole expedition had meanwhile been sanctioned by the Treasury and in due course the Report was published.[2] Apart from maps and plans of the principal buildings, and zincographic reproductions of photographs of public buildings and other features of particular interest, it contained Wilson's comparatively short account of the actual survey and a long description of his archaeological discoveries, with a preface by James enunciating his opinions on tradition and historical sites.

The Report aroused widespread interest and did much to stimulate public support for the Palestine Exploration Fund. Wilson had done well. He had fully performed his main task and, in spite of various harassments and changes of plan, his expenses had only exceeded the money subscribed by five per cent, most of that due to unexpected delays on the journey home.

The Sinai Survey 1868-9

Further surveys of Western Palestine were undertaken between 1865 and 1878 under the sponsorship of the Palestine Exploration Fund, but these had little or no official connection with the Ordnance Survey. But in 1867 the Survey was induced to take part in another Middle Eastern expedition, which again had the full approval of the War Office.

The idea seems to have originated with the rector of Ulcombe in Kent, the Rev. Pierce Butler, an Arabic scholar who in 1853 had accompanied his brother exploring the Sinai Peninsula. His desire to revisit the area found enthusiastic support from a nephew of James's, Captain H. S. Palmer, RE, then commanding the Survey Division at Tonbridge, with the result that Palmer in an application to his uncle, initiated a plan which it was hoped would, from small beginnings, lead to an exploration of the whole peninsula. James gave his approval, and the Royal Geographical Society and the Royal Society were persuaded to sponsor an appeal for funds. The objects of the proposed survey were to elucidate the topography of the Exodus, and to make a general study of the geology, botany and zoology of the region. Although the survey was a necessary background to these investigations, it was not so much a prime consideration as with the work in Palestine.

Butler died early in 1868 but the project continued, and the period till the autumn was spent in gathering a team of experts including Wilson who shared the direction of the expedition with Palmer. Among other scholars who joined the party was Professor E. H. Palmer, the distinguished Arabist. Sufficient money was in hand by the autumn and the party, which included four sappers, landed in Sinai on 12 November 1868.

The immediate object was to produce a manuscript map of as large an area as time would permit, at the scale of two inches to one mile. Particular attention was to be paid to the traditional Mountain of the Law, Jebel Musa, and also to Jebel Serbal, its rival for this distinction. A large-scale survey of the famous convent of St Katherine was also to be made. The party met with many difficulties from the extreme ruggedness of the ground and the rigours of the climate, but completed its work by April 1869. All were home by the end of May and the Treasury made a grant of £500 for the compilation and publication of their results.[3] These appeared in three parts but not until March 1872 despite the nominal publication date of 1869. The first was a general account with a preface by James, a chapter on the Biblical background of the area by the Rev. C. Williams, and others by the experts who had made studies of the natural history and antiquities. They were satisfied that the traditional Jebel Musa was indeed the Mountain of the Law. The second part contained maps, plans and sections, and the third was devoted to reproductions of one hundred and fifty of the three hundred photographs taken. As a typical contemporary touch thirty-six stereoscopic views were published separately in a box with a stereoscope.

Notes

1 See Edna Healey, *Lady Unknown, a Life of Angela Burdett-Coutts* (Sidgwick & Jackson, 1978).
2 C. W. Wilson, *Ordnance Survey of Jerusalem*, 4 vols. (1865).
3 C. W. Wilson and H. S. Palmer, *Ordnance Survey of the Peninsula of Sinai*, 5 vols. (1869).

15
The Last Years
of James's Superintendency
and the
Transfer to
Civil Control
1864–1880

The Last Years of War Office Control 1864–70

THE MOVEMENT TOWARDS CIVIL CONTROL

The final decision on the basic scales soon raised questions about the military nature of the survey. On 18 March 1862 Edward Ellice asked in the House of Commons for an account of the manner in which the Vote of £71 000 in the year's Estimates for the Ordnance Survey was to be appropriated; among other things, he wanted to know what was 'the sum (if any) to be expended upon the defence or any other survey not strictly in connection with the general survey of England and Scotland now in progress'. The return made by the War Office to this enquiry showed that the sum of only £13 000 was required for surveys for national defence which included £6000 for military survey round London.[1]

The presentation of the annual *Report* of the Survey (1863) to Parliament occasioned further questions from members of the House. This time it was Mr Wyld, the map-publisher and Geographer to the Queen, who asked for a breakdown of the annual cost of the Ordnance Survey Department including military pay and every contingency. The House was told in reply that for the six years from 1858 a sum of something under £40 000 was attributable to the cost of military surveys. This accounted for little more than five per cent of the total cost of the survey department during that period.

Inevitably the conclusion to be drawn was that the cost of the Ordnance Survey was not a proper burden to be borne by the War Office Vote. Indeed, reading the *Report* for 1863, one might assume that the time was ripe for the severance of the connection with the War Office. The original objective of the Survey – the making of a military map of England and Wales on the scale of one inch to one mile – had apparently been essentially achieved, since the *Report* stated that the engraving of the eight remaining sheets would be finished in outline before the close of that financial year, and the engraving of the hills was proceeding as rapidly as the nature of the work admitted. But, in fact, the military map of England and Wales was not finished until much later – in 1870.

James could not refrain from emphasizing the wisdom of the decision of the Government to proceed with the cadastral survey by recounting two stories of the utility of the large-scale surveys to the civil public. He described, as remarkable examples of the uncertainty which existed about the extent of highland or moorland properties, the case of an estate that was bought for a nobleman in Northumberland, the area of which was found from the Ordnance Survey to be 10 000 acres less than it was stated to be and actually bought for; and that of a baronet in Perthshire who found that he had been letting a farm estimated at about 30 000 acres which turned out to be more than 40 000. At the other end of the social scale, in Westmorland, the Irish reapers had gone to the agents for the sale of the plans to find out the acreage of the fields they had been engaged to reap and had thus obtained justice without an appeal to the law.[2]

By 1865 the Department had certainly widened the range of its activities in directions that were not obviously military. The survey of Jerusalem and the levelling from the Mediterranean to the Dead Sea had been begun, the Treasury had ordered a survey of the Isle of Man in consequence of a request from the Tynwald, and a large party of surveyors was employed in London completing the 1:1056 plans which had been surveyed in block outline some fifteen years before.[3]

Again, little military relevance was to be found in the operations of the Boundary Department. This was first formed at Southampton by Hall in 1849, but in 1864, after the final decision had been made by the Government to proceed with the cadastral survey, a Boundary Office was established in London under the command of Lieutenant-Colonel John Bayly. It was responsible for the delineation of boundaries in England but not in Scotland, where the duty remained with the officers in charge of divisions. The task of mereing and recording public boundaries for the new 1:2500 survey was large, complicated, exclusively civil in character and was seen as deserving supervision by a comparatively high-ranking officer. Bayly headed the Boundary Department until 1873; then, after a year when it was temporarily in the hands of Captain Coddington, the office was placed in the charge of Major R. O. Jones, who retained the position until 1891, by which time he had become a Major-General, senior in military rank to the Director General, Sir Charles Wilson.

In 1867 large numbers of maps had to be provided for the Boundary Commissioners under the Representation of the People Act of the same year. Initially sets of plans were required for the Assistant Boundary Commissioners to take with them when making their local enquiries throughout England and Wales; for this thirteen sets of plans of the counties and two hundred and seven sets of the boroughs were prepared. The boundaries of the parliamentary divisions, hundreds, wapentakes, and also the parish and petty-sessional divisions were to be shown on the plans of the counties; and on those of the boroughs, the parliamentary, parish and municipal boundaries. For this preliminary enquiry five officers from the Ordnance Survey and Topographical Depot, with six of the Royal Artillery and seven of the Royal Engineers, were employed as Assistant Commissioners to accompany the eighteen barristers who acted in the same capacity. The Boundary Commissioners, having received the reports of the Assistant Commissioners and having agreed upon the extensions or alterations to the boundaries which they wished to recommend to Parliament, instructed James to prepare the plans for their report. This entailed the making, often by enlargement or reduction, and the printing by lithography, of no less than 2032 copies of 261 plans, a total of 530 352, all of which had to be coloured by hand. It would have been impossible to undertake this vast amount of printing and colouring in the Ordnance Survey without causing a serious interruption in its normal work, but James was able to arrange for most of the printing to be done by the Stationery Office.

The radical reorganization being undertaken in the War Office from 1868 onwards, under the direction of Edward Cardwell, Secretary of State for War, was to include the changes in the control of the Ordnance Survey which all these activities portended. Cardwell was faced with the difficult task of improving the efficiency of the Army whilst at the same time reducing expenditure.[4] The anomalous nature of the Ordnance Survey, which while very large and costing a great deal of money found from the War Office Vote was apparently little concerned with purely military matters, naturally came under close scrutiny, and in 1870, under the provisions of the War Office Act of that year, the Ordnance Survey was transferred to the Office of Works,* although the Topographical Depot remained in the War Office under the Commander-in-Chief.

At the time of the transfer James gave an account of the history, progress and cost of the Survey up to 1870 in a special report to Cardwell,[5] which was also sent, for information, to the First Commissioner of Works. James seized the opportunity to point out some of his difficulties and to forestall some of the criticism he knew would soon be forthcoming from his new masters:

> The changes in the amounts voted for different years, sometimes by decreasing them and sometimes by increasing them, have . . . made it difficult to preserve an accurate balance between the sums voted and expended, and have caused an increase in the cost of the survey.

James had had many years experience of putting facts to departmental committees and Royal Commissions and presenting the best possible face to public and official enquiry. He concluded:

> In the report of the Committee of Officers appointed by Maréchal Niel, Ministry of War in France, to examine the maps, plans and other publications of the Topographical Departments of all the nations represented at the Paris Exhibition in 1868, it is stated that 'the Ordnance Survey is a work without precedent and should be taken as a model by every civilised nation', and I have every reason to believe that the series of plans now published gives entire satisfaction to the people of this country. It is, therefore, of the utmost importance, both for the proper conduct of the survey and on the ground of economy that the organisation which has produced this result should be carefully preserved after the transfer of the survey to Her Majesty's Office of Works. The

---

* At the time the Office of Works was the only civil department with any claim to suitability for sponsoring the Ordnance Survey.

essential feature of this organisation is the combination of the considerable number of officers, non-commissioned officers and men of the Royal Engineers–(20 officers and 4 companies)–with a large body of Civil Assistants. By this organisation the survey is methodically conducted and the plans produced in the most perfect manner at the least cost.

Clearly the Board of Works was meant to understand from the outset that although War Office control could be discarded, the soldiers of the Royal Engineers could not.

PROGRESS OF THE SURVEY 1864–70

The grant for the prosecution of the cadastral survey was increased in 1867–8 and again in 1868–9, in the latter year by as much as thirty per cent, an increase which the Treasury directed should be applied, in the first instance, principally to the survey of the mineral districts, for which the Ordnance plans on the 1:2500 scale were in great demand. James recruited another three hundred staff, but since it was impracticable to increase the number of draughtsmen at the same time as that of the surveyors who had first to make the field survey, the full number which the increase in the grant allowed was not reached.[6] A considerable sum was therefore devoted to enlarging the office at Southampton, and purchasing a large stock of copper plates and the surveying instruments which would be required when the full complement of employees was made up.

By the end of the decade the English counties to the north of the Mersey-Humber line had all been surveyed on either the six-inch or the 1:2500 scale, and many small tracts had been covered at 1:2500 in the industrial areas of the Midlands and South Wales. The survey of the metropolis of London at 1:1056 was almost completed but it had proved a most formidable undertaking and had greatly retarded progress elsewhere. In Scotland the survey at either six inches to one mile or 1:2500 had extended as far north as the Caledonian Canal with some patches beyond it. In the south of England the main areas of completed 1:2500 survey were around London and in the Hampshire Basin.

In Scotland the survey of the Highlands was being held up because the proprietors of the numerous deer forests objected to the presence of the surveyors between 1 July and 20 October, and because it was not possible to work there before April or after November owing to the severity of the weather and the snow lying on the mountains. James had to find winter work for the surveyors elsewhere:

> We must more generally adopt the system I introduced last year with surveyors in Argyllshire. They were brought down from Oban in a steamer in October and employed during the winter in Flintshire and Cheshire. I propose in like manner to bring a large number of the surveyors from Inverness-shire, Ross-shire and Sutherlandshire and employ them during the winter in Cheshire and Derbyshire to work southwards. The surveyors now in the south will be employed in Sussex, Hertfordshire, Hampshire and Essex, the principal object being the completion of the counties round London in the first place; but the surveys of the mineral districts in Denbighshire, Cheshire and Derbyshire will proceed at the same time.[7]

The final sheet of the one-inch Ordnance map of England and Wales was published on 1 January 1870.* If, as James assumed, the work started with the measurement of the Hounslow Heath Base in 1784, the whole map had taken eighty-six years for its completion. In Scotland, the one-inch map had been published as far north as the Firths of Forth and Clyde, and the engraving of the sheets up to the Moray Firth was in progress.[8] There was still no complete map of the United Kingdom at a uniform scale.

MAP SALES AND AGENTS

In 1866 there were fundamental changes in the arrangements for the sale of maps, plans and other publications of the Survey.[9] For many years agents had been established in the principal towns of the kingdom, some one hundred and fifty in number, to whom a discount of twenty-five per cent was allowed. They obtained their supplies from Southampton but paid all charges for carriage and were not permitted to return unsold or obsolete maps; after May 1858 the agents in London obtained their maps from the Topographical Department of the War Office, where a stock was kept. In January 1866 the Secretary of State for War decided, with the approval of the Treasury, to discontinue the country agencies and to appoint six selected publishers to whom all issues were to be made from Southampton. They were to receive thirty-three per cent discount, to pay all costs of carriage, and again no return of

---

* Presumably sheet 108. Sheet 100, Isle of Man, was published in outline in 1873.

maps was allowed. Four of these were London agents – Letts Son and Co, Longman and Co, Stanford, and Wyld. The other two were W. and A. K. Johnston in Edinburgh and Hodges and Smith in Dublin. The store of maps which the Government kept in London was abolished, the new agents being supposed to keep enough maps in hand to meet the demands of the public.

At the same time a decision was taken, and endorsed by the Treasury, establishing the principle, which was to remain in force for nearly a century, for calculating map prices. Survey and map production costs up to and including the engraving of the copper plate, or the making of the photographic negative for zinc printing, were reckoned as chargeable to the Exchequer; the remaining costs – printing, storage and distribution – were to be covered by the sums charged to purchasers. The immediate effect was a number of price changes; the six-inch large sheet was reduced by half, but the one-inch was increased from two shillings to two shillings and sixpence for a full sheet and from sixpence to one shilling for a quarter sheet.

The changes in the prices of the maps and the arrangements for their sale had the effect of diminishing the receipts by about £2000 during 1867,[10] but James confidently stated that the cost of the publication, for which £7000 was included in the Vote, would be recouped during the next year. However, the following year showed a further decline so that even adding in the paper value of the free distribution to public departments the sum of £7000 was not realised. James covered himself in May 1868 by pointing out that sales had decreased under the new agency arrangement, but the Treasury decided that a sufficient period had not elapsed to enable them to form a judgment as to its financial effects, so the system survived for another four years.

Sales continued to decline in 1869 and although there was a slight recovery in the two following years, the total value of sales and issues never approached that of 1866. In 1872 a correspondence took place between James, the Office of Works and the Treasury about the establishment of a map depot in London. James recommended that the map depot should contain one set of maps open to public inspection and that it should be at the Boundary Office, where orders could be received and sent to Southampton for supply. But the First Commissioner of Works decided to take a house at No. 1 St Martin's Place and to stock it with maps so that issues could be made directly; the staff was to be brought up from Southampton. James also proposed that agents should again be appointed in all the main towns and that postmasters throughout the country should sell Ordnance Survey maps; the Treasury were now prepared to make a change and agreed to the former proposal but refused to appoint postmasters. The new agents drew their maps directly from Southampton and were allowed a discount of twenty-five per cent; by the end of the decade they were established in 125 cities and towns, including London where there were as many as ten agents, Edinburgh where there were three, and Dublin. Ordnance Survey depots for the direct sale of maps were also opened in the Post Office building in Edinburgh and at the Ordnance Survey Office in Phoenix Park, Dublin. All these measures brought about some improvement in the values of sales, but the level remained disappointingly low. As might have been predicted, the official map-shops were not welcomed by the agents in the private map-trade, and there were many protests.

A New Broom

THE BOARD OF WORKS COMMITTEE OF ENQUIRY

Within six months of the transfer of responsibility, the First Commissioner of Works had set up a Committee of Enquiry into the Ordnance Survey. The members, Douglas Galton, Henry A. Hunt and Herbert Murray, took six months to complete their enquiry, and presented the results to the First Commissioner on 29 June 1871 in a confidential report,[11] which showed a certain lack of sympathy with many of the views expressed by the Royal Engineer officers who were interrogated.

The first matter of dispute was about the need for a separate Boundary Department. James told the Committee that the Boundary Department was formed in 1849 in consequence of the numerous errors which arose and the heavy expense which was incurred when the divisional officers had the investigation of the boundaries. He considered it necessary that these duties should be entrusted to an officer of experience and judgment. The other officers interviewed seemed to hold a similar opinion, but the Committee found that the reasons given for continuing the present system in England did not appear to be conclusive. It recommended that an endeavour should be made to alter a system which it thought entailed unnecessary public expense.

Although the Committee recognized that the question of the necessity for the various scales at which the maps were published was not included in the scope of its instructions, it took up a number of points from among the opinions expressed by persons who, in some cases, could only be described as interested parties. This was particularly true of the views of Stanford, the map agent and publisher. He found little demand for large-scale maps – which presented him with a storage problem – and provided the Committee with support for the idea that large-scale maps of towns should be produced only if the municipal authorities or others requiring them were willing to defray the cost of making and printing them.

The selection of detail shown on the 1:2500 maps came in for criticism. The Committee saw a strong tendency to introduce minute details into the maps for the purpose of improving their appearance; the surveying of the interior of buildings such as the Crystal Palace, of the rails, turntables, crossings and sidings at railway stations, and of gravel walks in gardens was quite unnecessary and resulted in considerable expenditure which might well have been applied to more useful objects.

Furthermore, it was suggested in evidence that the duties of the officers of the Survey Department should be confined entirely to the actual survey and preparation of the maps on the various scales required, and that the engraving and printing should be done by contract under the control and supervision of Her Majesty's Stationery Office in London. The Committee agreed in principle, but it was not then prepared to recommend the ending of the existing system because the engravers employed at Southampton were for the most part entitled to superannuation allowances, and the discontinuation of their services would entail an annual payment of upwards of £4000. Nevertheless it held that it would be to the advantage of the public to have the printing and engraving done by contract as soon as the present staff of engravers could be reduced, and, therefore, that no new engravers should be appointed.

In another money-saving gesture the Committee recommended that unless some great public advantage were to be derived from it, the arrangement sanctioned by the Treasury for the presentation to certain persons and Heads of Departments of copies of all publications of the Survey Department should be discontinued, limiting the free distribution to the complete sets to be deposited for reference in the Public Record Office in London, the General Register House in Edinburgh, and the Record Office in Dublin.

However, in certain important matters Galton and his colleagues did endorse the views put to them by the officers of the Survey. The Committee appeared to accept the time scale for the final stages of the mapping programme. It considered that a survey department would still be needed after the survey had been completed, for the purpose of revising the maps. The rate of industrial progress in the country, as well as experience in Ireland with revision for valuation purposes, indicated a revision cycle of about fifteen years, but as the maps of England were not used for valuation, there were large districts where so frequent a revision would be unnecessary.

The Committee was also prepared to accept the principle of military direction, but the officers were not to escape entirely unscathed from its criticism and suggestions. The Ordnance Survey, it believed, was an agreeable service for the officers employed upon it, and placed them in a comparatively independent position. It was probable, therefore, that it would continue to attract good officers from the Corps of Royal Engineers; even if the scale of pay were reduced there would be a wide field to choose from. However, the district or divisional survey officer was entrusted with considerable sums of money to pay the men employed under him, and if he were to be held responsible for any losses incurred, it might be desirable to continue the present rates of pay. One advantage of the military system and military pay was that officers and men could be returned from the survey to their ordinary duty without any claim for compensation, whereas if a salary were substituted it was not improbable that, on removing employees from the survey, claims for compensation or pensions might arise.

More damaging to the interests of the officers were the recommendations on rank. The Committee concluded from former reports of the progress of the survey that it had hitherto been considered sufficient for the officer in charge to hold the rank of Colonel; indeed, for a long while it had been an officer of the rank of Lieutenant-Colonel. Of the eighteen officers now engaged on the survey, sixteen had joined as lieutenants. Whilst admitting that there were certain positions in the Survey which required special qualifications and peculiar experience, it considered that the duties could be efficiently performed by officers of the rank of Captain or Lieutenant, and the Committee saw no reason why, so long as the military system prevailed on the Survey, the country should not obtain the full economic advantage of that system. It believed, therefore, that the scale of ranks of officers to be employed should be laid down and adhered to, to the greatest practical extent.

The divisional officers whom the Committee consulted laid great stress on the advantages of the system of military supervision, which gave them a much greater hold over the employees and infused much greater regularity into the organization than could be obtained otherwise. On the other hand, the Civil Assistants complained that they were always kept in a subordinate position, that there was no such classification for pay or position as prevailed in the rest of the Civil Service, and that any increments of pay which were accorded to them were dependent upon the opinion which the divisional officer had of their work. It seemed to the Committee that these complaints rested on the assumption that the Survey was a permanent institution and it was unfortunate that some colour had been given to this assumption by granting superannuation on discharge to the Civil Assistants. At the present rate of progress it would not be long before a much smaller staff would suffice for subsequent revision, and civilians who were on the footing of established servants of the Crown would become a permanent charge on public funds without rendering any service in return.

Moreover, if the Survey were to be considered as a school for educating Royal Engineer officers and soldiers, as the Committee thought it should, the amount of revision remaining after the completion of the original survey would not afford more than sufficient work for that purpose. Indeed, it would be preferable to employ more soldiers in the place of civilians. It therefore did not appear to be desirable to take any steps which would have the effect of placing the Civil Assistants in a more permanent position than they then occupied, and it was strongly recommended that for the future new appointments should only be made on the distinct understanding that no claim for superannuation would be recognized or allowed upon retirement from the service, or upon the services of the employees being dispensed with. No appointment in any capacity as Civil Assistant, either temporary or permanent, and no increase whatever in the rate of pay, should be made by the Director without the previous sanction of the First Commissioner of Her Majesty's Works. None of the evidence submitted to the First Commissioner by various Members of Parliament appeared to bring forward any special grounds for inducing the Committee to recommend any increase in the pay of the Civil Assistants.

The Committee aimed a final shaft at James by saying that the provision of special services must necessarily impede the legitimate work of the Survey, especially in such cases as the surveys of Jerusalem and Sinai for which officers were temporally detached from their divisions.

Evidently, the Survey's new civil masters were strongly in favour of retaining its military character, but they were partly influenced by the financial advantages of so doing. Herbert Murray, in a minority report, preferred to state the argument more clearly. He said that, although the survey was undoubtedly commenced as a military measure, it had long ceased to have anything to do with military objects. It was not intended as a school for educating officers of the Royal Engineers. It had been for many years, and still was, a purely civil business in the conduct of which the Government was of the opinion that practical economy was obtained by the employment of the skilled intelligence which was at their command among the military engineers whose services could not be dispensed with and who in peace-time could not be more usefully employed. He did not think that any real economy would result from the constant change of the officers who really superintended the bulk of the expenditure, which occurred during the field operations. The regimental promotion of these officers was by no means rapid, and the requirements of economy would be sufficiently met by the rule that no officer above the rank of Second-Lieutenant should be appointed a divisional officer of the Survey. If that were the case, any increase of pay which the officer might receive on his promotion would fairly represent the additional experience he had gained. Nor did he think that experience in other departments of State would sustain the opinion that the administration of any department was improved, economically or otherwise, by frequently changing the individual at the head of it.

The Report of the Board of Works Committee had very little effect upon the work of the Ordnance Survey. The Boundary Office continued to function under a senior officer, and the content of the plans remained virtually unchanged. Apart from a reduction in 1876, the civilian strength gradually increased during the decade, whilst that of the military gradually declined.* But the service of the civil staff ceased to be pensionable, and this 'concession' was not fully restored until 1906. The view of the Committee and of the Board was that since the Army was there, it was as well to employ it and at least derive some benefit from its existence in peace-time. The acceptance of this state of affairs was then used as an argument for further depressing the lot of the Civil Assistants.

The discontent of the members of the civil staff and public agitation on their behalf eventually led to the appointment of a Departmental Committee on the Pay and Conditions of Service of Ordnance Survey Employees, which reported in 1881. Whilst the findings were apparently intended to unify the principles of grading the work and pay of employees, the continued refusal to treat the Civil Assistants

---

* In 1870 the civil and military figures (less officers) were respectively 1367 and 409. In 1879 they were 1495 and 268.

of the Ordnance Survey in the same way as other Civil Servants with regard to superannuation strengthened the thread of disaffection which was to continue for many more years.

PROGRESS 1870–80

The loss of responsibility for the Ordnance Survey did not diminish the War Office's interest in its products; on the contrary, its demands in 1871 were more numerous than ever before. James characteristically remarked that this was true of most Government departments, as the importance and value of the cadastral mapping became more recognized as it proceeded, and the resources of the Survey more fully appreciated. The War Office was concerned with the condition of the one-inch map, which the Secretary of State described as being very defective south of Lancashire and Yorkshire, and a new map, based on reductions of the cadastral survey, was suggested.[12] James proposed to produce this map 'with hills' by having the hills drawn on a separate plate and printed by photozincography on an engraved outline. The hill features could be printed 'in colour if required'. A year later this proposition received the blessing of the Treasury, by which time some further thought had been given to it. The reductions were to be made from the six-inch scale to 'produce a new one-inch map on a perfect projection and from a perfect survey, so as to make the new one-inch map of the south of England uniform with that of the six northern counties. This was the 'New Series'. It was drawn on a single Cassini projection (origin Delamere Forest) and comprised 360 sheets, each 18 inches by 12 inches; there were two forms: outline with contours and the hachured hill version. The quarter-sheets of the Old Series north of the Hull-Preston line were renumbered from north to south, but were otherwise unchanged.

The work did not proceed very rapidly. By 1877 twelve outline sheets had been published, and at the end of the decade the total had only risen to twenty-three, all in Middlesex, Kent, Surrey and Hampshire. One sheet only had been published 'with hills'.

The Scottish one-inch, benefiting from its later start, was from the outset composed of uniform sheets (24 inches by 18 inches) on a single projection (Bonne – origin 57°30′N, 4°00′W)* and, as regards planimetry, was entirely derived from larger scales. Between 1874 and the end of the decade its progress, if slow, was considerably more rapid than that of the New Series, amounting to twenty-two sheets, most of them hachured, twice the size of the English maps. The engraving was done in two stages. After the outline had been cut, an electrotyped duplicate was made to which the contours were added so that the outline map could be printed without further delay. The engraving of the hills, which was done on the original plate, took very much longer and the hill map often did not appear until several years after the outline. The hill map was difficult to revise because alterations to the outline damaged the hachures, but it was not until 1889 that completely separate hill plates were made.

Somewhat better results were achieved with the large-scale survey itself. In 1877 the field survey of Scotland was completed and the whole force of field surveyors in Great Britain was concentrated in England.[13] At the request of the Secretary of State for War the two divisions withdrawn from Scotland were ordered to carry out the survey of the eastern counties of England.[14] But at the end of the decade a great deal still remained to be done. Of the area of England and Wales south of Lancashire and Yorkshire, only about two-fifths had been surveyed, mainly in the south-east and in the mineral districts. Progress had been retarded in many ways, principally perhaps by the staff reductions of 1876. The weather, too, had been unusually hampering, especially in 1872 when the rainfall recorded in Southampton for the year was fifty per cent above the average for the previous seventeen years. As a consequence of this great rainfall, large districts had been flooded, the surveyors in many parts of the country had been unable to go on the ground and many had suffered in health from constant exposure to the inclement weather.

Some of James's rather eccentric enthusiasms must have done more to hinder than to help. His interest in meteorology led to observations being regularly taken in all the field divisions and at Southampton. Another project – the computing of the mean height of all the counties in the kingdom – cannot be regarded as other than a waste of time. Certainly more maps might have been printed if less effort had been directed towards the reproduction by photozincography of Domesday Book, the Black Letter Prayer Book and various historical manuscripts. James had successfully contrived to

---

* The first Scottish one-inch map was published in 1856, at about the same time as the first Irish one-inch. It seems probable that the decision to use the Bonne projection for both the maps was taken under Hall, and that he was advised by Yolland.

ignore the criticims of the Departmental Committee of Enquiry of 1871, but on the subject of 'special services' it was undoubtedly right. Naturally James saw photozincography in quite a different light. He considered 'that few arts have been so successfully employed or more generally used by the Government since its discovery'.

Not all the 'special services' undertaken were attributable to James's hobbies. There was much extra-departmental activity in the preparation and printing of maps for the Foreign Office, particularly in relation to the North American boundary, and for the Census Commissioners of 1871 who were making extremely heavy demands on the Department for details connected with the areas of civil and ecclesiastical divisions of the country. On this topic James warned that if the same amount of information should be required for the census of 1881 it would be necessary to form a special department of the Survey to collect it from the extended area which would then be included in the Ordnance plans.

Between 1873 and 1876 the Local Government Board, which was investigating anomalies in the civil divisions of the country, made continuous demands on the Survey for maps at the one-inch and six-inch scales showing county, township, parish, and Poor Law Union boundaries. For those counties to which the cadastral survey had not then been extended, the existing maps were on the one-inch scale only, and in these areas the work was laborious and difficult, absorbing a substantial amount of effort in the field to the detriment of progress.

Methods and Processes of the Ordnance Survey

In his first annual *Report* of the progress of the Ordnance Survey and Topographical Depot, for the year 1858, James had announced:

> We are also preparing for publication a detailed account of the manner in which all the operations of the Survey are now performed, to serve as a book of instruction for those who join the Survey and for the guidance of the officers entrusted with our Colonial Surveys and also for the instruction of the officers of the Staff College and the cadets at Woolwich and Sandhurst.

Little more was heard of this project until he revealed in February 1875, in his final *Report*, that the work had been completed and was with the printers.[15] However, from 1873 onwards he had had separate sections printed at the Ordnance Survey with no reference on the title pages to the actual authors. The complete volume published in 1875 was entitled *Account of the Methods and Processes Adopted for the Production of the Maps of the Ordnance Survey of the United Kingdom, drawn up by officers of Royal Engineers employed under Lieut. General Sir Henry James RE FRS etc., Director General*. It included an introduction written by James:

> The perfection to which the work of the Ordnance Survey has been brought in all its details has led to numerous applications from Foreign and Colonial Governments for descriptions of the several processes employed . . . In drawing up this Report each separate part has been written by the officer at present, or very recently, in charge of the work and thus an account is given by men who are thoroughly and practically acquainted with the work in all its various branches. But it is only too well known how difficult it is to give full instructions by any written description and the work as it is in operation should be seen to be properly understood . . . It would be almost impossible to name the processes and modifications which from time to time have been invented by those employed upon the Survey. Such a report would include the description of the process by which the links of the chain are roughly cut to their required length, and the refined methods by which the standards of lengths of all nations have been determined. It would also include a special description of the ruling machine by which the finest lines on copper are cut, and of the method by which the duplicate by the electrotype process is made, with such perfection that no want of evenness of tint can be observed in the original or any imperfection on the duplicate. But there is one process for which the Ordnance Survey has received very favourable notice which deserved some special remarks. The art of reducing plans by photography was introduced by me in 1855 and by this process we not only effect an enormous saving amounting now to several thousands a year but the reductions are made more accurately than they could or can be made by any other method. But this art has been rivalled by another which I discovered in 1859 and named Photozincography. The chief value of the latter consists in the facility with which the photograph of the drawing, which it is desired to copy, can be transferred to a zinc plate and printed therefrom with great rapidity and at a very trifling cost, in permanent ink.

James was generally quite fair in this introduction in attributing credit to other officers, with the exception of the discovery of photozincography, about which, perhaps, memory played him false. The volume continued in print for many years with an increasing number of addenda and corrigenda recording deviations from the processes and methods outlined in the main text. A second edition, published in 1902, was little more than a reprint of the 1875 edition with a later set of addenda and corrigenda.

James — his Departure and his Successors

The *Report* for 1875 was signed not by James but by 'J. Cameron, Major-General' and dated 25 February 1876. James had evidently left the Survey, but there was no valediction for the departed Director.

It would perhaps be ridiculous to suggest that there was a conspiracy of silence about the resignation of Sir Henry James. Nevertheless, his departure from the Ordnance Survey seems to have occasioned only a single article in the *Hampshire Independent* of 11 September 1875, where a correspondent preserving his anonymity under the label 'Civilian' heaped on the departing James the obloquy of all the dissatisfied Civil Assistants in the Ordnance Survey. The writer expressed

> a renewal of hope in the fact of the appointment of a gentleman to the office of Director who combines large practical experience of the Department with kindliness of disposition and uprightness of character . . . While the Survey is to continue under the direction of a military man, a no more fitting officer could be found than Lt. Gen. Cameron CB, FRS etc. His predecessor with the most consummate tact and diplomatic skill increased the renown of his Department and persistently drew public attention to its manifold merits on the judicious principle, we suppose, of one of the characters in Tristram Shandy that this is not a world to hide your virtues in . . . General Cameron, who has been engaged on the Survey for nearly 40 years, has a splendid opportunity of so remodelling and consolidating the administration of this Department that the old prestige attaching to an Ordnance Survey map may be restored, and that the Civil Assistants, without whom the work could not possibly be conducted, may be treated in a more equitable and more righteous way. The appointment of General Cameron to the Directorship has given great satisfaction to the Civil Assistants. He cannot use finesse and he has not the diplomatic skill of his predecessor, but he has qualities far more desirable. It is hoped that the time of vaunting and trumpet blowing respecting the Ordnance Survey is over and that General Cameron will initiate a policy of internal reform which may obviate the necessity of a searching Governmental enquiry.

From this and much else that followed it would appear that Sir Henry James was less than popular with at least some of his civilian staff. Little has been written about him. There was no lengthy obituary when he died, no biography. *The Times* of 16 June 1877 recorded:

> Death of Lt. Gen. Sir H. James. Lt. Gen. Sir Henry James Royal Engineers, late Director of Ordnance Surveys of Great Britain from which post after 20 years service he retired in 1874, died at Southampton yesterday aged 74 years.

This brief notice was sandwiched between nineteen lines of 'with regret' for the authoress the Hon. Mrs Norton, and fifty-four lines on the drowning of two Oxford undergraduates.

The obituary in the *Royal Engineers Journal* for July 1877 contained very little other than a bare recounting of what he did and where, and when he was promoted. The only personal comments were that he reached the ripe age of seventy-four and that his services towards popularizing the study of palaeography and philology had been great. The remark that Sir Henry James was the author of many works of scientific value was perhaps more than the truth, since his name appeared on many of the works of his subordinate officers, including the fundamental work of Alexander Ross Clarke on the Figure of the Earth which was for some time attributed to James rather than to Clarke. Cameron wrote a private manuscript memoir of him soon after his death, a copy of which survives in the National Library in Dublin among the Larcom Papers. It was left to Colonel Vetch, writing a brief note in the *Dictionary of National Biography*, to imply that he had his differences with his junior officers, since he was 'unpleasant if opposed'.

Something of a mystery attaches to the departure of James from the Ordnance Survey. He was promoted Lieutenant-General and Colonel Commandant on 28 November 1874 when, according to the obituary notice in the *Royal Engineers Journal*, he ceased to be Director of the Ordnance Survey. It was not, however, until 18 August 1875 that he was caused to resign from the post of Director apparently on grounds of ill health.* James mentioned in his valedictory circular dated 19 August that he was suddenly taken ill when about to visit the Isle of Mull during a duty tour the previous autumn and had not since regained his usual strength.[16]

James remains an enigmatic figure. His long rule as Superintendent of the Survey, Director of the Topographical and Statistical Department and finally as Director General of the Ordnance Survey, was marked by an initial period of intense activity which was of great importance for the future of the Survey. In his later years his actions were touched with despotism and eccentricity and there seems to have been a complete absence of any warm feeling between the Director and his staff. The determination and dedication with which he set about establishing the objectives and the long-term programme

---

* Before 1876 there were no rules relating retirement from the Army to age, and officers could continue to serve until they died. In 1875 James was 72.

of the Survey between 1854 and 1863 must be set against those aspects of his personal character which alienated his subordinates and dimmed their initiative. Perhaps his worst fault was that he remained too long.

Major-General John Cameron had had almost a lifetime's experience of the Ordnance Survey when he became Director on 11 August 1875, a week before James resigned. He had been in charge of the Dublin Office from 1846 to 1852 and was Executive Officer of the Survey from 1852 to 1873 when he left on his promotion to Major-General. He must have known James very well indeed and if, as appears from the letter in the *Hampshire Independent*, he was indeed a kindly and courteous man, his failure to signalize James's departure in any way may have meant that there was a deep rift between them. Cameron remained in charge of the Ordnance Survey for less than three years. These were marked by the reductions of 1876, amounting to ninety Civil Assistants and fifty-four labourers, which inevitably reduced the rate of progress.[17] His period in office seems to have been otherwise unremarkable, but one of his actions was to have a long-lasting effect. In 1875 he lent several of the more important instruments used in executing the survey to the Loan Exhibition of Scientific Apparatus at South Kensington.[18] Some of these remained permanently on exhibition there, notably a set of Colby's compensation bars, the BO three-foot theodolite, the two-foot Troughton and Simms theodolite and Airy's zenith sector.

Cameron died suddenly from pneumonia on 30 June 1878 and was succeeded by Colonel A. C. Cooke who, by contrast, had had only a little previous Ordnance Survey experience and none later than the middle 1850s when he was a division officer in Scotland. However, he had been responsible between 1859 and 1869 for the Topographical Depot as Executive Officer under James, and must therefore have been quite closely in touch with events at Southampton. Cooke was the first head of the Ordnance Survey to use the title 'Director General' when signing the annual reports.

Notes

1 PP 1862 (134) XXXII.
2 OSR 1864, pp. 3–5: PP 1865 [3467] XXXII.
3 OSR 1865, p. 3: PP 1866 [3636] XLI.
4 Brian Bond, *The Victorian Army and the Staff College 1854–1914*, ch. 4.
5 PP 1870 (268) XLIII.
6 OSR 1868, p. 3: PP 1868–9 [4124] XXXVI.
7 PP 1870 (268) XLIII.
8 OSR 1869, p. 3: PP 1870, C. 61, XLIII.
9 OSR 1866, p. 3: PP 1867 [3834] XLI.
10 OSR 1867, p. 3: PP 1867–8 [4008] XLII.
11 Report of a Committee of Inquiry into the Ordnance Survey, 29 June 1871, No. 27969.
12 OSR 1871, p. 4: PP 1872, C. 511, XLVII.
13 OSR 1877, p. 3: PP 1878, C. 1986, LXI.
14 OS Library G3484.
15 OS OSR 1874, p. 10: PP 1875, C. 1204, LX.
16 OS Library G3484.
17 OSR 1876, p. 3: PP 1877, C. 1706, LXVIII.
18 *Ibid.*

16
The Mature
Topographical
Survey

The Large-Scale Plans – Function and Content

By the middle of the nineteenth century field procedures were well established and stabilized, but the cartographic requirements which regulated the map content were largely undefined and were still the subject of controversy. The final stage of the scales dispute had centred on the need for a map larger in scale than the six-inch; the supporters of the 1:2500 included engineers and agriculturalists, but ninety per cent of its advocates based their arguments on its use for land registration, conveyancing, land valuation, tithes and rating.[1] At the time, James was hesitant about justifying a large-scale survey on cadastral grounds but Charles Trevelyan took a different view in a footnote to James's Minute of 7 May 1855:

> As the relations of landlord and tenant apply to every part of town and country, to give certainty and facility to their transactions is an important item in that aggregate of public utility which constitutes the justification for the 1:2500 scale.[2]

The conclusion is unavoidable that the original purpose of the plans was primarily cadastral and that it remained so. Yet, like the final form of the Irish six-inch, the map was not simply cadastral in character. It was originally plotted by parishes but from 1873 the sheets were 'filled-in' to the county boundaries and, after the start of the first revision in 1891, it became the practice to fill in sheets completely, an arrangement not ideally suited to cadastral purposes because the sheet edges cut through the land parcels. Moreover, the 1:2500 map included much detail not required in a cadastral survey, although it ignored natural relief apart from spot heights and some slope drawing. It is not surprising to find that frequent minor changes in the content of the map were made throughout its life. In general the content was progressively reduced, which could be interpreted as a move towards a more definitely cadastral form; field names were omitted after 1888, interiors of public buildings, hedgerow timber and other minor details were discontinued after 1892, and from 1895 'unimportant' detail was no longer shown.[3]

Many years later Winterbotham made a revealing comment on the content reductions. He thought it was doubtful if the omission of gates and individual trees in hedges resulted in 'any real economy' and 'on the whole the omissions seem to have been ill-advised'.[4] These features, he said, were 'reliable and conspicuous' points on which a revision survey could be based, thereby giving a clue to one of the purposes of the 1:2500 map: to meet the needs of the Ordnance Survey itself. The basic scale survey provided the source material for all the derived maps, apart from the contours which were surveyed independently, and had therefore to include all the features which were shown on these maps except for a few details, such as the road classification, for the small scales. The 1:2500 maps had to satisfy two needs, those of the cadastral survey on the one hand and of the Ordnance Survey's topographical data bank on the other; the reductions in content were almost always of features that were not essential to either. Some objects facilitated the survey itself; what other justification could be conceived for showing flagstaffs?

The plans came to be used for many other purposes, but these were mainly the coincidental uses that could be found for any accurate large-scale map; some were very important, but had little or no effect on the map content. There arose the concept of the 'general map' – one not catering for any particular requirement, but useful as a base to which other information could be added to suit a wide variety of needs.

Topographical Methods

THE CHAIN SURVEY

The method of topographical surveying developed in Ireland known as 'chain surveying by triangles' was adopted for nearly all the large-scale surveys of Great Britain carried out in the latter part of the nineteenth century. The control consisted of triangulation stations about 1 to $1\frac{1}{2}$ miles apart for the 1:2500 scale, but greater or less than this if the map scale was to be smaller or larger. This lower order triangulation was never fully adjusted to the Principal Triangulation; every county or group of counties was surveyed on its own origin and there were discrepancies where the county triangulations met.

For the chain survey each surveyor, who had a labourer to assist him, was equipped with a chain of 66 feet divided into 100 links, with ten marking arrows, a ten-link offset-measuring rod, a measuring tape, and a ten-foot station staff, shod with iron at the lower end and having a small red and white flag at the top. The unit of work was a triangle formed by adjacent triangulation stations; the lines chained from one station to another were designated 'main lines'. Before starting to chain, the surveyor would reconnoitre the ground and decide what lines additional to the main lines would be necessary to pick up all the detail within the triangle. These additional lines were known as 'split lines', of which there might be three or four running across the triangle between points selected on the main lines, and 'detail lines' of which there would be a relatively large number, connecting points on previously chosen lines and sited for the particular purpose of fixing detail. For the 1:2500 scale maps the offset length was limited to one chain (100 links). If an offset was more than 80 links the surveyor was not permitted to estimate its direction; instead the right angle had to be constructed using an 'offset triangle' with measured sides in proportion to 3, 4 and 5. During his reconnaissance the surveyor would have this limitation of offset length very much in mind when deciding what chain lines would be necessary to fix all the detail as economically as possible.[5] He would sketch in his field book a General Line Diagram, showing main and split lines and probably some of the detail lines. The General Line Diagram would be supplemented by as many Detail Line Diagrams as might be necessary to show the often complicated network of detail lines. These line diagrams, while constituting an operational plan for chain survey, also provided a record of chained distances referred to the pages of the field book on which the detail itself was recorded.

When chaining sloping ground, the chain, or successive parts of it if the slope was steep, was often held horizontally and a plummet or drop arrow was used to mark the ground position of one end of the chain. Horizontal distances were thus obtained without measuring the slope by theodolite or clinometer, which had been normal practice in Ireland where the observed slopes served the additional purpose of providing ground heights above datum level. However, in an early description of Ordnance Survey field methods in Britain, a table of corrections to the measured length for various inclinations of the chain shows that the horizontal equivalents were sometimes found by measuring the angle of the slope.[6]

The surveyors, who were either civilians or sappers, were organized into sections of eight to twelve men. Each section was supervised by a superintendent, usually a non-commissioned officer. As a rule, one member of each section, assisted by one or more labourers, would be permanently employed on finding and marking the tertiary triangulation stations, and fixing marks on the ground at intervals along the main chain lines to ensure that the chaining of these lines would be as nearly as possible rectilinear.

Each surveyor recorded his chainages and offsets together with sketches of the concomitant detail in his field book. All field book entries had to be in ink, the surveyor carrying 'a fountain ink bottle suspended from a breast button'. Erasures in the field book were forbidden and corrections were made by crossing through the item concerned and rewriting, attested by the surveyor's initials. The section superintendent inspected the field books daily, and periodically verified each surveyor's work by measuring parts of it in the field. Whenever distances could not be directly measured by chaining owing to difficulties of the ground, additional points might be fixed with a theodolite.

The precision of chaining required for 1:2500 mapping was that there should never be a discrepancy of more than 2 links in 1000, with a maximum possible discrepancy of 15 links in any one line. The comparision between the chained lengths of main lines and the lengths computed from the triangulation was made in the division office to which the superintendent sent his weekly progress report, accompanied by a trace showing the progress of each surveyor's work. The lengths of the split lines were also tested at the division office by laying them down on an accurate plot of the main lines.

The trace was then returned to the superintendent with correct lines ticked off and lines needing to be rechained crossed through in ink.

In uncultivated and wooded districts and in mountainous areas the framework for detail survey was provided mainly by five-inch vernier theodolite and chain traverses or by a mixture of traverses and local chained frameworks depending on points fixed in traversing.[7] Where traversing was used as the main method of detail survey control, the district was divided into blocks of convenient size, bounded by common lines such as roads, paths and rivers. The surveyor undertaking a particular block first ran a traverse round it, connecting as he went all accessible triangulation stations. He then ran intermediate traverses at suitable intervals across the block, always noting the angular misclosure on reconnecting with the main traverse. Subsidiary traverses were run to connect isolated houses or other detail which could not otherwise be fixed and it was a rule that all such traverses must close on some station of the traverse from which they were started. So far as was convenient surveyors of adjoining traverse blocks were required to start from the same triangulation station and the 'meridian' of the traverse work was to be 'carried through from block to block as far as practicable', since this was said to be 'an advantage in the plotting'.[8] This contemporary explanation is thought to mean that arbitrary 'meridians' were used and that the system of observation was that in which the bearing is carried forward and recorded at each station as the reading of the horizontal arc of the theodolite with the telescope pointed along the forward line; the method is suitable for traverses to be plotted by protractor at the map scale, no computation of co-ordinates being made.[9] With care the results can be satisfactory when the sole object of the traversing is to fix detail, assuming that the over-all triangulation control is adequately dense. Surveyors employed on traversing were each normally assisted by two labourers.[10]

In general, however, traversing was avoided whenever possible in the original surveys for the 1:2500 map. Even for the 1:500 and 1:528 town plans great ingenuity was shown in providing sufficient subsidiary triangulation stations and intersected points so that traversing would only be required in 'crooked alleys and courts'. For instance, for the 1:1056 survey of London a multitude of tall poles, each with fishing-rod joints guyed at successive heights, were used as temporary triangulation intersected points to be observed during the early part of the day before there was much traffic. The points thus fixed were then used to control the detail survey by chaining and offset measurements alone. It was not until 1897 that precise traversing with computed co-ordinates was first used for the control of detail survey in urban areas. In 1912 the loss of tertiary triangulation points in the outskirts of London became a serious handicap in revising the 1:2500 maps, and precise traversing with permanent ground marks was introduced for a time to provide the necessary control.[11]

The apparent prejudice in the Ordnance Survey against traversing as a method of providing control for large-scale surveys seems illogical. It probably originated in Ireland in the years 1830–33 for reasons which were quite valid at the time; the difficulty in finding and eliminating errors from careless traversing compared with the certainty and simplicity of the chain-triangle method was probably the decisive factor.

PLOTTING AND EXAMINATION

In Great Britain the plotting of the triangulation points was done on paper by measurement from the sheet-lines with beam compasses.[12] The sheets for six-inch maps covered 6 miles east to west by 4 miles north to south (36 inches by 24 inches); for the 1:2500 scale the cover was 1½ miles by 1 mile, so that there were sixteen 1:2500 sheets to each six-inch sheet; the 1:500 town sheets covered 24 chains by 16 chains, so that there were twenty-five such sheets in the area of one 1:2500 sheet.

All plotting was done by men other than those who were employed on the field work. After the triangulation stations had been plotted for a given sheet and checked by the computed lengths of triangle sides, the plot was given to the line plotter who constructed the framework of chained lines from the line diagrams of the field books. The line plotter distributed any admissible differences between the triangulation stations, making any small proportionate adjustments which might be necessary for points along the line where interior (i.e. split or detail) lines joined or detail was marked. The split lines were all expected to plot without appreciable error since they would all have been previously checked on the submission of the superintendent's weekly reports; similarly the detail lines were expected to plot to scale exactly since for these shorter lines the accumulated error of the chaining should have been negligible at map scale. Any interior lines which did not plot accurately were included in an error list which was sent to the section superintendent who arranged for the rejected lines to be rechained. When all the lines had been finally accepted the line plotter inked up his plot in blue showing triangulation stations by small triangles and the junctions of chain lines (usually marked on the ground and called 'picket points') by small circles. This precise line plot at map scale together with the field books became a complete record of the surveyed framework for the map detail.

The points of this framework were pricked through from the line plot onto a sheet of drawing paper on which the manuscript map was to be drawn. The detail plotter drew the measured lines by joining the pricked points, checking their length as he went; he was followed by a third person who made a trace from the drawing paper showing all the triangulation and pricked points of the surveyed framework by black dots. The trace was then laid over the original line plot and any discrepancies between the positions of the traced points and those on the original plot were marked on the trace in red. The differences, if any, were then investigated and corrected. It was only after these very rigorous checks had been completed that the detail plotter was allowed to start plotting the topographical detail of the map.

The plotted detail included all items fixed in the chain survey by direct measurement – Colby's phrase for this had been 'actual measurement' – either by cuts along chain lines, offsets, or occasionally by chained triangles where an offset would have been too long. It also included any detail plotted graphically from theodolite traverses. The detail plotted was not, of course, absolutely complete and features and ornament (woods, rocks, marshland etc.) not recorded in the field books were added later, during the field examination of the manuscript map traces.

The partially complete manuscript map was then divided into rectangular sections by pencil lines: a 1:2500 map into six equal sections by one east to west line and two north to south lines, and a six-inch map into four equal sections. An ink tracing of each section provided documents of suitable size to be fitted in a sketching case for field examination; roads and fences were in black, buildings in red and water features in blue.[13] The examiner was an experienced surveyor and had to be a reasonably good draughtsman since his work was mainly graphical; his method of verifying the accuracy of the plotted detail was basically the comparison of directions and intersections on the ground with the corresponding directions and intersections on the trace of the manuscript.[14] The examiner used the same method to fix minor detail and ornament which had not been included in the chain survey; this would include footpaths, embankments, trees, details of railways and the large number of objects essential to the completion of the manuscript map. He would add explanatory remarks where necessary, particularly against features such as pits, shafts, conduits and weirs. The completion of the survey of the coast line with the accurate representation of cliffs, rocks and the foreshore was an important part of the examination, which included the determination of the points on rivers to which the ordinary tides flowed. The examiner had also to give all the information necessary for the subdivision of the land into serially numbered parcels whose areas would be subsequently measured on the completed map. In this he was required to indicate the various types of ground – arable, pasture, woodland, moorland etc. – supplementing symbols with notes and, in cases of doubt, defining the parcel limits which he would recommend. Another duty for the examiner was the collection of names.

The procedure for constructing the 1:500 town maps was, in general, the same as that for the 1:2500 maps, apart from the line plot. For so large a scale no adjustment of error by the line plotter was allowed. A separate line plot was therefore not used and the triangulation and traverse points together with the chain line framework were plotted directly on the manuscript map sheet; any line found to be in error was remeasured in the field.[15]

The completed manuscript map was examined on the ground by the division officer, and then, with its concomitant traces and documents, at the divisional headquarters office. Bench-marks and spot heights were inserted under the direction of the officer in charge of the levelling for the area. At headquarters in Southampton the manuscript maps were again examined before being reproduced by lithographic printing.

The Depiction of Relief

Hill-sketching was subject to control by contours from about 1843 in Great Britain and from about three years earlier in Ireland. Eventually the whole of Great Britain and Ireland was hill-sketched in this way as the basis for the hachures on the published one-inch maps. In England and Wales the hachures of the Old Series maps south of the Hull-Preston line were all replaced by later versions based on the contours.

CONTOURING

The contourer's work was done in three parts: levelling, marking the contours on the ground and surveying them, and finally plotting the contours.[16] For the levelling a five-inch theodolite was used since this could measure horizontal angles if necessary, and an eight-foot contouring staff graduated similarly to an ordinary levelling staff, with a sliding vane which could be fixed by a clamping screw and observed up to a distance of 10 chains or so. The contourer would start from a convenient Ordnance Survey bench-mark and would run a line of levels with the telescope line-of-sight horizontal until he obtained a point on the ground at the altitude of the contour which he wished to delineate. Having marked this point with a picket, he moved his theodolite to a place of roughly the same altitude as, and about 10 chains from, the picket. He then set the line-of-sight of the theodolite horizontal and his staff man put the foot of the staff on the picket and clamped the sliding vane in position when the contourer signalled that it was precisely on his line of sight. The staff man then moved along the general direction of the contour, finding a point on it at each significant bend by shifting the staff until the contourer signalled that the staff vane was on his line of sight. They continued in this way until the staff man was about the same distance on the far side of the theodolite as the starting picket was from it, having left a mark at each staff station and a picket at the final station. This procedure was repeated until a convenient length of contour was marked out on the ground and connections made to any other near-by bench-marks; the closing error had not to exceed 0.1 foot in flat country or 0.3 foot in hilly country.

The contour was then surveyed and plotted in the field in pencil on a six-inch reduction of the 1:2500 map or on part of the six-inch map where this was the basic scale. In areas of dense detail this was done by running chain lines connected to exactly defined points such as fence junctions, and measuring offsets to the marks placed on the line of the contour. In hilly country where detail was sparse, the chain lines were the legs of a traverse for which the horizontal angles were measured with the theodolite; vertical angles also were measured if the corrections of the slope lengths of these lines to their horizontal equivalents were significant. Where the ground was steep, time was saved by making connections to bench-marks by vertical angles. The traverses were plotted in the field using a scale and a protractor and the contours were plotted from the offsets. Later the contours were penned in blue, with dots at each staff station and small circles at the 'permanent' pickets; these were pickets at intervals of about one-third of a mile along each contour line, and were left in place when, after the contours had been finally checked, all other pickets and marks were removed. The heights of the triangulation stations were entered as well as the closing errors of the levelling lines, so that the field documents, together with the levelling book, formed a complete record of the work. The linear mileage of contours to be run increases generally with the altitude and an experienced contourer was expected to complete in a month all the operations of contouring in 8 square miles below the 200-foot level, in 5 square miles between 200 and 500 feet, and in 2 to 3 square miles at higher altitudes.

Contourers were grouped in field sections of four to eight, with a labourer as staff man for each contourer. A senior surveyor, designated superintendent, was in charge of each section. Whilst it was part of the superintendent's duties to check some of the work of each contourer, the general examination of the contouring was done by specially selected men, each assisted by two staff men, who checked the contourers' work using the same methods of survey, but working along each line in the opposite direction to that in which it had been originally surveyed. Since the contours were still marked on the ground, the work of checking them was expected to proceed at about five times the original rate.

Contours surveyed by these methods were called instrumental contours, and their altitude error was not expected to exceed 0.3 foot. In Lancashire and Yorkshire and in the Scottish counties Kirkcudbright and Wigtown, interpolated contours with a vertical interval of 25 feet were added by sketching. Between 1860 and 1882 a simple water-level[17] (essentially a U-tube partly filled with water) was employed in surveying these interpolated contours and the adjacent instrumental contour ground marks were used as starting levels, field methods being otherwise similar to those for the instrumental contours.[18] Interpolated contours with the same vertical interval were also used for the six-inch maps of some counties in northern Ireland, but it seems likely that these were fitted in between the instrumental contours, on the assumption that the intervening ground slope was even, without any additional levelling.[19]

HILL-SKETCHING

Once the contours were plotted and sketched the hill-sketching could proceed. The hill-sketcher worked on a base map, which was an outline reproduction of the contoured map, fixed in a sketching case. The scale of the base map was six inches to one mile for about half of Great Britain and for the remainder mostly two inches to one mile, one inch to one mile being used in the north-west of Scotland and for a few small areas in England and Wales. The hill-sketcher's instruments were a prismatic compass, a protractor, a six-inch plotting scale and a hill-sketcher's scale, which was graduated to show the horizontal interval at the scale of the hill-sketch between adjacent contours for various angles of ground slope, ranging from very small slopes up to 45°. Starting at a point plotted on his base map the sketcher would take a compass bearing to a distant point estimated to be at the same level as the starting point and where the ground slope was seen to change. By plotting this bearing on his base map and pacing the distance to the selected point he obtained a chord to an estimated contour giving the general direction which the curved guiding strokes of his shading must follow. He continued by making a succession of such chords and guiding strokes; then taking account of all known altitudes from instrumental and interpolated contours and also from spot levels, he would fill in the space between guiding strokes with 'touches' (short strokes), each representing a horizontal line, thus building up a picture of ground relief in which the variations in ground slope were represented by corresponding variations in the density of the shading. The thicknesses and number of the strokes and the resulting variations in the density of the shading were left to the experience of the hill-sketcher. In the Ordnance Survey, therefore, the hill-sketchers did not rely entirely on any systematic grading of shades in relation to slopes, such as had been designed by Colonel J. E. Van Gorkum[20] in Holland, although a formalized 'scale of shade' was used during training. The uniformity of the Ordnance Survey hill-sketches was obtained by the constant comparison of work done by different men in similar areas and, of course, the assistance of the contours and spot levels. The results were sufficiently consistent for it to be said that in good sketches the maximum breadth of horizontal strokes for very steep mountain slopes was $\frac{1}{45}$ inch, whilst the minimum breadth used in low and nearly flat country was $\frac{1}{500}$ inch; and that the average proportion of light to shade was 1:3 for a 45° slope and 25:1 for the minimum slope which could be indicated by shading. Since in nature no 'unbroken' slope is steeper than about 45°,* slopes steeper than this were shown by the hill-sketcher with lines perpendicular to the direction of the contours to indicate rocks, broken ground, quarries and cliffs.[21]

The pencil hill-sketch was inked in with a mapping pen and black ink. The hill-sketcher did not start this until he had shaded a considerable area, since he could then improve the general representation by exaggerating or reducing the effect of some of the ground features and so produce a sketch which would display the main characteristics of the relief of the area as well as those local intricacies of ground which could be properly shown at the scale of the sketch. The completed sketches were inspected in the field by the officer in charge of the division and then sent to the one-inch drawing office. These sketches were the originals for the hill-draughtsmen, who produced one inch to one mile hachured hill drawings by brushwork, using Indian ink.

Methods and Processes of the Ordnance Survey, published in 1875, describes, not very clearly, how the hill drawing was done:

> . . . The drawing must in fact appeal to the eye in a much greater degree than the original sketches do; it must become more artistic and less mechanical in its handling . . the draughtsman's first duty is to make a rough comprehensive draft . . . so as to divide the ground by zones into a certain number of altitudes in order to guide him afterwards in giving the proper general strength of shade in proportion to the altitude . . . He then proceeds to bring up each feature in his drawing gradually to its due prominence by faint shades of colour washed and toned down over and over each other.

It is difficult to avoid being rather sceptical about the value of all this, especially as the final result rested solely with the engraver who could do nothing more than cut the hachures on the copper plate. Furthermore, all the information derived from observations on the ground was contained in the field sketches so that the brushwork embellishments were merely gilding the lily. In defence, it has been argued that the hill-drawings were interpretative, and were intended to reveal the finer points of the field sketches more clearly to the engraver and to ensure that all ranges of hills were not made to look the same height.

The Archaeological Survey for the Large-Scale Plans of Great Britain

In the course of the large-scale survey of Great Britain, many archaeological and historical features and sites were surveyed and marked on the plans (Plate 12). A powerful influence at the time was the

---

* On steeper slopes the earth breaks away and in Ordnance Survey usage the word 'slope' no longer applies.

rise of national and local archaeological societies which occurred after 1840; these soon began to make themselves heard and to offer help. In 1855 the Society of Antiquaries of Scotland requested that 'all remains, such as barrows, pillars, circles and ecclesiastical and other ruins' should be noted by the Survey;[22] this was agreed with the proviso that the Society 'endeavour on their part to assist the surveyors with local information through the co-operation of the resident gentry, ministers, school-masters and others'.

The pattern set by the survey of Ireland, and the influence of Colby, can perhaps be detected in James's order of 1865 referring to

> the necessity of officers making themselves acquainted with the local history of, and (by personal inspections) with the objects of antiquarian interest in the districts which they are surveying in order that all such objects may be properly represented on the plans and fully described in the Name Books.[23]

and again, in a circular of 1867:

> . . . the officers are specially directed to read up the histories of counties in which the survey is in progress.

James must have been aware of the way in which the antiquarian work of the Survey in Ireland had tended to exceed the level acceptable to the Board of Ordnance, but nevertheless his genuine interest led him to collect as much archaeological information as possible. In 1867 he drew up a short account of several famous monuments (Stonehenge, Callernish and some Irish megaliths):

> for the guidance of officers on the survey as to the manner in which the present state of the antiquities of the kingdom should be sketched and described for record. This account is illustrated with plans, sketches and photographs and has been included in the list of publications on sale.[24]

Another indication of his interest was recorded in the annual *Report* for 1872:

> A portion of Wiltshire, including Stonehenge, has, at the request of the Society of Antiquaries, been ordered to be surveyed, in order to preserve an authentic record of the remains of antiquity there before the plough has effaced them.

James's ideas on the identification and depiction of archaeological features were usually good, but he was a man of decided opinions and was sometimes prone to error. It was he who insisted that the North Downs trackway should be called the Pilgrim's Way on Ordnance maps, without any basis in historical fact, causing much trouble in later years when it was necessary to correct it.

The system which James created was first laid down clearly in *Instructions to Field Examiners* in 1884 and was to persist with no significant change until 1920.[25] Superintendents were to receive briefs about antiquities taken from literary sources at the Office; they were to enquire whether the features were extant and, if not, whether their sites could be established. Examiners and revisers were to make enquiry on the spot for other antiquities and any newly discovered. Everything was to be endorsed by the local authority and entered in the Name Books. A fairly comprehensive list of features likely to be met with was given and the type faces to be used for antiquities of different periods were defined, AD 1688 being the limiting date. Particular care was to be shown in the accurate representation of slopes of earthworks and in the treatment of 'site' antiquities; the Office was to be the arbiter in all doubtful cases. The twelve paragraphs on archaeology in the *Instructions* were, in most respects, a model of the best which might be hoped for at the time.

However, those Name Books which survived the Second World War – almost all Scottish – show that worrying out the details of local archaeology under this system was still a chancy process. A typical episode is found in a letter from a Mr Joseph Hall, dated 14 January 1865, and preserved in the Name Book for Ancrum parish, Roxburghshire. He had been examining the hill-sketches for the county and wrote about local Roman sites, making the suggestion that since the Eildon Hills had a marked three-peaked form the Roman name TRIMONTIVM belonged there, a view held by Roy and generally accepted in later years. An examiner resisted this suggestion and preferred to attach the name to Burnswark on the evidence of the forged 'Richard of Cirencester', a nuisance whose influence on opinion dogged the Survey's work until 1920. The letter was sent to James through the local officer but there is no evidence that he ever saw it. A reply came from the Office accepting most of Hall's suggestions but making no comment about TRIMONTIVM. This obvious and serious gaffe remained on the plans.

Supplying 'site' antiquities became common during the large-scale survey and has since been a feature of Survey practice. Attention was drawn to them usually by local people; they were mainly find spots of hoards of bronze implements, ancient coins, pottery, human remains and so forth. Evidence for them was entered in the Name Books and, since many never found any other publication, the loss of so many of these records in 1940 was a heavy blow, but the hints supplied by their appearance on the maps have often led later field workers to important discoveries. A quantity of valuable local tradition found its way onto the maps, examples being the identification of Kett's Oak beside the Norwich-Wymondham road and the showing of the annual 'Penny Hedge' in Whitby Harbour. Many authentic sites of historic events were shown but there were such inexplicable oddities as the 'Hanging Walls of Mark Antony', a feature on the lower slopes of Cross Fell near Kirkby Thore which is, in fact, a group of old cultivation terraces. Another was the long persistence of the name Heriri Mons attached to the Roman fort site at Tomen-y-mur in Merionethshire. This Latin name was applied correctly by the early cartographer Speed to the whole Snowdon region, and the process by which it became attached to a site on the southern verge of that area remains a mystery.

Clearly there were serious flaws in the system, which might have been avoided by study of the earlier practice in Ireland. In 1896 David Murray was to note that, although the Society of Antiquaries of Scotland had duly circularized the conveners of counties and the landed proprietors, the end-product had been unsatisfactory.[26] Material had been collected uncritically and without method; there had also been many omissions. In England relations with the societies were more fruitful, but the pattern of the occurrence of antiquities and historical notices over the whole of the large-scale plans produced before 1893 makes it clear that a principal factor in success or failure was the officer in charge in the field. Although skilled in their own work, surveyors could not also be antiquarians, nor could they be expected to show any special zeal in this nebulous field. Much was missed. There was no expert central control to see that descriptions were correct, surveys adequate and areas thoroughly combed for features. The Irish Survey had employed professionals to ensure the best authority for its work but none was appointed in Great Britain until after the First World War.

Place-Names – the Mature System

The principles evolved by Colby were still current half a century later, and were restated in the description of the treatment of place-names included in *Methods and Processes of the Ordnance Survey*:

> The greatest care is taken to obtain the correct orthography of the names to appear upon the Ordnance Plans and that no names of importance are omitted. The detail examiner obtaining the names with the residential authorities, these are further verified by the superintendent of the party or other competent person who finally examines the whole of the work and then compares the names locally collected with the extracts supplied to him.

In practice a great deal of elaboration had taken place since the 1830s. The passing of the Survey Act in 1841, primarily designed to smooth the path of surveyors who were thenceforward responsible for laying down local administrative boundaries, also facilitated the work of place-name collection. In at least one county the seemingly more inquisitorial nature of the enquiries connected with the place-name sheets had led to friction. From Shropshire it was reported in 1831 that Henry Still, a young Ordnance surveyor,

> was seen going into several of the farmyards in this neighbourhood and taking down the names of farms, this caused great alarm and he was pursued by some special constables to a public house.[27]

But after 1841 the collection of names proceeded more smoothly under the legal umbrella of boundary surveying, and the stipulation of the Act that the 'Clerk of the peace of each county shall deliver to surveyor, a list of all the cities, towns, boroughs, parishes etc' must have assisted the toponymic work.

One of the administrative consequences of the Act was the creation by Colby of a section dealing with boundary matters within the Ordnance Office and, during the 1840s, this section accepted responsibility for the names of parishes, in conjunction with the survey of their boundaries. A separate series of Ecclesiastical Name Books (the forerunners of the Administrative Name Books) was accordingly created and was in use until 1879, when the boundaries of ecclesiastical parishes began to be replaced by those of civil parishes. Ecclesiastical Name Books have survived for a number of counties, those for Durham and Cumberland, dated from 1850 onwards, being the earliest.

Other features and places within the Ordnance plans were recorded in the complementary Object Name Books. Spellings were collected by the field surveyors, using the same printed form (OS 21) as in the Ecclesiastical Name Book. The 'objects' were both natural and man-made. The former included hills, streams, and woods, and the latter such domestic and industrial buildings, roads, canals and railways, and antiquities as fell within the scope of the plans. As a general rule less historical research was undertaken in connection with these names than with parishes – where the name was of legal importance – and local people, rather than documents, were consulted as authorities. The internal *Instructions* gave a systematic brief on place-names, extending to twelve pages:[28]

> For the name of a house, farm, park, wood, or other part of an estate, the owner is the best authority. For names generally the following are the best individual authorities and should be taken in the order given:
> Owners of property; estate agents; clergymen, postmasters and schoolmasters, if they have been some time in the district; rate collectors; road surveyors; borough and county surveyors; gentlemen residing in the district; Local Government Board Orders; local histories; good directories. Assistance may also be obtained from local antiquarian and other societies, in connection with places of antiquarian and national interest.
> Respectable inhabitants of some position should be consulted. Small farmers and cottagers are not to be depended on, even for the names of the places they occupy, especially as to the spelling. But a well-educated and independent occupier is, of course, a good authority.

From a group of surviving Object Name Books for Lancashire it is possible to see that these detailed instructions were heeded in practice. It is recorded that a blacksmith and a gamekeeper were consulted as well as representatives of most of the recommended categories.

On the question of documentary sources, the *Instructions* ruled:

> If possible, the names should be obtained or seen in a written or printed form; when taken down from word of mouth, errors are very liable to occur in the spelling. Estate maps, valuation rolls or rating books, tithe maps and their references, newspapers, notices or advertisements, or other documentary evidence, should always be referred to when available.

This goes a long way to account for the authorities actually quoted; these ranged from Bradshaw's Railway Guides to voters' lists. It became the practice to paste into the Name Books local advertisements, and even printed invoices and letter-heads in which the place-name was given, in support of particular spellings.

By 1850 the essentials of a standard system had developed into a matter of routine, for surveys of new areas and the work of revision alike. Improvements were to be made later, but the belief that local usage should be recorded and preserved remained inviolate. In 1887 it was reiterated succinctly:

> The system of the Ordnance Survey is whilst giving due weight to the various authorities, to adopt the form of the name which is well-established usage amongst educated people at the time of the survey.[29]

In the light of this doctrine it seems clear that, although the surveyors had been encouraged to grasp and use the etymological roots of language, especially with regard to parish names, the evidence of the past had not been allowed to override modern practice.

At the same time it is true to say that the Survey became a conservative – or at least stabilizing – influence in the spelling of local names, tending to perpetuate its own forms. As it had rescued names from oblivion so, too, it helped to ensure that they remained on the map. The later Object Name Books came to regard earlier Ordnance plans as their best authority, and the *Instructions* go into some detail to ensure that

> names which have already appeared on the Ordnance Survey maps should not be altered, or new names inserted, except on the best authority,

and

> important place-names such as those of hills, valleys etc should not be considered obsolete because they are no longer generally known . . .

No name was to be changed without the support of 'at least two good authorities'. Ordnance spellings were, of course, still challenged by a string of local pundits, and some were amended; but only occasionally in nineteenth-century England – as at the time of the dispute with the Local Government Board over the spelling of parish names – was the whole basis of its nomenclature under question.[30] Welsh and Gaelic names, however, continued to be a particular source of dissent.

Notes

1 H. St J. L. Winterbotham, *The National Plans*, OS Professional Papers no. 16 (HMSO 1934), p. 15.

2 A copy of the Minute and footnote is included in OSR 1855–6, illustration no. 20: PP 1857 [147] XXVII.

3 Winterbotham, *National Plans*, pp. 101–2.

4 *Ibid.* p. 23. For H. St J. L. Winterbotham see Ch.25.

5 J. C. T. Willis, *An Outline of the History and Revision of 25-inch Ordnance Survey Plans* (HMSO 1932), pp. 5–6.

6 *Account of the Methods and Processes adopted for the Production of Maps of the Ordnance Survey of the United Kingdom* (HMSO 1875), p. 69.

7 *Ibid.* p. 43.

8 *Ibid.* p. 44.

9 Winterbotham, *The National Plans*, p. 38.

10 *Methods and Processes* (1875), p. 44.

11 Winterbotham, *National Plans*, pp. 38–9.

12 *Methods and Processes* (1875), p. 44.

13 *Ibid.* p. 45.

14 Willis, *History and Revision of 25-inch OS Plans,* p. 6.

15 *Methods and Processes* (1875), p. 48.

16 *Ibid.* pp. 97–9.

17 Some water-levelling was done before 1860 according to E. Frome, *Outline of the Method of conducting a Trigonometrical Survey*, 2nd edition (1850), p. 81, footnote.

18 Winterbotham, *National Plans*, pp. 46–8. See Appendix IV.

19 *Report of the Departmental Committee . . . to inquire into the present condition of the Ordnance Survey, Minutes of Evidence*, p. 135: PP 1893–4 [6895] LXXII.

20 Major-General Sir J. Carmichael-Smyth, *Memoir upon the Topographical System of Colonel Van Gorkum* (1828), p. 11. See also Frome, *Outline of . . . a Trigonometrical Survey*, pp. 59–62.

21 *Methods and Processes (1875)*, p. 100.

22 *Proceedings of the Society of Antiquaries of Scotland* II, pp. 102–9.

23 Quoted in Winterbotham, *National Plans*, p. 86.

24 OSR 1867, p. 7. PP 1867–8 [4008] XLII.

25 *Instructions to Field Examiners* 1884, revised and reissued 1905, paras. 157–67, in OS Library.

26 David Murray, *An Archaeological Survey of the United Kingdom* (Glasgow 1896), p. 23.

27 De la Beche Papers, 'Letters copied from a book in the possession of the Ordnance Survey . . . 1830–1841', p. 26, in the National Museum of Wales, Dept. of Geology.

28 *Instructions to Field Examiners* 1905, paras. 168–206.

29 PRO OS 1/9 3499A.

30 This dispute is partially documented in PRO OS 1/9 3499A.

17
The Expansion
1880–1891

Cause and Effect

Lord Cairn's Land Transfer Act of 1875 remedied some of the weaknesses of the 1862 Land Registry Act, and made provision for the keeping in the Registry of a public map to which the private maps describing properties could be referred. When the orders issued under the Act came into operation the 1:2500 Ordnance map, where it existed, was specified as the public map. The 1875 Act also introduced the concept of general boundaries, no longer insisting that the division between one property and another should be precisely defined.* However, the registration of title continued to be voluntary.

In 1878 a Select Committee was appointed by the House of Commons to inquire into and report upon the steps that should be taken 'to simplify the title to land, and to facilitate the transfer thereof'. The Committee, reporting in 1879, said with reference to maps:

> As regards scale and accuracy the recent Cadastral Survey of England and Wales, so far as it has gone, leaves little or nothing to be desired . . . your Committee believe that it is impossible to overrate the value of a correct official survey as a means of preventing confusion of boundaries and facilitating the identification of property, and they earnestly recommend that the important work of surveying England and Wales . . . should be resumed and completed with as little delay as possible.

In the last sections of the Report, the Committee advocated 'the immediate completion of the Cadastral Survey of England and Wales, and its obligatory adoption . . . for identifying and describing property'.[1]

These recommendations were accepted and it was 'determined that the staff of the Survey should be about doubled so that the work should be completed in 1890 instead of in 1900, as was previously contemplated'. The survey was to be carried on from nine towns which were chosen as convenient centres for the mineral districts and metropolitan counties;** it was proposed to work outward from these centres until the whole country had been completed. A map attached to a Return to an Order of the House of Commons dated 7 July 1881 shows the order in which it was intended that the counties should be taken up.[2] This was declared to be so arranged as to give the greatest facilities for conducting the work with economy and efficiency from the different centres.

One consequence of the acceleration of the large-scale survey was that the method of making the derived six-inch map, which had hitherto been engraved, was greatly changed. This map had for some time been made by transferring a manual tracing of a photographic reduction of the 1:2500 onto copper and then engraving; the process was tedious and costly with the result that the publication of the six-inch lagged several years behind the 1:2500. The new method, first applied in 1881, made use of photozincography and enabled a printing plate to be made directly from a paper print taken from a photographic negative (reduced to six-inch scale) of the 1:2500; impressions could be printed at once from this plate, doing away entirely with engraving. The drawing of the 1:2500 was modified so that it could be photographically reduced without becoming illegible, and there was an unavoidable coarsening of the larger scale, both in line-work and lettering. But this simple method of photographic reduction did not survive long without modification. In 1882 some of the ornament and names on the 1:2500 were still drawn on an exaggerated scale but 'such ornament etc as would crowd the detail too much on the reduced scale was drawn on the manuscript plan in cobalt, which is not reproduced by photography'. The cobalt drawing did not include any of the line detail itself, which remained coarsely drawn on the 1:2500. Before the end of the decade modified drawing and direct reduction had both

---

* In England and Wales property boundaries are usually related to physical features such as walls, hedges or ditches, but the exact property divisions do not, as a rule, coincide with these features, which are normally included within one property or the other. The physical features constitute the 'general boundaries'; they identify a property but do not precisely define its limits. When the position of a boundary has been exactly determined, it is known as a 'fixed boundary'; in this country the information needed for 'fixing' boundaries is often lacking or contradictory.

** The nine centres were Bedford, Bristol, Chester, Derby, Hereford, Ipswich, Norwich, Plymouth and Reading.

been abandoned. Instead, blue impressions were made of the 1:2500 and on these the six-inch was redrawn 'in a style suitable for reduction'. The final development was to make the blue impressions at an intermediate scale – twelve inches to one mile – so that the six-inch drawing became more manageable. Greater accuracy was claimed for the photozincographic process as the possibility of error in the tracing and engraving was eliminated.[3] Moreover, the over-all saving was estimated to be over £100 000, and it became possible to publish the six-inch map simultaneously with, or even before, the 1:2500. Because of the photographic methods used and the limited size of negative, the six-inch maps were thereafter published as quarter sheets.

The 1:2500 plans themselves continued to be reproduced by zincography, that is, by means of paper transfers made by manual tracing from the manuscript plans, until 1889 when photozincography was adopted – a transfer made from a photographic negative being substituted for the manual tracing. This change, which appeared to be a significant step forward, was to be short-lived in face of the difficulties encountered when the plans came to be revised in the 1890s.

Staffing Problems of the Expansion

In 1882 Cooke described the difficulties of an expansion of this sort in an extended account which included a justification for retaining the existing arrangements for staff and supervision:

> . . . the superiority of the results [of the Ordnance Survey compared with the Tithe Survey] is due to the fact that the work is checked at every stage and that care is taken that the productions of all the surveyors should harmonise together. This system requires very careful organisation and supervision and of necessity very experienced men to superintend and carry it out and it is principally the difficulty of finding such men which limits the power of the expansion of the Ordnance Survey. The work of the Survey is carried out as a military organisation under the superintendence of officers of the Royal Engineers who have under their control four companies of Royal Engineers and a large number of Civil Assistants and labourers.

He went on to deal with the Survey's system for recruiting and training its civilian staff:

> It has been found by experience that it is better to engage the [civilian] Survey employees as young as possible and to train them onto the several duties and that it is not desirable to engage trained and consequently highly paid Civil Engineers . . . On the Ordnance Survey . . . the different stages of the work are carried on by different persons who thus form checks on each other and this system has also the advantage that it allows the employment of men in many stages of the work at very low wages.[4]

On 26 April the War Office wrote to the Office of Works saying that, as a consequence of the promotion of Colonel Cooke to the rank of Major-General, it was necessary to appoint an officer to succeed him as Director General. On the recommendation of the Commander-in-Chief, the Secretary of State had selected Colonel Stotherd RE, the next senior officer then employed on the Survey, for this appointment, and had submitted his name for the approval of the First Commissioner of Works.[5]

The Office of Works replied that the removal of Colonel Cooke from the direction of the Survey at that juncture would be most ill-timed and would tend to prejudice the completion of the work by the date currently specified, namely 1890. The whole of the services of the Ordnance Survey were in the course of reorganization and augmentation and it would take twelve months to carry into effect the changes contemplated; in the meantime the Department must be regarded as being in a transitional state. The letter continued:

> To make any changes in the Directorship of the Survey at the present moment would be an act of administration so prejudicial to the interests of the public that the First Commissioner hopes that Mr Secretary Childers may see his way to allowing Col. Cooke to remain in the Survey for another year. The First Commissioner will regret losing Colonel Cooke's services at any time but to sever his connection with the great work which he is directing at so critical a moment would be followed by consequences which would not fail to provoke great discontent throughout the country.

The War Office seems to have been convinced, and on 12 June agreed that Cooke, now Major-General, should be retained for a further period of one year, as a special and exceptional case in the circumstances. On receiving this information Cooke wrote a letter to the Secretary in which he said that he hoped the War Office would now take into consideration letters from Colonel de Courcy Scott and Colonel Carey* concerning their retention on the Ordnance Survey. He pointed out that if they had to leave that year the result would be that within six months the three most responsible posts at Southampton, including his own, would have new occupants and that this would be very undesirable.

---

* Executive Officer and Officer in charge of Reproduction and Examination respectively.

But the War Office had exhausted its capacity for acquiescence and the two officers were replaced very shortly afterwards.

Cooke's year of extension expired in April 1883 and on the 7th of that month Stotherd took up duties as Director General. With the expansion still in progress he too found it necessary to defend at length the organization of the Survey. Writing in 1885 he said:

> This organisation has been productive of incalculable advantage to the service, effective military supervision has thoroughly leavened the civilian element and has established habits of discipline, punctuality, order and regularity, which are essential in carrying out the minute details of a great work of this nature in which a large number of men are employed, while it has effected a considerable saving of expense and materially increased the amount of work produced per man. Various authorities have at different times recorded their opinion in favour of this military organisation.[6]

He then listed the various statements that had been made in the past in support of the military organization, beginning with that of General Roy (stated to be 'director of the survey' in 1791, the year after his death) and ending with the Report of the Board of Works Committee of 1870. He went on:

> There were on 31st December 1885 employed on the Survey 28 Officers, 2 Warrant Officers, 364 NCOs and Sappers of the Royal Engineers and 2846 Civilians, Total – 3240. The full establishment of Officers is 31 and that of NCOs and Sappers is 452, so that the latter is 86 short. This is due to the withdrawal of recruits and men from the survey companies during recent military expeditions, an otherwise exceptional state of affairs . . . Arrangements for completing the original cadastral survey of the United Kingdom by the year 1890 have been completed and estimates drawn up with this object in view. These estimates have been framed with reference to the number of employees, military and civil, now on the Survey and to the present organisation of the force. Any material disturbance of these conditions would undoubtedly tend to prevent the fulfilment of what has been promised to Parliament. It is especially essential to keep up the strength of the military element as any reduction in this direction increases cost.

The continued use of a large military force in the Ordnance Survey in peace-time was quite unique in the civil departments of Government, and had to be justified by essentially economic arguments. Such arguments were even more critical in the face of the likelihood of the gradual running down of the Survey as it completed the basic mapping of the country, and from the military point of view it was imperative that they should be kept in the forefront of the minds of those in power in Whitehall. That the military system was efficient and remarkably successful cannot be denied but the result of the constant reiteration of its economic advantages was to deny to the Civil Assistants many concessions they might well have been granted.

Although the position of the military as a whole might have been regarded as reasonably secure in the middle of the decade, that of the Director General was in some respects not so. On 16 September 1886 the War Office informed the Office of Works that, under Article 102 (1) of the Royal Warrant of 10 June 1884, which enforced the retirement of a colonel at the age of 57, Colonel Stotherd would be retired from the army on 25 November next. The War Office added:

> This contingency was not specifically provided for in the terms of the understanding arrived at in 1881, as the action of the Warrant in this sense had not then been foreseen; but as the working of the Warrant develops it becomes practically a condition which has to be reckoned with.

Stotherd lacked the Corps seniority to escape the provisions of the Royal Warrant by promotion to Major-General, and the War Office recommended that Colonel Sir Charles Wilson be appointed in his place.

The discovery that the operation of the Royal Warrant produced such precipitate retirement caused a flurry of correspondence between the War Office, the Treasury and the Office of Works. Eventually it was agreed that the Director should be paid a fixed civil salary in lieu of any army pay or pension, but that such service would not count towards a civil pension because it was of a temporary character and because the Director did not hold a Civil Service Certificate. The salary agreed on was £1200 per annum, which compared unfavourably with the £1344 10s. received by Stotherd.

A great deal of confusion seems to have arisen over the implementation of the new arrangements in the case of Sir Charles Wilson, but circumventions were always possible. In a letter to him from the War Office, the Deputy Adjutant General wrote:

> I am directed by His Royal Highness the Field Marshal Commanding-in-Chief to inform you that as you are in the receipt from the Office of Works of a consolidated salary, a portion of which is intended to represent the full pay of your rank, it has been decided by the Secretary of State for War that your appointment as Director General of the Ordnance Survey shall be regarded as a Military Appointment.

By the middle eighties the ratio of military staff to civilian was about 1:8, and the complaints of such a large number of pseudo Civil Servants could not be entirely ignored. In 1888 another Departmental Committee was set up to study the rates of pay which should be linked to the various classes of work and different types of duty. When these rates had been settled and approved by the Director they were communicated in a confidential paper for the guidance of division officers in order to ensure, as far as practicable, uniformity in the recommendations they made on the pay of individuals. These instructions were often referred to by the staff as the 'Secret Circular'. A copy was attached as an appendix to the minutes of evidence of yet another Departmental Committee appointed to enquire into the position of the Civil Assistants employed on the Ordnance Survey, which sat in the summer of 1891. The Chairman of this Committee was Lieutenant-Colonel George Leach, who had for many years been employed on the Ordnance Survey and had become the First Secretary of the newly-created Board of Agriculture which had assumed responsibility for the Survey in 1890.[7] Leach had certainly been a most able survey officer but it was most unlikely that he would entertain any very liberal views about the civilian staff.

The Departmental Committee reported in March 1892.[8] It observed that the military organization of the survey which worked so admirably and so economically in Ireland had been maintained throughout the English survey and, with some small modifications, still existed. The numerous divisions of the survey were identified under twelve heads, so far as they concerned the principal duties of assistants engaged in producing the finished plans: observers, computers, chain surveyors, plotters, tracers, examiners, draughtsmen, typers and stampers, area computers, levellers, contourers, and the members of the boundary division (who, aided by meresmen appointed by the justices, ascertained the boundaries of the various fiscal divisions). Most of the plotting, tracing, typing and stamping and area computing was done by boys. On the question of superintendence, the Report noted that successive directors of the Survey had expressed strong opinions as to the great value of the military organization, both as regards efficiency and economy, opinions which were reflected by the Departmental Committee in 1871. The Civil Assistants desired a larger share of the superintendence but it appeared, from a return furnished by the Director of the Survey, that a considerable number of Civil Assistants were already employed as superintendents. The numbers of Royal Engineer and civil superintendents were respectively 83 and 95, but 42 of the latter, the Report added somewhat disingenuously, were pensioners who had shown ability as superintendents when they were serving soldiers, and after their discharge from the Engineers were re-employed as Civil Assistants. The civilian staff also complained that comparatively young soldiers were often made superintendents over the heads of Civil Assistants of more experience and ability as workmen, but the Report regarded this as inseparable from the system. Any change would be certain to lead to a large increase in the cost of the Survey without increase of efficiency. The Committee was therefore of the opinion that any alteration in a system which had worked so well for upwards of fifty years and had produced such excellent results, both as regards efficiency and economy, would be most undesirable, and further that the Civil Assistants who joined the Survey with full knowledge of that system under which they were brought up and trained had no reasonable ground for complaint.

The Report pointed out that it would obviously be undesirable to pay the civil branch higher than the superintending military branch. Applications for employment on the Survey were numerous and there was no difficulty in filling vacancies. The work was popular and liked by the employees; men rarely left the Survey. Frequently the sons of former Civil Assistants were employed, and there were many instances of men who had left the Survey for other employment or who had been discharged, asking to be taken back. All this showed that the pay then given was sufficient to attract and retain the class of men required. Under those circumstances the Committee was unable to recommend any material alteration in the rates of pay. Such alteration would much increase the cost of the Survey, and it appeared to them to be unnecessary and undesirable. It would be cheaper, the Committee thought, and in many respects preferable, to increase the force of Royal Engineers employed on the Survey. The Committee of 1871 had come to the same conclusion.

A considerable part of the Report dealt with promotion, which included the whole question of incremental pay. The pay of all the employees of the Survey, both civil and military, was gradually increased according to the character of the duty on which they were employed, their length of service, and the quantity and quality of their work. Each man was stimulated to exertion by the knowledge that if his work and progress were good he had the prospect of an increase of pay. In some cases of exceptional merit increases were given twice in a year. The Director, Sir Charles Wilson, considered that the increases during the main years of expansion (1883–6) were abnormally high and absorbed too large a proportion of the total sums voted by Parliament. In the subsequent years the amount voted for the prosecution of the survey was reduced, and it was therefore necessary to reduce the expenditure by discharging a number of the Civil Assistants. The Director had decided that the most judicious course, having regard both to the work and the interests of the Assistants as a body, was to diminish the number of increases of pay so as to enable him to retain as many of the Assistants as possible.

Another point strongly pressed on behalf of Civil Assistants was that, instead of receiving increases of pay on the recommendations of the Officers under whom they were employed, they should receive fixed annual increments as in other public departments. A proposal on these lines was included in an Appendix to the Report but, as the Committee had previously remarked, the Survey was a great map manufactory, and a scheme of this nature would be unsuited for any manufacturing department:

> No private manufacturer would listen for a moment to such a proposal if put forward by his employees, as his expenditure must be governed by due regard to the cost of production of the article manufactured.

In its summary of recommendations the Committee found that it would not be desirable to alter the present system of military superintendence; that no alteration was necessary in the rates of pay, but that amongst the deserving young employees advances of pay should be given somewhat more rapidly; and that it was not desirable to alter the system of promotion. But the Committee proposed improvements in the travelling and dislocation allowances for Civil Assistants of considerable service, and some improvements in the sick pay and medical attendance due to them. Finally it recommended that retirement should be compulsory at a fixed age.

Such recommendations could provide little comfort for the civil staff, who still considered they were at a disadvantage compared with other Civil Servants. To more general critics of the conduct of the Ordnance Survey, the repetition of the entrenched views of decades of Directors only confirmed that the time was ripe for a considerable shake-up of the whole organization.

Revision

On 30 December 1882 the Treasury gave approval for the first time for some experimental revision surveys to be made as a means of finding out the probable cost and difficulties of such work. Two districts were chosen for the experiment. One was a small part of Yorkshire and Lancashire including the town of Clitheroe, which had been surveyed in 1844–9; the 1:1056 plans of the town were to be revised at that scale, but the remainder, which had been drawn at six inches to one mile, was to be 'revised' at 1:2500. The second district was an area of about 25 000 acres in Cornwall which had been surveyed at 1:2500 before 1860 for military purposes.

Little more was recorded about these experiments, but General Cooke, on his departure from the Ordnance Survey, was able to speak of the likelihood of a future systematic revision with a certain degree of confidence:

> I am very glad to have been able to arrange before leaving that as soon as the survey has been completed a revision of it shall be commenced as this ensures the continued existence of the Department and will allow of the service of many being retained who would otherwise have to seek employment elsewhere.

Three years later Stotherd, in his farewell memorandum, referred to the same subject:

> The question of a general and periodical revision of the maps of the Survey has recently become a subject of increasing importance. I am glad to have been able to put forward a detailed scheme and estimate for submission to the Lords of Her Majesty's Treasury on this important point. The necessity for a periodical revision has been more than once affirmed by their Lordships and I trust the decision on the financial basis on which this work is to be carried out, will not long be delayed. The necessity for periodical revision is evident, unless it is intended that the whole of the money amounting to several millions Sterling expended on the Survey is to be lost.

The Treasury decided in December 1886 that it was desirable to begin the revision at once, and the Director General of the Survey was, at the same time, authorized to draw upon the sum of £5000 provided in the Estimate for 1886–7. Their Lordships, however, in authorizing this expenditure and agreeing to the insertion of the sum of £15 500 in the Estimate for 1887–8 'wished it to be clearly understood that, in agreeing to the commencement of the revision, they do not bind themselves to any fixed term for its completion, or to the annual provision of any fixed sum for carrying it out'.[9]

Wilson was able to say in his *Report* for 1886 that arrangements had already been made for starting the revision of Lancashire and Yorkshire, as the surveys of those counties were thirty-five to forty-five years old, and were originally made on a scale of six inches to one mile. The next counties to be taken up were to be Edinburgh, Haddington, Fife, Kinross, Wigtown and Kirkudbright, which had also been surveyed on the six-inch scale more than thirty years before.[10] These counties became known as the 'replotted counties'; the decision to 'revise' them by replotting at 1:2500 from the six-inch field books and then bringing them up to date by 'examination' was one of the Ordnance Survey's worst errors. Yet it is easy to see how it came about.[11]

James, fighting the Battle of the Scales, had given evidence before the Select Committee on the Ordnance Survey of Scotland in 1856:

Question 340   (Mr L. Davies) Do you mean that when you took the measurement for the six-inch survey, your survey was of such a character that you could at once execute the 25-inch map?

Answer   (James) Yes; we might have to take the manuscript plan on the ground, but no re-measurement would be necessary.

Question 341   (Mr Denison) But you must return to the ground?

Answer   (James) Not to take measurements, but the eye must pass over the plans.

The consequence was that authority was never given for the resurvey at 1:2500 of these English and Scottish six-inch counties. Wilson, faced with having to get the job done, and hamstrung by James's unequivocal statements, chose to avoid a confrontation with the Treasury over the provision of more funds for a resurvey, and to tackle the task as 'revision'. The division officers responsible for the revision of Yorkshire and Lancashire were in no doubt about the quality of the work they were producing. On 1 June 1887 Captain R. C. Hellard (DO3)* wrote:

I must say I am rather sceptical about the accuracy of these plans bearing comparison with that of the ordinary 25-inch plans – and from the time required to revise such work I should think there cannot be much saving on a revision as against re-survey . . . .

Captain E. J. Boyce (DO2) wrote on 4 November 1889 to Major F. P. Washington:

I did not like the method that was adopted for Eccles and I reported unfavourably of the accuracy of the work – but EO [Lieutenant-Colonel J. Farquharson] did not agree with me on this point – for I found that if check lines were run through the work the detail was in places bodily out of position – in some places by as much as 25 and 30 links – this I consider was due to the very long lines and offsets of the old survey.

The management, in the person of the Executive Officer, (and presumably the Director General), refused to admit that anything was wrong, even when the gravest doubts were cast upon the economy of the revision as well as its accuracy. Captain K. MacKean (DO10) writing on 2 June 1887 said '. . . it would probably, if not certainly, have been cheaper to have resurveyed the work . . .' But Farquharson's mind was made up, or had been made up for him, and all he had to say was that 'the work looks good and I see no reason to doubt its accuracy'.

In fact he had every reason to doubt it. All his division officers doubted it and had told him so. The only likely explanation is that Wilson was under great financial pressure and the threat of reductions. In 1885 Stotherd had clearly recognized, as a conclusion from the Clitheroe experiments, 'that considerable areas will have to be entirely resurveyed to produce a map on the 1:2500 scale', but this necessity was not mentioned again in the years that followed. Instead, the annual *Reports* contain quotations from the discouraging Treasury Minute of December 1886, together with nervous expressions of hope that no reductions would be made in the funds allotted to the Survey.

The results were disastrous. Winterbotham, writing in 1934, was in a good position to put this into perspective:

Since [the 'replot'] periodical revisions have struggled with a growing evil. Skilled revisers, finding serious errors, have pushed them into unimportant parcels; anywhere, in fact, where property lines and areas were not important. Then these same areas have fallen to the builders.[12]

More Changes in Map Distribution

The arrangements for the sale of Ordnance Survey maps underwent yet another change in 1885, decided on by the Office of Works, against the advice of Stotherd. The Depot in St Martin's Place was closed from 1 January and the sale of Ordnance maps was placed under the direction of Her Majesty's Stationery Office, who appointed Stanford of Charing Cross sole agent for England and Wales; the numerous local agencies were terminated. In Scotland and Ireland the Edinburgh and Dublin Depots were still maintained and there were also local agents in these countries. The arrangement with

---

* Executive Officer was usually abbreviated to EO. DO was used to mean either Division Office or Division Officer.

Stanford was a provisional one which was to run for a couple of years; he obtained a 33⅓ per cent discount on the price of maps, and he gave the normal trade discount of 25 per cent to any map-seller in the country.

In May 1886 the Stationery Office, wishing to replace this temporary agreement, offered a contract for the sole agency for ten years on the same terms. Tenders were invited for the annual premium each applicant was prepared to pay for the sole agency. The contract for England and Wales was in the event again awarded to Stanford whose tender was for £600. Scotland and Ireland were then dealt with in a similar manner and contracts were made with A. and C. Black in Edinburgh, and Hodges, Figgis and Co. in Dublin. Wilson disliked the new system and said so in the annual *Report* for 1886. He did not believe the interests of the Survey could be well served by a sole agent who was himself a publisher of maps based on the national survey. Predictably sales decreased in 1886, but rose again the next year.

However, the activities of the private map publishers were not escaping the attention of the Government. A Treasury Minute was issued in August 1887 dealing with copyright in Government publications, arising from correspondence which had passed between the Treasury and the Stationery Office. The Minute declared that the law gave to the Crown the same right of copyright as to a private individual. Copyright in documents created by servants of the Crown belonged to the Crown:

> The majority of documents issued under the authority of Government have no resemblance to the works published by private publishers and are published for the information of the public and for public use in such manner as any one of the public may wish, and it is desirable that the knowledge of their contents should be diffused as widely as possible. In other cases the Government publishes, at considerable cost, works in which few persons only are interested and which are published for the purpose of promoting literature and science. These works are of precisely the same character as those published by private enterprise. In order to prevent an undue burden being thrown on the taxpayer by these works and to enable the Government to continue the publication of works of this character to the same extent as heretofore it is necessary to place them as regards copyright in the same position as publications by private publishers. If the reproduction of them or the most popular portions of them by private publishers is permitted, the private publisher will be able to put into his own pocket the profits of the work which ought to go in relief of the general public, that is to say, the taxpayers.

The Treasury Minute then classified Government publications under several headings and considered two classes of works the reproduction of which should be restricted. One of these included charts and Ordnance maps. The Minute continued:

> ... it seems desirable that the Copyright [in these classes] should be enforced in the interests of the taxpayer. Notice of the intention to enforce the copyright in any work should be given to the public. In the case of future works this notice can be given by prefixing to the work a notice to the effect that the rights of copyright are reserved.'

As a result of this instruction, from 1888 the note 'All Rights of Reproduction Reserved' was inserted on impressions of Ordnance Survey maps.

How the copyright regulations were to be worked out in relation to commercial map publishers was elaborated five years later by the Dorington Committee.

Notes

1 *Select Committee on Land Titles and Transfer*, pp ix, xiii: PP 1878–9 (244), XI.
2 PP 1881 (415), LXXV.
3 OSR 1881, p. 5: PP 1882, C. 3221, LII.
4 OSR 1882, p. 8: PP 1883, C. 3556, LIV.
5 PRO 4749D.
6 OSR 1885, p. 4: PP 1886, C. 4684, LII.
7 See p. 185.
8 *Report of the Departmental Committee appointed to inquire into the Position of the Civil Assistants of the Ordnance Survey*: PP 1892, C. 6692, LXIV.
9 OSR 1886, p. 7: PP 1887, C. 5005, LXVI.
10 *Ibid.*
11 H. St J. L. Winterbotham, *The Replotted Counties*, Supplement to Ordnance Survey Professional Papers, New Series, No. 16, (1934), p. 3.
12 *Ibid.* p. 4.

18
The
Dorington
Committee

The Ordnance Survey under Attack

The first half of Wilson's period of office was a time of anxiety and uncertainty for the Ordnance Survey. The large-scale mapping of the country was nearing completion but the Treasury refused to make any unequivocal commitment towards revision. Consequently the total strength dropped almost as rapidly as it had risen during the expansion, falling by nearly one thousand in five years, with the threat of worse to come. The loss of Clarke had deprived the Department of its only outstanding mathematician and geodesist; in the printing shop the experiments begun in 1886 for producing maps in colour made disappointingly slow progress and the publication of the first quarter-inch map in outline, unrevised, was a dismal failure. The decision to replot the six-inch counties was a major professional blunder whatever the circumstances.

This depressing catalogue of events was not entirely unrelieved. During the last year of Stotherd's directorship the electric dynamo had come into use to power 'an arc-light of about 10 000 candles' which was used during the dark weather of the winter for making photographic prints, with very good results; electric power was also used for lighting the new photographic and printing building. A steam-driven letterpress printing machine was introduced at about the same time together with a new forty-ton-pressure copper-plate press. For the first time photographic negatives, of size 45 inches by 30 inches, capable of covering a map up to 40 inches by 26 inches, were brought into use. This meant that any plan that could cost more than £2 to trace for a new edition was more cheaply photozincographed from existing impressions. In many instances plans which would have cost more than £20 to trace for reproduction were reproduced by photography for 25 shillings. Photozincography was at last coming into general use.

The old problem of making reductions by photography for the one-inch map was now satisfactorily solved. James's method had been to make an impression in carmine from the six-inch 'on which such parts of the detail as it was desired to retain were penned in (in indelible ink) in the particular manner required'. The carmine was removed by 'washing with chloride of lime' and the drawing was then ready for reduction by photography. In 1882 it was recorded that the reductions were being made 'by the pentagraph' because photography had 'not been successful', but by the end of the decade the photographic method had re-established itself. This time the generalized drawings were done on blue impressions of the six-inch; the blue outline, being 'non-photographic', disappeared when the reductions were made.

But these successes and improvements, though important, were really only in matters that were at the time peripheral to the Survey's main troubles, which were the uncertainty about future resources, the uncertainty of the commitment to revision, the bad state of small-scale mapping, the professional weakness in the fields of science and geodesy and the discontent of the civil staff. Complaints began to be heard on all sides in increasing volume.

It was fortunate for the Ordnance Survey that it was directed by Sir Charles Wilson during this critical period. His experience with the Survey had included the mapping of Jerusalem and he was also well known for the part he had played in events that were quite unconnected with Southampton, notably the Nile Expedition for the relief of Gordon which he had joined in 1884 in the middle of a tour of duty with the Ordnance Survey as officer-in-charge in Dublin. The presence of a public figure of high standing at the head of affairs must have had a powerful influence in maintaining the prestige of the Department in these difficult years.

Another timely circumstance was the transfer of the Ordnance Survey from the Board of Works to the Board of Agriculture on 1 April 1890,[1] which brought fresh minds to bear upon its current problems. The appointment of Lieutenant-Colonel George Leach as Secretary of the Board meant that the Survey's difficulties would not be neglected through a lack of understanding. In the words of Wilson's biographer:

> [Leach] was perfectly conversant with the work of the Department. He was therefore able fully to appreciate and to support the proposals made by Wilson for improving the work of the Survey.[2]

The association of the Ordnance Survey with the Board (later the Ministry) of Agriculture was to last for over seventy years, an indication that this understanding was maintained.

Although from time to time critics of the Ordnance Survey and its products had found opportunities for expressing their feelings, the year 1890 saw the opening of a new era of public discussion. Henry Tipping Crook, a civil engineer from Manchester, opened the attack in September with an address to the British Association in Leeds. His lecture was published in the *Scottish Geographical Magazine* later that year[3] and was repeated before a meeting of the Manchester Geographical Society.[4]

Crook began by pointing out that for the year ending December 1889 the value of sales only reached the paltry sum of just over £13 000, whereas Sir Henry James, nearly twenty years before, had estimated that when the Survey was complete, the yield would be £30 000 per annum. It would be difficult indeed to find a parallel for a work of equal magnitude yielding such disappointing results. Crook considered that there were only three ways in which this state of things could be explained. These were: that the present generation required fewer maps, that the maps were not accessible and therefore not known, and that the maps did not meet popular requirements. The first explanation, he said, was obviously untenable, there was a good deal to be said for the second, and after careful examination and enquiry he had come to a decided conclusion that there was far more importance to be attached to the third. The one-inch map was easily the most important of the series to the bulk of the map-buying public and something more than the mere difficulty of obtaining it was required to account for its unpopularity.

He maintained that the Department had attempted, or had been directed to undertake, far more than it had the means to carry out. The cadastral surveys had, during recent times especially, occupied the chief share of the Department's energies to the exclusion or indefinite delay of the original and more popular work. It had almost abandoned cartography for land surveying. Maps had given place to plans. No-one would dispute the advisability of carrying out the parent survey on the largest required scale, but like most scientific undertakings the Survey had suffered from constant Parliamentary interference. Since the general lines on which the Survey was to proceed were finally determined in 1863 the chief difficulty had been the throttle-valve of the Treasury and, after more than a century's existence, the Department had not yet completed one of its works. Apart from mere skeleton or index maps it had not yet produced on any scale a uniform map of the British Isles. In consequence of the length of time which it had taken and the neglect to provide for a timely revision, most of the maps were obsolete and of little more than historical interest. Crook went on to say that no-one who knew anything of the subject questioned the original accuracy and finish of most of the maps which the Ordnance Survey had produced, nor of the valuable work which had been done in the advancement of geodetical and astronomical science.

He gave in their probable order of importance the reasons for the apparently low estimation in which the maps were held by the public:

1. Age; for want of revision large portions of even the twenty-five-inch, and more particularly the six-inch and one-inch maps, were very incorrect, and in many cases quite obsolete.
2. Bad impressions, or impressions from old or worn-out plates.
3. Complexity in the one-inch through overcrowding of detail which caused confusion, since the map was printed in only one colour.
4. Deficiency in information as to ground forms, particularly in the six-inch map, with the exception of Lancashire and Yorkshire.
5. Want of uniformity.
6. High price, particularly in the case of the six-inch quarter-sheets, and on all scales where sheets were partially blank.
7. Lack of explanatory detail with the maps.
8. Inaccessibility. The general public knew little or nothing about the maps because of the system of sale, the bad indexes and the absence of information as to the age and style of maps published of particular districts.

Crook supported all these allegations with a mass of detail and many examples. He found that the Ordnance maps had no chance in competition with inferior but very much cheaper and more up-to-date reproductions which managed to get the whole of a locality on a single sheet. He maintained that, if the maps for which the nation had paid so large a sum were to be freely circulated, the Department must learn to cater for public requirements. If private individuals found a remunerative sale for cheap reproductions of the Survey, the Department must compete with them not necessarily as to price, but the price and quality combined must be such as would turn the scale in favour of the Ordnance map.

The basis upon which the prices of the different maps were fixed did not seem to him to be rational. It lay in a refined distinction between the cost of production and the cost of publication. The cost of production was supposed to end with the engraved copper plate in one case and with the photographic plate in the other. The subsequent processes of printing, preparing new editions, cost of storage etc., on which the prices were based, were called expenses of publication. These were heavier in the photographic process and the price of the maps produced by this method was therefore greater. Thus, while the total cost of map-making had been greatly reduced by the introduction of photozincography, the nation getting more work for the same money, nevertheless the selling price of the maps had been raised by sixty per cent. The system which could produce such an absurd result as this was surely in need of reform.

Crook found no grounds for complaint in the great cadastral map. He considered that it fully answered all that was required of it and was a work of which the Department could feel justly proud, but already he saw large portions of it becoming disgracefully obsolete. Consequently the smaller scales reproduced from it were similarly so. Again and again the necessity for revision had been pointed out. Every Director General had pressed the matter on the attention of the Government. He recalled that in 1882 the Treasury had recognized the necessity of a revision of the Survey which should be constantly in progress at such a rate as would complete the whole in every fifteen years at least. But it was not until December 1886 that they decided that a start should be made, including in their memorandum the following extraordinary passage:

It is to be clearly understood that in agreeing to the commencement of the revision they do not bind themselves to any fixed term for its completion or to the annual provision of any fixed sum for carrying it out.

He thought that this sort of thing was absolutely fatal to the proper conduct of the Ordnance Survey. It was a repetition of the indecision and blundering which had cost the country so much in the past and to which most of the deficiencies of the Survey were attributable. It would be a good plan if, for the information of the map users, the Treasury memorandum were printed in red on the margin of every sheet which had not been revised for more than fifteen years.

Crook maintained that, while the cadastral plans and the town plans could never expect to have anything but a limited sale, they might have been more largely utilized if the arrangements for sale and distribution were put on a reasonable basis. As had been pointed out by Sir Charles Wilson, the compulsory use of Ordnance Survey maps for valuation, for taxation and for transactions affecting land would be an important step.

Crook's attack produced a reply from Wilson, who said that the Ordnance Survey could not be held responsible for the obsolete character of many of the maps or for the system under which they were now sold to the public. No-one was more sensible than the Director of the Survey of the pressing need for a revision of the maps, but the question was really one of money which it was for Parliament and not for the Department to decide. He considered that Crook had underestimated the pressure which had from time to time been brought to bear upon the Government to complete the 1:2500 survey of Great Britain, and however much one might have regretted it, it could hardly be surprising that the survey was pushed forwards at the expense of revision. The result was that in many places revision had now to be regarded virtually as resurvey.

Wilson went on:

I gather from your paper that one of the faults you find with the Department is that it does not construct maps for popular requirements such as a combination of sheets so as to give large towns like Leeds with their environs on a single sheet. I think that in this you are rather ignoring the principle on which, rightly or wrongly, the Ordnance Survey has always been conducted. The Department is directed to make maps on certain scales, which were settled after many years of controversy, for state purposes. The construction of special maps for popular use was designedly left to private enterprise and any attempt to compete with private firms in 'catering for the public' has been discouraged. I may remind you that the guide book maps to which you allude are all based on the Ordnance Survey and could not have been produced and sold at such slight cost without it. The public thus and in many other ways indirectly derive benefit from the great national survey.

Wilson clearly did not believe in shouldering the responsibilities of his masters or in presenting a united official front to the world, particularly in his denial of responsibility for obsolete maps and for the sales system. The impression remains that he agreed broadly with most of Crook's criticisms and welcomed the opportunity of making public the difficulties with which the Ordnance Survey had to deal. The practice of using public gatherings of learned bodies as a forum for the debate was followed by the Director General in February 1891, when he read a paper on the methods and processes of the Ordnance Survey at a meeting of the Royal Society of Arts in London, for which he was awarded the silver medal of the Society.[5] It was in this paper that he attributed the comparatively high price of English maps to the $33\frac{1}{3}$ per cent discount allowed to the map agents 'for handing the maps over the counter'. This statement seems to have provoked Edward Stanford to join the critics with a publication of his own – *The Ordnance Survey from a Business Point of View* (1891), in which he enumerated the grievances of the agents, from the lack of credit and exchange facilities to the unfair competition of government retail shops.[6]

In March 1892 Henry Crook returned to the attack with a pamphlet entitled *The Maps of the Ordnance Survey as they are and as they ought to be*, which consisted of a reprint of papers he had presented to the British Association in 1890 and 1891, prefaced by a general sketch of the Ordnance Survey, bringing together the threads of his previous arguments, some of which were more finely developed. It began:

> The movement for the reform of the Ordnance Survey gathers force. A recent order of the House of Commons sanctions the appointment of a Select Committee to enquire into the present management of the Ordnance Survey and the best mode of accelerating the production and publication of correct maps of Great Britain and Ireland . . . It will often be found that opinions differ on the value of the maps from the simple fact that the productions of different periods are being spoken of. The number of those who have a general knowledge of the whole work of the Survey is so small that the faults of the Department practically escape notice, and the taste in cartography is so low that by continuous self laudation the Survey has engendered in the public mind an idea that its work is beyond criticism.

He pointed out that if a tourist wanted an accurate map of any particular district and found that the Government did not supply it, it was no consolation to be told that the beauty and accuracy of the Ordnance Survey work was the admiration and envy of the civilized world. Yet this was the stereotyped official reply to criticism of every kind. It was as if driving in the Scottish Highlands and finding cause to complain of the state of the roads, one were referred by the highway authorities to the encomiums bestowed on the work of the late General Wade.

He took up a point raised by Wilson in correspondence. Wilson had argued that, when comparing the English one-inch with similar maps of other countries, it should be remembered that the latter were military maps, whereas the military character of the British one-inch had had to give way to the civil requirements of the State. Crook found it difficult to tell exactly what was meant by this unless it was an attempt to explain the failure of the one-inch to satisfy either civil or military requirements. Perhaps he had inside information, for only a month later a Committee of the War Office sat to consider and report on the military map of the United Kingdom.[7]

Crook went on to refer to

> . . . tolerably successful experiments in printing in colours which had been made by the Ordnance Department . . . It was being said that they were not appreciated because there was no demand for them. However, it would be most irrational to expect any demand under the circumstances since, firstly, no-one knew of their existence, and secondly, the issue was confined to two one-inch sheets, for the areas of Ramsgate and Beaconsfield.

His final thrust was at 'the latest abomination issued from Southampton', the Advance Edition of the outline one-inch map produced by photozincography.* He did not think anything quite so degraded had been published by any government during the previous twenty years.

Crook would have found plenty of people within the Ordnance Survey who would have agreed with him about the Advance Edition.** He was extraordinarily well informed; so much so that a later age, more suspiciously aware of the devious ways of publicity and lobbying, might have regarded him as a 'plant'. If this was so, the desired result was soon achieved.

---

* With the object of speeding up the production of the New Series.

** The Advance Edition of the outline map was surpassed in ugliness by the Temporary Advance Edition with Hills, for which the hachures were redrawn at two inches to one mile for reduction and printing in brown by photozincography. The Survey's own verdict was that the map 'cannot be considered satisfactory' and it was happy to announce its withdrawal in 1898.

The Dorington Committee 1892

In April 1892 Crook wrote a long letter to *The Times* in a similar vein of criticism,[8] and in June *The Times* published two leading articles on the unsatisfactory state of the maps,[9] in which particular attention was paid to the quarter-inch. But on 26 April the Board of Agriculture had issued the terms of reference for a Departmental Committee:

'To inquire into and report upon the present condition of the Ordnance Survey and especially to consider:

1 What steps should be taken to expedite the completion and publication of the new or revised 1-inch map (with or without hill shading) of the British Isles?

2 What permanent arrangements should be made for the continuous revision and speedy publication of the maps (1:500 (towns), 25-inches, 6-inches and 1-inch scales)?

3 Whether the maps as at present issued satisfy the reasonable requirements of the public in regard to style of execution, form, information conveyed, and price; and whether any improvement can be made in the catalogue and indexes?'

The members of the Committee were:

Sir John Dorington, Baronet, MP, as Chairman

Sir Archibald Geikie FRS, FGS, etc.

Lieutenant-General A. C. Cooke CB, RE

Mr Henry Primrose CSI

Mr William Mather MP

Mr Henry Roby MP

Mr Charles Brickdale

Major Duncan Johnston RE, Secretary

In addition to the oral evidence, the Committee obtained statements in writing from a large number of civil engineers, borough surveyors, land agents and others, and from the Valuation Office in Dublin. It studied a considerable amount of documentary material and visited the Ordnance Survey Offices at Southampton. It examined thirty-one witnesses, including the following, who were called for in this order:

Colonel Sir Charles Wilson, Director General of the Ordnance Survey

Mr H. T. Crook, 'a Civil Engineer who has given much attention to the maps of the Ordnance Survey'

Mr J. Bartholomew, Map Producer

Mr J. Wyld, Map Agent and Map Producer

Mr E. G. Wheler, Commissioner to His Grace, the Duke of Northumberland

Mr E. Stanford, Sole Agent for Sale of Ordnance Survey Maps, and Map Producer

Mr T. Currie, of the firm of Keith Johnston and Co., Map Producers

Sir Archibald Geikie FRS, Director General of the Geological Survey

The Committee reported on 31 December 1892. The Report and Minutes of Evidence contained nearly half a million words and provided a vast amount of complex and sometimes conflicting information about the Ordnance Survey. However, the recommendations were nearly all accepted by the Board of Agriculture and established principles which were to guide the Survey for many years to come. Most important of all, the period of uncertainty about the future of the Department was brought to an end.

Under the first head of reference, the Committee acknowledged the reasons for the delay in completing the New Series of one-inch maps. It approved the course which the Survey Department had taken in producing an Advance Edition by photozincography so as to complete the map for the whole country in 1892. This edition, though necessarily rough, was satisfactory for its temporary purpose, but its temporary character might with advantage have been more distinctly indicated on each sheet. The meaning of the expression 'Advance Edition' now put on the maps would have been made clearer if the word 'temporary' were prefixed to it. It did not appear practicable to the Committee to envisage the completion by present methods of the hill-shaded map before 1910, though it was intended that a Temporary Advance Edition should be completed by 1900.

The second head of reference was dealt with in three parts. On the one-inch map, the Committee accepted that there need be no difficulty in bringing it up to date at a reasonable cost by means of a revision independent of the larger scales. This revision could be executed in four years at a quite modest expenditure, and once brought up to date a comparatively small annual sum, probably not exceeding £2000 for field work, would suffice to ensure the constant revision of the map, provided that arrangements could be made for the supply to the Ordnance Survey of information by local authorities or by the Board of Trade about alterations to roads, canals, docks, important extensions to towns and large engineering works, just as notice of alterations to railways was at present provided. The revision should be so arranged that the whole country should be gone over and the map brought up to date in periods of fifteen years. Each map should bear the date to which it was corrected or revised, and no map should be sold by authorized agents which bore a date of publication or revision older than fifteen years.

The public was disappointed, the Committee thought, that the 1:2500 scale plans of Lancashire, Yorkshire and the six Scottish counties had not been completed by 1890 as was supposed to have been promised. There was no doubt that the resurvey of these counties on the 1:2500 scale had not been authorized by the Parliamentary Committee of 1862, and consequently was not included in the work estimated to be completed by 1890. On the assumption that the cadastral survey of Great Britain was to be completed in 1890, the work of substituting the 1:2500 for the six-inch scale in the eight counties mentioned had been called 'revision'. This term was inappropriate. The Director General had stated in evidence that the work done in producing the 1:2500 scale plans of Lancashire and Yorkshire had amounted in many parts to resurvey. The Committee therefore recommended that in future the term 'revised' should be applied only to the bringing up to date of a map on the same scale as that on which it was originally drawn, and that 'resurvey' should be the term applied to work such as that then in progress in Lancashire and Yorkshire and in Scotland, as well as to the production of the 1:2500 scale maps in Ireland.

The large-scale maps were excellent in quality and fully met the purposes for which they were designed, but the very largeness of the scale led to their rapidly getting out of date. From this the Committee concluded that while the old one-inch map was still excellent in many parts of the country, although as much as seventy years old, the six-inch maps drawn between 1840 and 1850 were in some districts nearly useless. This was very apparent with the 1:2500 plans surveyed since 1854, and even more so in the town plans on the scales of 5 feet and 10 feet to one mile. Scarcely any of them had been revised and it was urgently necessary that 'so splendid a work as these maps of Great Britain and Ireland' should not be destroyed for want of a regular system of revision. The Committee urged that the revision of the 1:2500 survey should be commenced without delay, with the object of bringing the maps up to date in the next ten years and thereafter revising them within periods of fifteen years.

The advantage to the municipal authorities in the possession of such a map as that on the ten-foot scale was very great but there was no corresponding advantage to Government and to the general public, because the 1:2500 maps, if kept up to date, met every requirement from the ordinary public point of view. The Committee therefore recommended that the state should no longer maintain the town maps, but that town authorities should be required by statute to do so.

Under the third head of reference, the Committee considered the principal complaints and suggestions brought to its notice, under no less than twenty-seven different headings.

It had received a good deal of evidence on the insufficiency of contours on the present maps of the Survey, which was contrasted with the more elaborate contouring of the Lancashire and Yorkshire plans. Many of the demands for additional contours came from persons who would be quite satisfied with sketched contours, since they were required as representation of the ground rather than for accurate engineering purposes. No contouring, however close, would obviate the necessity for special contouring and levelling for the execution of engineering works, and the Committee therefore hesitated to recommend any great expenditure for extending the present system of contours as thoroughly as had been suggested. If any work were undertaken to increase the number of contours shown, the distinctions between instrumental, water-level and sketched contours should be clearly marked by adequate characteristics. The provision of contours at 250-foot intervals above 1000 feet, interpolated by water-level, was the most important and should be carried out as early as possible, as it affected a comparatively small area of the country for which the map had not been completed in this particular. The Committee was of the opinion that the 25-foot and 75-foot contours should be confined to large areas of low-lying land, where they would be very useful. At the six-inch scale accuracy in the positions of contours on the map was essential and the contours should therefore remain in black.

The Committee had examined the proposal that colour-printed maps should be produced and that private firms should be permitted to publish them. After detailed consideration it recommended that a coloured edition of the one-inch should be made to meet the requirements of the War Office. The general outline and writing should be printed in black, the water in blue, the hills in brown and the contours and altitudes in some other tint. The Committee did not agree that the railways should be inserted in red as desired by the Military Committee, since where the roads were marked in colour, the railways were better distinguished in black. It might be desirable to offer a thin paper edition, folded ready for the pocket. The Committee thought that, apart from the engraved one-inch map, the one-inch map with hills, the new one-inch coloured map for military purposes (which it recommended should also be sold to the public), the quarter-inch map and the ten-mile map, any other maps on the one-inch or smaller scales should be left to private enterprise. It recommended that reproductions of the Ordnance Survey's maps should be permitted on certain conditions. First, any privately published map should not be a mere reproduction of the Ordnance Survey map but should have some genuine difference, either in form or matter. Secondly, any firm wishing to publish such a map should send an application to the Board of Agriculture for transmission to the Controller of the Stationery Office in whom the copyright of the publications was vested. Thirdly:

> A certain amount should be paid for the privilege of copying an Ordnance map, either as a lump sum or as a royalty on the copies of the maps sold, as may be hereafter agreed upon, but this sum should be rather an acknowledgement than a substantial payment.

As an indication of what the Committee meant, it referred to a map which one of the witnesses, Mr J. Bartholomew, had produced from a transfer of the one-inch map of the Loch Lomond district which had been supplied to him. It had been reproduced, in colour, like other maps by Mr Bartholomew, on a smaller scale, largely for sale to tourists; the trade should be allowed to produce maps of this character on payment of the cost of the transfer and of a small acknowledgment to secure the rights of publication.

The objections of map users to the cost of purchasing several sheets in order to cover one urban locality were sympathetically received by the Committee, which declared itself in favour of single combination sheets for such areas. Another complaint about the high cost of the hand-coloured impressions of the large-scale plans led to its recommending that hand-colouring should be abandoned and replaced by cross-hatching. It added that hedgerow timber, single trees, as well as trees, shrubs and paths in gardens, should not be shown on the plans in future, as these features were generally thought to be of little value.

There was some substance in the charge that non-existent footpaths were shown on the large-scale plans. It was clearly impossible for the Ordnance Survey to discriminate between public and private footpaths, and the note at present inserted at the foot of each sheet met this difficulty as far as possible. However, more definite instructions were needed for the field surveyors to prevent the insertion of temporary tracks.

A key to conventional signs such as on the latest edition of the one-inch map should also be added, the Committee thought, to the margins of the six-inch, 1:2500 and town-scale maps, and it suggested the separate publication of a pamphlet containing, with other matter, a full explanation of the conventional signs. A cheap edition of the one-inch should be prepared by transfer to zinc or stone, and consideration should be given as to whether a portion of the edition could not be sold folded ready for use. It did not endorse the complaint that Ordnance Survey maps were too expensive, with the exception of the photozincographed six-inch map, the price of which should be on a level with that of the engraved map.

The Committee dealt at length with the subject of place-names, particularly those of Welsh origin. It recognized that errors had occurred which should have been avoided but also acknowledged the difficulty of the problem.

> First [the source of error] arose from the varying dialects of Wales, which render it almost impossible for one person to be an authority in all counties, and secondly from the incorrectness of form, name and spelling as well as from occasional paucity of the names collected owing to the want of knowledge of Welsh possessed by the Surveyors who collected the names. Every Survey party should have been provided with a Welsh-speaking person. In consequence of the precaution not having been taken, lead works have been described as slate works, copper works as manganese works. The sound of a name is in the first instance incorrectly caught, and written down by a person ignorant of the language; this is then conjecturally corrected, from the faulty pronunciation so written down, by a person having no local knowledge. Thus, Caer-gorlan, the field of the sheepfold, becomes Caer-goleu, the field of light, and Cae Fali, Mary's field, becomes Cae-Valley, a mixture of Welsh and English.*

Despite such defects in practice, the Committee endorsed the principles adopted by the Ordnance

*Evidently Colby's practice of employing Welsh-speaking surveyors in Wales had not been maintained for the large-scale surveys of the 1870s and 80s. The checking of all the Welsh names had been done by a single referee, Mr Rowland – a Welsh scholar of repute and author of a Welsh Grammar – and after his death by his widow, both of whom were presumably unfamiliar with all the dialect forms and local usages.

Survey for the spelling of Welsh place-names and quoted Rule 15 of the book of instructions used by the surveyors:

> When names have assumed a corrupted form which is thoroughly established, their orthography should not be altered even when they are known to be etymologically wrong; as, for instance, 'Hylas' for 'Heol-las'.

In its recommendations, the Committee advised that Welsh names should be checked by a local enquiry conducted by persons able to communicate with the people resident in the locality, and that the results so obtained should be looked over by competent Welsh scholars. But it was

> strongly of the opinion that when any method of spelling has been distinctly established in a locality it should be followed, and that no attempts should be made, by change of spelling, to attach a meaning to a name for which there may be no authority, and which might be at variance with that adopted in the locality.*

The closing paragraphs of the Report contained an extraordinary recommendation designed to allow the Director General to make public the extent to which Treasury or other Governmental restrictions prevented him from carrying out his responsibility for revision. The Committee said that it was of the greatest importance to define and distinguish between the responsibility of the Director General of the Ordnance Survey and that of the Treasury. It therefore recommended that the state of revision of the cadastral survey and that of the one-inch map should be entered in the annual report of the Director General; further, that the Director General should distinctly state whether he found that the sums provided were what were necessary for keeping up the revision of the cadastral and one-inch surveys at the intervals for which they were arranged. The Director General should also include in his annual report all suggestions made by him to the Minister under whom he was placed which he considered essential for the conduct of the Survey, as it was important that the public should know whether the Department, which they regarded as directly responsible for the progress of the Ordnance Survey, was in a position to fulfil its duties.

In conclusion the Committee was convinced that 'the basis for the Ordnance Survey' was 'perfectly accurate and satisfactory'. The great necessities of the Survey were obviously completion and early revision and with these none of the suggested improvements should be allowed to interfere. But, given the acceptance of the various recommendations which it had made, it confidently expected that the public would have 'no reasonable grounds for complaint as regards this great national work'.

The Results of the Inquiry

The Board of Agriculture, in consultation with the Director General, considered the Report of the Departmental Committee and in a Minute dated 22 December 1893 issued its instructions and observations.[10] So far as the recommendations of the Committee related to matters within the exclusive control of the Board, it was prepared to agree to them with certain exceptions. However, matters involving financial issues had to be determined by the Treasury, and the Board could only hope that financial exigencies would permit full provision to be made for meeting the requirements of the Survey within a reasonable period.

It was able to report that earlier in that year the Treasury had approved the addition of ninety-three Royal Engineers to complete the strength of the survey companies, so that the revision of the one-inch map could be started independently of the revision of the cadastral survey, and it proposed that the Director General should call the attention of the Board to any parts of the map which might have remained unrevised for a period exceeding fifteen years. The Board did not approve the recommendation that agents should withdraw from sale maps bearing a date of publication or revision older than fifteen years, although it hoped that the sale of such maps would, before very long, take place only in rare and defensible circumstances. It had been thought hitherto that the one-inch hill map would be completed, partly by photozincography and partly by engraving, in 1900, and the wholly engraved map in 1910. The dates which the Board now proposed to keep in view in the preparation of the annual estimates were 1898 for the combined photozincographed and engraved maps, and 1902 for the engraved map, an acceleration which would be in entire consonance with the Committee's wishes.

For the 1:2500 and six-inch maps, as for the one-inch map, no fixed date could be prescribed before which revision should be made; however, the annual reports should contain diagrams showing the dates of the commencement and completion of the last survey of each individual county. By this means a periodical review of the position would be secured, and the Board would be able to determine

---

* These principles, sometimes referred to as the 'Dorington rules', were used for many years as a guide to the Ordnance Survey's learned advisers on Welsh and Gaelic names.

what proposal it should submit to the Treasury for consideration and settlement. But it could not agree that the Director General should record all suggestions made by him to the Minister. It would, in the opinion of the Board, be contrary to usage and sound principle, that questions upon which it did not find itself in agreement with an officer acting under its control should necessarily be made public.

Expenditure of a substantial sum would be required to give effect to the Committee's proposals on contouring, and the case was not strong enough to justify submitting these proposals for Treasury sanction, until provision had been made for the completion of the present programme of the Survey, and the revision of the six-inch and 1:2500 maps. On the use of Ordnance maps by private enterprise the Board did not consider it desirable to formulate any general rules, but would deal with any individual applications as they were received, on the lines indicated.*

Approval was given for the preparation of combined sheets round important towns and in tourist areas on the six-inch and one-inch scales; such sheets had already been issued for the Isle of Wight, the Isle of Man, and Brighton, and a combined sheet for Chatham was in hand. But a financial difficulty stood in the way of adopting generally the recommendation of the Committee so long as the whole proceeds of the sale of maps were appropriated in aid of the Vote for the expenses of the Stationery Office, whilst a very large proportion of the cost of their production was necessarily charged to the Vote of the Ordnance Survey. The Board concluded with the observation that the Report was in itself conclusive evidence of the thoroughness and searching character of the investigation, and it had no doubt that the labours of the Committee would prove of considerable public advantage and permanent benefit to the Survey.

The Board's Minute was deliberately non-committal about the interval between successive revisions of the 1:2500, but behind the scenes T. H. Elliott of the Board and S. E. Spring Rice of the Treasury seem to have agreed in January 1894 that the interval would be twenty years 'by 1910'.[11] Two years later, in 1896, this figure appeared in the Survey's annual *Report*, and from that time it remained unchallenged until after the First World War.

As a result of the Inquiry, the procedures for collecting Gaelic and Welsh names were improved. Even before the Committee began its sittings, a Place-names Committee had been appointed in Scotland under the auspices of the Royal Scottish Geographical Society to advise on the forms to be adopted for names of Gaelic origin. This Committee was presided over by Dr James Burgess CSI and worked until 1899 after which it lapsed.[12] (Its assistance continued to be acknowledged in Ordnance Survey annual reports until 1905!) When the revision of the one-inch map in Scotland was begun in 1893, the Place-names Committee advised the Gaelic-speaking reviser whom he should consult in each locality, and afterwards examined his findings. The recommended versions were then sent to the Ordnance Survey, where 'the ultimate decision with regard to the orthography' rested with the Director General.[13] A similar practice was adopted in Wales when the first revision of the 1:2500 and six-inch maps was undertaken about the turn of the century. Welsh-speaking revisers were employed who submitted the names to the best authorities they could find. The results were then studied by Welsh scholars who were appointed on the advice of the County Council for each county as it was revised.[14] All the Scottish and Welsh authorities agreed to follow the Dorington rules.

The Dorington Committee's recommendations were of long-lasting effect, and forty-five years were to pass before there was another thorough examination of the Survey's major functions. The course taken by the Inquiry and its outcome might almost be regarded as laid out in advance in Henry Crook's pamphlet, and the place accorded to him as the first witness after the Director General was surely significant. He undoubtedly exercised a greater influence on Ordnance Survey affairs than any other private individual throughout its history.

---

* The Board failed to draw attention to an important point that had escaped the notice of the Committee: permission to copy a particular Ordnance map did not give a commercial publisher unrestricted access to later revised editions of that map.

Notes

1 Under the *Act for establishing a Board of Agriculture for Great Britain*, 52 & 53 Vict. c. 30, August 1889.

2 Charles M. Watson, *The Life of Major General Sir Charles Wilson* (London 1909), p. 365.

3 Henry T. Crook, *Scottish Geographical Magazine* 1890, VI, pp. 510–22.

4 Crook, *Journal of the Manchester Geographical Society* 1890, VI, pp. 228–38.

5 *Journal of the Royal Society of Arts* 1891, pp. 258–66.

6 Edward Stanford, *The Ordnance Survey from a Business Point of View* (1891), p. 14 *et seq.*

7 Report of Committee on a Military Map of the United Kingdom (War Office 1892), A237.

8 *Report of the Departmental Committee appointed by the Board of Agriculture to inquire into the present Condition of the Ordnance Survey*, App. III: PP 1893–4, C. 6895, LXXII.

9 *Ibid.* App. IV.

10 *Minute of the Board of Agriculture, 22 Dec. 1893, on the Report of the Departmental Committee*: PP 1893–4, C. 7257, LXXII.

11 PRO SO 490.

12 *Scottish Geographical Magazine* 1913, XXIX, p. 322.

13 *Scottish Geographical Magazine* 1891, VII, pp. 257–9.

14 See, for example, OSR 1899–1900, p. 15: PP 1900, Cd. 327, LXVIII.

19

A
Period of
Consolidation
1894–1913

Under the normal rules Wilson, as a Colonel, would have been retired from the Army early in 1893 at the age of fifty-seven, but representations from the Board of Agriculture to the War Office resulted in his retention as Director General for a further twelve months,[1] the Board arguing that his services should not be lost to the Department whilst the important changes recommended by the Dorington Committee were being put into effect. On his departure from the Ordnance Survey, the Board of Agriculture expressed its appreciation of the admirable manner in which he had discharged the duties of Director General. After a few months on the unemployed list, Wilson took up the appointment of Director General of Military Education at the War Office.

The four Directors who in succession led the Ordnance Survey for the next sixteen years were neither well known outside the Survey nor particularly distinguished within it. Fortunately the impetus given to the affairs of the Department by the Dorington Committee carried it forward through these years without any very great help from the officers at the head of it.

As was now customary, the senior lieutenant-colonel employed on the Survey was nominated as the successor to Wilson. This was Brevet Colonel John Farquharson who took up the post on 14 March 1894. Farquharson, who was Executive Officer at Southampton at the time of his appointment as Director General, had joined the Survey in 1872 as Lieutenant I. C. MacPherson, and had served in it continuously in various field divisions, apart from four years away on other duties. In 1888, while Executive Officer, he had changed his name. Farquharson continued as Director General until March 1899, his term of service being extended in circumstances which are not clear as the seventeen pages of correspondence relating to them were at some time removed from the file. It appears, however, that he retired from the Army in 1896, three years before he left the Ordnance Survey, and it is a matter for conjecture whether this unusual occurrence was in any way connected with the removal of the papers. Clearly many objections would have been raised to the establishment of such a precedent.

His five years as Director General covered a period when many changes to methods and processes were being introduced, most of them arising from the recommendations of the Dorington Committee. Farquharson himself, in a lecture given to the Royal Geographical Society shortly after his retirement from the Ordnance Survey, considered these changes to be 'a very dryish subject which, however interesting to specialists or those who have taken part in it, can hardly be made interesting to a general audience for it must necessarily in a large measure, consist of dull figures and uninteresting dates'.[2] Nevertheless, the specimens of work which Farquharson associated with his lecture reflected a great deal of solid experimentation and practical development.

Farquharson was succeeded by Brevet Colonel D. A. Johnston, who was granted the substantive rank of Colonel on appointment. From 1879 to 1884 Johnston had served as Division Officer at Derby and, after an interval away from the Survey, had been placed in charge of the Trigonometrical Branch in 1889. From 1891 until 1893 he combined this office with that of officer in charge of examination, photography and printing; on the face of it this was a large responsibility, but the Trigonometrical Branch was not very active at this time and Johnston's main interest seems to have been in the Zinc-Printing Department. He was followed in 1905 by Colonel R. C. Hellard, who also had spent his early years in the Survey (1883–7) in the Derby Office. Later Hellard took charge of the Dublin Office (1896–8) and was Executive Officer at Southampton throughout Johnston's directorship. The last of the four, Colonel S. C. N. Grant, represented a complete break with recent tradition, as he had served neither in a division office nor as Executive Officer. For the three years from 1893 to

1895 he had been in charge of one-inch revision, and in 1900 became head of the reproduction departments, where he remained until his appointment as Director General in 1908.

Map Sales and Agents

Towards the end of 1895, as a sequel to its comments on the Dorington Report, the Board of Agriculture appointed a Departmental Committee – known as the Hayes-Fisher Committee after its Chairman, William Hayes-Fisher MP – to consider the arrangements for the sale of Ordnance Survey maps. Among the witnesses was Mr Piggott, the Controller of the Stationery Office, who gave an account of the system then in force. He was well qualified to do this, having held office since 1885, when his Department entered into the contract with Stanford.

Edward Stanford, who had been sole agent for Ordnance Survey maps since 1885, was examined at length. He described some of the problems of trying to manage a very large stock of maps to meet the requirements of a public which was not particularly well informed. A considerable proportion of his evidence was taken up with a discussion of the morals of the surprisingly large number of people who appeared to order a map simply to trace off what they wanted and then to return it as not being what they had asked for. Apparently this was such a serious matter than Stanford had put a notice in his catalogues and other publications:

> Persons purchasing Ordnance Survey maps are particularly requested to satisfy themselves before leaving the premises that the maps are those they actually require, as by the rules of the Depot they cannot, after removal therefrom, be again received or exchanged for others.

When it was suggested that he sold old hand-coloured 1:2500 maps in preference to the newer uncoloured sheets, because of the higher profit, Stanford replied that part of the trouble was the delay in getting stocks sent up from Southampton. He agreed that the sending of a telegram might get a quick response but it would be an expensive business; it would have been a great convenience to him to have had direct telephonic communication with the Ordnance Survey. The Office at Southampton was not in fact connected with the Post Office telephone system until 1914.

There was a good deal of opposition from map-sellers to the sole agency system. Stanley Philip, whose firm had themselves submitted a tender when the contract was put out, did not like the idea of an agent being advertised as the sole agent, since the public seemed to suspect that other agents were somehow not doing a *bona fide* business. He knew of several instances where his firm had tendered for the supply of maps and been unsuccessful, not on the grounds of price, but simply because people thought that by going to the sole authorized agent the customer must necessarily be better served.

Among other publishers, George Bacon argued that the sole agent creamed off the best of the business, and Arnold Foster MP, representing Cassell and Co., said that the sole agent's margin between the $33\frac{1}{3}$ per cent allowed to him and the 25 per cent that he allowed to the trade was too small. Mr Stanford, he thought, had compensated for this by developing a very large direct-sale business.

Mr Smyth, Assistant Secretary to the Post Office, discussed the whole question of the use of sub-postmasters as agents for the sale of Ordnance Survey maps and the incentives and controls which would be necessary to make this a going concern. There would be a considerable increase in work for the Post Office which it would have to pay for itself, and some account of this would have to be taken in the financing of such a scheme.

When Farquharson was examined, he came out as strongly opposed to the present system of a sole agency. Nevertheless, he thought that an agent in London, with increased facilities, should be provided with a complete stock of maps at public expense, which would not amount to the monopoly of sale which a sole agency might imply.

The Committee reported to the Board of Agriculture in July 1896.[3] It thought the present system of distribution was not likely to result in as large a sale of maps as would be possible in other circumstances. Much of the evidence showed that, if the maps were better known and more readily obtainable, especially in the provinces, their sale would be increased. Maps were essentially local publications, and the arrangement, however efficiently carried out, by which the demand could only be satisfied through a single London agent drawing his supplies from Southampton, was conducive to much practical inconvenience. Where the sole agent carried on a retail trade, it was more in his interest to sell one map to a retail customer than three or four copies of the same map through the trade, although this was manifestly to the disadvantage of the Exchequer and the public. Nor could any system of appointing sub-agents, such as had been tried since 1893, be expected to remove all the drawbacks inseparable from a sole agency. Another objection, which it considered of much importance, was that under the current system the Ordnance Survey was out of touch with the public and could not take note of their requirements. Even when the Survey was in a position to meet a popular demand it could not do so if there was a prospect that the profits received by the sole agent might be detrimentally affected. For example, in April 1894 the Board of Agriculture proposed to issue a cheap edition of the one-inch map upon thin tough paper to be sold to the public at sixpence a sheet, but it was thought that this experiment might injuriously affect the sole agent's position and the scheme had to be abandoned. The Committee thought it right to say that general testimony had been borne to the satisfactory manner in which Mr Stanford had carried out his contract, but did not hesitate to recommend that the present system should no longer be continued, that the Ordnance Survey should resume control of the sale of its maps and that the proceeds from sales should be appropriated in aid of the Survey Vote. The Government should retain full freedom to produce and publish maps in any form it thought desirable and to increase or lower the prices as it considered proper.

The Committee was satisfied that there was a necessity for a complete and full stock of the maps to be maintained in London, convenient of access both for sale and for reference by the public and by public departments. It was also satisfied that it would be both undesirable and expensive to maintain a government depot for that purpose. It proposed therefore that a single agent should be appointed for the sale of maps in London, that he should keep a credit stock of all Ordnance Survey maps produced, and that tenders should be invited for the appointment. An agent should be appointed for Edinburgh, Dublin and each of the larger provincial towns, who would keep a credit stock of the one-inch and six-inch maps in local demand and, where thought desirable, of the plans on the larger scales. In addition to the agents in London and the provinces, any book or map-seller should be allowed to order maps directly from Southampton or London at a discount of twenty-five per cent, providing payment for the maps was made and the cost of packing and carriage defrayed. The Committee recommended that post offices should be used both to advertise the products of the Survey and as agencies for the transmission of orders to Southampton.

These recommendations were generally accepted by the Board and the new system came into effect on 1 January 1897. Stanford was appointed as the London agent holding a complete stock of the maps for England, and Menzies of Edinburgh was similarly appointed for Scotland; in Dublin, Hodges, Figgis and Co. retained the agency, but the complete stock of maps for Ireland continued to be held in the Ordnance Survey Office in Phoenix Park. In addition, 138 provincial agencies were established.

At the same time an arrangement was concluded with the Postmaster-General whereby Ordnance Survey maps could be ordered at 746 head post offices throughout the Kingdom, in towns which had no appointed agent. The orders were transmitted to Southampton and the maps sent direct to the purchasers. The post offices were supplied with map indexes and explanatory pamphlets, but would-be purchasers were unable to see the maps they were ordering.[4]

Although map sales and net receipts rose, the new system did not bring any great advantage. Purchasers, for the most part, continued to patronize the old sole agents and in 1897 less than one-quarter of the sales were made through the provincial agencies. No applications at all were received from over one-half of the authorized post offices, and only an average of two from each of the remainder. The resumption of direct wholesaling from Southampton, together with the preparation of indexes and other documents, placed a 'heavy burden on the staff', and at first there were delays in filling orders, partly because so many were wrongly completed or because the wrong money was sent.

In the next few years sales through the Post Office continued to be very disappointing, never rising to as much as £250 per annum, and in 1906 the scheme was abandoned.[5] On the other hand, the provincial agents gradually gained a greater share of the market at the expense of the main agents. The volume of sales continued to rise until the end of the century, but the trend then reversed and in 1904 and 1905 there was a decline leading to another change in the marketing system. The previously appointed agencies continued with the six-inch and larger scales under the same conditions as before, but the distribution of small-scale maps to the trade was placed in the hands of a wholesale agent – T. Fisher Unwin.[6] Initially Unwin's agency was confined to England and Wales but a year later it was enlarged to include Scotland and Ireland. This led to a change of main agent in Scotland, where W. and A. K. Johnston replaced Menzies; Stanford continued to act as main agent in London. In the enigmatic words of the annual *Report* for 1910–11, these measures 'were . . . on the whole to a certain extent successful'. The sales of small-scale maps under the administration of Fisher Unwin showed little improvement, the gross values for 1906–7, 1908–9 and 1910–11 being respectively £8173, £6798, and £8313.

At the instance of the Geographical Association it was decided in 1903, with the consent of the Treasury, to supply schools with specially printed Ordnance Survey maps at a very low price.[7] The price was fixed to cover the cost of preparing the maps in the cheapest manner possible, and they were issued on a written undertaking that they would not be placed on sale but would be used for educational purposes only. Over 46 000 were supplied in the first year.

CROWN COPYRIGHT

The application of the law of copyright to the products of the Survey had, from the days of Mudge, always contained an element of uncertainty. In 1816 the argument centred on the name of the 'proprietor', and although in the opinion of the law officers of the Crown the imprint containing Mudge's name on an Ordnance map satisfied the requirements of the current Copyright Acts, this remained a matter open to dispute.

When the Copyright Act of 1911 was passed, the doubt about the proprietorship of Government publications was removed. A clause of the Act read:

> ... where any work has, whether before or after the commencement of this Act, been prepared or published by or under the direction or control of His Majesty or any Government Department the copyright on the work shall, subject to any agreement with the author, belong to His Majesty, and in such case shall continue for a period of fifty years from the date of first publication of the work.

In a letter to the Secretary of the Board of Agriculture, the Treasury commented:

> ... the Board will observe the above clause places for the first time all Government publications, including Ordnance maps, upon a definite footing, irrespective of the question of authorship, which has hitherto rendered it doubtful whether proceedings could be taken with success in cases of infringement of Government copyright.[8]

The administration of Crown Copyright in Ordnance Survey maps established by the Act (1 & 2 Geo. 5, Ch. 46) was vested in the Controller of H. M. Stationery Office.

Land Registration

> The use of the maps for the purpose of Land Registry is not ... nearly so general as was probably intended when the progress of the Cadastral Survey was specially accelerated by the Government.

In these words the Ordnance Survey recorded the failure of the Land Transfer Act of 1875, and to drive the message home repeated it year after year from 1894 to 1905. But after 1897 a more hopeful note was struck:

> But the Land Transfer Act of 1897 may possibly increase the use made of the Ordnance Survey maps for this object.

This Act introduced the principle of compulsory registration of title* within a specified area of a county, and was applied first to the County of London in stages in 1899 and 1900. From 1889 onwards the Ordnance Survey had provided some assistance to the Land Registry, but only in the form of two or three Civil Assistants who were employed in the preparation and maintenance of the public index map. The application of the Act to London caused a great increase of work and raised many problems connected with mapping and revision which led to a prolonged disagreement between the Ordnance Survey and the Land Registry.

A Committee representing the Treasury, the Ordnance Survey and the Land Registry, met in July 1898 to consider the arrangements best suited to the mapping work of the Land Registry. It came to the conclusion that this work (estimated at fifty or sixty registrations a day) would be too large to be undertaken by a Map Department which was merely a branch of another organization such as the Ordnance Survey. But the Director General made it clear that, in his opinion, if the means were provided, the Ordnance Survey could easily carry out the survey work for the Land Registry, and a rider to this effect was added to the Committee's Report. Nevertheless he signed the Report and its main conclusion was put into effect at once. Colonel Washington, late Royal Engineers and for some time the Ordnance Survey's division officer at Norwich, was appointed Director of a Survey and

* But only after application had been made by the County Council.

Mapping Department within the Land Registry, to which sixteen Civil Assistants were transferred from the Ordnance Survey in 1898.

Another Committee, similarly constituted and with the same terms of reference, was appointed in 1899 and gave particular attention to the Director General's rider of the previous year, but by this time the Ordnance Survey was feeling the effects of the withdrawal of officers and men to serve in the South African War and Johnston was much less positive in his willingness to undertake the work. The deliberations of this Committee and of others which followed are well summarized in the *Report* of the Stewart-Wallace Committee of 1928:[9]

> The majority of the 1899 Committee foresaw serious difficulties in connection with the Ordnance Survey if a separate Land Registry staff was maintained, performing somewhat similar duties, but under different conditions of employment. This, it was felt, would lead to competition between the two Departments, and as the work of the two Departments was regarded as not being so materially different as to justify any important variation of pay or privilege, it was recommended that the Survey and Map Department of the Land Registry should, as soon as possible, be permanently transferred to the Ordnance Survey, a special division for London being formed and housed either in the same building as the Land Registry or in the immediate neighbourhood. The Chief Assistant Registrar, however, was unable to concur in these recommendations, as he was of opinion that if they were adopted the efficiency of the Land Registry would be seriously impaired. The Lord Chancellor's Department supported the Chief Assistant Registrar, and expressed the opinion that the system of compulsory registration would be in danger of breaking down if the Mapping Branch was not part of, and under the same control as, the Land Registry. In view of this position the Treasury, while in agreement with the views of the Committee, did not feel able to press them upon the Lord Chancellor at the time and sanctioned a separate establishment for the Mapping Branch of the Land Registry. In 1901 a Committee appointed by the Lord Chancellor to enquire into the organisation and working of the Land Registry Office, on which neither the Treasury nor the Ordnance Survey Department were represented, found that a considerable amount of map revision, as opposed to the more detailed work in connection with individual applications, had been and was being done by the Land Registry. They recommended that before compulsory registration was put into operation in any area the large scale Ordnance Survey maps of the district should be brought up to date, and expressed the view that this could be done most conveniently and economically by the Ordnance Survey and not by the Map Department of the Land Registry. The cost of this revision should be charged on the Land Registry or the Local Authority. They thought the Land Registry Map Department might reasonably be required to keep maps up to date after compulsory registration had been put into force, but that it was very desirable that any work of revision done by the Land Registry in this connection should be utilised by the Ordnance Survey, subject to proper checking in order to prevent discrepancies arising between the Ordnance Survey and Land Registry maps. In endorsing the Committee's recommendations under this head the Treasury laid down that the cost of preliminary revision for compulsory registration should be met by the municipality concerned.

The Survey and Mapping Department of the Land Registry revised large parts of the 1:1056 map of the County of London and surveyed considerable areas where this map had not been published; in 1905 the Land Registry proposed to put their surveyed and revised plans on sale to the public, but the Ordnance Survey objected on the grounds that there would then be two plans of the County on the same scale produced by two public Departments. It was also claimed that the new surveys, as distinct from revision, should not, in any case, have been done by the Land Registry. Another Committee was appointed in 1905 to enquire into the overlap between the two Departments. The outcome was that the Land Registry revision was incorporated into the Ordnance Survey 1:1056 plans, printed and published by the Ordnance Survey, but marked 'Land Registry Series', an arrangement which continued until 1923. Between 1906 and 1909 the Ordnance Survey extended the 1:1056 plans to cover an additional 8000 acres in the County of London, in accordance with the principles recommended by the 1901 and 1905 Committees. The latter had also recommended that the revision of areas in London exceeding 20 acres should be carried out by the Ordnance Survey.[10]

The argument was to go on for many more years. Leaving aside the tribal feelings of the two Departments, it rested on two matters of substance: the ability of the Ordnance Survey to produce up-to-date maps when they were wanted by the Land Registry and the ability of the Ordnance Survey field staff to understand the requirements of the Land Registry and in particular to interpret deeds on the ground. The second difficulty was avoidable, because the interpretation could be done in the Land Registry itself and presented to the surveyor in the form of specific questions which he was capable of answering. The first problem was more intractable, and was not solved until the adoption of continuous revision in the middle of the century.

A new system for indexing registration was brought into use in the Land Registry in 1907.[11] This was the General Map, which was divided into sections, each section being an extract of the Ordnance Survey bounded by topographical features, usually roads, and not by sheet-lines. In this way the map was modified to the form commonly used in other countries for cadastral purposes, and the inconvenience of sheet-lines which cut through property units was eliminated.

Cartographic Developments

ACCOMMODATION AND MACHINERY

One of the first matters confronting Johnston after his appointment in 1899 was the pressing need for extension of the Zinc-Printing Department to accommodate the increasing amount of colour printing. As an alternative to taking temporary premises outside, a proposal was made to utilize Ordnance House, the official residence of the Director General, for some of the offices. Detailed discussions took place to decide on the amount of money which should be paid to the Director General in lieu of the official residence and the accompanying perquisites such as rates and maintenance.[12] By the end of the year the Treasury had agreed to pay an allowance at the minimum rate proposed by the Director General, but with the proviso that Colonel Johnston's successor would have no claim to this allowance. The need for a new zinc-printing building had been argued each year since 1896, but work on it was not started until 1901 and not finished until 1903.

The lack of good accommodation had seriously retarded the full adoption of improved methods. The photographic process known as heliozincography,[13]* by which images could be transferred to the printing plate with or without change of scale, had been introduced in 1893; in theory, this removed many of the difficulties of colour printing in register by doing away with the paper transfer, but a camera was still necessary for making the negative which was exposed to light in contact with the sensitized printing plate. The Vandyke process, which had been brought into use in 1900, made it possible to transfer the manuscript drawing to the sensitized printing plate by direct contact without using a camera. In order to get good results from either of these methods the plans had to be suitably drawn and kept perfectly clean. This latter condition was difficult to fulfil in view of the large amount of work done on each plan, and the fact that in the old offices of the Ordnance Survey the air was often laden with smoke and dust. In general, however, the difficulties were overcome, but only by taking great care. So successful was the Vandyke process for the reproduction of the large-scale plans that a further payment of £400 was made to the inventor, Conductor Vandyke of the Survey of India, raising the total paid to him to £700. By this payment the Government secured the right to use the process for the work of any government department in the United Kingdom.[14]

The provision of electric light throughout the Ordnance Survey Office at Southampton was completed in 1900. The cost of electric lighting had been found to exceed that of gas, but electricity was more suited than gas to the drawing and other work done at the Office, and could hardly fail to promote efficiency since it kept the air cleaner and fresher.

Very careful investigations were made into the best and most economical system of arranging the machinery and supplying motive power in the new zinc-printing building. Captain P. H. Du P. Casgrain RE had been sent to visit a number of installations in the United Kingdom, Canada and the United States, and the scheme which he devised – to work all the machinery by 'electro-motors' – was accepted. The electro-motors took up little space and had the further advantage that they worked without vibration.

The substitution of electricity for steam proved economical and convenient, although the reliability of the Corporation's supply was not yet all that could be desired. By 1904, nineteen out of a total of twenty-eight hand-printing presses were operated by electricity, an electrically-driven grinding machine for lithographic stones had been obtained and found to be very useful, and the lift in the new printing building had been designed for working by electricity.[15]

THE ENGRAVED ONE-INCH MAP

One of the principal publications of the Ordnance Survey, the black engraved one-inch map of the United Kingdom with hills, was completed in 1902. The amount of labour that had been involved in its preparation was probably not generally realized, although it could be gauged from the fact that it took four to six months to make the hill drawing from the field sheets, and one to two years to engrave a map the size of a full English sheet. The whole of this had to be done by highly skilled draughtsmen and engravers. With the completion of the hill map the preparation of separate hill plates could be taken up more vigorously for those parts of England and Wales where they did not exist before, and for the Scottish and Irish sheets.**

* The plates were exposed to sunlight whenever possible; hence the name of the process.
** The existence of separate hill plates greatly simplified colour printing at this time.

The last and perhaps the most beautiful version of the engraved hachured map was that made by double printing from two copper plates, with the hills in brown. It was introduced in 1889 and greater legibility was justifiably claimed for it. In later years Winterbotham, in a burst of nostalgia, described it as 'a delightful map, that small engraved sheet, with its beautifully clear outline and hills'.[16]

Early in 1903 the last of the revised one-inch outline maps of Ireland was published, completing the one-inch revision of the whole of the United Kingdom, and making available to the public for the first time a reasonably up-to-date one-inch outline map prepared on a uniform system. The second revision had been started and good progress was being made with it.

THE ONE-INCH MAP IN COLOUR

The encouragement given by the Dorington Committee led soon to a productive period of cartographic experiment and development. There were other circumstances which favoured these advances, including the improvements in reproduction methods and the use of electricity for power. Moreover it could hardly have been coincidence that two of the Directors at this time, Johnston and Grant, had each had several years experience in charge of the reproduction branches of the Survey.

Early in 1897 sanction was received from the Treasury for the publication of the experimental one-inch map in colour,[17] which had been produced for the War Office, and which embodied revision lately carried out for the one-inch engraved map. Experiments in colour had first been mentioned rather casually in the Ordnance Survey *Reports* for 1886 and 1887:

> A negative is taken for every distinct colour and these negatives are so manipulated by the photographer and retoucher that each negative retains the detail of one colour only. A carbon transfer from each negative is made and the transfers are separately laid down on zinc plates to the same size. The colours are afterwards printed in the ordinary manner.

The process actually used for the standard coloured one-inch series was quite different, although its basis remained the engraved map. The 'manipulation' was not carried out on negatives but on transfers to zinc.

From the copper plate of the outline edition a transfer was taken and laid down on a zinc plate known as the 'index plate'. From this several 'set offs' were prepared on thin zinc sheets. The required detail for each colour was inked-in on the separate set offs and the corresponding unwanted detail removed. The printing plates were made by direct transfer from the set offs, and as all of these had been prepared directly from the index plate, good registration was ensured. For the hachures, a transfer was taken directly from the copper hill plate, where it existed, and laid down on either zinc or stone. Where there was no separate hill plate an impression was taken of the combined detail and hills, from which the unwanted outline was removed by scraping and cleaning before transferring to zinc.[18]

On the coloured one-inch the detail was in black and the water in blue, but the remaining colours – brown for the hachures, burnt sienna for first and second class roads, and red for contours – gave the map an over-all brown tinge, although this was to some extent lessened after 1904 by the addition of a rather harsh green for woods. The roads, which had not been particularly conspicuous on the engraved map, became very prominent, but the old difficulty with the legibility of names was not entirely overcome in the heavier hilly areas especially where the hachures, the green woods and the black wood or park symbols were combined. The map took on the character of a rather dingy road map, without clearly distinguishing the main roads from the remainder. Farquharson was not entirely satisfied with it; when he retired in 1899 he said that although much improvement had been made, the standard of colour printing was not yet equal to the best achieved in the trade. By 1903 the coloured one-inch map of England and Wales had been completed, that for Ireland was about half finished and a similar map for Scotland had been authorized.

The first published coloured one-inch sheets were not classified as a new edition, as they reflected variously the New Series and its first revision; for many years they were merely referred to as the 'one-inch map in colour'. From 1906 the small sheets corresponding to the engraved map were combined on new sheet-lines to meet a War Office requirement for larger sheets, and were issued as the Large Sheet Series. The description 'Third Edition' was applied to those sheets, both large and small, which incorporated the small-scale field revision (the second revision) of 1902–12.

MORE NEW MAPS

The early history of the engraved quarter-inch map of Great Britain is fragmentary. According to the *Report* for 1892 the engraving of 'a general map of the Kingdom' at this scale was begun as early as 1859. In 1872 work was stopped and it was not until twelve years later that it was resumed and completed without revision at the request of the Director General of the Geological Survey, but the map was not published. Subsequently a demand for quarter-inch transfers from map-publishers led to the map being placed on sale in its existing state. Henry Crook described this map as 'bad in design, bad in execution, entirely obsolete and artificial, and grossly inaccurate in places with regard to material detail', and in 1892 *The Times* referred to it critically in a leading article. The Ordnance Survey did not dispute these strictures but preferred to describe the defects in the map more kindly as 'known imperfections'. In its *Report* the Dorington Committee accepted the Director General's explanations for the inferior quality of the map and recommended that it should be 'perfected' and the hills added once the New Series one-inch had been completed.

The transition from the black quarter-inch map, which had drawn upon itself such opprobrium, to coloured versions followed closely on the change to the coloured one-inch, the new styles being broadly similar. Between 1900 and 1903 a hill edition with brown roads, blue water and green woods appeared, based on the old outline, but revised. It was a charming map, simple, clear and legible even in the hills. These were shaded but not hachured, the shading being produced by photographing a brush drawing and photo-etching on copper.[19] The Second Edition, started in the years before the First World War, was produced in larger sheets. It preserved the same style, but the delicacy of the First Edition coloured map was not maintained, particularly in the hill-shading which tended to be significantly heavier.* In 1902 a start was made on a fully-coloured map series at half an inch to one mile. The military authorities had required and published such a map of certain areas and the agents of the Ordnance Survey had for some time urged that there was a demand on the part of the public for a similar map. The first version closely resembled the coloured editions of the quarter-inch and the hill-shading was produced by the same method but lacked the delicacy of the early quarter-inch sheets. Names were typed and were subsequently criticized as 'cramped and inferior'; in this respect the map fell a long way behind the quarter-inch with its engraved writing. Another version was made between 1906 and 1908 on larger sheets in two forms, one with both hill-shading and layering, and the other with hill-shading only. The layered form was not one of the Ordnance Survey's most beautiful productions: the typed names remained, the layer/hill-shading combination was very heavy and the layer colours rather ugly. Winterbotham, writing in the 1930s, was explicit:

> . . . a vile bottom green and an equally dreadful bluey top layer . . . the colour might have been laid on with a trowel.[20]**

In the more hilly areas the layering was elaborate and particularly thick; on the Alnwick sheet there were no fewer than seventeen layer colours. Where the relief was lower the combined style was more successful, although the colouring remained unattractive. Nevertheless, the map had 'the germs of success'; it was in fact an important exercise in experimental cartography and needed only simplification and refinement to become admirable.

Another cartographic venture at this time was a map at the scale of 1:1 million[21] produced in accordance with the recommendations for a map of the world made at the 1891 International Geographical Congress at which Great Britain was represented. It was published in 1905 and by later international standards was a very simple map, printed in only three colours. There were two sheets covering Great Britain and Ireland.

The rapid development of colour printing by zincography† enabled the Ordnance Survey to begin experiments for colour-printing geological maps, which had hitherto been mostly hand-coloured. The engraving of geological maps had always been carried out by the Ordnance Survey but before 1901 the hand-colouring had been done by a contractor. In that year, because of the contractor's inability to cope with the demand for the revised geological sheets based on the one-inch,[22] the Ordnance Survey formed a hand-colouring department, which soon afterwards was allowed to run down as more sophisticated methods of colour printing were developed. Between 1889 and 1896 the Geological Survey had published colour-printed maps at the quarter-inch scale, based on the much-criticized

---

* It is recognized throughout that cartographic judgments on such matters as delicacy of colouring are matters of individual taste, and that a single printing may include some variation in quality.

** However, in his handing-over notes to McLeod, Winterbotham confessed that he was partially colour-blind.

† Lithographic stones were introduced for colour printing in 1896 and gradually came to be regarded as essential in work of the highest quality. After 1936 their use declined.

quarter-inch engraved map, but these had been printed by the trade under arrangements made by the Stationery Office. Colour printing at the one-inch scale began at the Ordnance Survey in 1902 and the results were very successful, the colours being far better than on the hand-coloured maps and the cost considerably lower. At about the same time, on the recommendation of a Departmental Committee of the Board of Education which reported in 1900, the Ordnance Survey undertook, for the first time, the publication and sale of geological maps.

The descriptive pamphlet suggested by the Dorington Committee also appeared in 1902.[23] This useful little booklet gave the published coverage and sheet-numbering system of the various series and an explanation of the information contained on the maps including the extent to which the contours were instrumentally surveyed or only sketched in different parts of the country. Abbreviations and comparative tables of characteristics and symbols, covering both current and former systems, were given and defined, and there were sample cuts from a wide range of the publications of the Survey. A revised edition was published in 1908.

A great deal of space was given to printing and publication in Johnston's annual reports which were voluminous affairs and, in common with most other Ordnance Survey Reports, repeated whole passages, word for word, year after year. In 1899 he published a table of comparative printing statistics for the current and previous years, giving for each scale the number of impressions and the number of printings. A total was arrived at by adding 'impressions' and 'printings' together. This error went unnoticed for several years, and it was not until 1903 that the totals of printings and impressions were shown separately.

Progress in the Field

Card revision, first used in County Louth in 1860, was adopted in 1894 for the 1:2500 revision in Great Britain. The 'cards' were impressions on paper of one-sixth of a 1:2500 map, which gave a size convenient for handling in the field. But the revisers found them difficult to work on. They had trouble in carrying construction lines and detail features across the edges because the cards could not be made to join together exactly. It was soon realized that the material from which the cards were made had distorted, so that even before the revision began the map had lost its true shape. In the Ordnance Survey *Report* for 1895 the problem was brought into the open:

> The principal difficulty has arisen from the distortion of the paper on which the first editions, or original surveys of the map were printed. In many cases the length or breadth of the printed map was found to be as much as a chain different from the correct length or breadth and the distortion was not uniform in any one direction nor in any one part of the map.

These defects could only be remedied by fitting the cards together by 'shining-up*'. With the introduction of the tracing-paper 'field trace' (1900–1907) some of the immediate problems disappeared, but inevitably a time of reckoning came when the second revision (started in 1904) had to be added to the results of the first. Generally the plans revised by the card system were found to be unacceptable as a basis for new work.

Another unfortunate consequence of the card revision was that photozincography was no longer used for reproducing the 1:2500 plans. Instead there was a reversion to transfer-making by manual tracing, this time from the cards after they had been fitted together by shining-up. There was thus no manuscript record of the revised plans, apart from the cards themselves, an evil which persisted until the adoption of the Vandyke process and the reviser's trace.

By the turn of the century the town surveys had been completed – although their revision was restricted as a result of the recommendations of the Dorington Committee – and the 1:2500 maps of Great Britain had all been published. The first revision of the 1:2500 map was finished by 1909 except for Lancashire, Yorkshire, the six Scottish counties and the Isle of Lewis, which had been surveyed originally on the six-inch scale. The advice of the Dorington Committee on the definition of 'revision' seems to have been forgotten, because from 1907 onwards these counties were shown in the reports as having undergone a complete 'first revision' and to have been among the first to be taken up for a 'second revision'. A genuine first revision of Lancashire and Yorkshire was begun in about 1904 (except for the revision of The West Riding which began in 1901) and of Haddington and Edinburgh

---

* Shining up: the recompilation of a distorted document to fit a true framework, in this case the correct size and shape of the sheet. The distorted document was cut into pieces and reassembled so as to spread the errors introduced by the distortion over the whole area. The cuts were usually selected to avoid close detail on the map, and therefore the distribution of the 'correction' was discontinuous and arbitrary.

in about 1905. Also in 1904 a second revision was started in south-eastern England, Berwick and Peebles. Subsequent events were to prevent the second revision from ever being completed.

The South African War 1899–1902

The outbreak of the South African War affected the Survey in two ways: it led to a considerable drain on personnel and concurrently brought much additional work.[24] Seven officers were at once sent to South Africa, where most of them were employed on general Royal Engineer duties and not on survey. Only one was replaced: a net loss of six out of a total establishment of twenty-four. As well as the non-commissioned officers and men of the Survey Companies who were sent overseas for survey work, reservists left to join the colours and many others volunteered for active service. The total number of maps printed for the War Office during the financial year 1899–1900 was 374 538, entailing 766 818 printings, whereas the largest number printed in any previous year had been 64 850, made up of 102 850 printings. The *Report* for this year remarked naïvely: 'Every soldier proceeding to South Africa has been provided with a map.' In the next year two complete sections (one commanded by Major C. F. Close) were despatched to South Africa, and in 1902 two more were sent, and another to Mauritius. The annual *Report* included the vague comment: '. . . it is believed that [these sections] have done very useful work'.

Not all those who served in the theatre of war were enthusiastic about the maps. Lieutenant-Colonel H. M. Jackson RE thought that less than one per cent of the maps sent out were used,[25] and Close, who was invalided home early in the war, recalled that the high quality paper on which they were printed made them very suitable for lining uniforms to keep out the cold winds of the veldt.[26]

Two survey sections mapped about 13 700 square miles at various scales, while mapping sections at Pretoria, Bloemfontein and Cape Town printed a total of about 460 000 maps, many in colour, of which about 308 000 were issued. The Ordnance-Survey-trained sappers were generally effective, but active service was not popular with them, particularly with the senior men, because of the loss of their departmental pay which was regulated by ability and experience.

A Revival – the First Years of Close's Directorship

Colonel C. F. Close succeeded Grant as Director General in August 1911. His previous experience of the Ordnance Survey consisted merely of being briefly in charge of the Trigonometrical Branch in 1900 and commanding one of the survey sections sent to South Africa. But he had worked with the Survey of India and on boundary commissions in Africa, and in 1902 was appointed Chief Instructor in Surveying at the School of Military Engineering where he wrote his *Text Book of Topographical Surveying*. In 1905 he became Chief of the Geographical Section of the General Staff. He must have been greatly dissatisfied with much that he found on rejoining the Ordnance Survey in 1911.

The discontent of the civil staff had once more reached a point which made it necessary to appoint another Departmental Committee to enquire into their pay and classification. Anxiety was created because numbers were being reduced steadily, even among the sappers, with the disbandment of the 16th Survey Company in 1906.[27] However, some improvements in conditions had been realized since the last committee of enquiry. In 1894 the Treasury had sanctioned 'the boon of superannuation' to some Civil Assistants, and in 1906 all Assistants whose conduct, work and health were good were placed on the pensionable establishment after fifteen years service, but pay was reduced by amounts of between five and ten per cent, depending on the length of service. Under this scheme, 679 members of the staff were admitted to the establishment of whom 101 had formerly served as Royal Engineers.[28] But the new scale of pay which had been authorized in 1909 was a fixed scale, with three classes of work recognized within each trade. This system created disappointment amongst the staff, particularly because it took thirty-five years to reach the maximum rate. Added to this the pension scheme of 1906 was considered to compare unfavourably with the old superannuation scheme which had been withdrawn in 1870. The Departmental Committee published its report in 1911,[29] having taken evidence from both staff and officials of the Ordnance Survey. This volume of over a quarter of a million words reveals the gulf which existed between the military direction and the civilian members of the staff.

The recommendations of the Committee, which contained a series of detailed proposals for the removal of grievances, was the first important matter that Close had to deal with on taking over as

Director General. He referred in his first *Report* to the evidence given by the representatives of the Assistants on the disadvantages under which the various groups were labouring.[30] The facts were stated temperately and reasonably by the representatives, he said, who managed their case well and indicated clearly the difficulties attendant upon the applications of the 1909 pay scale. He added that he had recommended the adoption of the proposals of the Committee, and that the Board of Agriculture and the Treasury had approved them without any substantial modification. This provided the authority for the new scales of pay, allowances and classification of the Assistants, Temporary Assistants and Labourers of the Ordnance Survey which had been published in a paper presented to Parliament. Close believed that, as far as could be judged, the new scale would work well; there were necessarily some minor matters which required adjustment and still some individual cases which needed investigation, but he hoped and believed that it would not be long before it would be possible to report that, so far as was known, no Assistant was classed below his deserts and no genuine grievance unredressed.

Some measure of the success which Close achieved in his relations with the staff was to be found a year or so later when, in November 1913, on the occasion of his wedding, he was given a complimentary concert and presentation at Southampton before a large and enthusiastic assembly of all ranks of the Survey, both male and female.[31] In responding to a congratulatory address, Close said that there were two ideas in regard to the work and administration of the Ordnance Survey which he had kept in view in carrying out his duties as Director General. The first was that there should be as little internal friction as possible and that all should try to work together with mutual confidence. The second was that all should endeavour to increase the prestige and enlarge the reputation of the Ordnance Survey, not only in the opinion of fellow countrymen, but also in the opinion of those abroad who were interested in their work. Close acknowledged the assistance he had been given, not merely by the officers and superintendents of all sections of staff, but more particularly by the men's Associations. On more than one occasion he had been prevented from making mistakes by reason of conversations he had had with the representatives of these Associations who were, of course, in close touch with the desires and wishes of the men they represented. In this connection he thought it would be proper for him to say, as it was common knowledge, that they were endeavouring to establish a pension scheme for those men in the service (the artificers and labourers) who were then not entitled to pensions.

These remarks brought forth great applause from the audience. The weight of feeling in his favour on this occasion could probably be assessed by the very handsome silver rose-bowl, weighing 112 ounces, which was presented to him.

On his appointment Close immediately began to restore the scientific reputation of the Survey by completing the work of testing the triangulation. An apparent revival of interest within the Ordnance Survey in geodetic work had taken place between 1909 and 1911 when the Lossiemouth Base was measured and linked to the triangulation.[32] On the face of it a revival was an unlikely event at this time, and in fact the test had been initiated from outside. From the beginning of the century some doubt had been felt by scientists about the accuracy of the British triangulation compared with more recent European work, notably by Sir George Darwin, the Astronomer Royal. Various proposals had been made for strengthening the British network and eventually the measurement of a test base, suggested by the Council of the British Association for the Advancement of Science and supported by the Royal Society, was given the approval of the Board of Agriculture. For several years the Department remained silent about this episode, and it was not until 1912, when Close made public what was being done in his first annual *Report*, that any official reference by the Ordnance Survey was made to the test measurements.

In this *Report* Close said that no survey department could afford to neglect the scientific aspects of its work. The department which ignored its scientific duties tended to fall into routine and to adopt the habit of accepting methods which were supposed to be just good enough but which, as a fact, were never good enough in the long run. He added, tactfully, that this was no reflection on the labours of his predecessors to take advantage of the progress of science and of mechanical and artistic ingenuity; they laid a good foundation, their ideas were in advance of their time and they would have rejoiced to see the Survey doing its best to meet the wants of a new age.

Following these principles, he arranged for work to begin on a 'revision of the geodetic levelling', subsequently known as the Second Geodetic Levelling. To provide permanent marks for the new levelling, the 'Fundamental Bench-Mark' was designed[33] (Plate 14), and to establish a more reliable sea-level datum, tidal stations were erected at Dunbar (1913), Newlyn (1915) and Felixstowe (1917).

Close was far from complacent about the current state of small-scale maps. He considered the one-inch map in its coloured edition as good of its kind but by no means representing the last word in cartography, although he admitted that here he was on somewhat controversial ground, since no general agreement could be expected on questions of taste. Although the coloured one-inch map occupied a high place amongst the maps of the world, he believed its relative position some years earlier had been higher. The half-inch map as it existed in 1912 drew from him some very reserved comments, and he categorized it as being 'provisional' in character. He looked forward to the early production of a half-inch map from an engraved base with much lighter layer tints.

The cartographic advance which began in 1897 reached its culmination with the production of the *Killarney District* map in 1913 (Plate 15). A sophisticated combination of contours, layers, hachures and hill-shading was used, which was very successful in the Killarney mountains, the black dotted contours remaining perfectly clear against the hachured, layered and shaded background. The bluish 'shadow side' shading which made the hachures on the shaded side appear to be printed in a darker brown, and the unobtrusive layers (changing at 300 and 1250 feet) were extremely effective. The main weakness of the *Killarney* sheet, apart from its expense, was in the use of black dots for different purposes. The dotted contours were faultless on the open hill-sides, but in the valley bottoms and on the lower ground, vegetation and enclosure boundaries were shown by nearly identical dotted lines and the contours were not easy to follow. A few other district maps (*Snowdon, Aldershot, Leith Hill, Glasgow, Ilkley*) were produced in a similarly elaborate style. None of the later tourist sheets succeeded in matching the concepts of relief depiction embodied in the *Killarney* style, the effects of which were only achieved by printing between thirteen and sixteen impressions of colour.

Close's ultimate intention was to produce a new improved one-inch series in the *Killarney* style, with a similarly redesigned half-inch to follow. With this object in mind he set about reducing the number of one-inch series, and obtained approval in 1912 to discontinue the all-black hachured map and the version with hachures in brown. This left only the engraved outline map and the coloured edition. Several sheets of the new design were in preparation when the 1914 war brought production to a halt, never to be resumed.

During the first decade of the century the revision of the large-scale plans in Britain went ahead in the manner planned but doubts were growing about the twenty-year revision cycle; for some localities it was too long and for others too short. The effect of the Finance (1909–10) Act made this weakness only too clear. The newly-formed Land Valuation Department was immediately faced with the task of carrying out a general valuation but, because of the cyclic revision system, the sets of maps provided for the valuers were not all up to date. In March 1911 the Ordnance Survey agreed to undertake a partial revision of nearly 5000 plans, concentrating on the close town areas, within eighteen months – the shortest possible time. Only the detail required by the valuers was to be added and this at first excluded boundaries and areas; later the Chief Valuer changed his mind and asked for the areas of altered parcels. The revision was executed with great vigour, but many short cuts were taken, and much inferior work was added to the plans. Ultimately this revision had to be done again; but errors once incorporated throw suspicion on the whole work and make subsequent revision much more difficult and costly. It is hard to see what could have been done to avoid these evil consequences. The root of the trouble was the Ordnance Survey's inflexibility, both in the method of cyclic revision and in the craft system, which depended for its success on checking and supervision. Once these were relaxed, as they were in 1911, the standard of work tended to drop.

Close had other reasons for feeling sour about the whole episode:

> The cost of preparing a special revision of Ordnance Survey maps for the purposes of Land Valuation has been about £80 000. This comes under the Vote for the Ordnance Survey and the money has been found, not by adding to the Ordnance Survey Vote, but by delaying normal revision.[34]

It was in connection with the 1911 valuation that Close introduced the 1:1250 enlargements that were to prove so satisfactory for this purpose[35] and which were later adopted by the Land Registry. The difficulties of the revision itself stimulated another innovation of great importance; Close argued that revision would be greatly simplified and accuracy preserved if a system of traverses in and around towns was surveyed with 'each important traverse point marked in a permanent manner'.[36] On this basis an unlimited succession of revisions could be undertaken without progressive loss of accuracy. Close also developed the concept of 'J' points – junction points of fences etc. unaltered since the original survey – which could be used as starting points for revision in rural areas.[37]

The lapsed state of the Scottish Place Names Committee did not escape Close's attention, and in 1913 he suggested that it should be revived; it was accordingly reconstituted with Dr W. J. Watson as Chairman and Mr John Mathieson (Superintendent of the Edinburgh Division, Ordnance Survey) as Honorary Secretary. It continued to work within the Dorington rules, as a report to the *Scottish Geographical Magazine* shows:

With regard to the important class of Anglicised names the Committee is of the opinion that although, as a rule, *the names must be regarded for ordinary map purposes as stereotyped*, it is nevertheless of great importance for philological and historical purposes that the genuine traditional forms as pronounced in Gaelic should be ascertained and preserved.

For the purposes of the Ordnance Survey, the main function of the Committee was to identify the correct Gaelic names 'where the map spelling did not accurately represent the local pronunciation in Gaelic'.[38]

A Pre-War Summary

When war broke out in 1914 Close was half-way through the normal tour of five or six years as Director General. He had been appointed Director in 1911, when he was only forty-six, and he seems to have felt that the Army might make better use of him on more active service. In March 1916 he wrote to the Board of Agriculture putting forward this suggestion.[39] In the event, his services as Director were retained and were continued into the post-war reconstruction period until his retirement in 1922.

The situation of the survey at the outbreak of war was generally satisfactory, partly because of the efforts of Close in the previous three years. The 1:2500 of Ireland was finished; in Great Britain the first revision (including the replotted counties) was finished and second and third revisions were in progress. The second one-inch revision had been completed in the field and a new and handsome one-inch map was in preparation. The geodetic aspect of the Survey had been revitalized and a second geodetic levelling had been started. The staff were for the most part satisfied with the new scales of pay and conditions of service, and relations between management and men were probably better than they had ever been before. Until 1912 only the officers had been named in the annual reports, but Close enlarged this list to include the superintendents and the senior clerks, a step which was indicative of changed relations and which must have given wide satisfaction. In 1913 the Lords Commissioners of the Treasury approved the expenditure of a small annual sum for the grant of awards to employees of the Department who devised or suggested improvements in methods or materials leading to economy or increased efficiency.

In the same year the first proceedings in the history of the Survey for the enforcement of copyright were taken. An Ordnance Survey quarter-inch map had been reproduced as a road map and, with a few slight alterations, had been published as a new production and sold at a low price. The circumstances were brought to the notice of the Stationery Office and the Treasury, and a prosecution under the Act of 1911 ensued. The case was tried at the Guildhall in London in October 1913 and resulted in the firm concerned, H. G. Rowe & Co., being convicted and fined, and an order issued for the destruction of all plates and copies of the infringing maps.

Notes

1 PRO 4749D.

2 *Geographical Journal* 1900, XV, pp. 565–98.

3 *Report of the Departmental Committee appointed by the Board of Agriculture to consider the arrangements to be made for the Sale of Ordnance Survey Maps*: PP 1896, C. 8147, LXVIII.

4 OSR 1896–7, p. 14: PP 1897, C. 8555, LXXII.

5 OSR 1906–7, p. 13: PP 1907, Cd. 3668, LXVIII.

6 OSR 1905–6, p. 15: PP 1906, Cd. 3064, XCVIII.

7 OSR 1903–4, p. 7: PP 1904, Cd. 2195, LXXIX.

8 PRO OS 1/233.

9 A Departmental Committee convened by the Lord Chancellor; Quoted in H. St J. L. Winterbotham, *The National Plans*, Ordnance Survey Professional Papers, New Series, No. 16 (HMSO 1934), pp. 72–3.

10 *Ibid.* p. 70.

11 *Ibid.* p. 73.

12 PRO 4749D.

13 *Methods and Processes adopted for the Production of the Maps of the Ordnance Survey*, 2nd edition (HMSO 1902), p. 179.

14 OSR 1902–3, p. 24: PP 1903, Cd. 1688, LV.

15 OSR 1903–4, p. 21: PP 1904, Cd. 2195, LXXIX.

16 Winterbotham, *Geographical Journal* 1932, LXXIX, p. 17.

17 OSR 1896–7, p. 4: PP 1897, C. 8555, LXXII.

18 *Methods and Processes . . .* pp. 185–6.

19 OSR 1902–3, p. 10: PP 1903, Cd. 1688, LV. For Photo-Etching see *Geographical Journal* 1925, LXV, p. 305.

20 Winterbotham, 'The Small Scale Maps of the Ordnance Survey' *Geographical Journal* 1932, LXXIX, p. 22. See Ch. 25.

21 OSR 1901–2, p. 9: PP 1902, Cd. 1243, LXXXIII.

22 J. S. Fleet, *First Hundred Years of the Geological Survey* (1937).

23 D. A. Johnston, *Ordnance Survey Maps of the United Kingdom – a description of their scales, characteristics etc.* (1902).

24 OSR 1899–1900, p. 3: PP 1900, Cd. 327, LXVIII.

25 H. M. Jackson and P. H. Du P. Casgrain, *Reports on Survey and Mapping Sections in South Africa* (1903).

26 C. F. Close, 'Fifty Years – a Retrospect', *Empire Survey Review*, April 1932, vol. 1, no. 4.

27 OSR 1906–7, p. 10: PP 1907, Cd. 3668, LXVIII.

28 *Ibid.* p. 3.

29 *Report of the Departmental Committee appointed by the Board of Agriculture and Fisheries to inquire into the Pay and Classification of Ordnance Survey Staff*: PP 1911, Cd. 5825, XXXVII; also *Minutes of Evidence*: PP 1911, Cd. 5826, XXXVII.

30 OSR 1911–12, pp. 13–14: PP 1912–13, Cd. 6372, XLII.

31 *Southern Daily Echo*, 13 November 1913; *The Hampshire Advertiser County Newspaper*, 15 November 1913.

32, 33 See Ch. 21.

34 Quoted in Winterbotham, *National Plans*, p. 80.

35 OSR 1911–12, p. 9: PP 1912–13, Cd. 6372, XLII.

36 OSR 1912–13, p. 8: PP 1913, Cd. 6903, XXXVIII.

37 J. C. T. Willis, *An Outline of the History and Revision of the 25-inch Ordnance Survey Plans* (HMSO 1932), p. 8.

38 *Scottish Geographical Magazine* 1913, XXIX, p. 322; italics in quoted passage are author's.

39 Board of Agriculture PRO F 191/16, 15 March 1916.

20
Ireland –
The Land Question
And After,
1871–1918

The Land Question

Outside the realm of officialdom, the landed gentry had been the most important factor in the history of the Irish survey. They had debated it and enquired into it in their capacity as members of Parliament; they had dictated the names and boundaries of demesnes and to a large extent of townlands; they had developed their estates with the aid of the six-inch map and sold them with the aid of the Landed Estates Court surveys. In the last three decades of the century, however, the power of the Irish landlord was declining as public opinion became convinced that the peasantry should be helped to buy their farms, borrowing part of the purchase price from the Government and repaying it by instalments on easy terms.[1] This principle was applied first to the tenants of glebe lands at the time of the disestablishment of the Church of Ireland in 1869 and then, a year later, to all tenants whose farms passed through the Landed Estates Court. Although these early measures of land reform were largely ineffective, they served to warn the Ordnance Survey of the likelihood that tenement maps might soon be as important as the townland maps produced in the plantation era.

At first it seemed as if the six-inch scale, already so versatile, could be adapted to the new situation. In the Valuation Office, farm boundaries had already been added to the printed impressions in hand colouring. To meet an anticipated demand for tenement maps, it was decided in 1871 to print lithographed editions of twenty-five copies in which the boundaries would appear in red.[2] The experiment was not repeated, presumably because the maps became out of date too quickly, but it was an interesting if little-known example of an Ordnance Survey property map.

Another chapter opened in 1881 with the Land Commission established by the Gladstone Government to buy estates for resale to the tenantry. Six-inch sales increased dramatically at this time, and the question of expediting the revision suddenly took on a new urgency. Accordingly, it was decided to revise two counties at once, to replace chaining as far as possible by intersections and alignments, and to provide additional personnel for the Irish six-inch by cutting down on town surveys.[3] Quicker reproductive methods, mooted as long ago as 1871, were also reconsidered; but in the absence of an Irish 1:2500 it seemed best to continue printing the six-inch as finely and clearly as possible, and the experimental publication of county Leitrim by lithography in 1885–8 did nothing to change this opinion.[4] Engraving was made less laborious, however, by omitting garden ornament, from 1885, and by a more sparing use of stipple; the latter was achieved by shading, not demesnes as such (which would in any case have been deprived of significance by the coming land reforms) but only 'parks and ornamental ground'.[5]

The pace of Irish rural change seemed to be accelerating when under the Ashbourne Act of 1885 purchasers were allowed to borrow the full price of their farms and to spread the repayments so thinly as to make buying cheaper than renting. To the officer in charge at Mountjoy, Colonel Sir Charles Wilson, it seemed hard for outgoing landowners to have to pay for any special surveys that were necessary, and he therefore revived the cause of an Irish cadastral map that James had dropped twelve years earlier. In the old days the six-inch scale had been justified on the ground that the typical Irish estate was a townland or block of townlands. If, as now appeared, the properties of the future were to be farms of twenty or thirty acres, there was a case for enlarging the scale of the national map. This line of reasoning was supported by the survival in many areas of the so-called 'rundale' system, in which tenants' holdings were intermixed in a confusion of minute parcels. Where rundale plots were unfenced, as was usually the case, it had not been customary to survey them, and in Griffith's valuation they were generally lumped together to yield a composite total. But if these scattered holdings were soon, under Government sponsorship, to become separate properties, then the consolidation of rundale plots and its essential preliminary, the mapping of rundale, became themselves a matter of public concern. And maps of rundale demanded something larger than six inches, as Wilson demonstrated to a Royal Commission in 1886 by exhibiting a specimen of it on both the larger and the smaller scale.[6] His persistence was rewarded a year later when the Treasury authorized a 1:2500 map of Ireland.

The result was a considerable increase in the Irish field force and a corresponding enlargement of the Mountjoy office. The relation between the two was now less intimate, however, than in the days when there had been only one revision division to cover the whole country. The new headquarters at Cork (1891–1911), Ennis (1891–1914) and Belfast (1902–22) were classed as 'English divisions working in Ireland', a description that was even more appropriate for the division that surveyed part of Ulster in 1900–1908 from a headquarters office in Carlisle.[7] The new survey, as these arrangements implied, was in the main a routine application of methods perfected on the other side of the channel. The chief difference from southern Britain was in the previous existence of a six-inch map, a fact that led Wilson, now Director General, and some at least of his successors, to hope that the 1:2500 might be replotted, as had been done in Lancashire and Yorkshire, in the manner that James had declared to be feasible thirty years before.[8] But the Irish survey had not been tight enough for this dubious practice to be generally adopted. The original primary triangulation proved adequate for 1:2500 purposes, but completely new secondary and tertiary triangulations were observed except where some counties, or parts of counties, were replotted from the original six-inch survey; as a rule, however, the detail had to be rechained. Although the Principal Triangulation had been published for about forty years, no attempt was made to base the new triangulation on it, and for a second time the survey was made county by county. Consequently suggestions for plotting the new maps on a single meridian were not taken up; on the contrary they were coaxed into the existing six-inch framework with an exact fit between sixteen new sheets and one old one.[9] Further, the old large-scale plans of towns based on the original triangulation were reduced to 1:2500 scale and dropped into the new survey with the minimum of adjustment. There was, therefore, an area round each of these towns where considerable fudging had to be done.

Despite the relevelling of Ireland in 1887–90 and the revival of contouring in 1890, there was no alteration in the low-water datum.[10] For the new levelling, the heights of the junction points as obtained by Cameron in 1855 were accepted and the relevelling adjusted to them. The lines connecting the twenty-two Airy tidal stations to the primary network were also relevelled, producing differences of up to 0.757 foot, but this may have been due to the instability of the original marks. Between the primary lines a network of secondary and tertiary lines was observed to give the heights required for the 1:2500 plans.

Place-names were changed as little as possible, and antiquities were dealt with by referring doubtful cases to experts nominated by the Royal Irish Academy, with results that varied sharply in merit. As in Britain, the six-inch map was retained both as a reduced form of the 1:2500 and as the largest scale for publishing 'mountain and moorland', a category that was revised on six-inch cards *pari passu* with the survey of cultivated areas. Mountain and moorland were interpreted rather liberally in Ireland to include the Aran Islands and several other closely settled areas.

The Irish 1:2500 proved more costly and laborious than Wilson had expected, in spite of its economical management. Much of the expense was due to the fine texture of the landscape, with enclosures at a density that sometimes exceeded a thousand per sheet, more than had been encountered in any rural area of Britain. Even so, progress had been faster than in the James era and the six-inch engravers were quite unable to keep up with it. After 1897 engraving at this scale was abandoned in favour of heliozincography (the 1:2500 had been zincographed from the beginning), and it may be seen as a tribute to the continuing importance of the Irish six-inch that successful efforts were made to introduce this technique without any diminution in sheet size.[11] But unlike the 1:2500 the new six-inch was not an all-Irish product, for it was not until 1915 that the Dublin office was equipped for photography; before that, the maps were printed at Mountjoy from plates prepared at Southampton. Their style was basically that of the English six-inch, with the interesting difference that Irish houses, being generally smaller, were shown in black, except in towns of more than 4000 people, instead of being cross-ruled. Given the choice between the six-inch and the 1:2500 Irishmen continued to favour the smaller scale. Even government departments like the Land Commission, for whose benefit the 1:2500 had been introduced, avoided using it except in areas of unusually close detail.[12]

Colour and its Problems

When he retired, Wilson placed the Irish 1:2500 first among the achievements of his directorate.[13] In England, however, he is more generally associated with a reaction against the cadastralism of James in favour of smaller scales. Irish opinion played little part in the new vogue for military and travelling maps. At the Dorington inquiry of 1892, for example, the only Irish voices came, predictably, from the Valuation Office.[14] And the main achievement of the Valuation Office at this period was to reverse the general trend by side-stepping the Board of Agriculture's new ban on further urban surveys; in 1894–5 it obtained permission for the Survey to produce a set of Irish town plans by photographically enlarging the 1:2500 to 1:1250.[15] But grateful or not, Ireland was given or promised all the new small-scale maps provided for Britain under the Dorington plan. Perhaps because of its limited purchasing power it was often slow to get its share. Sometimes, on the other hand, the country's very smallness and unimportance gave it a useful role as testing ground for semi-experimental novelties. The extent to which new Irish maps could actually be produced in Ireland varied according to their technological requirements, with a general tendency to diminish. In the copper-plate era Dublin and Southampton had stood on equal terms, and a number of the British maps were actually engraved at Mountjoy. But with greater technological complexity, and new economies of concentration, there was increasing pressure to centralize the final stages of the map-making process.

The first stage of the small-scale revolution, at least, presented no serious problems. After a long period of being revised in the office from the larger scales, the Irish one-inch was brought up to date in 1898–1901 by a field division that had been formed for that purpose in England.[16] Another revision, this time incomplete, took place in 1909–13. But although a few modern conventions were introduced, it was impossible to assimilate the map completely to its most recent English equivalent. For one thing, except for some greatly altered sheets it was engraved on duplicates of the existing plates, from which much of the original detail was brought forward. And in any case there were differences between the two countries that made it undesirable to carry uniformity too far. Thus Irish baronies and parishes, deprived of practical significance by the Local Government Act of 1898, were omitted after that year, their successors – the rural and urban districts – being shown in red on a special administrative one-inch edition of 1903–4. Then there were townland names, which had always presented difficulties at this scale. To omit them was to leave the map unpleasantly bare, for Ireland has few of the farm names which diversify the English one-inch; to include them can be confusing, for where the settlement pattern is dispersed, as in most parts of the country, there is nothing to attach them to. As a compromise, the new map selected townland names to give a general name-density of about one per square mile, and spaced out the letters in a way that distinguished them from names of villages and hamlets.[17] The chief weakness of the revised one-inch was the absence of contours from most of the map. Some sheets did not have their contours engraved until 1919.

It was in the field of colour printing that Mountjoy suffered most from the changing technological balance of the new century. As early as 1889 one of its printers had produced some impressive two-colour hill work by transferring a hachured sheet to stone, scraping off all the detail except the hills, and double-printing the result with an outline impression of the same sheet; but these experiments were interrupted after a report from the Survey's Dublin agent that there would be no worthwhile market for coloured maps in Ireland, and the only similar work done in the next few years was an unpublished military manoeuvre map of the Curragh district.[18] Double-printing was also made possible by engraving separate hill plates for the last three sheets of James's hill map,[19] but the resulting mixture of black and brown was put in the shade by the 'fully coloured' version of the 1898–1901 revision which appeared in 1901–6. The latter was produced from a specially installed steam press, in brown for hachures and tree symbols, green for woods, blue for rivers and waterlines, and burnt sienna for roads, as well as black. It was an unexpectedly difficult task, partly because of the inexperience of the staff and partly because of the extreme fineness (an old Mountjoy characteristic) of the engraved work to be transferred. In the end a large part of the map was printed at Southampton.[20] But in spite of its indifferent technical success, the fully-coloured soon took the lead in public favour, selling an average of fifteen copies per sheet in 1909–12 as compared with 4.4 copies of the black outline and 0.4 copies of the black hill map over the same period.[21] In the light of these figures it was considered pointless to continue with the fourth variety of one-inch map, started in 1909, which offered a black outline, newly revised and in some cases contoured, with brown hachures printed from separate plates.[22] A portion of this last map had found its way into print, but it was soon almost as completely forgotten as the quarter-inch triotint map.

From 1904 onwards almost all Irish colour work was carried out in England. It included the 1905 edition of a ten-mile map originally issued by James and a new quarter-inch map published in sixteen inconveniently small sheets in 1904–5. Both these maps were also available in black and white. In 1912–18 there followed two varieties of a coloured half-inch map of Ireland in twenty-five sheets, one with contours and hachures in brown, the other with layer colouring. The latter was described by Close as one of the most legible topographical maps in existence and chosen as one of the illustrations for his *Text Book of Topographical Surveying*. It later formed the basis for the standard official topographic map of the Irish Republic. Of equal interest are the fully-coloured one-inch tourist maps of the environs of Killarney (1913), Cork (1918) and Dublin (1918). Despite the Irish subjects of these coloured maps, none of them can be said to belong to the history of the Dublin office. There was a revival of colour printing at Mountjoy in 1915, but this was overtaken by events before it had done more than produce a draft edition of the Dublin one-inch geological map.

Towards Home Rule

From the nineties onwards, political trends were running counter to the centripetal forces operating within the Survey itself. For the first time since the memoir crisis, the affairs of Mountjoy occupied the stage at Westminster. Some of the criticisms now levelled at the Survey probably had little significance outside the ritual of parliamentary obstruction that was practised by the Irish party in the House of Commons at this period, and a good deal of it applied as much to Britain as to Ireland: slowness of revision and publication, for example, or – another old favourite – poor quality of paper. But some grievances were more distinctively national. At a time of heavy Irish unemployment, the transfer of office work from Dublin to Southampton encountered strong opposition, and there were even proposals, echoing the controversies of Larcom's day, for an entirely separate Irish survey establishment on the analogy of the one provided in 1906 for the Irish geological survey. Meanwhile the Gaelic revival had provided new grounds for attacking the Survey's treatment of place-names, while other complaints ranged from the non-publication of the old memoirs to the fact that Roman Catholic churches were described on the maps as chapels. But whether through apathy or as an expression of approval, the Survey's Irish output encountered very little local criticism of a purely cartographical character.

Close's directorate, distinguished as it was in many other respects, was not a happy time for the Irish office. From about 1912 the approach of Home Rule produced a certain reluctance to carry important new projects across the channel from Southampton,[23] and the 1914–18 war brought a considerable reduction of output (the 1:2500 was finished just in time to avoid the crisis) and of staff. Behind the scenes, the history of the 1840s was quietly repeating itself. Re-enacting the part once played by Mulcaster, Close prepared for Home Rule by drawing a sharp distinction between the cadastral and the military. The Irish six-inch, together with the unremunerative and burdensome 1:2500, under whose weight the Survey had uttered many a groan in its recent annual reports, he proposed to hand over to independent survey departments in Dublin and Belfast; the one-inch and everything smaller would remain at Southampton as an imperial service.[24] However, when the separation took place in 1922, the arrangements that were made were rather different from those Close had in mind.

Notes

1 For a general account of the subject, see E. R. Hooker, *Readjustments of Agricultural Tenure in Ireland* (1938).
2 Mountjoy Letters 3576 (1870). OSR 1870: PP 1871, C. 301, LVI.
3 Mountjoy Letters 4169 (1880), 4279 (1881).
4 Mountjoy Letters 3601 (1871), 3910 (1877–8), 4668 (1884–5). OSR 1885: PP 1886, C. 4684, LII.
5 Mountjoy letters 8370 (1890).

6 Mountjoy letters 4765 (1885). *Report on the Land Law (Ireland) etc.* 1887, Map B. J. Farquharson, 'Twelve Years work on the Ordnance Survey, 1887–1899', *Geographical Journal* 1900, XV, p. 597 (discussion).

7 OSR 1899–1900: PP 1900, Cd. 327, LXVIII. OSR 1900–1: PP 1901, Cd. 709, LX. OSR 1901–2: PP 1902, Cd. 1243, LXXXIII. For a short history of the Irish 1:2500 see OSR 1914–15, p. 2: PP 1914–16, Cd. 7953, XXXI.

8 Mountjoy letters 5049 (1887–9), 8568 (1890–91), 4934 (1899), 5503 (1899–1900), 5507 (1899–1900), 5610 (1900), 5620 (1900). C. W. Wilson, 'Methods and Processes of the Ordnance Survey', *Scottish Geographical Magazine* 1891, VII, p. 250.

9 Mountjoy letters 8499 (1900), 5004 (1899). N. MacNeill, 'The Ordnance Survey of Ireland', *Administration* (Dublin), 1966, XIV, p. 18.

10 Mountjoy letters 1773 (1894). Levelling office letter book (1887–90) in the OSO Dublin.

11 Mountjoy letters 3989 (1897–8).

12 *Report of Her Majesty's Commissioners of Inquiry into the Procedure and Practice and the Methods of Valuation followed by the Land Commission, The Land Judges Court, and the Civil Bill Courts in Ireland, under the Land Acts and the Land Purchase Acts*: PP 1898, C. 8734, 8859, XXXV, qq 4526–6257.

13 Southampton circulars, 13 March 1894, in the OSO Dublin.

14 *Report of the Departmental Committee appointed by the Board of Agriculture to inquire into the condition of the Ordnance Survey*, PP 1893–4, C. 6895, LXXII, Appendix II, pp. 232–3.

15 Mountjoy letters 1676 (1894–5).

16 Mountjoy letters 4008 (1897–8).

17 Mountjoy letters 4880 (1898–9).

18 Mountjoy letters 7026 (1889), 5267 (1899).

19 Mountjoy letters 1765 (1894).

20 Mountjoy letters 5060, 5508B, 6681, 7707, 7838 (1899–1905).

21 Mountjoy letters 14423 (1912).

22 Mountjoy letters 14509 (1912). Officers' memos, 1908–10, no. 89.

23 P. G. Madden, 'The Ordnance Survey of Ireland', *Irish Sword* 1962, V, p. 163.

24 PRO OS 1/6/S03 (1913–16). OSR 1920–21: PP 1921, Cmnd. 1308, XV.

21
A Geodetic Revival
–The Test
of the Triangulation
and the
Second Geodetic
Levelling
1909–1921

The Test of the Triangulation 1909–12

After the completion and publication of the Principal Triangulation in 1858, little geodetic work was done during the rest of the nineteenth century; during this time the trigonometrical parties were fully occupied in observing the secondary and tertiary triangulation required for the 1:2500 mapping of the United Kingdom. But meanwhile great improvements were being made in the design of theodolites, giving increased accuracy and speed in use combined with lightness in construction. Equally important was the discovery in 1896 of 'Invar', a nickel-steel alloy with a very low coefficient of expansion, which could be rolled into wires or tapes and used for measurement when suspended in catenary. This enormously increased the speed of base measurement and also allowed it to proceed over comparatively rough ground. However, any doubts about the Principal Triangulation were concerned with the angular measurements, not with the bases.

The probable error of an observed angle of the Principal Triangulation was $\pm 1''.23$ and about the turn of the century the question arose as to whether this was good enough to stand comparison with the more modern European geodetic frameworks which had an angular probable error about one-third that of the British work.[1] Between 1904 and 1908 there were discussions in the Royal Astronomical Society and at meetings of the British Association for the Advancement of Science, and in 1908 a test measurement was authorized in an area remote from the Lough Foyle and Salisbury Plain Bases to find out if any error had accumulated in the Principal Triangulation.

A base was chosen on the southern shore of the Moray Firth near Lossiemouth with an extension to join it to the stations at Knock of Grange, Corriehabbie and Mormond Hill, which formed part of Figure 9 of the Principal Triangulation. In September and October 1909 the base of about 4.5 miles was measured in sections, each section being measured three times with Invar tapes 100 feet long in catenary. All measurements were in terms of the ten-foot Ordnance intermediate bar $O1_1$ which had been standardized at the *Bureau International des Poids et Mesures*, Sèvres, in 1906, by J. R. Benoit of France and Major W. J. Johnston of the Ordnance Survey. The bar was tested against two four-metre bars in terms of the international metre and converted to standard inches by the factor: 1 international metre = 39.370 113 standard inches. It was deduced that at 55.4°F the length of bar $O1_1$ was 119.995 983 9 standard inches. The logarithms of lengths expressed in standard inches were converted to inches of O_1 by adding a constant 1.999 998 55.[2]

For standardizing the Invar tapes it was proposed to use bar $O1_1$ to lay out a one-hundred-foot base at Southampton, but the terminal marks of this bar were originally on the centre line and were unsuitable for bringing into coincidence with the Invar plaques at the ends of the base. Additional marks on the flanges of the bar had been made at Sèvres, but it was found that these were rapidly deteriorating. So two pairs of platinum plugs were let into the flanges of another bar $O1_2$* which was compared with bar $O1_1$ and then used to set out the base.

* $O1_2$ was a bar similar in all respects to $O1_1$

The final value for the Lossiemouth Base is given as 23 525.979 44 standard feet,[3] not the feet of bar O_1 used for the Principal Triangulation. The difference is small, reducing the base by one part in 300 000 to 23 525.900 feet of O_1 at 62°F.

The base extension suffered from considerable lateral refraction at Bin Hill where the large masonry 'Earl of Seafield's Cairn' was only 19 inches from the line of the ray from Bin Hill to the west end of the base at some 40 feet from the instrument. In 1912 Bin Hill and four other stations were reobserved; in addition to those from ground level at Bin Hill, observations were also made from a scaffold which raised the line of sight about 10 feet above the cairn.

The triangle Mormond Hill – Corriehabbie – Knock of Grange is poorly shaped (the angle at Knock of Grange being over 136°), and the adjustment of the test triangulation gave differences of about −1″ at Mormond Hill and +1″ at Knock of Grange from the adjusted angles of the Principal Triangulation. The sides as then calculated were all shorter than the corresponding sides of the Principal Triangulation as shown in the accompanying table:

Side	Principal Triangulation	Test Triangulation	Test–Principal Triangulation	Ratio
Mormond Hill–Corriehabbie	feet of O_1 247 660.01	feet of O_1 247 655.91	feet of O_1 −4.10	One part in 60 000
Corriehabbie–Knock of Grange	120 524.16	120 521.03	−3.13	39 000
Knock of Grange–Mormond Hill	145 861.40	145 859.85	−1.55	94 000

At this same time the French had been reobserving and recalculating their meridional arc, including the remeasurement of its bases. Although the results were not complete, the French were able to provide the latest value of the side Cassel – Les Harlettes, which formed part of the cross-Channel connection of 1861–2.[4] This side depended only upon the Paris Base to which the Principal and test triangulations could therefore be related. Working from the measured length of the Lossiemouth Base, the calculated lengths of the other bases were all longer than measured by the following fractions:[5]

Salisbury Plain	1 part in 45 000
Lough Foyle	88 000
Paris	42 000

The conclusions from the test triangulation were that the linear errors of the Principal Triangulation were similar to those to be expected from modern triangulation carried out in chains of triangles over similar distances.[6] The likely error of any side was about one inch in one mile. If a new triangulation were made it would be unlikely that the distance from Dover in the south to Saxavord in the north would be altered by more than 25 yards in 700 miles. It could be concluded that the agreement of the bases at Lough Foyle and Salisbury Plain was not accidental, and that the Principal Triangulation was of a standard comparable to that of work in Europe and elsewhere.

But there was still a possibility that there were errors in the individual figures of Clarke's adjustment which had been masked by the great figural strength of the triangulation. In the 1920s test computations of the figures covering East Anglia and Yorkshire confirmed that there were local errors which exceeded the average error of the whole Principal Triangulation. No funds were then available either to repeat the triangulation or to carry out further tests.

Minor Triangulation and Meridians

According to Winterbotham in *The National Plans,*[7] there were originally forty-two county origins in Great Britain. In 1912 Close proposed that the number should be reduced to eleven, and six counties (four in Scotland and two in England) were transferred to neighbouring origins before financial stringency put a stop to the work in 1919. However, diagrams in *The National Plans* show thirty-eight origins in all and *Notes on Minor Triangulation,*[8] reprinted in 1933, gives details of forty-four origins, including the six transferred and Caerloch, the origin for Kincardine, which *The National Plans* shows as on The Buck (Aberdeen). These discrepancies are not easy to resolve as the Ordnance Survey possesses no list of the original county origins or of their first accepted geographical co-ordinates, and so it is difficult to establish the initial situation and the subsequent history.

It would appear that the six counties transferred between 1912 and 1919 were:

Scotland: Roxburgh, Stirling and Dumbarton to Lanark Church Spire.

West Lothian to The Buck.

England: Northumberland to Brandon Down.

Essex to St Paul's Cathedral.

Trigonometrical data were also prepared for the transfer of Selkirk, Dumfries, Cambridge, Huntingdon and Suffolk.

The co-ordinates of the primary and secondary stations to be transferred were rigorously computed on the new origin, but the tertiary stations were calculated from the old angle books on the new framework. It was a somewhat laborious procedure but the work was accomplished with the very limited man-power available immediately before and during the First World War. In 1915 the prefix 'N' was added to the sheet numbers of counties published on a different meridian from that previously used – the first counties to be affected in this way were Essex and Stirling.

Although Close's scheme was materially to improve the convenience of the large-scale plans, it also provided problems for the future. Winterbotham, who as a captain had been the officer in charge of the Trigonometrical and Topographical Division at Southampton in 1913–14, was to claim in 1934, when he was Director General, that Close altered some of the meridians purely for the sake of eliminating them from the cartographic system, and indeed, as in the case of Middlesex and Essex, 'had introduced far worse troubles of "fudge" than he cured in convenience'.[9]

In 1924 H. L. P. Jolly, Research Officer of the Ordnance Survey, made an investigation to see if the secondary and tertiary triangulations could be related to the Principal Triangulation.[10] He found a very confused state of affairs. Some initial distances in the secondary work were taken from the Principal Triangulation; near Rhuddlan Marsh they were from Mudge's values. Very few of the surviving calculation books were dated. Some triangles were computed by the chord method, others were calculated by Legendre's theorem. He concluded that it would be difficult to bring the secondary and tertiary systems into sympathy with the Principal Triangulation.

But the field observation books of the secondary and tertiary triangulations were still available and were entirely reliable. The positions that had previously been obtained from them were difficult to use because the observations had been related either to Mudge's out-of-date triangulation or to the Principal Triangulation before its adjustment was complete. In the 1920s it was decided to check a number of the old secondary stations and, if necessary, to put in new centre marks, a process known as 'restoration'. Clarke's positions for the Principal Triangulation were accepted and from these the co-ordinates of the restored secondary stations were calculated using the old angle books. The general results were very good but the work was abandoned when the retriangulation was authorized.

The Magnetic Survey 1913–15

The magnetic resurvey of the British Isles was begun in 1913 by the Royal Society, but the co-operation of the Ordnance Survey was essential for its successful completion. When the first magnetic survey had been carried out in 1885–95 under Sir Arthur Rücker and Sir Edward Thorpe, the Ordnance Survey had supplied the maps needed in the field, and the same assistance was again asked for by the Royal Society. Close willingly complied, since the values of magnetic declination and those of the annual change were of special interest to the Ordnance Survey.

Close and Captain E. O. Henrici (in charge of the Levelling Division) represented the Ordnance Survey on the Royal Society committee for the magnetic survey, and by February 1914 one observing party of three men from the Ordnance Survey had been formed to assist Dr George Walker, who directed the work. A new four-inch micrometer-theodolite, supplied by Troughton and Simms, was to be used in fixing the points from which the observations were to be made. By March 1915 Dr Walker had observed 112 points out of the scheduled total of 200. Close was quite justified in pointing out that without the co-operation of his Department, progress would not have amounted to half of what was actually accomplished.[11]

During the course of the magnetic survey Captain B. F. E. Keeling, the officer in charge of the Trigonometrical Division at Southampton, made some interesting discoveries about the accuracy of the tertiary triangulation. In providing Walker with azimuths the Survey had apparently guaranteed a precision of 30 seconds of arc. But the azimuths were determined by reference to the sides of the third order triangulation, and in some instances it was found that they could not be guaranteed to within two or even three minutes. The original tertiary calculation books had unfortunately been destroyed and, as Keeling remarked, 'further investigation would mean rather heavy work'.[12] He proposed to deal with the inaccuracies either by recomputing a portion of the relevant triangulation from the angle books, or by determination of the azimuths using astronomical methods. Close chose the latter remedy and commented on the great misfortune of the calculation books having been destroyed:

> I have always felt that the trig records have been badly managed and wrote on the subject to Farquharson in 1897 . . . As to the trig records, I should be glad if O Trig would fit out a scheme for the creation of a suitable room in which to house them.[13]

The special repository for the records does not seem to have been made, and the problems of inadequate documentation were to be keenly felt in future years.

Walker's work was eventually published in the *Philosophical Transactions* of the Royal Society for 1918,[14] occupying a whole volume. All the stations of the magnetic survey had been marked on the ground; these now assumed a national importance and became the responsibility of the Ordnance Survey and were thenceforward subject to the various Acts of Parliament which related to the Survey.

In February 1919 a committee composed of representatives of the Royal Society, the Ordnance Survey and the British Association proposed that the Ordnance Survey should periodically carry out future magnetic surveys, advised by a committee of the Royal Society. Two months later the Board of Agriculture and Fisheries approved the joint committee's recommendations.[15]

The Second Geodetic Levelling of England and Wales 1912–21

The areas between the main levelling lines of the initial levelling[16] had been single-levelled to provide the heights required for the 1:2500 plans. When these were first revised, both primary and branch lines were relevelled where necessary and all new work closed on old bench-marks. At the second revision from 1904 onwards similar methods were adopted but the levelling soon ran into difficulties, mainly because many bench-marks, new and old, were unstable or had been disturbed. It was apparent that the levelling was accurate enough only for local engineering purposes and that it could not indicate if there had been any alteration in the general ground level or determine any relative movement of land and sea. The prime need was for a new levelling based on stable bench-marks and executed with modern instruments and by modern methods, in both of which there had been great advances. Accordingly, in 1912, a new geodetic levelling was begun.

For the Second Geodetic Levelling, tidal stations were set up at Newlyn, Felixstowe and Dunbar, and 115 Fundamental Bench-Marks, about 30 miles apart, were constructed on solid rock at sites chosen with the help of the Geological Survey (Plate 14). The war considerably delayed the work and the economies which followed curtailed the extent of the network so that parts of south-east England, East Anglia, Wales and the south of Scotland had to be omitted. In the end only 86 of the Fundamental Bench-Marks were incorporated.

Zeiss levels were used for the levelling. This instrument had its spirit-level fixed to the side of the telescope and embodied a prism device so that the leveller could see the bubble without moving from the eye-piece end of the level. By means of a vertical screw, the telescope and spirit-level could be tilted until the images of the end of the bubble were brought into coincidence as seen through the prism. Some instruments had a parallel plate attachment by means of which the leveller could read the staff to the third decimal of a foot and estimate the fourth place from the reading on a graduated drum.

The levelling staves originally used were made in the Ordnance Survey workshops but a better version, designed in the Ordnance Survey and manufactured by the Cambridge and Paul instrument company, was taken into use in 1914. This staff was made from one piece of wood with an Invar strip, about 0.5 inch wide, let into a groove in its face. The Invar was firmly secured at the bottom of the staff but was otherwise free to move lengthways. It had graduations at 0.02 foot intervals, engraved and painted black. Each staff was provided with circular bubbles at two different heights so that the staff-holder could see if the staff was vertical. There were two handles on the staff against which sticks were held so that the staff could be kept still.

In addition to the Fundamental Bench-Marks, special gunmetal marks called flush brackets were cemented into the faces of buildings about every mile along the primary lines. This type of bench-mark was designed to support the levelling staff by means of a bracket which could be hooked on. In between the flush brackets, bolts or rivets were let into the horizontal surface of a brick or stone about every quarter-mile.

The datum for the new levelling was mean sea-level at Newlyn as derived from the mean of hourly readings for six years from 1 May 1915 to 30 April 1921. The Dunbar tidal station started operating on 1 May 1913 and that at Felixstowe on 9 July 1917. From the readings to 30 April 1921, mean sea-level at Dunbar appeared to be 0.81 foot above, and at Felixstowe, 0.04 foot below, the Newlyn Datum. Although part of the difference at Dunbar was caused by the lower average barometric pressure, the inescapable conclusion seemed to be that mean sea-level at Newlyn and Dunbar differed.

In calculating the levelling, recent refinements, in particular those due to Lallemand of France,* were incorporated. These took count of the distinction between 'dynamic' and 'orthometric' heights which arises because the Earth is not a stationary sphere but approximates to a spheroid (or ellipsoid) rotating daily about its shorter, polar, axis. Gravity is strongest at the poles and weakest at the Equator, and to raise unit mass from sea-level to a given orthometric height (i.e. a height expressed in the ordinary units of measurement) requires more work at the poles than elsewhere on the Earth. One may imagine a series of 'equipotential surfaces' surrounding the Earth, for any pair of which the work done to raise unit mass from one to the other is uniform throughout. The 'geoid' (or an idealized sea-level) is one such surface and is the datum to which heights are usually referred. Above the geoid there are an infinite number of equipotential surfaces, the orthometric heights of which are least at the poles and greatest at the equator although the dynamic height is uniform throughout any one surface. In spirit-levelling the 'horizontal' line to which the height difference in each space levelled is referred is (or should be) tangential to the local equipotential surface. To this extent therefore the operation determines differences of dynamic height and a small correction is required for levelling extended in a north/south direction to reduce bench-mark heights to their more generally useful orthometric values. The correction (to be added to the height of the more northerly mark) is:

$$0.005302 \text{ H} \sin 2\phi \delta\phi \sin 1''$$

where H is the mean height of the two bench-marks,

ϕ is their mean latitude

$\delta\phi$ is the difference in latitude in seconds of arc.

The derivation of this correction is explained in *The Second Geodetic Levelling*[17] which gives the orthometric height differences of all lines levelled and also the dynamic heights of all Fundamental Bench-Marks.

The differences of orthometric height between the Fundamental Bench-Marks of the Second Geodetic Levelling were calculated, giving values for the closing error of each circuit. The worst closing error was in the circuit including Matlock, amounting to 0.4771 foot in a circuit of 290 miles. The closing errors were distributed by a least squares solution, the maximum correction being 0.1092 foot on the line from Hibaldstow to Matlock. The total length of the levelling was 3009 miles.

In 1912 the International Association of Geodesy (IAG) agreed to classify levelling according to accuracy criteria worked out by Lallemand.[18] For these, three types of error were specified:

ηr The probable accidental error of the levelling derived from forward and back levelling differences for each space between bench-marks throughout the network. This figure included an allowance for the probable systematic error.

σr The probable systematic error derived from the apparent systematic differences between forward and back levelling of whole lines (or substantial sections of lines).

σR The probable systematic error derived from the least square analysis of circuit misclosures.

For 'levelling of high precision' (the most accurate category) the limiting values prescribed and those attained by the Ordnance Survey were as follows:

IAG limiting values	OS values
ηr ±1.0 mm per km	±0.46 mm per km
σr ±0.2 mm per km	±0.18 mm per km
σR ±0.2 mm per km	±0.12 mm per km

It was evident therefore that the Ordnance Survey's work was well up to the best international standards.

---

* Charles Lallemand (1857–1938) was head of the *Service du nivellement général de la France* from the time of its creation in 1884, until his retirement in 1928. He became President of the International Union of Geodesy and Geophysics in 1919 and held this office until 1933.

Notes

1 H. St J. L. Winterbotham, *An Investigation into the Accuracy of the Principal Triangulation of the United Kingdom*, Ordnance Survey Professional Papers, New Series, no. 2 (HMSO 1913), p. 3.

2 *An Account of a Geodetic Base Line at Lossiemouth, in 1909 etc.*, Ordnance Survey Professional Papers, New Series, no. 1 (HMSO 1912), p. 18.

3 *Ibid.* p. 25.

4 Winterbotham, OS Professional Papers no. 2, p. 7.

5 *Ibid.* p. 17.

6 *Ibid.* p. 4.

7 H. St J. L. Winterbotham, *The National Plans*, OS Professional Papers no. 16, (HMSO 1934), p. 37.

8 *Notes on the Minor Trigonometrical Work of the Ordnance Survey*, compiled under the Direction of Colonel C. F. Close etc. (HMSO 1914).

9 Winterbotham, 'Handover Notes' to MacLeod, p. 73. Ordnance Survey Library.

10 H. L. P. Jolly, A Report on the Investigation of the old Triangulation and Calculation Books. Typescript dated 11 March 1924. Computations Branch O.S.

11 PRO OS 1/8. Close to Major Hall, War Office, dated 24 March 1915.

12 PRO OS 1/8. Memorandum by B. F. E. Keeling regarding the accuracy of the tertiary triangulation.

13 PRO OS 1/8. Memorandum dated 11 May 1915.

14 George Walker, 'The Magnetic Re-survey of the British Isles for the Epoch Jan. 1, 1915', *Phil. Trans.* 1918.

15 PRO OS 1/8.

16 See p. 145.

17 A. J. Wolff and H. L. P. Jolly, *The Second Geodetic Levelling of England & Wales 1912–21* (HMSO 1922).

18 *Comptes Rendues de la Conférence Géodésique Internationale, 1912*, II, p. 252.

22
The
Ordnance
Survey
1914–1918

The Survey and The First World War

At the outbreak of war in August 1914 the Ordnance Survey was one of the few government departments equipped and prepared for its war-time role; in the following four years the greater part of the organization was turned entirely to war work, leaving only a small fraction to continue the peace-time programme. The contribution of the Ordnance Survey to the war effort included over thirty-two million maps supplied to the Forces – a prodigious volume of production at this time.

The involvement of the Ordnance Survey in purely military matters was far greater in the First World War than in the Second. The provision of survey units, their reinforcements and stores, and the formation of the Overseas Branch of the Ordnance Survey were all within the Director General's sphere of responsibility. But the recognition by the Army of the importance of artillery survey, in the development of which the survey units of Royal Engineers played a leading part during the war, led to the transfer of this function to the Royal Artillery in 1919. This was one of the reasons for the decline of Engineer survey in the 1920s which eventually helped to bring about the separation of the Ordnance Survey from the Royal Engineer military survey organization in the 1940s.

The problems of map production and supply were not new to the British Army, but the scale of these operations in the Great War was unprecedented. On the outbreak of war the General Staff was wrongly convinced that the struggle would be short and decisive. This attitude was reflected in the initial lack of provision for survey support – a complacent reliance on the suitability of existing French maps pervaded a generally unprepared GHQ. Indeed, three survey sections were held in readiness by the Ordnance Survey but the War Office decided that their services would not be needed.[1]

As the war progressed through its three operational phases – mobilization and deployment of the British Expeditionary Force and the manoeuvres of 1914, ending with the so-called 'race for the sea'; the beginning of trench warfare and the static war of attrition; and the final mobile phase – so the character of the survey work changed to meet the varying demands made on it.

THE WESTERN FRONT

During the first months of the war, the Ordnance Survey was deprived of almost all its military and most of its civilian strength. Sixteen of the twenty officers on the active list left immediately to join the British Expeditionary Force and were inadequately replaced by six retired officers. Of the 326 warrant officers, NCOs and men present at the commencement of hostilities, 322 were in active service within a year. In response to Kitchener's appeal for a Volunteer Army, 623 of the 808 civilian staff eligible to enlist had joined up by June 1915.[2]

The full complement of the Topographical Sub-section of the General Staff at GHQ in France was at first one officer, in the person of Major E. M. Jack RE (General Staff Officer 3rd Class) and a clerk.[3] Known as Maps GHQ, such a ludicrously small group could do little to remedy the cartographic deficiencies suffered by commanders in the field in the first months of the war. The *Official History* records the difficulties experienced in the retreat from Mons:

> . . . with the uncorrected maps [French 1:80 000] then at the disposal of the British Force, a commander might well hesitate before involving his columns, with the enemy on their heels, in so large and blind a mass of trees.[4]

Again, late in August 1914, at Le Cateau, although troop dispositions had been made on the ground by II Corps:

. . . it was difficult to identify places by the map, for the only one then available was the French uncontoured hachured map of the 1:80 000, to which the British officers were not accustomed.[5]

It was perhaps in response to problems such as these that in the same month Maps GHQ was augmented by one clerk and a box car. In addition to the small headquarters section there was also a Printing Company RE, part of which was located at GHQ, but its role became uncertain when, in October 1914, the two Corps sections provided for the First and Second Armies were sent back to GHQ, minus their transport, as unnecessary encumbrances.[6]

This state of affairs was soon changed. The importance of maps and survey first became clear in the Battle of the Aisne in September 1914, when the Germans 'stumbled on the discovery which shaped the First World War; men in trenches with machine guns could beat off all but the most formidable attacks'.[7] The cartographic implications of this change in the method of warfare was far-reaching. It was during this battle that the earliest demands were made for large-scale maps on which to depict trenches. It was also the only part of the British battle-area which had been mapped on the French Topographical Survey's new scale of 1:50 000, and throughout the lengthy duration of the battle practically all artillery shooting was done by obtaining ranges and angles of sight from the map.[8] It was to be some time before 'map shooting' was to be possible for other less well-mapped areas.

It was apparent that the slender resources of Maps GHQ would not be able to cope with the new demands for maps, but even so, the provision of a survey unit was accidental. During the retreat from Mons and the Battle of the Marne, it was evident that German artillery fire was directed to its target by signals from aircraft. This possibility had also been recognized in Britain before the war by Fuller, when he wrote:

It appears to me that special aeroplanists will have to be trained for artillery observation, and that these and their aeroplanes will have to be allotted to those guns detailed to carry out the decisive artillery attack.[9]

It should not, therefore, have needed a demonstration by the Germans to prompt the British into the practical application of artillery and aircraft co-operation. When ordered by the War Office to devise a similar system, the Ordnance Survey set up experiments on Salisbury Plain in October 1914 to fix the position of an aircraft when it signalled, using a theodolite and plane-table. Once the viability of the method had been demonstrated, the 1st Ranging Section RE, commanded by Captain H. St J. L. Winterbotham, and staffed by four other ranks, accompanied the 8th Divisional Artillery to France in November 1914. As such, it was the first survey unit to be sent out to France by the Ordnance Survey, but even before it arrived its methods had been superseded by Lieutenants Lewis and James of the Royal Flying Corps, who had begun to adapt wireless telegraphy to artillery observation during the Battle of the Aisne.[10] Thus it happened that the small nucleus of expert surveyors in the 1st Ranging Section was available for field survey work at a time which coincided with the advent of static warfare and the recognition of the need for large-scale maps. Augmented by eleven topographers from the Ordnance Survey and three Royal Engineer units which were already in France, the Ranging Section began surveying in January 1915.

The 1st Ranging Section proved the worth of a highly trained survey team in the preparations for the Battle of Neuve Chapelle in March 1915. By the time the British guns were deployed to support the first stage of the offensive,

the positions of most heavy and siege batteries had been fixed by survey, and the maps and bearings of all prominent points in the German area accurately ascertained . . . by the Ranging Section RE, under Captain Winterbotham, working under Major E. M. Jack of the Topographical Section, General Staff.[11]

It was at this early stage that Winterbotham earned almost legendary fame as a surveyor with the gunners, as Jack recalled after the war:

when he [Winterbotham] fixed the position of one of the first 15-inch howitzers that arrived in France, and laid out directions and told the gunners that if they fired in a certain direction with correct elevation, they would inevitably hit a distant and invisible target, they attributed to him occult powers, and called him 'The Astrologer' – a name that has stuck to him ever since.[12]

Winterbotham's section was renamed the 1st Ranging and Survey Section in April 1915, and was transferred from the 8th Artillery Division to Maps GHQ, under the direction of Jack.

The main task of the Section in 1915 was to make an entirely new map at the scale of 1:20 000. The decision to undertake a new survey was based on the total inadequacy of enlargements to that scale from the existing French 1:80 000. In one month the Ordnance Survey plane-tablers of the 1st Ranging and Survey Section covered the whole of the British front, extending from Ypres to Béthune. The comparative superiority of this still crude material over previous maps demonstrated the need for continued improvements in field survey work. The 1:20 000 was to become a most highly valued map: ideal as a trench map and suitable for artillery, it also covered enough ground to allow planning for troop movements.

As the deep lacerations of trench warfare spread across the face of France and Flanders, so the survey organization under Jack expanded in an effort to maintain a cartographic record of the front lines. The strength of the British Expeditionary Force grew and was distributed among the new First. Second and Third Armies. The 1st Ranging and Survey Section likewise expanded and between July and September 1915 was divided into three topographical sections, one assigned to each Army, incorporating maps and printing sections. Each Army thus had its own map-making organization. Winterbotham, now a major, was the commanding officer of the Topographical Section, Third Army.

It was this Section which, in October 1915, published the first British 1:10 000 map (57D SE4 Ovillers),[13] another scale which proved to be essential in trench warfare. The ground survey of forward areas was a particularly dangerous operation and, in order to avoid it whenever possible, compilations were made using the old French cadastral plans as a reasonably accurate framework which could be filled in with information obtained from air photographs.

The expansion of the Western Front was matched by a further growth in the survey organization. The topographical sections, unable to cope with the mass of work, gained an increase in complement and were transformed into field survey companies (the word 'field' distinguishing them from the survey companies of the Ordnance Survey) in February 1916. It was at this point that Captain M. N. MacLeod RE became the commanding officer of the 4th Field Survey Company RE. In 1917 the survey strength was again reorganized into larger units known as field survey battalions.

MacLeod was to specialize in mapping from air photographs.[14] Air photography of enemy positions was first carried out by the Royal Flying Corps on 13 September 1914,[15] but the technique was initially ineffective, failing to provide the vital evidence of enemy preparation for attack. As aerial photography improved in quality it became more and more valuable in the elucidation of topographical and military detail such as the depth and nature of trenches, positions of trench-mortars, ammunition stores and gun emplacements, and early in the war the Ordnance Survey seconded draughtsmen to Maps GHQ to transfer this detail from the air photographs to the maps. There was, however, an intractable problem in using such photographs – the difficulty of removing the variations in scale caused by differences in the height of the ground and by non-vertical exposures. It was eventually solved by MacLeod who invented a device which produced an approximate rectification of the photographs so that, in flat country, detail could be traced-off within a framework of points provided by ground survey.

At the beginning of the war, observation from aircraft contributed greatly to the locating of hostile batteries, compensating for the early unreliability in flash-spotting and sound-ranging,[16] which were later to become the most important methods of counter-battery work. Flash-spotting, which entailed the observation of gun flashes and the direction of counter-fire onto them, was revolutionized by the development of the 'flash and buzzer board',[17] which allowed telephone communication between the Group Headquarters and the survey posts, for synchronizing all observations. The locating of the enemy gun positions was then done by intersection, for which an essential prerequisite was the accurate fixation of the positions of the observation posts. This survey was necessarily undertaken at first by the topographical sections because of the lack of gunners trained in surveying, but to make good this deficiency the Third Army Field Survey Company set up a most successful school of instruction in March 1916 for Observation Group personnel.

The principle of sound-ranging was to locate a gun by recording the times at which its report reached various fixed positions; the technique used by the British was based on the French system designed by Lucien Bull of the Institut Marey in Paris, and developed by him and Lieutenant W. L. Bragg RA.* By the winter of 1916–17, twenty sound-ranging sections had been formed and were allocated to the field survey companies. In the battle zones, frequently shrouded by a pall of smoke or gas, or visually obliterated by mist or driving rain, this was often the only practicable method of locating enemy batteries. Its success can be judged by the following captured German Order dated June 1917:

> *Group Order.* In consequence of the excellent sound-ranging of the English, I forbid any battery to fire alone when the whole section is quiet, expecially in east wind. Should there be occasion to fire, the adjoining battery must always be called on, either directly or through the Group, to fire a few rounds.[18]

The high point of artillery survey in the First World War was undoubtedly reached on the occasion

---

* Later Sir Lawrence Bragg CH, Director of the Cavendish Laboratory.

of the first great tank battle which took place at Cambrai in November 1917. Brigadier-General H. H. Tudor, who commanded the Artillery of the 9th Division, was searching for a means of mounting a surprise attack (a novel idea in what were otherwise tediously slow and expensive operations), and suggested that total reliance should be placed on survey methods of gun-laying, instead of allowing preliminary registration by the usual practice of trial and error, which advertised the army's intentions well in advance of the actual assault.[19] Tudor's ideas led to the development, largely by Major B. F. E. Keeling, OC 3rd Field Survey Battalion, of unregistered shooting or 'predicted fire'. Its spectacular success at the Battle of Cambrai must have depended on the preparatory work of the Royal Engineer surveyors.

The basis of 'predicted fire' was map shooting. Each heavy and siege battery had to be surveyed and its position plotted on an 'artillery board', on which the map, or plain gridded sheet, was mounted so that distances and angles could be determined accurately by means of a large graduated arc centred on the battery position. These boards, which were supplied by the Ordnance Survey to all batteries, greatly facilitated the determination of the correct line and range of artillery targets. This was the secret of the historic tank surprise, about which an eminent military historian wrote:

> . . . on November 20th, 381 tanks . . . rolled forward in the half light upon the astonished Germans, without even the courtesy of a preliminary bombardment to announce their coming.[20]

The organization of survey work had grown beyond all early expectations. By the middle of June 1917 Jack, promoted to Colonel, had the over-all direction of nearly five thousand officers and men, and his immediate subordinate, Lieutenant-Colonel Winterbotham, who had been transferred from the Third Army to GHQ, was his Technical Assistant with responsibility for all survey innovations and improvements.

THE OVERSEAS BRANCH OF THE ORDNANCE SURVEY

Until 1917 most of the maps required for the Western Front were printed by the Ordnance Survey at Southampton, but from the beginning there was also some provision for printing in the field. When the first three armies were formed at the time of the expansion of the British Expeditionary Force in 1915, each was assigned a 'maps officer' and an Army section of the printing company, the combination being unofficially known as the Maps and Printing Section. Apart from distributing the maps printed in England, these sections were also responsible for reproducing small numbers of maps for headquarters use. When the topographical sections of the Armies were formed, they assimilated the maps and printing sections.

By 1917, however, the constant demands for new editions of trench maps and the dependence on Southampton for their supply led to unacceptable delays. The decision was therefore taken to establish an Overseas Branch of the Ordnance Survey (OBOS) in France, initially at Wardrecques, near St Omer. Here, although their proximity to the front lines was a disadvantage, were readily convertible buildings close to the Aire Canal, allowing the transportation of large consignments of material from England direct to the site. A total establishment of 149 (of whom 46 were Women's Auxiliary Army Corps) with two officers was finally approved.[21] Even though OBOS only became operational in the closing stages of the war, its output was phenomenal. On 21 March 1918 the Germans opened their offensive on the Somme, and the temporary incapacitation of two field survey battalions created enormous demands on OBOS for map supply. On 27 March six quad-demy machines went into action, working continuously round the clock and turning out over 300 000 maps by the beginning of April. But the war had entered its final mobile phase with the beginning of the German offensive in the north, and it was clear that OBOS would have to move quarters. A new site was selected at Aubengue near Boulogne, although printing continued at Wardrecques until June, when the new premises were ready. Over one million maps, involving more than two million impressions, had been produced at Wardrecques.

The final British offensive began on 8 August and demanded continuous map printing at OBOS. From 7 to 17 August, three consecutive shifts operated the four machines then available, turning out over 400 000 impressions in the ten days. Although the need for trench maps ceased with the signing of the armistice on 11 November 1918, it was decided that OBOS should continue until the spring on German mapping, the plates for which were shipped out from Southampton. The termination of war-time for OBOS was marked by a Royal tour of inspection by Princess Mary at the end of November, after which the personnel were slowly transferred back to Southampton.

THE HOME FRONT

I am commanded by the Army Council to convey to the President of the Board of Agriculture and Fisheries their thanks for the great services rendered by the Ordnance Survey during the war.

The Ordnance Survey has trained and provided the bulk of the personnel required for survey work in this war, and it has prepared and printed over 20,000,000 maps for the Armies abroad and at home; it has always been ready to give expert advice on technical matters . . . it has provided large quantities of stores for survey and observation work, and although the provision of these stores at the beginning of the war did not strictly fall within its province the exact knowledge possessed by the members of its staff has enabled the Ordnance Survey to supply material as no other department could have supplied it.

I am to add that the great services which have been rendered are a proof of the value of the military element in the Ordnance Survey; the fact that that Department has been under the guidance of officers of the Corps of Royal Engineers has made possible throughout the war the very effective co-operation of the Ordnance Survey and the Geographical Section of the General Staff with the Armies in the Field.

Letter from the War Office, 14 December 1918[22]

It is perhaps ironical that the Ordnance Survey should have so fully justified its 'military element' for the first time in war while under a civil authority. The Ordnance Survey was a strange institution, largely because of the dual capacity in which its Director General held office. As Director of a civil department he was responsible to the President of the Board of Agriculture and Fisheries for its work, which was the maintenance of the survey and maps of Great Britain; he was also responsible for the efficient operation of the troops under his command, and for their training for war duties. It was this *alter ego* which became dominant during the war. The Ordnance Survey provided a steady flow of officers and men, trained in the 19th (Reserve) Survey Company RE, and for many the war was to be their first experience of surveying. The training provided by the Ordnance Survey was always praised as sound but, before the end of the war, the supply of Ordnance Survey men was exhausted, and the survey units in France became dependent on men with only an elementary knowledge of surveying or topography taken from other units.

The catalogue of the Survey's achievements reflects the enormous effort necessary to match the demands from the Western Front – a million maps required in less than a month, terrain models, artillery boards to be built to specifications determined in France, and the supply of trained surveyors. Jack reflected in later years that

> . . . it was men . . . many of whom could turn their hand to almost any kind of survey work required – observing, computing, plane-tabling, drawing – and all of whom were expert in at least one branch, who formed the backbone of the Field Survey Companies during the war, and without whom the excellent survey organisation that developed would have been impossible.[23]

The supply of maps, unlike ammunition and petrol for which time taken on the road was irrelevant as long as a daily provision was forthcoming, was effective only if the maps arrived at the right time at their specific destinations. One of the most formidable accomplishments of the Ordnance Survey during the war was the ceaseless stream of maps which flowed from Southampton to France from November 1914 to November 1918. The ordinary route was by steamer to Le Havre and thence to Rouen, Abbeville or Calais. Urgent maps were sent by train to London, checked by MI4, escorted onto the Folkestone train, shipped to Boulogne and speeded to GHQ.

Just before the war the War Office had prepared a four-sheet 1:250 000 map covering Belgium, and the Ordnance Survey was required to extend its coverage southwards to the 47th parallel in France. Printed in five colours, and modelled to some extent on the French 1:200 000, the new maps displayed a certain economy of style over the earlier sheets. The War Office had also prepared outline plates from the German 1:100 000 series and the Ordnance Survey undertook, early in the war, to make the accompanying colour plates. Another small-scale map which was found essential for administration was the 1:500 000 map of France, which was also used for indexing the large-scale maps.

The first provision of larger-scale mapping, mainly for use by the artillery, was made by the Ordnance Survey after the Battle of the Aisne in 1914. This was primarily done by enlargement from the French 1:80 000 to the scale of 1:40 000 which was the general administrative scale in trench warfare, or to 1:20 000, for the artillery and infantry alike. Colours were added to the photographic enlargements to distinguish roads, water and contours. The second edition was redrawn, but all the distortions and inaccuracies of the original map remained and it was all but useless for the artillery, creating the need for new field surveys. Southampton was also involved in the preparation of the larger-scale 1:10 000 maps from 1915 onwards. The work of reproducing these compilation maps was extremely laborious and was done partly by the Service Géographique and partly by the Ordnance Survey. The basic maps of all scales were reproduced in a variety of forms to depict specialized information such as traffic, roads and bridges, railways, enemy order of battle, water supply, hostile battery positions and geology.

The use of the large-scale maps at the Front had its corollary at home with the development of artillery training maps at the scales of 1:40 000, 1:20 000 and 1:10 000.[24] These were produced by the Ordnance Survey from the end of 1914 onwards for the War Office. During the war years the 1:20 000 was reduced photographically from the six-inch scale, until 1918 when it was redrawn; it was printed in two colours – a black outline with the contours drawn at metric intervals in brown. The sheets were overprinted with a system of squares – the forerunner of the grid – which had been developed in France.

The method of describing positions within a square by rectangular co-ordinates was proposed by Brigadier Fanshawe RA and was universally adopted in the British Army.[25] The squares which appeared on the 1:20 000 and 1:10 000 training maps of Great Britain were the same as those used by the British Army in France. A large square with sides representing 5000 yards was designated by a letter, a 1000 yard square by a number, and the four quarters of that square by the lower case letters a, b, c and d. The choice of a non-metric unit for the squares on what was otherwise a metric map was made at the insistence of the Artillery, who failed to realize that the squares were designed as a means of location and not of measurement. The dispute occasioned by this decision was to be frequently resurrected in future years. In practice, the Artillery in France had to resort to the French system, which was based on projection rectangular co-ordinates, continuous from sheet to sheet, for calculating distance and direction; the French method was eventually adopted by the British, but not until the end of the war. Close himself felt that 'if we had taken our courage in our hands and started a metric grid at the beginning of the war, we should have saved many difficulties'.[26]

Among the many services performed by the Ordnance Survey for the armies at the Front was the provision of artillery boards. These boards, first made by the Third Army in 1915 after the pattern of a French example, were specially constructed so that they would not warp as a result of atmospheric changes. The artillery boards became a normal item of Army supply in 1916, but their production was subject to many delays. In the meantime the Ordnance Survey had perfected a zinc-covered board, which it continued to make in large numbers, on which the map, or gridded sheet, was fixed by tacking it to the board. It was the simplest and most satisfactory of all. Another excellent feature which made these boards popular was the American-cloth cover and carrying handle. Over 11 000 artillery boards were supplied from Southampton during the war.

There can be no doubt that the services rendered by the Ordnance Survey to the war effort were made possible by the successful interaction between the Department, the survey battalions in France and the War Office. It could not, as Close phrased it, 'be put down quite formally as a matter of logical organization' – it was in effect 'a typically British arrangement' and 'the thing worked'.[27]

The Olivier Committee 1914

On 11 May 1914 the three members of a Departmental Committee, Sir Sydney Olivier, Mr F. Atterbury and Sir Charles Close, were briefed to consider the arrangments between Fisher Unwin and the Board of Agriculture and Fisheries, and the effect of his agency on sales and on the availability of the small-scale maps to the public. The advertisement of the maps, the trade discount allowed on them, as well as the possibility of reducing the sale prices, were also points to be considered. The Olivier *Report on the Sale of Small Scale Maps*, presented on 26 August, was confidential and unpublished,[28] but is of considerable interest as it clearly reveals the attitude of the agents, and to a lesser extent, that of the public, towards the products of the Ordnance Survey.

It soon became apparent, as the examination of the witnesses proceeded, that the national survey was confronted with stiff opposition in the commercial world of map-publishing. Indeed, the name of Dr Bartholomew occurs with almost the same regularity as that of the Department throughout the Report. As the representative of Menzies said of the Ordnance maps: 'We can do very little with them, I am sorry to say, we have such a great competition locally'.[29] This was scarcely surprising, since the locality was Edinburgh, home of the Bartholomew firm. Unwin's contractual obligation to promote the Ordnance Survey map could not have been easy to fulfil when the booksellers were 'so drenched with the Bartholomew map, which they talked of as the Ordnance map . . . that they had the Bartholomew habit almost'.[30] It had long been a stumbling block to the commercial viability of the national, state-produced map that Philip's and Bartholomew's maps should have had the words 'Ordnance Map' printed conspicuously on them, in spite of the fact that the use of these words by private map-publishers had been prohibited in 1911. Bartholomew was also able to undercut the market by giving larger discounts and distributing his stock on a sale-or-return basis, a practice which the harassed Mr Unwin strongly deprecated. The Government had certainly improved the State discount by raising it from forty-five per cent to fifty-three per cent by 1912,[31] but the effect of this had been to neutralize the gain resulting from any increase in sales, and the sole wholesale agent was still unable to give favourable discounts to the trade.

From the questions posed by the Committee it is evident that the Department considered that there was only one serious competitor in the field of cultivating the 'map habit' among the public. Asked by the Chairman 'whether on account of your efforts we are gaining ground on Bartholomew, which is what we want to do', Unwin referred to the recent increase in intake of Ordnance Survey maps by W. H. Smith and Son, replying tersely: 'We could not have made this increase . . . but that we have supplanted Bartholomew's considerably . . . Messrs W. H. Smith and Son do not buy these for love.'[32]

There were numerous minor criticisms of the Ordnance Survey small-scale maps: the very pale buff covers soiled easily, and for this reason were not displayed on bookstalls as often as desirable; the protective envelopes in which the maps were housed inhibited the public from examining the maps; the explanatory leaflets were too comprehensive and it was therefore difficult to absorb their information; the road classification on the Ordnance small-scale maps was inferior to that of the Bartholomew half-inch map for the use of motorists. The list was lengthy. It may have been a depressing experience for Close, but many of the witnesses' comments were justified.

Although generally the trade witnesses were not in favour of any reductions in prices, it was recognized that there was indisputably a demand for cheap holiday-type maps which was then being met by private production. The Committee stressed that 'the Ordnance Survey maps are national maps, paid for by the public, and it is only right that they should be available to the public at the lowest possible prices', and concluded, unaware of the years of retrenchment ahead, that the maps could be reduced in price, thereby effectively undercutting the private market.

Although the terms of reference of the Committee applied only to small-scale maps, the evidence had shown that there was a considerable demand for town maps at scales between one inch and six inches to one mile. This demand had hitherto been met by the German firm of Pharus which used Ordnance Survey material as the basis for its maps, which were very cheap. It was strongly felt that this was one area of map production in which the Ordnance Survey should provide a competitive alternative.

The final recommendations of the Committee covered eleven points:

1 That the existing contract with Fisher Unwin as wholesale agent be terminated as soon as possible, on the ground that the scale of discount given by the Ordnance Survey was not justified by the results achieved during the currency of the 1906 contract.

2 That the Department should take over the sale of the small-scale maps, operating directly from Southampton.

3 That agents for the sale of small-scale maps should be appointed in all principal towns and be allowed a discount of $36\frac{1}{3}$ per cent on all sales, and that maps should be supplied to railway stalls at a discount of 45 per cent. All superseded sheets were to be returnable.

4 That the prices of the one-inch and half-inch maps be reduced from one shilling and sixpence to one shilling for unmounted maps; from two shillings to one shilling and sixpence for mounted and cased maps. There was to be no change in the price of two shillings and sixpence for mounted and dissected maps because the profit margin on these was already narrow.

5 That there should be a reduction in the variety of small-scale maps available to the public.

6 That map covers should not soil easily and should be printed with a more attractive design.

7 That the powers given by the Copyright Act of 1911 should be freely exercised to prevent private firms from using the name of the Ordnance Survey on their maps.

8 That the outward method of folding maps, so convenient for the motorist, should be retained only for the half-inch and quarter-inch scales, as the inward method of folding was preferred by pedestrians for the one-inch map.

9 That the Department should endeavour to arrange for the stocking of maps of the locality at the local post office 'shop'.

10 That the Department should consider the advisability of approaching the principal booksellers of every large town, and offering them a map of the town on a suitable scale, and that the publication should be considered of medium-scale maps (between one-inch and six-inch) of tourist districts.

11 That adequate advertising material should be prepared and circulated as widely as possible.

The annual *Report* of the Ordnance Survey for 1914–15 made no mention of the Departmental

Committee on the Sale of the Small Scale Maps, since its report was confidential. It was evident that Close had already been planning changes in the form of the small scales then available to the public, but there can be no doubt that the final recommendations of the Committee lent added authority for some alterations and improvements which might otherwise have been sacrificed in the cause of war-time economy. Even so, the implementation of many of these recommendations was postponed until after the war, including the termination of Fisher Unwin's agency and the resumption of small-scale wholesaling by the Ordnance Survey.

Domestic Mapping 1914–18

THE SMALL-SCALE MAPS

In 1914 there were still at least five forms of the one-inch map in production: black outline; coloured edition, small sheet series; coloured edition, large sheet series; district maps, black with coloured roads; and the parish indexes. It had been suggested during the Olivier Committee hearings that this variety remained a source of confusion to the public, a factor which could discourage sales. It was accordingly decided to drop the small sheet coloured series, retaining only the large sheet size in the coloured edition, and the parish indexes were to be allowed to become obsolete. Close himself thought that the then current one-inch map of the 1897 type had three major defects. Firstly, the road classification did not meet the modern requirements; secondly, the hill features fell 'short of the possibilities of modern cartography', and thirdly, the existence of parish boundaries on the map served only to confuse the detail.[33] The Board of Agriculture and Fisheries had already approved the omission of parish boundaries, and the War Office Committee of 1912 had also approved a new road classification system which, with slight modifications, was to be adopted for the new one-inch map, the revision for which continued slowly throughout the war.

At the outbreak of war the half-inch map was held to be more important than the one-inch because it was the principal military map of the country. The new edition which had been in production since 1912 was characterized by lighter layering without hill-shading, but even so had found little favour with some of the witnesses in the Olivier Committee's hearings. The general opinion had been summed up by the representative of Cornish Bros., map-sellers of Birmingham:

> The contour in layers is not anything like so popular with the motorist, cyclist and the ordinary tourist as the Bartholomew. Frankly, I certainly think Bartholomew has it.[34]

He added, perhaps conscious that he had gone too far in praise of the opposition: 'I speak with all respect.' It was apparently felt that the Ordnance map did not show the same clear distinction between the layers as did that of Bartholomew.

The quarter-inch Ordnance Survey map was available in three forms in 1914: the outline edition in small sheets, the coloured edition in small sheets, and the coloured edition in large sheet form. To keep in line with the Committee's recommendation that the variety of small-scale maps available to the public be reduced to a minimum, it was decided gradually to abolish the outline edition and the small sheet coloured edition.

The type of paper used for the small-scale maps was a rag litho, hard-wearing and suitable for folding. Three weights were used in 1914: 55 lb per ream at twenty-seven shillings and sixpence, 67 lb per ream at thirty-three shillings and sixpence, and 83 lb per ream at forty-one shillings and sixpence. The one-inch and quarter-inch maps took six printings, the half-inch seven, and the proposed new one-inch map of the Killarney type would have had eleven. The cost of each printing naturally varied with the type of machine used but averaged about fifteen shillings per run of one thousand. This figure included a percentage for establishment charges and for electricity and repairs. The normal size of an 'edition' varied with different sheets; for the fully-coloured one-inch map, an edition of one thousand of an individual sheet would last about three years. The half-inch layered map was printed in a run of 2500 copies for each sheet, while for the unlayered version an issue of only six hundred copies per sheet would last for the same time, about three years.[35]

THE LARGE-SCALE PLANS

Sir Charles Brickdale, of the Land Registry, writing to Close in 1916,[36] pointed out that the work undertaken by the Land Registry in keeping the 1:2500 up to date for roads, estate development and fences was similar to that performed by numerous other departments or bodies. These included, he claimed, the Land Valuation Department, the Post Office, Middlesex County Council, municipal councils, urban and rural councils, water companies, gas and electric light companies – the list seemed interminable. Brickdale then made what must have seemed a highly provocative suggestion to Close. So that the same work should not be unnecessarily repeated by different organizations, it would surely be advantageous if only one central body could undertake the essential surveying and supply the others with the results. Furthermore, he continued, since Land Registry surveys were bound to follow closely on the heels of all actual constructions on the ground, the Land Registry was obviously best suited 'for the foundation of a co-operative scheme of this kind'.

As Close remarked, with laudable restraint, it was an interesting suggestion, and one which, as concerned the Ordnance Survey, needed rather careful handling. One of the reasons for this was the recent insistence by the Ordnance Survey on the existence of Crown Copyright in Ordnance maps. Also, by mid 1916 the new revision of the large-scale plans of London was complete, and the drawing was almost finished, but the revision of the six-inch sheets in general had had to be postponed because of the pressure of other work. During the course of the war, however, the revised plans could only be issued under certain restrictions, and it was not intended that the plans should be made public. Close had been requested by the War Office to deal with all questions of security affecting the issue of new maps and new editions of old maps of the United Kingdom, no matter by whom issued or published. As he pointed out to Brickdale, any revised maps of the kind he was proposing would sooner or later find their way into the hands of the enemy. Brickdale's proposal was thus neatly shelved for, as he replied to Close: 'I am ashamed to say that I had quite forgotten the wretched enemy.'[37]

The Effect of the War

As a result of the transfer of effort to military duties the gross domestic expenditure of the Department fell from £252 475 in 1913–14 to £101 640 in 1915–16. It had been intended that this process of reduction of spending on the revision of the Ordnance Survey maps should continue gradually throughout the war, but the Treasury, in a letter of 27 July 1915, required a further immediate restriction and still more drastic reductions in the following year.[38] This resulted in the diminution of the staff to a nucleus of one superintendent and three draughtsmen in the offices at York, Shrewsbury, Norwich and Belfast. Only one division each was maintained for England, Scotland and Ireland, the headquarters being at Bristol, Edinburgh and Dublin. Even so, these divisions were at less than half their normal strength. In the course of these reductions 314 civilians were discharged,[39] and by 1917–18 the gross domestic expenditure had dropped to £73 700.

The scale of these losses can be fully appreciated only when it is realized that a normal field revision division consisted on one officer and seventy other ranks and civilian assistants. The usual peace-time strength of the Ordnance Survey was seven full divisions, but by 1918 only three half-divisions remained, and the revision of the national plans was proceeding at three-fourteenths of its proper rate, with severe consequences in the ensuing twenty years. It is no wonder that Close, speaking in retrospect in 1931, should have remarked regretfully:

> . . . the Ordnance Survey was almost the only public department which did genuinely economise; it is a great pity that all public departments did not follow suit, and some of our present financial troubles are due to their failure to do so.[40]

Notes

1 Ordnance Survey, *A brief outline of the growth of survey work on the Western Front* (1919), p. 3.

2 Ordnance Survey, *The Ordnance Survey and the war 1914–1919* (1919), p. 4.

3 *Report on survey on the Western Front, 1914–1918*, (HMSO 1920), p. 5.

4 James E. Edmonds, *History of the Great War* (Military operations of the British Army in the western theatre of war 1914–18), (HMSO 1922), vol. I, p. 111.

5 *Ibid.* p. 142.

6 *Report on survey on the Western Front*, p. 53

7 A. J. P. Taylor, *English History 1914–45* (London 1970), p. 56.

8 Edmonds, *History of the Great War*, vol. I, p. 380.

9 J. F. C. Fuller, *Memoirs of an unconventional soldier* (London 1936), p. 26,

10 Walter Raleigh, *The War in the Air* (Oxford 1922), vol. I, p. 339.

11 Edmonds, *History of the Great War*, vol. III, p. 83.

12 This comment was made by Jack in the discussion following a lecture by Winterbotham entitled 'British Survey on the Western Front', *Geographical Journal* 1919, LIII, no. 4, p. 273.

13 *Report on survey on the Western Front*, p. 40.

14 See, for example, M. N. MacLeod, 'Mapping from Air Photographs', *Geographical Journal* 1919, LIII, pp. 382–403.

15 Edmonds, *History of the Great War*, vol. I, p. 379.

16 An account of these two methods is given in John R. Innes, *Flash Spotters and Sound Rangers, how they lived, worked and fought in the Great War* (London, 1935).

17 For a full description of this board, see *Report on survey on the Western Front*, p. 96.

18 L. Bragg, A. H. Dowson and H. H. Hemming, *Artillery Survey in the First World War* (London 1971), p. 38.

19 Edmonds, *History of the Great War*, vol. II, p. 6.

20 B. Liddell Hart, *History of the First World War* (London 1970), p. 435.

21 Ordnance Survey, *The Overseas Branch of the Ordnance Survey* (1919), p. 8.

22 Quoted in OSR 1918–19, pp. 6–8: PP 1919, Cmd. 247, XXVII.

23 E. M. Jack, 'The Ordnance Survey in relation to war', *Royal Engineers Journal*, 1930, vol. XLIV, pp. 263–70.

24 A set of these maps, mainly at the scale of 1:20 000, produced between 1914 and 1919, is held in the British Library, Map Library, Maps 150 d. 14 (2 vols.).

25 For a fuller description of the map referencing systems used in the British and French Armies, see *Report on survey on the Western Front*, p. 159–64.

26 Winterbotham, *Geographical Journal*, 1919, LIII, p. 272.

27 *Ibid.*

28 *Report of the Departmental Committee on the sale of small scale maps, 1914*, a printed document endorsed 'Confidential' and 'For Departmental Use': PRO OS 1/6.

29 *Ibid.* para. 16.

30 *Ibid.* para. 97.

31 *Ibid.* para. 46.

32 *Ibid.* para. 108.

33 *Ibid.* These opinions were expressed during the course of the hearings.

34 *Ibid.* para. 385.

35 *Ibid.* paras. 688–91.

36 PRO OS 1/5, dated 21 June 1916.

37 PRO OS 1/5, dated 2 July 1916.

38 PRO OS 1/8. OS 17159/15.

39 PRO OS 1/8. Memorandum on the state of the Revision of Large Scale Maps of the United Kingdom as affected by the War.

40 In discussion on Winterbotham 'The small scale maps of the Ordnance Survey', *Geographical Journal* 1932, LXXIX, p. 24.

23
Reconstruction
after The
First World War
1919–1922

Last time that the Ordnance Survey vote was under discussion, certain people proposed that as we had got all the maps we wanted for several years, the Survey should be abolished temporarily.

Sir Arthur Boscawen 1921[1]

The Economy Cuts and the Large-Scale Plans

The men of the Ordnance Survey had become accustomed to trenches during the war – living in them, mapping them or printing maps of them. Now that the war was over with the signing of the Armistice on 11 November 1918, they were to experience another restricting environment. Two committees had sat, one in 1916 on National Retrenchment[2] and the second in 1918 on National Expenditure.[3] Both made recommendations for the conduct of the Ordnance Survey which were calculated to achieve considerable financial economy. The implementation of the committees' proposals, however, was to cause greater financial problems in the next twenty years than they were intended to solve in the first instance.

The principal recommendations of both committees concerned the revision of the large-scale plans. It was here that the greatest cuts in expenditure could be made. Huge arrears in revision had accumulated during the war, and the Report of the 1916 Committee stated that as a permanent measure of economy, the period of years fixed for the revision of the six-inch and twenty-five-inch maps should be increased. In 1918 Close proposed a scheme whereby the plans at these scales of certain mountainous areas and of sparsely populated regions, then revised every twenty years, should in future be revised only once every forty years.[4] The Report of the 1918 Committee finally extended this recommendation to include counties with a population of less than one hundred per square mile. This was to affect about forty per cent of the United Kingdom.

Once the revised programme of revision was agreed, a corresponding reduction in man-power was made, and final Treasury approval was given in January 1920 for a Survey establishment of 1462, contrasting with the pre-war total of 2077. Practically all the old Survey hands had returned from the war by 1920, but the planned reductions meant that there could be no recruiting of new staff. But even before this the Ordnance Survey had received instructions that cuts would have to be made – a Treasury letter of December 1919 had stated that 'the underlying principle is that in the present financial crisis the keeping up of the Ordnance Survey at anything like its pre-war standard is a luxury which must be foregone'.[5] Only seven counties could be taken up immediately; these were Buckingham, Derby, Durham, Essex, Hereford, Northumberland and Oxford. Many counties not affected by the forty year rule were to remain unrevised for periods in excess of twenty-two years, while some of the 'forty year' counties were not taken up until the mid 1970s.

The terms of retrenchment affected the large-scale plans in other ways. No further changes in the county meridians were to be made, except in Essex and Northumberland which were already half completed; revisers were not to check old detail; new area books were no longer to be prepared, and the areas on the last published plan were not be altered unless the parcel boundaries had been changed or an error had been noted.

As far as the normal series six-inch map was concerned, no new sheets had been drawn for many years, with the result that even many of the more important counties (in terms of the demand from map-users) had to make do with obsolete maps. The exception was the London area: by 1920 the revised six-inch sheets, the drawing of which had been continued in the war years, were in course of publication. The attractive coloured special six-inch town maps made their appearance in 1920; the first map to be issued covered Southampton. The publication of these maps was the direct result of the recommendation made by the Olivier Committee in 1914, that the 'Department should consider . . . approaching the principal booksellers of every considerable town and offering them a map of the town on a suitable scale'.[6]

The 1918 Committee considered that some of the Ordnance Survey maps were sold at a price which did not cover the cost of the paper, printing, storage, sales expenses or any significant proportion of the cost of the survey. It had of course always been a matter of policy that the public should not have to pay towards survey costs when buying the maps. Nevertheless, it was felt that a considerable increase in the selling price of the twenty-five-inch plans 'would not lead to any diminution in the sales and would be accompanied by a gain to the public revenue'.[7] The price of a 1:2500 sheet accordingly rose from three shillings to five shillings, and that of the six-inch quarter-sheet from one shilling to one shilling and sixpence. In 1919 the production of the six-inch was restricted to full sheets and these sold at four shillings. In the same year it was decided that 1:1250 enlargements of the 1:2500 map should replace the 1:500 town plans which were in fact already largely discontinued.

The massive reductions in man-power were undoubtedly seen as the main way of improving the balance sheet of the Ordnance Survey. It was calculated that the actual saving in expenditure would amount to £150 000 a year, more than half the estimated cost of the Survey to the State for 1920. It was a short-term expedient which was soon proved to have been short-sighted; by cutting back the Ordnance Survey's revision programme the Government deprived itself of an essential corpus of material for putting much of its own legislation into effect.

The Small-Scale Maps

The small-scale maps were self-supporting to a great extent, but they did not altogether evade the cold eye of post-war retrenchment. The concept of the 'new series coloured one-inch' on the lines of the *Killarney* sheet, so proudly announced by Close in 1914,[8] had been shattered with the first explosions of the big guns in France; a cheaper alternative was imperative. The Olivier Committee had referred to the demand which plainly existed for a very cheap map, and had been shown a sheet which it was proposed should be produced as a special district map. It was to sell for sixpence a copy and was to be known as the 'Contoured Road Map'. The Committee pronounced that 'it should become a highly popular form of the one-inch' and confidently predicted that it would be 'sold in large numbers'. It was this map that became the pattern for the new one-inch series.

Such was the origin of the Popular Edition, whose new and improved cover bore the legend 'Contoured Road Map' (Plate 16). It sold, not for sixpence, but for one shilling and sixpence paper flat, or three shillings and sixpence for a folded, dissected and mounted copy; sheet 120, the first to be published, appeared on 24 June 1918.[9] Relief was shown by contours at intervals of 50 feet, but there were no hachures, layers or hill shading. On the early sheets the contours were finely drawn in orange; the general appearance was bright and legible in spite of the fact that the black outline and names were still derived from the copper plates. One important change was the omission of parish boundaries, which was to draw much criticism in the future; the sheet-lines were altered and the number of sheets reduced from 153 to 146. There was a marked emphasis on the road system, the first class roads being coloured in what Winterbotham later described as a 'violent red', but the new classification, showing width, quality, and surface, gave eleven classes of roads and made the map a firm favourite with the War Office. By 1922 the one-inch revision of England and Wales was nearly complete and 83 sheets had been published.

To accompany the Popular Edition it was decided to issue a series of district maps which were to be known as Tourist Maps; the first of these was published in February 1920 and covered Snowdonia.[10] * The Tourist Maps differed from the Popular Edition in showing the relief by a combination of hachures, contours and layers, sometimes resembling the *Killarney* sheet, although lacking the hill shading and other refinements. So the original roles of the Popular and Tourist maps were reversed. The new one-inch map series which had been proposed before the war had instead become the district maps, and the proposed cheap district road maps had become the national series.

The half-inch map, in its modified form with lighter layer colours (edition of 1912), continued in

* This Snowdonia tourist sheet was essentially an unrevised pre-war version. A revised Popular-based sheet was published in 1925. Altogether over twenty tourist sheets were published between 1920 and 1933.

production until 1931, while in the immediate post-war years the third edition of the quarter-inch series was completed. The latter was published in twelve sheets, the first to appear being sheet 10 in October 1919.[11] With its redrawn detail and handwritten names it was a complete break with the engraved and hill-shaded maps. Although layered and full of colour, it remained clear and legible and was probably the best of all the quarter-inch series, but only one class of main road was distinguished and woods were shown by an obscure black symbol. Publication was completed in 1921 and in the same year the drawing for the quarter-inch map of Scotland, for reproduction by heliozincography, was taken up.

With the new one-inch and quarter-inch maps came a new and attractive series of designs for map covers. It had been one of the contentions of the 1914 Committee that such an innovation would considerably enhance the sales potential of the maps. The appointment of Ellis Martin as Artist and Designer in 1919 was a welcome step towards the successful implementation of the Committee's recommendation. The familiar covers of the Popular Edition – red with a picture of a cyclist (later to become a hiker), seated map in hand overlooking a wooded landscape, and with a small inset showing the area covered by the map – date from this period. In 1921 three and four-colour covers, the most distinctive by Ellis Martin but some drawn by Arthur Palmer and others, were introduced for the tourist maps, and a selection of Martin's designs was shown at the exhibition of British Industrial Art in February.[12]

Other measures were taken to promote the sale of the small-scale maps, mainly following on the recommendations of the Olivier Committee. As advocated, the contract with Fisher Unwin for the wholesale agency was terminated in 1919, and the Ordnance Survey undertook its own wholesaling direct from Southampton. A special show-card for advertising the Ordnance Survey maps was printed in 1920, but perhaps most important, in view of the criticisms made in 1914, was the appearance of the newly-designed booklet, *A Description of the Ordnance Survey Small Scale Maps*. Published in 1919 and followed by a second edition in 1920, it provided, with its clear explanatory text and wealth of illustrations, a comprehensive and easily understood guide to the small-scale maps.

The Establishment of the Whitley Council

It was inevitable that the reductions in staff should affect morale and leave an atmosphere of unrest. The Ordnance Survey was naturally not unique in post-war Britain in this respect. The problem of securing good relations between employer and employed in industry had exercised the Government during the war years and in 1916 a committee under the chairmanship of the Right Honourable J. H. Whitley recommended the setting up of Joint Industrial Councils, District Councils and Works Committees. But it was the Civil Service – for which the proposed procedures were not intended – that responded with enthusiasm to the idea of 'Whitley Councils'.

On 19 March 1920 the Departmental Whitley Council for the Ministry of Agriculture and Fisheries held its first meeting, at which the Ordnance Survey was represented by three members of the Survey administration and four members of the civil staff.[13]

At this meeting the general objectives and functions of the Council were stated: to secure the greatest measure of co-operation between the Administration (the Official Side), in its capacity as employer, and the general body of the Staff (the Staff Side) in matters affecting the Department. The Council's terms of reference included the determination of the general principles governing the conditions of employment: working conditions, promotion, discipline, staff training and the encouragement of further education. It was the first time in the history of the Civil Assistants of the Ordnance Survey that a body had existed in which they could actively participate and voice whatever grievances and complaints they might have. In the early days it was a highly successful means of diverting and deflating what could have been unpleasant crises of staff restlessness in a depressed post-war Britain.

The first question to be dealt with that affected the Ordnance Survey concerned the hours of work at the Department. Such was the efficacy of the Departmental Whitley Council that new hours of work were quickly approved and came into force on 1 June 1920.[14] The former average of $43\frac{3}{4}$ hours per week was reduced to $39\frac{1}{2}$, on the understanding that there would be no reduction in output. In the same year the Ordnance Survey Whitley District Committee was founded to deal with matters which were within the competence of the Director General to decide. The first meeting of the District Committee was held on 29 September. The Official Side was chaired by Colonel G. F. A. Whitlock, the Executive Officer, and the Staff Side was led by Mr A. W. Ashmead. Among the several questions raised at this inaugural meeting, one dealt with the 'consideration of the case of Assistants who, on return to civil duties [after serving with HM Forces] are employed under less favourable conditions than formerly'. This potentially explosive situation of Assistants being worse off than before they left the Survey to fight for their country was quickly defused by Close. Justifiable grievances were immediately redressed, as no doubt they would have been without the intervention of the Whitley machine. But it was inevitably seen by the staff as a success for the new system and was a portentous beginning for the Ordnance Survey Whitley District Committee.

The second meeting, held on 10 March 1921, supported a resolution of the National Whitley Council regarding the communication of adverse reports on staff. It was agreed that in future no adverse entry should be made in the Qualification Return of any Ordnance Survey employee until the Assistant had been informed of the facts, and given every opportunity of 'explaining the circumstances'. This was another welcome advance in the rights of the Civil Assistants. The Survey in Ireland also participated in the Whitley scheme, the Irish Sub-Committee being formed early in 1921.[15]

The Separation of the Irish Surveys

On 1 January 1922 responsibility for the survey of the six counties of Northern Ireland was transferred to the Ordnance Survey of Northern Ireland, which continued to maintain close links with Southampton, and on 1 April the Survey of the rest of Ireland was handed over to the Provisional Government of the Irish Free State, which preferred to assert its independence at every scale and at every stage of production.

The fifteen warrant officers, NCOs and sappers of the Royal Engineers who were stationed at the Ordnance Survey in Phoenix Park in Dublin returned to Great Britain when the Survey was handed over. Lieutenant-Colonel J. E. E. Craster remained with the responsibility for completing the handing-over procedures.[16] It is indeed open to question just how well prepared the Irish Free State was to accept this new responsibility; some of their arrangements were certainly left until the last minute, as witness their failure to select a Director to replace Craster. Close, knowing that the Ordnance Survey estimate for 1922–3 included no provision for Ireland, wrote urgently to the Ministry of Agriculture and Fisheries on 13 March 1922, insisting that 'to preserve continuity, and to prevent the Survey of the Irish Free State breaking up through internal intrigues, it is most desirable that the Provisional Government should *at once* nominate a Director'.[17] This was evidently done, for at the end of the month Craster delivered the official 'Handing Over Report' to the Acting Director, Captain G. H. Mew. The report detailed the records, maps, books, documents, printing-presses, stores, machinery and buildings which the new Survey of Ireland was to acquire from the British Government. The Irish Survey claimed that it was entitled to certain instruments used in Ireland, but the Ministry merely remarked that 'the fact that an instrument or machine has at some date been used in Ireland does not, in the opinion of the Ministry, entitle the Survey of the Irish Free State to claim it'.[18] Eventually one of Colby's bars was handed over as a gesture of goodwill. Some people were surprised by the new Government's decision to refer to its official Survey Department as the Ordnance Survey of Ireland (*Hib.* Suirbheireacht Ordanais). But perhaps the retention of the name was not wholly inappropriate in a country where its previous bearers had achieved so much, and where both makers and users of maps remained keenly aware of their nineteenth-century inheritance.

Two New Posts for the Ordnance Survey

As a contrast to the constant diminutions in the Survey establishment at this time, two important new posts were created: Research Officer and Archaeology Officer. On 10 December 1919 H. L. P. Jolly joined the Ordnance Survey as its Research Officer and Scientific Adviser. The post had been Close's idea. He felt that continuity of approach was essential to the solving of many of the scientific problems which confronted the Survey, something which was ordinarily difficult to achieve with the constantly changing postings of the military officers. At first sight it is a matter for surprise that Treasury approval was ever given in times of financial crisis for an additional appointment on the Survey, but a glance at the tasks of the Research Officer suggests that he would have to have been a man of phenomenal attainments and energy in order to cope with what could well have occupied several men. He was entrusted with the charge of the magnetic survey, with investigations and calculations for the trigonometrical work as well as the responsibility for the trigonometrical records, with the determination of mean sea-level and the general reduction of the new geodetic levelling network. The bringing together under one head of these various scientific tasks must have seemed, on the face of it, to provide an economical use of man-power which would have appealed to the Treasury.

There was of course an analogy with the Indian Survey, of which Close had had experience, and where the Mathematical Adviser was a 'mathematical court of appeal' which in Britain was rarely needed. While Close no doubt knew exactly what he expected from the Research Officer, the two succeeding Directors General were 'completely at a loss what to do about it'.[19] Jack, after Close's departure, tried to use Jolly as the officer in charge of the parties for gravity and magnetic work, but this was strictly the province of the Trigonometrical Division, and the experiment was unsatisfactory. The dual nature of the Ordnance Survey perhaps made the appointment of a Research Officer a profitless measure in the long term. The double function of the Survey was seen as an efficient means of 'using and training in peace, upon the normal surveys of the nation, the military engineers necessary for war surveys'.[20] It followed that such training for the engineer officer would include a liberal dose of mathematics; moreover officers of special mathematical ability had usually been obtained for the Survey when requested. As Winterbotham was later to ask, who would have done the inevitable scientific work in war-time if, before the war, the Research Officer 'had become the arbiter on matters of adjustments, co-ordinate systems, changes of meridians, projections and the like?'[21]

Jolly, as a civilian scientist, therefore faced an understandable military prejudice, and did not come to experience the same measure of mutual esteem as had Isaac Dalby more than a hundred years before. His initial tasks, however, provided few hints of the uneasiness to come. He was largely responsible for the account of the revised geodetic levelling of England and Wales in 1921,[22] and he also carried out investigations into mean sea-level. This work was to be followed in 1925 by a magnetic resurvey of Britain. It was to be some time yet before the Research Officer was relegated to 'odd matters for international unions' or 'reviews for this or that scientific journal'.[23]

The second special posting to the Ordnance Survey was that of O. G. S. Crawford as Archaeology Officer on 1 October 1920. The appointment was the result of a question, raised only the previous year at a British Association meeting, as to how the antiquarian information printed on the Ordnance maps could be made more exact and useful.

The Beginning of the Debate on Air Survey

> I don't like to commit myself to any very definite opinion as to the future of air-photo work, though I can imagine circumstances in which it would be useful.[24]

Thus replied Close in 1919 to a Royal Air Force pilot anxious to obtain employment. In the same year Lieutenant-Colonel Moore Brabazon asked in the House of Commons whether the Ordnance Survey had taken steps 'to utilize the experience obtained during the war of air photography for mapping purposes . . . having regard to the fact that many of the maps are now out of date'. The official reply was given that the Ordnance Survey was studying the matter closely. It seems to have been forgotten that Jack, Winterbotham and MacLeod were among the highest authorities on 'the experience obtained during the war', but the post-war Ordnance Survey was faced with questions which were very different from those of military mapping in war: whether large-scale plans could be made and revised more economically from air photographs than by the well-tried methods of chain survey and examination, and whether reliable contours could be similarly obtained.

In spite of the coldness of the financial climate, a great deal of valuable research was being done at this time mainly under the direction of the War Office Air Survey Committee, which held its first meeting on 1 November 1920. The Committee had been formed under the aegis of Sir Charles Close and was originally composed of the Chief of the Geographical Section, General Staff, one other nominee from GSGS, one from the Ordnance Survey (Winterbotham) and two from the Air Ministry. The Committee's functions were threefold: to initiate research into apparatus and methods, to maintain a record of information, and to arrange for the interchange of information with any scientific departments that might be interested. The Ordnance Survey was thus directly involved in what was effectively a central clearing house for air survey information.

The Department could hardly be said, therefore, to be ignoring the potential of air survey methods and did, in fact, produce at least one map with the aid of air photographs. It appears that early in 1919 Close had discussed with Brigadier-General Hearson of the Air Ministry the possibility of preparing plans of towns using air-photo mosaics. It is not clear whether the finished product was intended for use by the pedestrian, motorist or pilot, but the resulting dark brown map, entitled 'Air Map of Salisbury' was published in 1919 at the scale of 1:5280.[25] It was the first civil 'map' produced partly by aerial methods by the Ordnance Survey, but even though it was 'compiled from Ordnance Survey plans and air photographs' it was not a true combination of ground and air survey. It had been found that each of the photographs comprising the mosaic, which had been supplied by the Air Ministry, was on a slightly different scale. To overcome this an outline map was produced by reducing the relevant 1:2500 sheets to twelve inches to one mile. The photo map was then completed by an artist who, by working from points shown on both the mosaic and the outline map, was able to make a picture virtually the same as the mosaic in appearance, but with the discrepancies of scale eliminated.[26] There were no outstanding points of interest in its compilation; the Ordnance Survey regarded it merely as an 'admirable artistic production' and printed five hundred copies of it to be sold at two shillings each.[27] No more maps of this kind were produced and the experiment served to emphasize the vast amount of work which still needed to be done before aerial methods could be successfully used by the Ordnance Survey.

The End of an Era – Sir Charles Close Retires

The directorship of Sir Charles Close – he was knighted in 1918 for his war services – endured to witness a further blow to the Ordnance Survey. Sir Eric Geddes, whose schemes for modernizing the railways had been sacrificed at the altar of public economy, presided over a committee on Government expenditure, which sat in February 1922.[28] The now legendary 'Geddes Axe' swung in all directions, abolishing five Government departments and cutting the personnel of the Ordnance Survey to one thousand. The twenty-year period for the revision of the large-scale plans of those counties with a population of over one hundred per square mile was to remain, but was to be restricted to boroughs, urban districts and areas which had undergone considerable change since their last revision.

Close's term of office spanned a watershed in the history of the Ordnance Survey. At the time when he retired, in 1922, scientific experiment had become a dispensable luxury, and unprecedented financial stringency was depriving the Department of its major *raison d'être* which was the provision of up-to-date large-scale plans. It must also have been a saddening experience for him to observe the deteriorating relationship between management and staff, after having done so much to improve it in his first years as Director General. His closing reflections on this subject are contained in an unpublished memorandum which he signed on 29 June 1922:

> It has long been felt by those who have studied the Ordnance Survey organisation that the old custom of employing a large number of somewhat underpaid civilians leads to discontent. This discontent has found a voice on many occasions during the the the past sixty years. The proper policy is to pay really well a smaller body of men, perhaps more highly skilled'.[29]

Notes

1 PRO OS 1/9, 24 Nov. 1921.
2 *Committee on Retrenchment in the Public Expenditure*: PP 1916, Cd. 8200, XV, p. 181.
3 *Select Committee on National Expenditure*: PP 1918 (132) IV.
4 *Third Report of the Select Committee on National Expenditure*, para. 63: PP 1918 (132), IV.
5 OSR 1919–20, p. 3: PP 1920, Cmd. 718, XXII.
6 PRO OS 1/6, 1914, p. 16.
7 *Third Report of . . . Committee on . . . Expenditure*, para. 64: PP 1918 (132), IV.
8 OSR 1913–14, p. 9: PP 1914, Cd. 7424, XLIV.
9 PRO OS 1/18.
10 *Ibid.*

11 *Ibid.*
12 A volume containing examples of these early map covers is in the Ordnance Survey Record Library, Southampton.
13 OSR 1919–20, p. 3: PP 1920, Cmd. 718, XXII.
14 OSR 1920–21, p. 3: PP 1921, Cmd. 1308, XV.
15 Minutes of the Ordnance Survey Whitley District Committee from 29 September 1920 to 2 December 1926: Ordnance Survey Library, Southampton.
16 These procedures are detailed in PRO OS 1/3, 1922.
17 PRO OS 1/3: letter dated 13 March 1922.
18 *Ibid.* letter dated 22 Feb. 1923.
19 Winterbotham's 'Handover Notes' to MacLeod, 1934, p. 22: Ordnance Survey Library.
20 *Ibid.* p. 23.
21 *Ibid.*
22 A. J. Wolff and H. L. P. Jolly, *The Second Geodetic Levelling of England and Wales, 1912–1921* (HMSO 1922).
23 'Handover Notes', p. 23.
24 PRO OS 1/11: letter dated 4 Jan. 1919.
25 A copy is in the British Library Map Library, pressmark 5730 (7).
26 PRO OS 1/11: Close to *Country Life*, dated 21 Jan. 1921.
27 PRO OS 1/11: letter from Winterbotham dated 9 Jan. 1920.
28 *Second Interim Report of the Committee on National Expenditure*, p. 49: PP 1922, Cmd. 1582, IX.
29 PRO OS 490.

24
Archaeology –
the
Crawford
Period

The First Archaeology Officer

During the war Close had met a young officer, Lieutenant O. G. S. Crawford, belonging to the 3rd Army Survey Section in France. Crawford, writing after the war, described the meeting:

> ... Winterbotham had sent me back to England with some maps to deliver to the Director General of the Ordnance Survey, who was to print them . . . My official business was quickly disposed of and we spent the rest of the interview discussing archaeology.

He resolved not to allow the acquaintance to lapse after the war, the last nine months of which he spent as a prisoner, after transferring to the Royal Flying Corps as an observer. He kept this resolve and later recorded:

> [Sir Charles] was very favourably disposed towards archaeology and had decided that the large scale . . . ordnance maps might legitimately be issued free to certain qualified persons in return for the use of the archaeological information they inserted, which would correct and amplify that already marked there . . . I made frequent visits to the Ordnance Survey during 1919, not only to get six-inch maps, but also to consult the original two-inch-to-mile drawings of the first (engraved) one-inch map, which marked many things not shown, or shown less clearly, in the published maps. I was becoming a sort of voluntary field-worker for the Ordnance Survey and I fancy that Sir Charles, impressed perhaps by the archaeological errors and deficiencies thus revealed, thought that he might do worse than take me on his staff permanently. As an ex-serviceman with plenty of survey experience I had the necessary qualifications. He therefore put the proposal to me and I at once jumped at it; for it was exactly the thing I wanted and had long ago decided to aim for, namely, to be paid for doing work I liked.[1]

In order to obtain official sanction for this post Close, moving behind the scenes, engineered a proposal from the British Association to the Minister of Agriculture, urging the appointment of an Archaeological Officer to the Ordnance Survey. The Minister agreed and Crawford joined the Survey in October 1920 at a salary of £250 a year. A twenty-year period now began in which a new approach was made to the handling of archaeology in the Survey. This was so completely dominated by the personality of Crawford that its history must be largely that of the man himself.

He was a man of strong individuality and prickly independence of spirit, born in 1886 the son of an Indian High Court judge and of Scottish descent on both sides. He was educated at Marlborough and Oxford and began his career as Junior Demonstrator in the Oxford School of Geography. His interest in field archaeology was fostered by contacts with H. J. E. Peake of Newbury and Dr J. P. Williams-Freeman, a pioneer in the archaeology of the chalk areas. Before taking up his post at the Survey he had already gained practical experience of archaeology both at home and in the Sudan. His war-time experiences taught him much about maps and their production; he also became aware of the scientific potential of air photography.

In the Survey hierarchy the Archaeology Officer came under the direction of the Executive Officer, but had the right of direct access to the Director General in the capacity of adviser. He had no staff and only minimal accommodation. In 1922 even this rudimentary situation nearly collapsed when the Ministry proposed to make his post a half-time job; disaster was averted by the intervention of Sir Hercules Read, then Keeper of the British and Medieval Antiquities at the British Museum, who was able to pull the necessary strings to allow the status quo to continue.

Crawford, and the comparatively unimportant activity which he represented, were regarded with some hostility by his military colleagues at the Ordnance Survey, an attitude which took some time to die down, and although the status of archaeology as a science steadily improved between the two world wars, he often ploughed a lonely furrow. His enthusiasm and energy sometimes proved an obstacle to success because he had a large stock of ideas, many of them unconventional, and was not always tactful in the way he pressed them on his colleagues and superiors. He was compelled to realize many of these ideas outside his official employment by founding and editing the internationally-esteemed periodical *Antiquity* in 1927, another cause of misgivings at Southampton.

The programme of post-war economy in government spending and the spate of new building which followed the war brought many changes which, in turn, affected Crawford's work. In the main this was to ensure the accuracy of archaeological information on maps of all scales by gathering new information and applying it to new editions as they appeared; if the rate of revision was severely reduced, corrections and additions were also restricted in proportion. Crawford was therefore always collecting more material for revision than could actually be applied to the maps. But first the point had to be made to those in control at Southampton, who had not envisaged a peripatetic Archaeology Officer, that without field-work little could be done to correct, much less amplify, archaeological information on maps. Many gross errors on the pre-1920 maps could be dealt with outright without leaving the office but much field-work was required for any real progress.

Crawford became the most capable and inspiring field archaeologist of his time, only lightly bound to his office and spending long periods travelling over the country on his bicycle, making direct observations on the ground, which he recorded for future use, and also making friends with those who could best help him in his work. These contacts enabled him to develop the system of honorary local correspondents, first applied in Wessex by Close before 1920, and a great deal of information was made available to the Survey at no greater cost than that of the six-inch maps which were issued. These voluntary helpers included such men as Dr E. Cecil Curwen of Brighton, who revolutionized the archaeology of Sussex after 1919 and placed all his work at the disposal of the Survey; no figure exists for the total number of correspondents operating between the two wars, but it was considerable. The scheme coincided with an increase in field activity among amateurs in many parts of the country, but Crawford had no professional help in the office until an assistant archaeology officer was appointed in 1938.

Early in his career at the Survey, Crawford wished to increase the competence of field archaeologists, with an improved flow of information for the use of the Survey in mind. A small pamphlet entitled *Field Archaeology, some notes for beginners issued by the Ordnance Survey* was produced in 1924, and proved extremely popular. It was subsequently revised and greatly enlarged by Crawford's successors.

Besides being an acute field observer, Crawford brought other qualities to his work. He was a place-names expert, a student of historical documents, early maps and other kinds of evidence deriving from geography, geology, botany and folk-lore, as well as being a skilled and sensitive photographer. With official consent he built up a large collection of full-scale photographs of early maps and plans covering the period from the sixteenth to the nineteenth century by gaining access to material in the possession of estate offices, large land-owning bodies like Oxford and Cambridge colleges and many other sources. These were photographed at Southampton and the collection became an important source for early names and topography as well as for extinct forms of land usage. Unfortunately the Southampton collection was badly damaged in 1940, but as the precaution had been taken to send a copy of each photograph to the Map Room of the British Museum the loss was not total. After his retirement Crawford published his testament as a field archaeologist in his book *Archaeology in the Field*.[2]

One of Crawford's most valuable contributions was the application of air photography to archaeology. While working on an excavation in the Sudan in 1914 for Sir Henry Wellcome he was impressed by the use of a box-kite to get vertical photographs of sites. In the latter part of the war, as an observer in the Royal Flying Corps, he was already aware of the way in which viewing country from a height in different conditions of weather, light, soil and crop-cover can reveal traces of man's earlier activities not visible from the ground. He also realized how the aerial view could sort out the different parts of a multiple site and establish the age sequence of its components by inspection alone. As a result of a lecture which he gave to the Royal Geographical Society he was able to form an association with Alexander Keiller which led to a programme of air photography in southern England whose results appeared in the classic publication *Wessex from the Air* in 1928.[3]

The value of air photography as an aid to revision was realized in the Ordnance Survey and he was permitted to do much of it in official time. He also became concerned about the fate of the large number of air photographs taken during the First World War in Iraq, Syria and elsewhere in the Middle East, and of those being taken by the Royal Air Force during training over Britain. He made a successful effort to direct much of the Middle Eastern material into the British Museum. Long and sometimes frustrating negotiations allowed him to receive a fair proportion of the material produced in Britain and this was arranged in albums by counties with six-inch map references. Here again there was disaster in 1940; most of the negatives were ruined but many of the albums survived. Crawford's two Survey Professional Papers *Air Survey and Archaeology* which appeared in 1924 and *Air-Photography for Archaeologists* issued in 1929 were, for all practical purposes, the only standard works on the subject until the publications of Riley and Bradford in 1944 and 1957.[4]

Period Maps

A number of special maps illustrating various archaeological and historical situations were published after 1924. This was not entirely without precedent. In 1793 the publication of Roy's map of Roman Scotland had shown the way, and during the Irish six-inch survey O'Donovan prepared several maps showing the limits of ancient Irish territories with an attempt to reconstruct the distribution of ancient woodland, but they were never published. The mid-nineteenth-century reproduction of historical documents also led to Sir Henry James's facsimiles of ancient maps.

The initiative which resulted in the publication of the first edition of the *Map of Roman Britain* in 1924 came almost entirely from Crawford. In 1920 he found that Close had been discussing a possible historical map of England at a scale of 1:1 million with the historian, Sir Charles Oman; an experiment had been made with a map of the Oxford area by showing all the antiquities and historical features on the Ordnance Survey maps covering it. The result was confusion and it was Crawford's delicate task to guide Close away from this impracticable scheme and get him to allow the preparation of a physical base map on which maps covering one period at a time could be compiled and printed. His own ideas on this subject had developed while he was at Oxford; they stemmed from his early conviction of the value of the distributional method in archaeological studies, in which the mapping of the known distribution of limited classes of archaeological objects and sites is used to clarify the observable evidence of the movements and settlement topography of early peoples, cultures and modes of life. Before 1911 the technique had made little impact[5] but in that year Crawford had given a lecture to the Oxford University Archaeological Society in which he used distribution maps to illustrate problems of the Early Bronze Age in Britain,[6] and the method was fairly launched. By 1914 his ideas had developed further and the chance to put them into wider practice came when he joined the Survey.

The model for the first *Map of Roman Britain* was a modest affair showing no more than roads and the places named in documentary sources. It was submitted to Jack (the new Director General) who, while he indicated his displeasure that the compilation had not received his official sanction, still allowed it to be drawn and published. It went on sale in August 1924, and the whole issue was sold in a few days. Official misgivings were allayed and a second edition was authorized which covered most of the country, carried greatly increased detail, and was printed on a layered base. This was published in 1928 and lasted with general success through a number of reprints (Plate 17).

Between 1928 and 1939 seven more maps were published covering four subjects ranging from *Britain in the Neolithic–Early Bronze transition* to *Seventeenth Century England*. One alone of these, *Britain in the Dark Ages*, continued in publication after the Second World War. The two-sheet first edition of this map appeared in 1938 and 1939 and carried introductory essays by Crawford which were a serious contribution to scholarship, as were the maps themselves.

Crawford's work with period maps was to give birth to an important international production of the same kind. He saw the possiblity of a map series covering the whole of the Roman Empire at 1:1 million, and suggested this in a lecture to an International Geographical Congress at Cambridge in July 1928. The idea was widely taken up and the first meeting of an International Committee with Crawford as secretary was held at Florence in April 1929. Further meetings took place in other European centres and several maps were compiled and printed. In 1933 the organization of the map was transferred from the Committee of the International Geographical Congress to that dealing with the 1:1 million Map of the World whose headquarters were then at the Ordnance Survey. The maps produced were very much on the lines originally laid down for the *Map of Roman Britain*, but the war disrupted the scheme and it was some time before progress was resumed. The contribution of the Ordnance Survey consisted in the compilation of two sheets of Roman Libya and others covering Lower Egypt.

The Beginnings of Archaeology Branch

In the later twenties the amount of work developing through revision, the collection and classification of air photographs, the preparation of period maps and an increasing correspondence was clearly beyond the capacity of one man. In 1930 Crawford was given the services of an assistant and in the next five years two draughtsmen were placed under his supervision to work on models for period maps. The last and most important addition to the staff was made in 1938 when Crawford's efforts to get an assistant with full archaeological qualifications succeeded and Mr W. F. Grimes from the National Museum of Wales became Assistant Archaeology Officer. This appointment caused difficulty because the Survey required a graduate but were unable to offer an adequate salary. At first the post found no takers, but eventually the offer was improved and Grimes joined the staff. This addition was too late to have much effect, for the years of peace were running out, but it established an important precedent for the period after 1945.

Work in the Branch slowed down after the outbreak of war in 1939, and when the danger grew in 1940 Crawford took thought for the materials and records in his care, and sought permission for their removal to a place of greater safety. This was only granted after the first weekend of bombing, and he then arranged for the use of an empty block of flats at Grove House, Nursling. For several days two vans were continuously employed moving the material. On the morning of 30 November the vans containing the last of the records and Crawford's private library were ready to leave, but the drivers had to attend a dental parade. So the lorries remained and were destroyed where they stood at London Road that evening.

Within a few weeks the Branch was disbanded. It was the end of Crawford's connection with the Survey and he retired early in 1945.

Notes

1 O. G. S. Crawford, *Said and Done, the Autobiography of an Archaeologist* (London 1951), p. 151 and *passim*.
2 O. G. S. Crawford, *Archaeology in the Field* (London 1955).
3 O. G. S. Crawford and A. Keiller, *Wessex from the Air* (Oxford 1928).
4 D. W. Riley, *Archaeological Journal* 1944, vol. 101, pp. 1–6; John Bradford, *Ancient Landscapes, Studies in Field Archaeology* (London 1957).
5 In Britain, Sir John Evans's maps in *Coins of the Ancient Britons*, 1864 and 1890, and by Lord Abercromby. In Germany, by Schlitz and Lissauer between 1904 and 1907.
6 *Geographical Journal* 1911, XL, pp. 184–203, 303–17.

25
The
Lean
Years
1922–1934

Close's Successors

Between 1922 and 1934 the Ordnance Survey was directed by two men of strikingly dissimilar character, Colonel (later Brigadier) E. M. Jack until 1930, and Brigadier H. St J. L. Winterbotham until 1934. Jack was a patient administrator, 'always tolerant and sympathetic, he had a notable gift for handling personal matters, and exceptional skill in pouring oil on troubled waters'.[1] He lacked the imagination and academic brilliance of his successor, but at a time when relations with the staff were difficult, his undoubted ability in personnel management was of crucial importance.

Evan Maclean Jack (1873–1951) was commissioned in the Royal Engineers on 25 July 1893. He was posted to Gibraltar for three years and then to St Helena, returning to England in 1903 to the Ordnance Survey where he served for four years, two in charge of the York office and two at Southampton. The next two years were spent as Assistant Commissioner on the Uganda-Congo Boundary Commission, after which he again returned to the Ordnance Survey, only to be sent on another boundary commission in Central Africa.

He was appointed a General Staff Officer in the Geographical Section of the War Office in 1913 but went to France with the British Expeditionary Force on the outbreak of war. He returned after the war to a subordinate appointment in the Geographical Section, General Staff, (MI 4), where his responsibilities included the preparation, storage and issue of operational and training maps for defence forces at home and overseas.[2] After the rigours of map supply in war, this job could hardly have taxed Jack's abilities to the full, and by 1921 he was in charge of the whole of MI 4 with the rank of Lieutenant-Colonel.

When Jack succeeded Close in 1922 as Director General, he was faced with the implementation of the draconian measures laid down by the Geddes Committee. The task of conducting the normal work of the Department with a greatly reduced staff prevented him from initiating any major changes, and for eight years he continued loyally to put into effect a mistaken policy, which was to result in an appalling reduction in the assets of the Department by allowing the revision of the large-scale plans to fall even further into arrears. His successor judged him to be 'sound, straight, kindly', but with a 'mental lag which pictured the circumstance of yesterday'.[3] He was promoted Brigadier in 1924 and retired in 1930.

The contrast between Jack and his successor must have been immediately self-evident. Harold St John Loyd Winterbotham (1878–1946) was a man of great ability, with an endless capacity for work. Yet he achieved very little, perhaps because he faced impossible odds. He was a prolific writer and had a flair for making witty and quotable comments on practically every aspect of Ordnance Survey work, past and present; he also made some striking claims on his own behalf. He was the first Director General (he said) who roamed around the country testing the maps and talking to agents behind the counter; he had 'done more about the air photo business than any other Englishman'. He was certainly brilliant, if egotistical, but he seemed to lack the capacity to get results, notably in the one field that he recognized as paramount: provision of adequate staff.

Winterbotham saw service in the South African War and later, in 1908, he was put in charge of the topographical survey of the Orange Free State, taking over the Colonial Survey Section which was then small party of two officers and four NCOs. Returning in 1911 to command the Trigonometrical Division of the Ordnance Survey, he completed the test triangulation at Lossiemouth. He succeeded Jack at MI 4 in 1922, and played a leading part in the founding of the journal *Empire Survey Review*. He was attached briefly to the Colonial Office in 1929 to inspect various colonial survey departments, and became Director General of the Ordnance Survey in 1930, a post which he occupied for only four years, at a time when the Ordnance Survey was in the 'absolute depths' with regard to the revision of the large-scale plans. Unlike Jack, he refused to accept the legacy of the Geddes Committee, and made ceaseless but ineffective efforts to increase the financial estimates for the Ordnance Survey. He calculated that it needed £400 000 instead of the £323 000 it received in 1935–6, and yet at the end, totally disenchanted, he could only say:

> . . . after four years I am no nearer driving the truth home than when I started. Such an increase is regarded as a joke in very questionable taste.[4]

Staff Problems

When Jack assumed responsibility for the Ordnance Survey in 1922, he inherited a discontented civilian staff whose mistrust of the military side of the Survey was manifestly the cause of many disagreements regarding recruiting, promotion and rates of pay. Fortunately these were largely resolved at an early stage through the machinery of the Whitley District Committee. The institution of regular promotion boards was the result of national acceptance of a report published in 1922,[5] and agreed to by the Ordnance Survey in December of that year. There followed through the ensuing eight years a succession of meetings of the Promotion Board Sub-Committee of the Whitley District Committee, until a suitable formula for the conduct of the boards was agreed by both sides.[6] Many of the Staff Side requests, such as their insistence on separate boards for technical and clerical grades, were acceded to by Jack.

Another difficult problem of this period was that of reclassification. In 1923 the Staff Side contended that, as civilian recruitment in recent years had been spasmodic or non-existent, many of the 'Normal' classification assistants* were of very long service and would have expected promotion long since.[7] It was felt that some of the older assistants had deserved earlier promotion but were no longer able to reach the standard of the 'Special' classification. The situation was further aggravated by the constant drafting into the civilian staff of Royal Engineers on completion of their military service at about the age of forty, who still had the prospect of twenty years service as civilians from their date of re-employment with the Ordnance Survey. The matter was eventually settled in 1930 by the promotion of several 'Normal' assistants at the age of fifty-seven.

New scales of pay and improved conditions of service for the civilian staff had been brought in by 1926. For the technical grades the most important reform lay in the reduction in 1924 of the number of scales of pay from fifteen to four; annual rates with regular increments were substituted for daily rates and irregular increases, and the age for reaching the maximum of the pay scale was reduced.[8] The negotiations for the clerical staff took much longer; annual scales were ultimately substituted for daily rates and most clerks received pay rises. To bring them into line with other government departments, the civilian clerical staff were in future to be recruited by public examination.

These were real improvements for the civilian staff, but their regular demands for the return of recruiting were the cause of prolonged disagreement with the management. They had borne the brunt of the reductions, and since no young assistants were being engaged it followed that no younger employees were being trained in the higher technical duties of the Department to fill the vacancies caused by retirement. Recruitment was, however, a point on which the Department had to maintain a rigid inflexibility. Not until the 1930s was there an increase in the Survey's complement of one thousand.

THE ABOLITION OF ENGRAVING

Until about 1914 the engraved plate remained unquestioned as the basis of the one-inch coloured map.[9]** From this time it was generally agreed that drawing combined with heliozincography provided a more efficient method of production, but the 120-year-old tradition of reproducing maps from

---

* In the Minute of the Board of Agriculture and Fisheries dated 23 Nov. 1911, commenting upon the Report of the Departmental Committee of 1911, and approving the new scales of pay, the Board agreed that the second classes and first classes of the new classification should be termed 'normal' and 'special' to 'prevent normally efficient Assistants from feeling aggrieved at being classified as 2nd class'.

** The change which led to the abolition of engraving was its replacement by drawing (in pen and ink on paper) and this was not linked in any direct way to the growing use of heliozincography. 'For the coloured [small scale] maps the engraving of copper plates [had been] reduced to a merely ancillary process; the plates were only used for the preparation of transfers, and the actual printing was done from stone or zinc'.

copper engravings was not abandoned lightly. One of the arguments put forward against the abolition of engraving was the enormous capital value stored in the copper plates.[10] Work of the highest quality was there intact, needing only periodic revision. Furthermore, the alterations which had been made in the plates of the large sheet series to make them suitable for use in making a coloured map had been carried out for nearly the whole of England. It had been a very costly exercise, and the engravers urged that to discard the result would be wasteful and extravagant. On the other hand, some loss was inevitable whenever one process of manufacturing was superseded by another.

The engravers were assured in 1920 by the Minister of Agriculture that no considerable reductions in the engraving department were envisaged.[11] But in September of that year several engravers were transferred to other duties, a move which caused disquiet, even though it was ostensibly occasioned by the Survey's being somewhat over strength. The older man who had spent most of his life acquiring the unique skills of this one department regarded a transfer to another, in which he had little or no experience, as a step towards his ultimate discharge, while the younger man saw his future advancement jeopardized.

The decision to abolish engraving was precipitated by the advent of the coloured Popular Edition one-inch map. A committee under Lieutenant-Colonel W. J. Johnston* appointed by the Director General in 1921 to consider the production of a coloured map, had expressed in its report a decided opinion that the best method would be redrawing, and reproduction by heliozincography, although it made no specific recommendations.[12] In spite of his earlier assurances, the Minister, briefed by Close, had already allowed for the abolition of engraving when he gave his undertaking to the Geddes Committee that the staff of the Ordnance Survey could be reduced to one thousand,[13] and Jack had agreed that the engraving department should be gradually phased out. By July 1923 the staff of seventeen established assistants and eight unestablished had been reduced to one who was retained for Admiralty work.[14]

In fighting the introduction of new methods and processes for the production of the one-inch map, the engravers seemed genuinely, or perhaps obstinately, unaware of the fact that the helio process had been used in the Ordnance Survey for twenty-five years, and that it was no new experiment. In this light, the patience and sympathy of Jack in guiding the employees towards the dissolution of their department was monumental. Official files provide ample evidence of the time and thoughtful consideration which he gave to the terms for a final settlement. Yet time after time he was accused of breaches of faith and broken agreements. The circular on the *Abolition of engraving and rules as to the disposal of engravers*,[15] which was issued on 5 May 1923, set out the terms of transfer, but it was greeted by a storm of protest from the Staff Side of the Whitley Council, who stated that 'the staff feel very strongly that they cannot accept the present terms as a final settlement without a lasting sense of grievance and dissatisfaction.'[16]

Six clauses governed the future of the engravers and showed the efforts being made to mitigate the adverse circumstances which were inevitably to face the staff affected. The second clause might have given some cause for alarm, stipulating that 'no engraver, whether established or unestablished, will be retained on the Ordnance Survey unless he qualifies on transfer for his new work within a period prescribed by the Director General', but Jack's assurances that 'Rule No 2 will be interpreted in a generous spirit, and, generally speaking, no engraver need have any apprehension as to his future, provided that he makes an honest attempt to fit himself for any new duties to which he may be allotted'[17] seems to have been accepted by the staff, but not by the engravers' union, who had earlier accused the management of adopting 'Victorian methods of administration'.[18]

The engravers were represented by the Amalgamated Society of Lithographic Artists, Designers, Engravers and Process Workers. This society figured prominently in the disputes and negotiations between staff and management for four years, harassing the Ministry with incessant correspondence in what was essentially an emotional conflict, characteristic of any enforced change in traditional ways. The Society's attitude was certainly counter-productive, generating unco-operative reaction from the Ministry which refrained from replying in detail to the letters on the grounds that 'we shall get into the position that we have to justify every change to this Trades Union'.[19]

The general dissatisfaction of the engravers with the way their situation had been handled was not entirely without cause. They believed that the decision to abandon engraving had been made on inadequate grounds, a belief made stronger by the apparent lack of any supporting documentary evidence. The question had been carefully considered by Close's 1921 Committee, but the report was confidential and its arguments and conclusions were not shown to the staff.

---

* Johnston was the officer in charge of the Publication Division.

Cost Accounting for the Ordnance Survey

> There are some things which I never understood and never shall – such as why the gates are shut on Friday and what use is cost accounting and what are we to do with our Whitley Councils?[20]

That the time-consuming inability of the Whitley Council to reach agreement should have occasionally exasperated Winterbotham is understandable, but his reference to cost accounting, however flippant, is more difficult to explain, especially in view of his earlier public statement that he was 'confident that cost accounting will continue to be of great value to us'.[21]

The Ordnance Survey scheme for cost accounting was prompted by the demand made by the National Economy Committee in the House of Commons, and by the Committee of Enquiry into Government Printing Establishments, which asked for definite information as to whether the prices of the small-scale maps covered the cost of production from first proof stage onwards. The latter Committee made radical recommendations which, had they been carried through, would have resulted in the transfer of the responsibility for the printing and sale of the Ordnance Survey maps to HM Stationery Office.[22] Fortunately the Ministry of Agriculture and Fisheries was able to submit cogent arguments against this advice and the Treasury finally agreed that the existing system should not be changed.

The principal objectives of the cost accounting scheme were to ascertain the efficiency of departmental control, the correct selling prices of Ordnance Survey maps, the cost of services performed for other Government departments, and the cost of the national mapping service.[23]

The Committee of Enquiry had assumed that there was a clear distinction between the stages in map production which were regarded as chargeable to the national Exchequer and the processes to be covered by the sale of maps. This supposition demonstrated the ever-present problem of communicating the way in which the Ordnance Survey worked to those with no previous knowledge of its operations. It would otherwise have been clearly realized that the stages of preparation in map-making were very closely interlocked. For example, while for some maps the negative was a mere stage in reproduction, for others the negative took the place formerly occupied by the engraved plates, revision was done on it and it had, for all practical purposes, to be regarded as the principal manuscript record.

Between 1928 and 1932 the work on cost accounting was experimental and was carried out with the help of a small group of specially trained staff loaned by the War Office.[24] It was recognized that the Ordnance Survey was an office of involved technical processes with much concealed interaction between the divisions, but even so the quantity of statistics that emerged during the course of the experiment was quite unforeseen. The major difficulty in working the scheme lay in the fundamental difference between the Ordnance Survey, as a State department, and commercial enterprises, which made it virtually impossible to apply normal accounting procedures. A business concern had to pay for whatever it received, and obtained the full benefit of the products it distributed. A State department, on the other hand, which was neither self-contained nor independent, frequently gave or took value without full recovery or payment. While such a system as a whole was probably economical from the point of view of the Exchequer, it increased the problems of studying a particular department's activities and added to the difficulties of cost accounting.

The cost accounting scheme did, however, highlight some of the probable causes of high production costs. Overheads were high because of the generous treatment of staff, compared with outside industry where leave, sickness privileges, superannuation or retirement gratuities, were all less favourable than those provided by the Ordnance Survey. Added to this the Survey's employees did not face the threat of being stood off during slack periods. It is true that the high cost of the superintending and administrative staff was partly due to the wealth of statistical material required of a government department, but the cost accounting experiment disclosed a considerable amount of unproductive supervision.[25]

Cost accounting also pointed out ways in which costs could be pruned. The numerous attractive map covers designed by Ellis Martin were expensive to produce and it was suggested that standard covers would be a better advertisement for the Survey because 'at present there are too many Ordnance Survey covers for the public to know them all'.[26] The small glossary of Gaelic words which was inserted in the Scottish Popular Edition of the one-inch map resulted in the printing and folding of these maps being more expensive than for any other small-scale map. Again, the purchaser of a complete set of quarter-inch maps was made a present of a case to hold the set, each case costing the Survey nine shillings; it was thought that this gift could be withdrawn.

One of the more interesting results of cost accounting was that it showed all map sales in terms of profit or loss for any sheet or for the series as a whole. A list was compiled of the Survey's issues together with their gross selling prices and profit or loss.[27] In the main this list justified the prices charged, which had previously been based on what was known to be insufficient evidence. The bulk of the sales were of maps which were linen-mounted and folded in covers, and satisfactory profits were made on these in general. The great losses occurred on those maps which were sectioned and mounted in covers, and also those on unmounted paper folded in covers. In particular the Ministry of Transport half-inch road maps, introduced in 1923, showed substantial losses from the very beginning. The reasons were not difficult to find, the principal one being that the Ministry of Transport's ideas on numbering roads changed more quickly than they had originally led the Ordnance Survey to expect. The maps were therefore soon out of date and much stock had to be cancelled.

When attending meetings of the Public Accounts Committee during the course of the cost accounting experiment, Winterbotham found the members surprisingly unversed in the functioning of the Ordnance Survey. After one meeting, characterized by a distinct lack of communication, he remarked:

> I was specially struck by a pleasant boy sitting on my left who had tried to follow the connection between the sad military history of a gentleman on my right, and the cost accounting of the Ordnance Survey. Failing entirely to make a connection he looked at me with bewilderment and asked who was really responsible for our work. When I told him the Ministry of Agriculture and Fisheries it knocked out of him all the little stuffing he had left. He gave it all up.[28]

A National Compromise: the Ordnance Survey in the Military Context

> In the Public Accounts Committee of the lower house a representative of the Treasury stated that the Ordnance Survey had always been considered 'an appanage of the War Office', whilst a conservative member asked how any public business could help but be mismanaged in military hands.[29]

Such was Winterbotham's embittered recollection of the largely inept interrogation he had received at the hands of the Public Accounts Committee in 1932. When Aneurin Bevan imprudently asked: 'Does the General think that the semi-military organization of his staff is the best way of doing the job which he has to do?' he was rebuked by the Chairman of the Committee for putting a question which was one of Government policy, and not for the Director General to determine. But Winterbotham had already answered: 'Emphatically I do, Sir.'[30]

Since its beginnings the Ordnance Survey had been a military department, with the military staff supplemented as necessary by civilians. When, in 1890, the President of the Board of Agriculture assumed, in respect of the Ordnance Survey, all the powers possessed until 1855 by the Master General of the Ordnance, he became the only Minister entitled to issue orders to the personnel of the Survey, including the officers and men of the Royal Engineers who were employed on it.

The sappers of the 13th, 14th, and 19th Survey Companies had from the first been scattered around Great Britain in locally based divisions. The officer commanding each of these divisions, which also contained civilians, usually held the rank of captain, with a sergeant as second-in-command. At Southampton the military held all the chief management positions. The Director General's immediate subordinate was the Executive Officer, who was usually a lieutenant-colonel or colonel, and the officers in charge of the various Divisions of the Ordnance Survey were all serving Royal Engineers, whose tour of duty was five years. This was occasionally exceeded in the case of senior officers.

The other ranks of the survey companies were recruited partly by competitive examination and partly as boy apprentices at the age of fifteen or sixteen by selection interviews. The latter were required to gain a first class Certificate of Army Education before enlisting at eighteen. There followed a year of military training at the School of Military Engineering at Chatham, and if they proved satisfactory, they served for twenty-one years on the Ordnance Survey. At the end of a soldier's service he was usually re-absorbed as a civilian, and he finally retired at sixty. For the serving soldier on the Ordnance Survey, the Ministry of Agriculture and Fisheries provided pay, allowances, rations, quarters, fuel and light, cost of educational instruction, travelling and medical expenses. The only charges borne by the War Office were for military clothing, training and pensions. The need for a civil-paid military presence on the Ordnance Survey was repeatedly questioned in the finance committees of the 1920s and 30s,[31] reflecting in part the anti-military sentiment of the times and also the failure on the part of civilians to comprehend the Ordnance Survey's military obligations to train soldiers for survey in war.

It had been held by all the Directors in the inter-war years that the officers, NCOs and men of the

Royal Engineers who served in the Ordnance Survey received excellent preparation for war while working on purely civil map requirements. This, however, was not enough to meet all military needs. Further training was necessary on the technical side and was provided by annual courses in military survey, lasting from April to September. Preliminary and advanced classes in trigonometrical and topographical surveying were held, at first at Bembridge in the Isle of Wight, and then at Fort Southwick on Portsdown. Additional training in topographical drawing and air-photo work was given in the winter months at Southampton, and the Trigonometrical Division of the Ordnance Survey was responsible for all-the-year-round training in trigonometrical computing.

But the operational training with other military units and headquarters was hardly adequate. Unlike the Artillery, which maintained a full Survey Company working continuously on special survey problems, the Royal Engineers were only able to provide, for exercises and manoeuvres, a Topographical Section which had been collected from all corners of the kingdom, and which only worked together for about a fortnight during the whole year. It was therefore ineffective in establishing and carrying out any operational role.

There was evidently a case for a permanent military training unit which would operate continuously. It was envisaged that men would complete a two-year tour with this unit which would be organized on the lines of its war establishment, with fully equipped topographical, drawing, litho and photo-printing sections. The idea was largely the brainchild of MacLeod, who devoted considerable energy to promoting his views on survey training.[32] He had held the post of Chief Instructor (Survey) at the School of Artillery at Larkhill from 1919 to 1923, where in 1919 he had formed, and commanded for a short time, the 1st Survey Company RA, a unique position for a Royal Engineer officer. His competence in the field of survey training was given recognition in 1922 when, still only a major, he was offered the post of Chief Instructor of Survey at the School of Military Engineering at Chatham, which he would have accepted, had not Jack offered him a post on the Ordnance Survey. MacLeod shrewdly reckoned that 'the latter seemed to me to hold out better prospects'.[33]

One of MacLeod's first moves on joining the Ordnance Survey in 1923 was to advocate that the 19th Survey Company should become a full-time training unit. This suggestion failed, for reasons unknown, to meet the approval of Winterbotham, then Chief of the Geographical Section, General Staff, and was shelved. After MacLeod took over at GSGS in 1929 he was able to put his ideas into effect. The three survey companies were reorganized to form the Survey Battalion RE and, in 1930, what had been the 19th Survey Company was detached from the Survey Battalion to form the 19th Field Survey Company which, unlike the Battalion, was not part of the establishment of the Ordnance Survey. Its formation was made possible, according to MacLeod, by his finding an ally in George Walker, Commandant of the School of Military Engineering and Inspector of the Royal Engineers, and it was largely because of his support that the Field Survey Company came into being.[34]

The main advantage of the existence of the 19th Field Survey Company was that it allowed a full six months training in trigonometry and topography before the men joined the Ordnance Survey. In this way the interruption of their work on the Survey was reduced to a minimum, and GSGS was satisfied by having an RE survey unit administered and commanded through the normal channels.

As well as preparation for military survey duties, the officers and men employed on the Survey had to undergo ordinary military training such as musketry and drill, and this caused further interruption to normal work; the fact that the men were paid by the War Office at these times could hardly compensate the Ordnance Survey for the time lost.

The position of the Royal Engineers of the Survey Battalion in relation to the civilian organization by which they were employed was that they were loaned by the War Office to the Ministry of Agriculture and Fisheries, who paid their wages. The relationship of the sapper surveyors, whose headquarters at Southampton was within the area of Southern Command, to military authority was shrouded in confusion and misunderstanding. Until 1927 their status was never officially set down in army orders. It frequently happened that Royal Engineers of the survey companies, who carried out their peace-time duties on Ordnance Survey work in areas of different military commands, were ordered by the respective GOCs to submit themselves for inspection and to other military discipline. There were difficult and sometimes acrimonious exchanges when it fell to the Director General to explain that, while he had no wish to demilitarize the Ordnance Survey, the military commands had no right to interfere with the procedures of the Survey, which was a civil and not a military body.[35]

Determined to end such fruitless altercations, Jack requested that a special order be issued explaining the position of the Ordnance Survey. *Order No 1264–Ordnance Survey* was accordingly published by GOC Southern Command in December 1927, and laid down the chain of authority to which the Survey was subject.[36] It was essentially a modification of a memorandum written by Close several years previously on 'The relations between the Royal Engineers of the Ordnance Survey and the Military Commands'. It established that the formal channel of communication between any Command and the Director General of the Ordnance Survey was via the War Office through the Ministry of Agriculture and Fisheries. Certain exceptions to this rule were made for the sake of administrative convenience. For example, military matters which were not concerned with policy were discussed directly with the War Office, and the line of communication was then between the Director General and the Director of Military Operations and Intelligence. Those cases of discipline where the powers of the Director General were insufficient to deal with the offender were referred to the most convenient Command for court-martial.

In the uncertain political climate of the inter-war years, the Directors of the Survey frequently found themselves, as had their predecessors in the previous century, justifying the employment of military personnel. The benefits which accrued to the Army from the arrangement with the Ordnance Survey were obvious, but those which the Ordnance Survey derived from the Army were not so readily discernible to government officials. The benefits of a military command seemed indeed to be somewhat intangible. It was a highly emotive subject, steeped in the traditions of the military origin of the Survey. Trying to foresee the future of the serving Royal Engineers of the Ordnance Survey, Winterbotham wrote in 1934 that he thought it 'probable that the present position will last just as long as officers and other ranks of the Royal Engineers provide the nation with specially good service – ordinary honest work will hardly suffice in a time of anti-military sentiment'.[37] The Staff Side of the Ordnance Survey Whitley District Committee justifiably complained that serving soldiers could not be expected to show the same efficiency as civilians because of the constant interruptions caused by absence on military duties. Important officials of the Ministry of Agriculture and Fisheries considered that the Ordnance Survey could be officered as efficiently from the civil surveying professions. These were small noises of discontent, it is true, but their persistence generated an uneasy atmosphere between military and civilian personnel.

The Royal Engineer officer could certainly claim some advantages not generally available to his civilian counterpart. Firstly, the officer had a thorough introduction to the study of ground forms – the basis of minor tactics. His survey training, begun as a cadet, continued at the School of Military Engineering, and then on the Ordnance Survey. Secondly, the officer's engineer training was invaluable to the Survey, and it could be said that much of the evolution in map printing in England in the nineteenth and early twentieth centuries was a result of invention and improvement by the Corps. The Royal Engineer officers also had frequent opportunity to experience survey work abroad. It seemed, therefore, that during the inter-war period the Royal Engineer officer was the best qualified to head the various divisions of the Ordnance Survey. A comparison of the enlisted man and the civilian did not, however, reveal the same measure of superiority. From a national point of view there was certainly a disadvantage in the disturbance and loss of time due to military training, but the soldier, who served for twenty-one years, could be removed from the Survey by the Director General at any one of several times during this period if he proved unsatisfactory. It was not as easy to shift the civilian bad bargain.

In the years from 1919 to 1935 the position of the civilians as a whole seemed even more vulnerable and insecure than before. Staff Side complaints at Whitley meetings were founded on a deep-seated objection to the recruiting policy of the Ordnance Survey.[38] It required little thought on the part of the civilians to realize that, given a fixed establishment, and the fact that soldiers retired into a civilian position on the Survey after active service, it would not take long before the only means of entry into the Ordnance Survey would be through the Royal Engineers. The increase in the proportion of soldiers during the early 1930s seemed to reinforce this argument. In 1930 the number of Royal Engineers of the Survey Battalion fell short of the peace-time establishment of 450 by almost 150. It was therefore possible to increase military strength within the limits of the authorized man-power but it was decided not to augment the number of Engineers *en bloc* as this would have meant the dismissal of civilians. It followed that the military element was only increased when a civilian retired, but this policy, which had been designed to give some protection to civilians in post, was seen by them as a deliberate means of decivilianizing the Ordnance Survey. Only when the military establishment was complete could civilian recruitment begin again, but this prospect was not regarded with much confidence by the civil staff.

The main justification for an essentially military organization for the Ordnance Survey continued to be that given by Herbert Murray in 1871.[39] A military survey capability had to be maintained in peace-time, and so it was a question of 'whether it should be maintained in idleness or doing unproductive work, or whether it should be kept in a productive Department, so that it earns its daily keep, as it were, while it is in training'.[40] Only if the two elements of this dual role became incompatible would the justification fail.

The Changing Face of Post-War Britain and the Large-Scale Plans

It was 'by the irony of circumstance, [that] the reduction of Ordnance Survey staff coincided with a period of great development'.[41] New houses, industrial estates and road-building projects had rendered even the most recent plans obsolete, and exacerbated the dislocation of the revision of the large-scale plans caused by the war. During the years from 1922 to 1933, the annual output of revised twenty-five-inch plans fell from about 2100 to just over 500. There had been no relaxation in the post-war policy of financial stringency; ten years after the Geddes Report, the staff of the Ordnance Survey remained at its 1922 quota of one thousand.

About thirty counties were taken up for revision on the 1:2500 scale during these years, and as revision became increasingly limited to areas completely altered and built over, field work tended more and more to approximate to resurvey and so the time required for each sheet constantly grew. The selection of areas of intensive change was, moreover, by no means easy, and many municipalities began to undertake their own revisions, which varied so greatly in quality as to be useless for national purposes.

One of the first measures adopted with the aim of cutting costs and speeding up production was the publication of areas of parcels to the plan edge only. In the same year, 1922–3, it was decided to discontinue the filling up of the border plans of a county with parts of plans of the adjacent county when that was drawn on a different meridian. The mounting pressure on the Department to find ways of hastening the process of revision inevitably reached the Drawing Section, which theoretically kept pace with field revision. Each edition of the 1:2500 plans was produced from a manuscript drawing which consisted of redrawn old work and new drawing from the recent revision. It was self-evident that if the need for redrawing could be eliminated much time and money would be saved, and furthermore there would be no loss of accuracy. It was with this objective that several experiments were undertaken in the late 1920s which hinged on the use of a special coated paper.[42] It was soon demonstrated that a good print of the old plan was a satisfactory substitute for redrawing, and that if this print was produced on paper coated with a celluloid solution the parts to be corrected could easily be removed by the application of a suitable solvent. This method was hailed as a great advance on the time-honoured tradition of painstakingly redrawing, and Jack ordered its gradual introduction in 1930. But within two years doubts as to the quality of the work were being voiced. The standard was not up to that of the old. Ink flaked off the new surface for no apparent reason, and by 1934 the special paper was used only when the amount of alteration since the last edition was so small as not to merit the redrawing of the plan. Much time and effort had been spent in merely proving the worth of the old methods, but it had been an interesting demonstration of the Survey's alertness to the possibilities of new labour-saving devices.

THE LARGE-SCALE PLANS AND AIR PHOTOGRAPHY

Jack's term as Director General was notable for another much more ambitious experiment, undertaken in 1925–6, again searching for a solution to the accumulating revision problem. While aerial methods were not generally thought suitable for revision work, the mapping of certain areas which were difficult of access – such as tidal regions, fenlands, extensive mudflats and foreshores – obviously might benefit from the technique. It was with this in mind that attempts had been made by the Air Ministry to provide photographic cover of the channel of the River Duddon and Poole Harbour between 1922 and 1924. Both efforts proved abortive, partly because of bad weather.[43]

Jack himself remained convinced that air photography offered distinctly valuable prospects[44] but that nothing definite could be decided until it had received a comprehensive test under Ordnance Survey conditions. In formulating his ideas he was fortunate in having the advice of Winterbotham who, as head of the Geographical Section, General Staff, still sat on the Air Survey Committee, on which he had represented the Ordnance Survey only a few years previously. The experiments, which were to be carried out in the Eastbourne area, were designed to answer three questions: whether alterations on the ground appeared clearly enough on the photograph to enable them to be identified; whether data shown on the photograph was sufficient to enable the position of all new features to be transferred to the plan with the requisite accuracy; and how much revision on the ground would be required after the completion of the photographic plotting.[45]

The Air Ministry was unable to provide official facilities, so civil firms were invited to tender for the aerial photography. The quotations varied from £5 per square mile to over £15 per square mile.[46] The cheapest, and therefore successful, application was from the Aircraft Operating Company who, after many frustrating false starts, finally completed the work in October 1925. The photographs were taken using an F8 camera with a fourteen-inch lens, borrowed from the Royal Air Force, but the pilot had to operate the shutter by hand because the minimum intervalometer setting was too long, which resulted in some rather erratic flying; then it was found that the first films were ruined by static electrical discharges.[47]

At first it was hoped that it would be possible to trace off the revision from rectified enlargements of the photographs. The negatives were projected directly onto a screen which could be tilted about two axes at right angles, and attempts were then made to obtain an exact fit to four points on the unrevised map. The method proved to be slow, costly and difficult, because it was often necessary to adjust a photograph in several separate parts; it was soon abandoned and replaced by the familiar procedure of resection and intersection, on the assumption that the plumb points and principal points coincided. The revision traces then had to be examined on the ground and features which were invisible (such as wire fences) or concealed (such as the centre lines of hedges) added. It was concluded that although the accuracy of the method compared favourably with that of ground revision, the cost, particularly in rural areas, was very much greater, amounting overall to an increase of over forty-five per cent. A second experiment near Brighton, begun in 1928, confirmed these findings, but suggested that a saving might be made in dense urban areas if some relaxation in the standard of completeness was accepted.[48] In spite of his initial optimism, Jack was led to conclude that air photography was not generally suitable for 1:2500 revision.

In 1933 the Ordnance Survey gave permission to the Air Survey Company to use Ordnance Survey plans as a basis for rectifying air photographs, but as a *quid pro quo* demanded free copies of the rectified photographs.[49] This was a useful arrangement and, as Winterbotham remarked, 'the present revision of Middlesex is quite largely based on them'. Notwithstanding Jack's earlier conclusions, by this time the Ordnance Survey had one Assistant Superintendent and about eighteen well-trained men constantly working on air photographs. The graphical method of revision had been refined by adapting the Arundel method[50]* for fixing control points, and introducing an epidiascope for transferring detail. The positions of the principal points were resected onto the plan from existing old detail; height control points were then selected on the photographs at significant changes of slope so as to define the main planar elements of the ground surface. These points were intersected on the radial line traces and transferred to the plan, where they served as the control points for taking off new detail from the photographs in the epidiascope. In spite of the financial restraints of these lean years, some important research was carried out, mainly under War Office direction, into several of the fundamental problems of air survey. The success of this work is very largely attributable to the Research Officers of the War Office Air Survey Committee, at first Captain M. Hotine, then Lieutenant J. S. A. Salt and finally Captain E. H. Thompson. Both Hotine and Thompson were brilliant mathematicians and Thompson was an outstanding engineer and instrument designer. As early as 1926 a large stereoplotting machine ('Big Bertha') was designed and manufactured by Barr and Stroud in consultation with the Committee, and in the early 1930s two versions of a much smaller instrument, a stereogoniometer, were made in association with H. G. Fourcade; later this instrument was redesigned and refined by Thompson. Two of the redesigned plotters were made by Barr and Stroud and sent to the Ordnance Survey at Southampton for experimental work; a Wild A5 stereoplotting machine was also acquired and installed. At about the same time Thompson designed the stereocomparator, manufactured by the Cambridge Instrument Company, which was to be widely used during and after the Second World War; one of these instruments was set up in the Ordnance Survey Office with the three plotting machines. The purpose of this impressive concentration of machinery was to investigate the relative advantages of analytical and analogue methods of making high precision surveys from air photographs. It was a great misfortune that the work was cut short by the war; both stereogoniometers were destroyed and the A5 severely damaged in air raids in 1940.

---

* The Arundel Method was so named after a trial air survey of a small area near Arundel carried out in 1926. The method was based on the linking together of radial line traces made from each photograph to form strips. See M. Hotine, *Simple Methods of Surveying from Air Photographs* (Professional Papers of the Air Survey Committee no. 3). It was later elaborated by combining and adjusting the strips into blocks.

GOVERNMENT ACTS AND THE LARGE-SCALE PLANS

The speeding up of revision was of prime importance, for in the period 1922–34 the Government passed six Acts which required the use of Ordnance Survey plans for their implementation, so that the geographical pattern of revision came to be dominated by requirements such as those of the Land Registration Act of 1925. This Act repealed the Land Transfer Act of 1875, and under the new laws the registration of title to land could, by an Order in Council, be made compulsory on sale in any specified county. An up-to-date plan was an essential preliminary to registration; by 1928 the time taken to revise any plan specifically for compulsory registration was so long that, at the suggestion of the Land Registry, a Departmental Committee under the chairmanship of the Registrar, John Stewart-Wallace, was appointed to consider the situation. One of the most important of the Committee's recommendations[51] was that the Ordnance Survey should take over, when staff arrangements permitted, as much as was practicable of the surveying work then being carried out by the Land Registry in both voluntary and compulsory areas of land registration. The Committee felt that it was 'impossible at present to recommend any permanent addition to the Ordnance Survey to cope with this work', but did recommend that the Land Registry should, as an experiment, undertake to pay the Ordnance Survey up to a maximum of £3000 a year for the next three years, to enable them to engage extra temporary staff. This additional staff, it was suggested, 'could be used by the Ordnance Survey, when not required for Land Registry work, on their normal revision, thus enabling them to get somewhat ahead of their programme.[52] The £3000 per annum was never paid, but Treasury authority for the increase in establishment of sixteen was obtained in September 1928. The pay of these men was estimated to cost £3000 a year, but the Land Registry was only charged for the work done.

By 1930 it became clear that the Department was not able to cope with the continuous revision needed for Land Registry purposes. Most of the work was now in suburban London, where industrial development had spread so rapidly that the revision of the plans was urgent. Unfortunately the old tertiary control had been obliterated and it was therefore necessary to retriangulate or traverse the London area. In 1930 a partial solution to the problem was found by disbanding the Norwich Office and re-establishing it in London, specifically to maintain a direct contact with the Land Registry. In 1934, when the compulsory registration order for Middlesex was made, the Ordnance Survey was receiving over four thousand survey cases* a year and an increase in the staff estimates of £20 000 was allowed for one year to enable the revision of Middlesex to be accelerated.[53]

Winterbotham's term of office saw a marked improvement in the relationship between the two departments, which was unfortunately not to survive him. The amount of personal attention which he gave to the problems of the Land Registry was such as to prompt Stewart-Wallace to say: 'How fortunate we have been in having a Director General of the Ordnance Survey who has taken steps to enable registration to be effected with ease and speed'.[54] It is evident that, in spite of the logistical problems which it posed, Winterbotham saw in land registration the means of establishing continuous revision at little cost to the taxpayer.[55]

The Town and Country Planning Acts of 1925 and 1932 also led to heavy localized demands on the Survey's meagre resources. It is true that the acts did not mention maps, but in the various orders issued by the Minister of Health, regulations were laid down which compelled local authorities not only to provide maps, but to ensure that they were up-to-date, causing an exasperated Winterbotham to comment that 'the Ministry of Health writes survey legislation into its instructions to all and sundry with entire disregard of the national survey'.[56]

The largely unsuccessful struggles of the Ordnance Survey to keep pace with revision led, in the early 1930s, to the formation of several private air and land survey companies, each vying with the others to provide a quick service for local authorities. But they too were unsuccessful, partly because of the growth of municipal surveying offices which desired to keep all surveying work in their own hands, and partly because there was 'imbued in the nation for one hunderd years the feeling that they pay for an Ordnance Survey, and they do not see any reason why it should not function'.[57]

Under the terms of the Slum Clearance Act of 1930 it was proposed to build a million new houses within the next few years. At current rates of progress this would have provided the Ordnance Survey with ten years' work, and in the event most authorities had to add the alterations themselves on the old plans.

Another Act which stretched the resources of the Ordnance Survey was the Land Valuation Act (1931). It was hoped that 3500 plans would be specially revised for this purpose in fifteen months, an

---

* A 'survey case' was a special survey or investigation carried out by the Ordnance Survey for the Land Registry.

almost impossible objective at this time. When the previous land valuation had been undertaken in 1912, the Ordnance Survey had a much larger staff and a greater degree of flexibility than in the 1930s. In 1912 the strength of the revisers in Great Britain was 343, and there was an additional staff of 188 revisers in Ireland which could be drawn on, bringing the total to 531. In 1931 the strength of revisers was 99, with no reserve of men. As a result of the immense acceleration of building after the war there was at least twice as much to add in the valuation revision of 1931 as there had been in 1912.[58]

Clearly the Ordnance Survey as it was could not be expected to fulfil all the demands of land valuation. Great efforts were made to increase the strength of the Survey; Assistants were kept on beyond retiring age, others who had retired were re-employed, and the normal drawing for the six-inch sheets was suspended. The minimum of information was to be shown on the twenty-five-inch plans for land valuation: only road construction and the points along the roads where property boundaries intersected.[59] The great and positive effort made by the Ordnance Survey to co-operate with the Land Valuation Department was ultimately of no avail because within a few months orders were received to suspend work. The specially engaged staff had to be dis-engaged and once again the national plans had 'suffered greatly in capital value'.[60]

The normal pattern of publication of the six-inch sheets, which followed closely on that of the twenty-five-inch, had not been maintained during the war. By 1925 approximately half the backlog had been cleared, and the publication of the six-inch maps in quarter-sheet form was resumed because of objections to the full sheet, which had been introduced as a measure of economy in 1919.[61] The reversion to quarter-sheets delayed the clearance of arrears, and the original plan for completing this by 1926 was further frustrated by the continual drafting of trained men for service abroad.* In 1930 it was 'still not possible to reduce the time between the publication of the twenty-five-inch and the six-inch to a desirable minimum'.[62]

The Small-Scale Maps

THE ONE-INCH MAP

In 1921 Johnston and Winterbotham had been commissioned by Close to consider redrawing the map of Scotland, instead of using the old engraved plates.[63] They spent some time examining foreign topographical maps before deciding in favour of redrawing; another of their major recommendations was that the lettering on the map should be in an improved style. The opportunity was also taken to adopt the same projection for Scotland as that used for England and Wales, making for the first time a continuous one-inch map of Great Britain. The Ordnance Survey had been 'for a century embarrassed by the fact that England was on the Cassini, and Scotland, by the obscure decision of some rash Director General, on Bonne, so that in spite of the Union the two countries would never join at the Border'.[64]

Another innovation in the Scottish map[65] was the larger sheet size which allowed for an overlap of one inch all round. The method of showing relief, by interpolating contours at intervals of 50 feet to supplement the surveyed contours, won universal approval from Scottish users. Those contours which marked intervals of 250 feet above sea-level were thickened. The map was drawn at the scale of two inches to one mile for reproduction by heliozincography and incorporated new styles of writing which were evolved on what was called the 'Perth sample'.[66] A striking change was the use of solid black instead of cross-hatching for built-up areas.

'In the light of experience', said Winterbotham in 1934, 'Close made a mistake in leaving off the Popular Edition all record of administrative boundaries. Indeed, from the moment he did so until today complaints continue to come in and we are putting Parish boundaries on the Fifth Edition.'[67]** The error of omission seems to have been quickly perceived, however, as parish boundaries were inserted on the new Scottish edition of the one-inch, the first three sheets of which were published by 1925. The whole of the drawing for Scotland was completed in 1931.

The drawback of the Popular Edition of England and Wales was that it had been produced from copper plates, and soon became difficult and exceedingly expensive to maintain because of the

---

* In 1927 51 men were employed abroad on colonial surveys, boundary commissions, or attached to military units.

** Writing to Close, 25.4.1931, Winterbotham explained the re-introduction of parish boundaries as due to the 'conservatism of the British Public', and that 'there have been so many insistent demands for them that Jack decided to re-introduce them'.

necessity for constant revision.* The usual interval for the revision of the one-inch sheets was fifteen years but now, for the first time, intermediate revision became essential to keep the road information up to date. The special roads revision was begun in 1925 and the results were incorporated on the one-inch and smaller scales as the sheets became due for printing or reprinting.[68] Publication of the Fourth or Popular Edition of England and Wales, based on the third revision of 1924–5, was complete in 1927, and the sheets continued to be reissued with road revisions until replaced by either the Fifth Edition or the War Revision Series.

The fourth revision, which was to be the basis of the Fifth Edition of the one-inch map, was begun in December 1928. The new map embodied many improvements and was considered at the time to be the zenith of the Ordnance Survey's cartographic achievements. It was known as the Fifth (Relief) Edition, and took its name from the elaborate technique employed in showing relief, apparently attributable to Winterbotham, who considered that 'that curious person, the average man . . . understands the idea of contouring, but is quite unable to visualise ground form from it, especially undulating or flat country.'[69] Jack had wanted a straightforward contoured map in the style of the Popular, the only difference being in the lettering, and in his *Report* for 1929–30 he commented that the details for the new map had been worked out by Captain J. G. Withycombe. Withycombe, who has been described as 'an artist by profession and by nature, as well as being a surveyor', had given a paper on lettering styles for the Ordnance Survey maps,[70] giving rise to the so-called 'alphabet controversy'. Winterbotham appeared, at least in private, to resent the credit given to one who took over the design at a late stage, and was quick to point out that the designing of the new map was 'entirely personal to myself'. There was considerable justification in this claim for, although the Fifth (Relief) Edition was truly heir to the *Killarney* experiment of 1913, it required less than half the number of printings. When Winterbotham was Director General, he told Close that 'the Killarney sheet hangs behind me on the wall, and it was there during the whole course of the colour designing of the new map'. He further itemized his qualifications as foremost designer of the map:

> I inherited, you see, the result of three things. First of all, the experience of the early experiments in '13 and '14. Secondly, an investigation which you called for soon after the war on modern continental cartography. And thirdly the designing of alphabets for the map of Scotland upon which we had come to a general conclusion before Withycombe took over.[71]

In fact, work on the specifications had been in progress during Jack's term of office. However, by the time the map appeared, there was no trace of the one feature for which Jack had been responsible. This was the decorative border, which was intended solely to add to the artistic value of the map. Winterbotham considered that it did not, and left it off.

The early sheets of the Fifth (Relief) Edition were undoubtedly beautiful productions. The new writing was mostly clear and legible, but the map was saturated with colour and even thicker in appearance than the Third Edition, partly because the whole sheet was covered with layer tints. The layers and the hachures (the sole surviving element of the engraved map) were in the same golden shade, but the hachures on the shaded side of the hills were overprinted in purple. Winterbotham said in 1932: '. . . layers, hachures and shadows must be regarded as mere aids to the general effect. The layer convention is really destroyed by the added colour of the hachures, the relative emphasis of the hachures is lost in the layers.' He added: 'The map must not cost more than the Popular and must not take longer to prepare'.[72] With a relief system of such complexity this was a difficult condition to fulfil, and in the flatter part of the country the effect produced hardly justified the effort.

Perhaps the most significant innovation of the Fifth (Relief) Edition was the use of a grid based on the Transverse Mercator projection. Winterbotham did not believe the public was ready for a grid, but it was introduced none the less as a result of pressure brought to bear not only by the military, but also by such pillars of the geographical establishment as the Royal Geographical Society. The grid was printed in 5000 yard squares, with the origin well to the south-west of Britain. Its introduction provoked intense discussion and interest, but it was not an idea original to the Ordnance Survey. As Winterbotham remarked: 'If anyone thinks we are being singular in the introduction of a grid system . . . we are one of the last in Europe to come to it'.[73]

Close had commented in 1924 that the grid might be used by civilians 'if there were an index of names accompanying each sheet as was suggested some years ago, though the war interfered with the carrying out of the project so that there is now no such index'.[74] The idea was resurrected with the beginning of the fourth revision of the one-inch map, and the compilation of a gazetteer was begun for

---

* Popular Edition sheets based on the engraved map were often redrawn when revised. After 1923 very little revision could have been done on the copper plates themselves.

departmental convenience to save time and labour in referencing.[75] As an experiment a gazetteer was published in 1931 for the Plymouth sheet, the first sheet of the Fifth (Relief) Edition, in a big issue of over five thousand copies. But only forty-one of the gazetteers had been sold by 1933, and in 1935 work on them was stopped.[76]

Winterbotham believed that convenient sheet-lines were an essential element in sales promotion. With the Fifth Edition in mind, he wrote in 1932:

> Recent years have made it abundantly clear that we must for ever be re-arranging sheet lines for the man-in-the-street's convenience or very naturally he will not buy.[77]

A decade or so later such a concept was to be regarded as wantonly extravagant because revision had to be incorporated not just once but on every overlap and on every special sheet; furthermore the sales of special sheets were usually at the expense of the standard series. So, apart from its cartographic elaboration, the Fifth (Relief) Edition had to carry the burdens of varying sheet sizes, large overlaps and special sheets. In spite of all Winterbotham's hopes for the new map, it had a limited life which was to come to an end in 1937.[78] Sales had shown that it was not popular with the public, and since it was costly to produce, it was discontinued. In 1934 Winterbotham had already decided to yield to the fashion for simplicity and produce a Fifth Edition without the relief plates.[79] The two maps were to be distinguished by a red cover for the relief edition and a blue one for the simpler style. Jack's original instinct to go for a purely contoured map had, after all, been vindicated.

The passing of the London Passenger Transport Act in 1933 led to the twelve-sheet London Passenger Transport Map. Overprinted on the black and blue plates of the Popular Edition were the administrative boundaries of the Metropolitan Police District, the London Passenger Transport Area, and the London and Metropolitan Traffic Areas.

THE HALF-INCH AND SMALLER SCALES

The revision of the half-inch map had been started in 1932, but its production was constantly delayed because of the numerous corrections and alterations which had to be made, such as the changing names of railways and the adding of new aerodromes and wireless stations. By 1930 the half-inch was hardly mentioned in the annual reports. This was because 'every available man was pushed into the country and the half-inch was set aside for better times'.[80]

In 1922 the quarter-inch map was published in atlas form, entitled the *Ordnance Survey Atlas of England and Wales*. It sold for thirty shillings and was accompanied by an 'Index to towns and villages'. The whole of Scotland was published at this scale by 1942, and was also issued as an atlas; shortly afterwards the two atlases were combined to form the *Ordnance Survey Atlas of Great Britain*.

It was decided in 1927 to change the sheet-lines of the quarter-inch series to a more rational layout. Two years later the roads were given the Ministry of Transport road numbers and the series was further enhanced by the addition of town traffic diagrams showing the principal routes through the chief towns. This map, which was in effect the Third Edition of the quarter-inch, was soon superseded by the Fourth Edition, which was in course of preparation in 1933.

Besides the change of projection to the Transverse Mercator and fewer sheets – eleven instead of twelve – the new Fourth Edition was quite different in appearance. It remedied the defects of the Third, but at some expense of clarity because of the over-all brown effect produced by the red and brown roads and the wholly buff and brown layers which had been adopted in order to release the green colour for the woods. Loss of quality in later printings led to the maps appearing to be overburdened with detail. The old two-inch alpha-numerical square referencing system was replaced by the 10 000 yard grid to keep in step with the Fifth Edition of the one-inch map. The quarter-inch scale, like the one-inch and half-inch, was also used for special district sheets; the South Central sheet covering an unusual area from London south to Bournemouth, west to Bath and north to Birmingham had been published in 1924 and had proved very popular.

The progress and publication of the other small-scale maps included the completion of the ten-mile map of Great Britain in three sheets. It was finished in 1927 and a special air edition was published in 1929. The Ordnance Survey was also responsible for producing the 1:1 million *International Map of the World* for Great Britain: sheets NN30 and NM30 were published in 1932.

Scientific Work

The Research Officer, Jolly, was becoming increasingly involved in international geodetic conferences. He was a regular participant in the triennial conference of the International Union for Geodesy and Geophysics (IUGG), where he reported on the geodetic work carried on in Great Britain. It fell to his lot in the early 1920s to spend considerable time in preparing reports on the determination of longitude, latitude and azimuth, and especially on the geodetic applications of wireless telegraphy. Such work, although it showed no immediate benefit to the Survey, was justified to Jack by the need for international co-operation; it also kept the Research Officer busy. By 1924 Jolly had become Assistant to the Secretary of the Geodesy Section of the IUGG and had produced translations of the 1923 Rome proceedings; he also became responsible for maintaining the correspondence between the Ordnance Survey and other geodetic organizations.

The Magnetic Survey, which was a recent addition to the scientific responsibilities of the Ordnance Survey, became due for revision in 1925. The Channel Islands, which had not been included in the previous survey, were selected as a suitable starting-off point. The revision took nine years to complete and resulted in a fairly dense pattern of observed magnetic stations, averaging about one every 25 square miles. The magnetic edition of the Physical Map of Scotland was published in 1934 and that of England was redrawn and a new edition published in 1933. The Second Magnetic Survey was finished before Winterbotham retired and the third survey, or second revision, was scheduled for ten to fifteen years later.

In 1927 the Ordnance Survey acquired another scientific interest: gravity survey. The accurate determination of the force of gravity throughout the kingdom had never been thoroughly investigated and was long overdue. The Survey co-operated with the Geographical Section, General Staff, and the School of Geodesy at Cambridge in making pendulum observations, but the work was carried out sporadically and only sixty-six stations were observed in six years. It was, however, another sphere in which Jolly participated, in particular by designing new pendulum apparatus which greatly reduced the bulk and weight to be transported.

Notes

1 *Royal Engineers Journal* 1951 vol. 65, pp. 442–5.
2 For a description of the duties of MI 4a, see *War Office List* (HMSO 1919), p. 103.
3 Winterbotham's 'Handover Notes' to MacLeod, 1934, p. 12.
4 *Ibid.* p. 13.
5 National Council for the Administrative and Legal Departments of the Civil Service. *Committee on Promotion. First Report* (HMSO 1921).
6 See, for example, OS circulars c.c.821 and 821A, *Principles and regulations governing promotion on the Ordnance Survey*, 23 May 1923 and 5 Dec. 1925; c.c.823 *Promotion boards* 5 July 1923.
7 Minutes of Ordnance Survey Whitley District Committee, 22 Nov. 1923, p. 120.
8 OSR 1925–6, pp. 2–3. The Ordnance Survey Progress Reports ceased to be Command papers after 1921.
9 OSR 1921–2, p.4.
10 See PRO OS 1/9 for the arguments against abolition put forward by the engravers' union.
11 PRO OS 1/9. Letter dated 2.9.1920.
12 *Ibid.* The report of this Committee does not appear to have survived, but it is referred to in 'Report on Engraving as a basis for small scale Ordnance Survey Maps, corrected to 4 April 1923'.
13 *Ibid.* Sir Francis Floud to the Treasury, 20 April 1923.
14 *Ibid.* Memorandum dated 27 July 1923.
15 OS circular, c.c. 819.
16 PRO OS 1/9: Whitley Staff Side report to the Director General, 15 Sept. 1923.
17 OS circular, c.c. 819.
18 PRO OS 1/9: R. Kneale, General Secretary of the Engravers' Union, to the Ministry of Agriculture and Fisheries. 8 Oct. 1920.
19 *Ibid.* Memorandum dated 28 Sept. 1920.

20 'Handover Notes', p. 29.

21 OSR 1931–2, p. 7.

22 *Report of a Committee of Inquiry into Government Printing Establishments*, pp. 111–25: PP 1927, Cmd. 2828, IX.

23 PRO OS 1/21.

24 *Ibid.* See the report on the Departmental Committee on cost accounting for the Ordnance Survey, 3 Aug. 1928.

25 For a fuller analysis see PRO OS 1/21, report by the Warrant Officer in charge of cost accounting, April 1932.

26 PRO OS 1/21.

27 *Ibid.* Warrant Officer's report.

28 *ibid.* Winterbotham to Watson, 16 April 1932.

29 'Handover Notes', p. 160.

30 *First and Second Reports from the Select Committee of Public Accounts*, Evidence, q. 3366: PP 1931–2 (42, 93) IV.

31 *Reports from the Select Committee of Public Accounts.* Evidence, q. 4082 and *passim*: PP 1929–30 (70, 137) V.

32 M. N. MacLeod, 'Military Survey', *Royal Engineers Journal*, 1923, XXXVII, pp. 619–26.

33 MacLeod, 'Autobiographical Notes', typescript in the Ordnance Survey Library.

34 *Ibid.*

35 PRO OS 1/110: memorandum by Close on relations between the Royal Engineers of the Ordnance Survey and the Military Commands, 7 Jan. 1920.

36 PRO OS 1/110.

37 'Handover Notes'.

38 Minutes of the Ordnance Survey Whitley District Committee, 20 Feb. 1924.

39 See p. 163.

40 *Reports from . . . Committee of Public Accounts*, Evidence para. 2051: PP 1930–1 (48, 114) V.

41 OSR 1929–30, p. 17.

42 See the OS Reports for these years.

43 See the OS Reports for 1922–3 and 1923–4, under *Air Photography*.

44 PRO OS 1/11: notes on informal discussions with Colonel Crosthwaite, Aircraft Operating Co. Ltd., 19 Dec. 1924.

45 *Report on the experimental revision of the 1/2500 Ordnance Survey plans with the aid of photographs taken from the air* (HMSO 1927); and PRO OS 1/11: Memorandum dated 16 Dec. 1924.

46 PRO OS 1/11. The Central Aerophoto Co. quoted £15 per square mile.

47 *Ibid.* Aircraft Operating Co. to Jack, 15 July 1925.

48 *Report on the Experimental revision of the 1/2500 Ordnance Survey plans with the aid of photographs taken from the air* (No. 2, 1928–30), p. 8.

49 PRO OS 1/73: Winterbotham to the Controller HMSO, 23 March 1934.

50 See J. S. A. Salt, Professional Papers of the Air Survey Committee, no. 8.

51 The recommendations of this Committee are printed in full in Winterbotham, *The National Plans* (HMSO 1934), p. 75.

52 PRO OS 1/31. A summary of the Committee's findings was given by MacLeod in a memorandum dated 24 Dec. 1935.

53 *Ibid.* Stewart-Wallace to MacLeod, 13 March 1935.

54 *Ibid.* Stewart-Wallace to Winterbotham, 22 Nov. 1934.

55 Winterbotham, *The National Plans*, p. 79.

56 PRO OS 1/73: Winterbotham to the Ministry of Agriculture and Fisheries, 3 March 1934.

57 PRO OS 1/31: Winterbotham to Air Commodore J. A. Charnier of Charnier, Gilbert Lodge and Co., 9 Aug. 1934.

58 PRO OS 1/28. Memorandum dated 6.2.1931.

59 *Ibid.* Winterbotham to the Ministry of Agriculture and Fisheries, 1.5.1934.

60 Winterbotham, *The National Plans*, p. 81.

61 PRO OS 1/53. An undated memorandum (*c.* 1924) gives background information on the protests against publication of the six-inch map in full-sheet form.

62 OSR 1929–30. p. 10.

63 'Handover Notes', p. 106.

64 *Geographical Journal* 1931, LXXVIII, pp. 353–6.

65 For an account of the Popular Edition of Scotland, see John Mathieson, 'The new one-inch to a mile Ordnance Survey map (Popular Edition)' *Scottish Geographical Magazine* 1932, XLVIII, pp. 98–103.

66 Winterbotham, 'The Small-scale Maps of the Ordnance Survey', *Geographical Journal* 1932, LXXIX, p. 18.

67 PRO OS 1/48.

68 OSR, 1925–6, p. 1.

69 PRO OS 1/48. Winterbotham to F. Debenham, Cambridge University, 21.5.1931.

70 J. G. Withycombe, 'Lettering on Maps', *Geographical Journal* 1929, LXXIII, p. 437. Jack's comment is in the discussion following the paper.

71 PRO OS 1/48. Winterbotham to Close, 12.10.1931.

72 Winterbotham, *Geographical Journal* 1932, LXXIX, p. 21.

73 Winterbotham, 'The use of the new grid on Ordnance Survey maps', *Geographical Journal* 1933, LXXXII, p. 46.

74 H. St J. L. Winterbotham, E. M. Jack and A. R. Hinks, 'The choice of a grid for British maps', *Geographical Journal* 1924, LXIII, p. 504. Close comments in the discussion following the paper.

75 PRO OS 1/49. Memorandum from the Director General to the Treasury, 29.11.1932.

76 *Ibid.* Memorandum dated 16.2.1935.

77 Winterbotham, 'Sheet Lines', *Geographical Journal* 1932, LXXX, p. 514.

78 OSR 1937–8, p. 5.

79 'Handover Notes', p. 111.

80 *Ibid.* p. 114.

26
MacLeod
and the
Davidson
Committee
1935–1939

MacLeod, the last of the inter-war Directors of the Ordnance Survey, was to exert a profound and far-reaching influence on the future of the Department. The medium through which he was able to do this was the Davidson Committee, appointed to enquire into the affairs of the Ordnance Survey soon after his taking over office as Director General in February 1935. The national projection with the large-scale series on national rather than county sheet-lines, the metric grid, the 1:25 000 series, as well as the system of continuous revision, were all recommendations of MacLeod's, later adopted by the Committee. Doubtless his predecessors would have agreed with the concept of a national series of large-scale plans, but neither Jack nor Winterbotham were evangelists in the cause of metrication. Winterbotham was positively averse to the 1:25 000 map, and considered that if the Ordnance Survey published maps on decimal scales, 'sales would diminish to vanishing point, and that Bartholomew and other people would burst out into Rolls Royces'.[1]

MacLeod had a practical eye for efficient management and aimed at transforming the Ordnance Survey into a 'genuine mass-production organization of the so-called sausage machine type'.[2] His hope that the Ordnance Survey would be made responsible for all government survey and cartography, including boundary commission work, colonial surveys undertaken by the Imperial Government, and the cartographic work done by the War Office and Air Ministry was, however, never realized.

Malcolm Neynoe MacLeod of the Raasay branch of the clan MacLeod was born in India on 23 May 1882. He passed out top of his batch at the Royal Military Academy, Woolwich, in 1900, collecting the Pollock and Queen Victoria gold medals, and prizes for military topography and geometrical drawing. After some fourteen years with the Survey of India – broken by extended periods of sick leave in England – he joined the British Expeditionary Force in France in 1915. He succeeded Winterbotham in 1930 as head of the Geographical Section at the War Office, a post he held until he became Director General of the Ordnance Survey. His service in war and with the Royal Artillery had left him with 'very strong views on map policy'. These views were largely militarily orientated, mainly because it soon became clear that another war was imminent, and the role which the Ordnance Survey was to play seemed confused, in spite of its experiences in the First World War. That this was so was to some extent the result of War Office indecision, but the loss of artillery surveying was also partly responsible.

MacLeod's term of office as Director General lasted from 1935 to 1943 and was dominated first by the Davidson Committee and then by the Second World War. With the expansion of staff in 1935–7, as a result of the Davidson Committee's recommendations, the rank of the Director General of the Ordnance Survey was raised to Major-General, although MacLeod was not actually promoted until 1939.

Winterbotham may have thought that the Ordnance Survey had sunk to the absolute depths on his arrival as Director General, but the situation had worsened by the time his successor took office in 1935. Indeed, during the previous year only 558 revised 1:2500 plans had been published, which meant that the average cycle of revision had increased from twenty to one hundred years. The importance which Winterbotham attached to prompt revision for land registration diminished in MacLeod's time under the enormous pressures imposed by the Town and Country Planning Act of 1932. The terms of the Act made it necessary that all planning schemes at their various stages should be illustrated by maps. Seventeen million acres of land, covered by planning resolutions, needed to be revised and, in order to comply with the Act, this work had to be completed within three years.

In many areas Parliament had been compelled to extend the period prescribed for the adoption of even a draft scheme on the sole ground that its preparation was impeded by the lack of up-to-date Ordnance Survey maps. Unable to meet the variety of demands made on it, the Ordnance Survey became the subject of investigation by a Departmental Committee under the chairmanship of Sir John Davidson, who was appointed by the Minister of Agriculture and Fisheries on 28 May 1935, with six other committee members: Brigadier D. F. Anderson (War Office), C. B. Collins (Air Ministry), R. N. Duke (Scottish Office), H. W. S. Francis (Ministry of Health), H. G. Richardson (Ministry of Agriculture and Fisheries), and W. R. L. Trickett of the Treasury.

The Committee was given four terms of reference:

1 to consider what measures were necessary to accelerate the revision of the Ordnance Survey maps in order to bring them up to date and thereafter to maintain them at a high level of accuracy, while providing for other public services undertaken by the Ordnance Survey Department;

2 to consider what immediate steps were possible in the meantime to revise Ordnance Survey maps to the extent necessary for the purpose of town and country planning schemes;

3 to review the scales and styles of Ordnance Survey maps placed on sale to the public and to recommend whether any changes were desirable;

4 to review the conditions upon which the reproduction of Ordnance Survey maps was permitted.

The Interim Report of the Davidson Committee

The more urgent problems of town planning and copyright required immediate consideration and were the subject of an *Interim Report* which was presented on 21 December 1935.[3]

Many of the 1:2500 plans required by the Town and Country Planning Act had already been revised by local authorities, who despaired of ever obtaining up-to-date maps from the Ordnance Survey. MacLeod thought that, if the Ministry of Health would accept work already completed by the local authorities, only three to four thousand plans would need immediate revision by the Ordnance Survey. Anxious that the normal revision of the large-scale plans should not be disrupted, he recommended that the town planning work should be incorporated into the general process of overtaking arrears in revision.[4] He had, however, overlooked the immediacy of the town planning requirement and had also seriously underestimated the staff needed and the cost of the whole operation. He eventually suggested that an interim revision could be undertaken with the aid of air photographs and to this end he instigated an experimental air survey in the Birmingham area.

MacLeod had originally wanted the Royal Air Force to take the photographs for the Birmingham experiment, which comprised about 400 square miles where the last ground revision had taken place in 1913. The Air Council, however, refused to allow Royal Air Force participation and insisted that civil firms should be used. MacLeod was forced, somewhat reluctantly, into the complicated and novel manoeuvres of drawing up contracts and inviting tenders from commercial firms for the flying work. The lowest estimate was submitted by Aerofilms Ltd., the British operating company for Hemming and Partners, and was accepted by the Ordnance Survey in June 1935. For £5 a square mile, the contractors guaranteed completion within four months.[5] But following the high optimism born of inexperience of the exacting Ordnance Survey requirements and a total disregard of the British weather, Aerofilms Ltd. were forced to admit defeat at the end of the year, and the results of the experiment were inconclusive. The reason given for this failure was that the contract had specified the use of a gyronavigational control apparatus within the aeroplane with which the pilot was quite unfamiliar, but MacLeod had been insistent that one of the most important objects of the experiment was to discover if, and how far, the quality of vertical air photographs could be improved by obtaining the highest navigational standard possible.[6] There was clearly a need for detailed and possibly prolonged scientific investigation, but the expectation that air photography would, sooner or later, greatly reduce both the time and the cost of revision in rapidly developing areas led to the contractors being given the opportunity to complete their work in the next season.

Reluctant to place complete reliance on aerial methods at this time, the Committee thought that for town planning purposes it would be sufficient to produce a revised map which showed new field boundaries, buildings and other physical features, but which omitted new bench-marks, names of new roads and the numbers and areas of parcels in which alterations had taken place since the last edition. By this means the production of a provisional edition would take only one year instead of the two years allowed for a full revision. But if the existing staff were to be employed on work for town planning alone, the programme of normal revision would be delayed still further. The Committee therefore regarded it as 'essential that there should be an immediate increase in the establishment of the Ordnance Survey' so that the production of maps for town planning and the resumption of normal revision could be carried out concurrently.

During the financial year 1935–6, 281 additional civilian staff were recruited, a substantial increase which necessitated a reorganization of the technical side of the Ordnance Survey. The amalgamation of the Trigonometrical and Levelling Divisions, the concentration of drawing at Southampton and the rationalization of the Field and Drawing Divisions led to practically all the technical work of the Department being organized into four, instead of seven divisions, dealing respectively with triangulation, levelling and contouring; large-scale survey, field revision and air survey; map drawing; and map-printing and publication.[7]

The increase and reorganization of staff were geared specifically to cope with town planning requirements and the need to attack the arrears in revision of the large scales. It was inevitable that before long there would be a conflict of interests with other departments which also relied on Ordnance Survey plans for the continuation of their own work; it was predictable that one of these would be the Land Registry, which expected the Survey to be able to produce revised plans within one year for areas of compulsory registration. The revision of Middlesex for Land Registry purposes was virtually complete by the end of 1935, but thereafter the Ordnance Survey had to state that it was unable to undertake the further revision of whole counties in anticipation of registration.[8] A marked growth of bad feeling quickly developed between the two Departments culminating in the cancellation of the 1928 agreement with regard to the type of plan which the Survey was required to provide.[9]

From this dispute originated MacLeod's recommendation to the Committee that the resurveying of urban areas at 1:1250 instead of 1:2500 should be considered. Each 1:2500 plan revised for the Land Registry had to be photographically enlarged to 1:1250 because the original scale was too small to permit the identification of individual properties in closely built-up areas. But this process revealed many minor discrepancies which passed unnoticed on the original scale. The most common were in rows of identical houses which appeared to be of different sizes on the enlargement simply because it was not possible for the draughtsman to draw each house exactly the same size at the smaller scale. The Survey was obliged to correct these distortions on the enlargements, immediately creating a discrepancy between the Land Registry plans, on which registration of title depended, and the Ordnance Survey plans, which were used by the public for similar purposes. MacLeod also pointed out that it created differences between neighbouring Land Registry plans. He then, rather tactlessly in the circumstances, proposed that the extension of compulsory registration should be postponed until there was a resurvey of urban areas at 1:1250.[10]

This suggestion unleashed a torrent of impatient correspondence from Sir John Stewart-Wallace. 'A conflict of plans', he wrote, 'which does not represent a conflict in holdings is, from the point of view of the Land Registry, a matter of small moment'.[11] His indifference as to 'whether or not the plans of the particular plots fit in with scientific accuracy on a map of the whole country' led him to remind MacLeod that Ordnance Survey maps were not conclusive evidence as to property boundaries; they were used only for the identification of registered land. The major point at issue was that MacLeod's recommendation to resurvey urban areas at the larger scale would increase the cost to the Land Registry, which paid the Survey for all work done on its behalf. Stewart-Wallace's concern was entirely understandable, for his department was in competition with unregistered conveyancing, which was untrammelled by the need for having any plans at all, much less plans based on a 'trigonometrical map of whole areas for which it had to pay'.[12] The Land Registry's plans for expansion were unhappily thwarted, not by unregistered conveyancing, but by the overwhelming demands of town planning. By 1937 the postponement of further compulsory registration was unavoidable. The Ordnance Survey could not guarantee the production of the necessary plans until mid 1939.

The second topic considered by the Davidson Committee in the *Interim Report* was that of copyright. The introduction of cheap processes of direct reproduction had led to the widespread copying of Ordnance Survey material, the source often being unacknowledged. The question of copyright had been reviewed in 1918, when it was laid down that map-making firms could continue to use their existing plates which partly comprised Ordnance Survey data, but no additions or corrections could be made to these plates if the information was derived from Ordnance Survey sources, unless royalties were paid after special permission had been given.[13] This decision led to complaints from local authorities, which held that they should be allowed to copy Ordnance Survey material without payment of royalties for work which they were obliged to undertake in connection with Parliamentary bills, and for the illustration of such schemes as those involving transport, lighting, water and power. In 1925 permission was granted for Ordnance Survey plans to be copied for public purposes on the understanding that local authorities would not produce large editions of the maps, nor indulge in widespread copying. This understanding was soon ignored. Editions, exceeding five hundred in some instances, of local authority maps directly based on those of the Ordnance Survey were printed without reference to the Department or to Crown Copyright. This in turn led to the considerable copying of these maps for private interests without payment of the royalty fees. The Department was compelled to revise the regulations. The new rules, in force from 1 December 1932, restricted a local authority's freedom to copy Ordnance Survey maps, without notification, to twelve copies made by the local authority itself, and limited the number to be made without royalty charge to fifty, again providing these were not produced by an outside agency. All copies had to carry a proper acknowledgement and the words 'Crown Copyright'.

After these regulations were made it soon became apparent that many local authorities did not possess their own copying facilities. The work was therefore put in the hands of private firms where supervision was practically impossible. Neither was it a simple matter to distinguish between local authorities and corporate bodies serving other public purposes, leading to unequal treatment between one applicant and another. It was obvious that the 1932 regulations could not be adequately enforced without a thorough investigation of the internal administration of local authorities and the activities of private firms, a task which would be impracticable as well as undesirable. As a general principle, the Davidson Committee saw no grounds for the exemption of either private firms or local authorities from the copyright law, arguing that 'if the Ordnance Survey Department were not maintained by Government, a very substantial additional expense would be thrown upon local authorities'.[14] Such cost would inevitably be met by the ratepayers.

The Committee therefore recommended that new regulations should be introduced, providing a uniform scale of charges 'applicable to all users of Ordnance Survey copyright material'. Exemptions or reductions were to be allowed 'but very sparingly', as in the case of learned and scientific publications where only small portions of a copyright map were reproduced without commercial profit. The new regulations were drawn up in a fifteen-clause draft proposal which was appended to the *Interim Report* and which provided the framework for a much tighter control over the copying of Ordnance Survey material. Private printing firms undertaking work for local authorities were required to obtain a special licence from the Director General before printing from Ordnance Survey material and were obliged to keep record copies of all reproductions for inspection by an 'accredited representative of the Director General'.

The new copyright rules were designed to exact a revenue in royalty fees which corresponded as closely as possible with the degree of use made of Ordnance Survey maps by other departments and organizations, public or private. The success of the new regulations can be judged by the fact that they did indeed cause a dramatic increase in income from this source, more than doubling it between 1935 and 1938, when it rose from £3176 to £7927.[15]

The Final Report of the Davidson Committee

> Evidence offered to this Committee soon convinced all the members that a bad blunder had been made by the Geddes Committee.
>
> MacLeod (1946)

After the publication of its *Interim Report* in 1936, the Davidson Committee turned its attention to the remaining issues of its brief, concerned with the measures needed to accelerate the revision of the Ordnance Survey maps, and the review of the scales and styles of the maps. The large conference room at 10 Whitehall Place provided the setting for prolonged discussions on these matters, during which ninety individuals and organizations gave evidence. While Davidson was certainly the captain of the Committee boat, MacLeod was unquestionably the navigator. Within a short time of his taking office as Director General he had a clear idea of the course he wanted the Ordnance Survey to steer in the future, and to a great extent manoeuvred the Committee in this direction. Indeed, when the findings were complete he was able to say that with 'one exception the . . . recommendations are based on proposals which I submitted to the Committee'.[16] The proposals entailed a number of changes in the British cartographic system, and it was with justification that he addressed a meeting at the Royal Geographical Society in January 1939 with the words:

> the Final Report . . . amounts to a new charter for the Ordnance Survey.[17]

MacLeod's recommendations, which were set out in a memorandum dated 30 December 1935, dealt first with the question of the large-scale plans and the National Grid.[18] The proposals uppermost in MacLeod's mind were that the twenty-five-inch and six-inch plans should be rearranged as single, continuous series, to replace the old County Series, that this rearrangement should be made the occasion for a complete overhaul of the 1:2500 survey, and that the maintenance of the plans thereafter should be a continuous process instead of by cyclic revision. He further proposed that all Ordnance Survey maps should be gridded, and that the grid unit should be the metre rather than the yard.

By approving the proposal for transforming the large scales to a national system, the Committee were, in fact, recommending that the 'old cartographic structure should be demolished and entirely rebuilt'.[19] That there should be no change in the 1:2500 scale for the basic plans was a point on which all the evidence was unanimous, as it was for the adoption of a single national projection, in place of the existing Cassini projections, for the 1:2500 maps, even though it meant altering the sheet-lines of every large-scale sheet. It was because MacLeod had foreseen the acceptance of these recommendations that he had already started the retriangulation of the country. It was to be expected that he would advocate the adoption of a national grid for all Ordnance Survey maps. Grids had been a cartographic necessity from a military standpoint since the First World War, and as the War Office was one of the Survey's largest customers (its payments rising from £20 000 in 1934–5 to £75 000 in 1937–8)[20] it was inevitable that the decision to incorporate a grid on Ordnance Survey maps should have been made. There was no opposition to the proposal but, in order to provide a choice for the layman, the Committee recommended that two versions of the small-scale maps should be published, one with a grid and one without.

The question of which unit of measure the grid should be based on was far less easily settled. It was an emotive issue which had last been raised when Jack and Winterbotham had introduced the 5000 yard grid to the one-inch series in the early 1930s, when the battle between metric and imperial measures had been won by the Empire. Now, however, the wind of change was blowing through the Ordnance Survey. 'It seems', wrote Hotine, 'absurd to base the unit of the National Survey on a yard, which no-one but a draper uses'.[21] MacLeod, more rationally, replied that 'the introduction of the metric grid is the best way of introducing the public gradually to a change which may, ere long, become very desirable, or perhaps absolutely necessary'.[22] Only sixty years before, it had been a penal offence to use metric weights and measures, but by the 1930s convenience and international co-operation had compelled their almost exclusive use for scientific purposes.

It was with some difficulty that MacLeod eventually persuaded the Committee of the necessity for the decimal spacing of grid lines, which could only be fully achieved by using metric units. Bound up with the principle of using a national grid was the effect it would have on the size and shape of maps. It was evidently desirable to have the sheet-lines based on the grid, when the most convenient shape for the twenty-five-inch plan would be square, covering one square kilometre of country. Furthermore, only 200 000 plans would be needed compared with the 240 000 for plans with sheet-lines based on imperial units and covering 1000 yards square; and as the mainland of Britain is almost exactly one million metres in length from north to south the grid co-ordinates could be limited to six figures instead of the seven which would be needed for a grid based on yards.

The great convenience of the kilometre square plan was that every smaller scale map on which the grid interval was one kilometre would show the extent of the 1:2500 plans which it covered; the inconveniences of the small square sheets were considered but were dismissed. The Committee therefore recommended that the national grid should be based on the international metre, that the 1:2500 plans in the new national series should be square, in place of the existing large rectangular plans, and that they should cover one square kilometre of ground. The Committee was careful to point out that the adoption of the metric grid unit did not necessarily involve the adoption of metric units by map-users. The decision had been taken, nevertheless, in anticipation of eventual statutory metrication imposed by government, and in the full knowledge that it would be extremely difficult and costly if the sheet-lines based on imperial measures had to be changed yet again at a later date.

MacLeod was to find it impossible to persuade the Committee to adopt his second objective, that of changing the scales of the maps produced by the Ordnance Survey. He had assumed, correctly, that the Committee would attempt to lay down a long-term policy for the Ordnance Survey which would cover the next fifty years. On this premise, and reasoning that major changes, if not implemented soon, would have to wait another half century, he suggested the following new scales:

1 the six-inch to be replaced by a map in a similar style on a scale of either 1:10 000 or preferably 1:12 500;

2 a new 1:25 000 map to be introduced;

3 the one-inch map (1:63 360) to be replaced within five years by the scale of 1:62 500;

4 the half-inch (1:126 720) to be replaced within five years by 1:125 000;

5 the quarter-inch (1:253 440) to be replaced within five years by 1:250 000.[23]

In principle Davidson was entirely sympathetic, stating that 'if the 1:2500 is accepted as the key plan, then clearly to my mind the proper course is to suggest that the series of national plans should be multiples or divisibles of that key plan'.[24] There were, however, two families of scales which broadly met this desideratum, one was favoured by Davidson, the other by MacLeod;* there seemed to be no basis for mutual agreement, and once again the question of scales became a cause of controversy.

The principal dispute focused on the fate of the six-inch map. Davidson preferred the alternative scale of 1:10 000 which, for the same sheet size, gave exactly sixteen times the area of the 1:2500. On the other hand, MacLeod argued that the 1:12 500 covered exactly twenty-five times the area of the basic plan, that it would contain twenty-five 1:2500 plans, and the grid square of 1000 metres would be exactly twice the size of the 100 metre square of the 1:2500, and further, that a 1:25 000 sheet of the same dimensions would contain exactly four 1:12 500 sheets. He conceded that the 'introduction of a 1:12 500 scale would probably cause a public outcry, while the change to 1:10 000 might pass unnoticed',[25] simply because the 1:10 000 was so close to the original six-inch scale. In the event the Committee decided to recommend that a 'new series of plans at 1:12 500 should be tried out in selected areas to see whether it would prove suitable as a replacement for the six-inch'.[26] This decision, made early in 1937, was modified in the *Final Report* so that it did not read as a recommendation but merely a suggestion that 'at some future date . . . a limited number of maps on the scale of 1:12 500 could be published "to ascertain the extent of the public demand for maps on that scale"'. The Committee had consulted representatives of the Ministry of Health, as a Department which made extensive use of the six-inch maps, to find out whether there would be any insuperable objections to an alteration in this scale. None of those consulted could point out any difficulties; equally, none were in a position to appreciate the advantages to be gained by a change in scale. Eventually, and after long discussion, the Committee took the majority view that the immediate inconvenience which would be incurred far outweighed the ultimate advantages and decided not to recommend any change.[27]

As far as the smaller scales were concerned, MacLeod evidently changed his mind with regard to the most suitable alternative for the one-inch and finally settled for the 1:50 000, but he recognized that the case for this scale no longer existed once the 1:12 500 and 1:10 000 had been rejected. He added that such a change would be

> a much bigger and more expensive operation than the other scales, and although the larger scale has some advantages I thought it better that its introduction . . . should not be undertaken at the present time, though it might be considered at a later date when the new Fifth Edition is complete.[28]

As it turned out, the 1:50 000 scale did not replace the one-inch until nearly forty years later.

Setting out the advantages and disadvantages of the proposed changes of scale in their final report, the Committee eventually recommended no change in the small-scale maps. At one stage, in 1937, it seemed that the members would be unable to reach a unanimous decision, a situation which nearly resulted in a minority report on the question of scales.[29] Davidson was finally won over to the opinion of Brigadier Anderson – that there was no need for any relationship between the large scales and the small scales. MacLeod had to admit defeat, but not without making it clear in private that he 'regarded the infraction of the principle of related scales preposterous'.[30]

This failure was to some extent offset by his qualified success in introducing the 1:25 000 map as a standard national scale. The *Final Report* quoted a 'number of witnesses' as having requested a map at this scale, yet in 1936 the Committee was not convinced that such a map would be worth its cost, and planned to recommend that only a few sheets be published in order to test reaction. MacLeod was a strong advocate of the 1:25 000 scale, believing that it 'would undoubtedly have considerable civil value and . . . enjoy a good sale' and that it might 'eventually replace the six-inch, with substantial

---

* The two scale series were:

(a)	(b)
1:2500	1:2500
1:12 500	1:10 560
1:25 000	1:25 000
1:62 500	1:63 360
1:125 000	1:126 720
1:250 000	1:253 440
1:500 000	1:633 600
1:1 000 000	1:1 000 000

The decimal scale (a) was preferred by MacLeod; initially Davidson preferred series (b).

saving in the cost of revision'.[31] This view was diametrically opposed to that of his predecessor, Winterbotham, who considered it 'a map ill adapted for civil use, competitive to the six-inch scale and, in effect, designed entirely for military purposes'.[32]

The 1:25 000 map was indeed a military necessity and its continuation had been specifically asked for by the War Office. The only limit to the rate of progress of the map, which had already been produced of certain areas by the Ordnance Survey for the War Office, was financial. 'Were unlimited money available', ran the military evidence set before the Committee, 'it would be desirable from the War Office point of view, that the Ordnance Survey should have sufficient personnel exclusively employed on the production of this map to complete the whole series during the next three or four years'.[33]

A 1:25 344 map of East Anglia had originally been produced as a confidential map in a block of thirty-six sheets during the war for defensive purposes. By 1918 it had been extended southwards into Essex, Kent and the London area and then became designated the Map of the Eastern Counties, with a modified British Cassini grid. After the war, however, the Geographical Section adopted the 1:20 000 as the medium scale, thereby losing much of the value of the mapping of East Anglia. The 1:20 000 sheets were ordered from the Ordnance Survey and paid for by the War Office on the understanding that they should remain unpublished and be marked 'Official Use Only', but after a review of War Office policy in 1923–4, and in the light of increasing expenditure, an attempt was made by GSGS to induce the Ordnance Survey to put the 1:20 000 map on sale, in order to recover part of the cost, but Jack had refused, possibly on the grounds that it would be competitive with the six-inch map. In the 1930s the 1:20 000 was replaced by the 1:25 000.

One of the more important military considerations which weighed heavily in favour of the 1:25 000 was that it was needed for the training of the Territorial Army. As the Director of Military Training, Major-General A. F. Brooke, pointed out: 'unless they are accustomed to this scale in peace, they will not be able to get full value out of it in war'. MacLeod's desire that the Ordnance Survey should provide for the entire military cartographic need was no less clear. 'It is my opinion', he stated, 'that the War Office should press strongly for [the 1:25 000 map's] introduction, especially as the cost will not be borne by Army Votes'. The military representative on the Committee was Anderson, the Director of Military Intelligence, whose attitude was that of reluctant acquiescence in, rather than strong support of, MacLeod's advice. MacLeod complained bitterly that as

> my advocacy is quite frankly based on military needs, you can well imagine the fact of its not being energetically supported by the official War Office representative greatly reduces its weight.[34]

In fact, the military requirements for the new intermediate scale were played down in the *Final Report*, no doubt as a matter of policy in times when the common sentiment was distinctly against the martial profession. Greater emphasis was placed on the suitability of the map for walkers and educational authorities. It was thought possible that a contoured 1:25 000 map of mountainous areas would be commercially viable, whereas the six-inch maps of the same areas were produced at a loss, but it was impossible to forecast the sales of the new map. The only other Survey publication at a similar scale had been the three-inch map of London, which had to meet keen commercial competition and did not offer a useful comparison. The Committee cautiously recommended therefore that 'a number of maps of selected parts of the country should be produced and put on sale at the scale of 1:25 000, and, if these are successful, that a complete series on this scale should be published with fixed sheet-lines conforming to the National Grid'.

The Committee had little difficulty in resolving the future of the town scales. Only sixteen authorities had been prepared to pay the Ordnance Survey for revision and as a result most of the town plans had become obsolete, the most important exception being the 1:1056 of the London area, where revision had been undertaken by the Land Registry and, after 1931, by the Ordnance Survey. The Committee agreed that the 1:500 was useful for local purposes, but was not a national necessity, and it was therefore unable to recommend the revision, republication or extension of the 1:500 plans.

The 1:1250 map, on the other hand, had proved invaluable for both land valuation and registration, and MacLeod strongly favoured it as the basic scale for urban areas. There was a well-established need for a survey on a larger scale than 1:2500 for the expanding towns, and while the 1:500 scale would involve an unjustifiable amount of extra work, the 1:1250 would cost only one-third as much again as the twenty-five inch. The Committee therefore recommended that 'when the revision of the 1:2500 plans is nearing completion, further investigations should be carried out with a view to establishing whether the requirements of urban areas would not more adequately be met by a survey on the 1:1250 scale'.

Having considered the question of scales the Committee pointed out the incongruity of certain Parliamentary Acts which stipulated the use of scales not produced by the Ordnance Survey. To avert the possibility of this happening needlessly in the future, it was suggested that any department initiating legislation involving maps should first consult the Ministry of Agriculture and Fisheries, who would in turn request the Director General to advise on the suitability of the intended scales.

Another subject reviewed was the special work done by the Ordnance Survey for other government departments on a repayment basis. The most important of these were the defence departments, Land Registry, Stationery Office and Geological Survey. No doubt bearing in mind the attempts of HM Stationery Office to take over all Ordnance Survey printing in the late 1920s,[35] the Committee emphasized the need for only one state cartographic organization, for 'only thus can the institution of a multiplicity of small branches each carrying out similar work be prevented'.

When it came to review the map styles of the Ordnance Survey, the Committee found that most of the evidence offered was based on personal prejudice born partly of ignorance of cartographic production problems. Satisfied that the Survey could itself deal with the question of style, the Committee made no recommendations for any change and considered only the subjects of contouring and parcel numbers.

'The standard of British maps in depicting relief is far below that of their planimetry', wrote MacLeod in an early draft on Ordnance Survey policy.[36] He favoured replacing the six-inch altogether by an adequately contoured 1:25 000, but was of the opinion that, if the six-inch were maintained, then it should be contoured at ten-foot intervals, but not necessarily with instrumental contours. Two months after making his first report to the Davidson Committee, he proposed that the six-inch 'or the map which replaces it should be contoured at 5 metre intervals'.[37] Once again he had introduced the highly controversial issue of metrication, but he was unable to get the Committee to deal with the point and they finally ignored it. The Committee agreed entirely that additional contours should be introduced, but left the 'details to be settled when the time is ripe for the Department to undertake the work'. This somewhat indecisive recommendation left MacLeod in a dilemma, for he was anxious that the work of additional contouring should be begun as soon as the report was published. It was impossible for him to forecast when metric units would be introduced, but he thought that the 'probability of their compulsory introduction is greater than it was even a few years ago'. He concluded that 'on the whole, as our levelling is recorded in feet I think it would be best not to anticipate changes, but to work in feet on the ground and to publish the contours in feet on the six-inch scale, but in metres on the new 1:25 000.[38] But for the intervention of the Second World War, which precluded any immediate action, this decision might well have been implemented. It was not until 1943 that it was ultimately decided to survey the contours at twenty-five-foot intervals, and incorporate the same data on the 1:25 000.

The other major question which arose out of the Committee's consideration of map content was that of parcel numbers. The system of parcel numbering on the 1:2500 plans had outlived its usefulness. Originally numbered in consecutive order within each parish, the parcels had subsequently undergone subdivision within the parish and, with the changes in many parish boundaries consequent on the Local Government Act of 1929, a further subdivision between parishes. Moreover, the abandonment of revision of whole counties in favour of selected areas had a devastating effect on the already confused methods of parcel numbering. The abolition of the system had previously been advocated by the Departmental Committee of 1892, but this recommendation had failed to win approval because of public opposition. Now that the Davidson Committee had recommended the introduction of a national grid, thereby providing a precise referencing system which could be adapted for parcel numbering there was, at last, no need for the parish numbers which were to be discontinued as soon as the national grid was introduced.

The Committee recommended that acreage figures should be retained. The brief reference to area measurement concealed the size of the problem of showing areas on the large-scale plans, which was tied up with that of parcel numbering. Under the old system of consecutive numbering, areas were computed for whole parcels, but under the new system, which had operated since 1922, areas were computed to plan edge only. This was highly inconvenient for the map-user who found his parcel to be on four different sheets, and had generated many protests, particularly from surveyors and land agents. Suggestions that revision should be extended to adjoining sheets to complete broken parcels, so that total areas could be shown in the margins of revised plans, were met with disapproval first from Winterbotham and secondly from MacLeod, who was anxious for the Committee to 'place on record an endorsement of the policy of "areas to plan edges only" '.[39] The Committee failed to support this policy in public, no doubt leaving it to the Director General to decide for himself which method to follow.

The main point before the Committee was the pressing need to accelerate the revision of the large-scale plans, and to devise a workable system for keeping them up to date. Only two scales, the one-inch and the twenty-five inch, needed to be considered, since all others were derived from them. Generally speaking, the smaller the scale of map, the longer it took to get out of date, and so the existing practice of cyclic revision for the one-inch map every fifteen years was thought to be adequate. The maintenance of the small-scale maps was done in two ways: by the complete revision of the whole sheet at intervals of fifteen years, and by partial revision, incorporating only specially important changes, such as new roads, at shorter intervals. The latter form had first been used systematically on the Fourth Edition of the one-inch map, contributing greatly towards its success with the public. It was both convenient to the users and economical to the Department, and the Committee recommended that this system should be continued.

By 1936 it had been amply demonstrated that the cyclic revision of the 1:2500 was inadequate for mapping the development which was taking place simultaneously over the whole country. It was a situation about which the Committee held strong opinions:

> To maintain cyclic revision and thus to permit continued deterioration in the knowledge that at some future date it must be remedied at ever growing cost, is not a course we could invite His Majesty's Government to contemplate.

The only alternative was continuous revision, which meant that changes on the ground would be surveyed shortly after they occurred, by surveyors permanently located in each area. The revised field sheet would be available to the public for consultation and copying on repayment, and could be reprinted when a new edition was justified by the demand and the amount of change.

The Committee was 'of the opinion that continuous revision was the ideal solution to the problem of obtaining up-to-date maps', and recommended that it be adopted as soon as possible. The Treasury was not at all enthusiastic about the increase in expenditure that the new system would generate, and its requests for cost analyses drove an exasperated MacLeod to retort that continuous revision 'was not, of course, as cheap as doing nothing at all'.[40] He silenced Treasury opposition by pointing out that unless the system were adopted quickly, the Ordnance Survey 1:2500 plans, on which many millions of pounds had already been spent, would become so out of date as to be useless. As a means of improving the efficiency, and therefore decreasing the cost, of such a revision, the Committee looked again at the possibilities of air photography.

The potential value of air survey was becoming clearer. In spite of set-backs, the results of experiments showed that it could be effective and economical in areas of rapid urban development. But it was evident that the resources of civil firms were not adequate to meet the exacting demands of the Ordnance Survey, and the Committee recommended that a special air survey unit should be formed, comprising personnel trained in air survey methods and equipped with aircraft fitted with suitable apparatus.

Trained men were also desperately needed for ground survey and revision, for 'the solution of the problem of the revision of the basic large-scale plans is principally dependent on the staff which can be made available for such work'. The total strength of the Ordnance Survey had by now been increased to 1334, but MacLeod envisaged that in order to overhaul the twenty-five-inch plans and thereafter maintain them, a further recruitment of five hundred new revisers and draughtsmen every year for four years would be needed.[41] The original calculations were based on an annual output of four resurveyed plans per man, and ten plans per man for continuous revision. The great disadvantage arising out of this mass recruitment was that there was no reserve of skilled labour which could provide an immediate supply of trained revisers, and it was estimated that immediate recruitment would not produce a fully trained staff until 1944. This new staff would initially be allocated to the job of overtaking arrears, but obviously, if continuous revision were ignored until all the arrears were dealt with, the first plans would again be out of date. The Committee recommended that 'as the plans in any one area are brought up to date, a number of men should be left behind to maintain that area under continuous revision'. MacLeod's estimate of the increase in staff was accepted by the Committee which judged that the maximum expansion required should reach an eventual total establishment of 4000, decreasing gradually to between 3000 and 3500 after fifteen years, by which time the plans for the whole country would have been completed and brought into the system of continuous revision. The enormous waste of time and money, incurred as a result of the recommendations of the Geddes Committee, was to be avoided in the future by the adoption of a 'settled policy . . . in relation to the Ordnance Survey, in order that continuity of effort should be maintained in the future'.

A full discussion of the Committee's recommendations was held at the Royal Geographical Society in January 1939.[42] The proposed changes in the conduct of the Ordnance Survey were generally approved and, in particular, the use of the metre rather than the yard for the national grid received great approbation. There was also unanimous enthusiasm for the new 1:25 000 map, especially from the educational representatives. But the war clouds had already gathered when the *Final Report* of the Davidson Committee was published in November 1938. Twenty-five years had elapsed since the outbreak of the last war which had so severely crippled the Ordnance Survey and now, on the point of recovery, it was swept into another global war. Fortunately the recommendations of the Davidson Committee survived to provide the framework for its restoration in the post-war period.

The Eve of War

Large-scale revision continued to be the chief work of the Department in the last year of peace. The work was based on the requirements of local authorities for town and country planning, but preparations were also made to begin the overhaul of the 1:2500 survey, as recommended by the Davidson Committee. The original town planning programme, begun in 1936, allowed for about 1400 plans, but more than 2500 had been revised for this purpose by 1939, practically completing the work. While the output of revised twenty-five-inch plans rose with the intake of new staff, the difficulty of obtaining accommodation for the draughtsmen at headquarters made it impossible to accelerate the fair-drawing of the revised plans at the same rate as the field work.

A special traverse of the city of Hull, which was undertaken as a test of the methods proposed for the overhaul of the 1:2500 in large towns, was fortunately completed. No new experimental air survey work was taken in hand; various practical difficulties had arisen to prevent the formation of the air survey unit recommended by the Davidson Committee, and these had not been overcome when war put a stop to civil air photography altogether.

The outbreak of war deferred the publication of the new edition of the one-inch map in the style recommended by the Committee, with a kilometre grid. This was to be the Sixth Edition, and it was proposed to call it the 'New Popular' because it resembled the Fourth Edition closely in style. Each sheet was to be uniform in size covering about 700 square miles. The drawing of a new half-inch map was also suspended.[43]

Notes

1 PRO OS 1/48. Winterbotham to Lt.-Col. A. F. V. Jarrett, undated.
2 PRO OS 1/144. MacLeod to Ministry of Agriculture and Fisheries, 2 June 1938.
3 *Interim Report of the Departmental Committee on the Ordnance Survey* (HMSO 1936).
4 PRO OS 1/113. MacLeod to Davidson, 3 Oct. 1935.
5 *Ibid.*
6 *Ibid.*
7 OSR 1935–6, p. 7.
8 PRO OS 1/31. OS to Land Registry, 13 Dec. 1935.
9 PRO OS 1/31. Ministry of Agriculture and Fisheries to MacLeod, 31 Dec. 1935.
10 PRO OS 1/31. MacLeod to Stewart-Wallace, 13 Nov. 1936.
11 PRO OS 1/31. Stewart-Wallace to MacLeod, 2 Dec. 1936.
12 PRO OS 1/31. Stewart-Wallace to MacLeod, 18 Dec. 1936.
13 *Interim Report*, p. 10.
14 *Ibid.* p. 11.
15 See OSR for the years 1936–8, under *Finance*.
16 PRO OS 1/114. MacLeod's comments on the *Final Report* of the Davidson Committee, 12 April 1938.
17 'Discussion on the Final Report of the Departmental Committee on the Ordnance Survey', *Geographical Journal* 1939, XCIII, pp. 314–32.
18 PRO OS 1/117.
19 'Discussion on the Final Report', p. 316.

20 OSR for 1934–5 and 1937–8, under *Finance*.

21 PRO OS 1/114. Memorandum on the metric system by Hotine, 29 Oct. 1935.

22 PRO OS 1/114. MacLeod's comments on Hotine's memorandum, 4 Nov. 1935.

23 PRO OS 1/117. Memorandum by MacLeod, 30 Dec. 1935.

24 PRO OS 1/114. 'Review of the General Position by the Chairman, 3 Feb. 1937.

25 PRO OS 1/114. MacLeod to Ministry of Agriculture and Fisheries, 22 Aug. 1936.

26 PRO OS 1/114. Decisions taken by the Committee up until 20 April 1937.

27 PRO OS 1/114. MacLeod's comments on the *Final Report*, 12 April 1938.

28 *Ibid.*

29 PRO OS 1/114. M. Collins (Secretary of the Davidson Committee) to MacLeod, 20 July 1937.

30 PRO OS 1/114. MacLeod to Collins, 17 June 1937.

31 PRO OS 1/117. Memorandum by MacLeod, 30 Dec. 1935.

32 Winterbotham's 'Handover Notes' to MacLeod, 1934, p. 182.

33 PRO OS 1/113. 'Present and prospective requirements of the War Office from the Ordnance Survey Department'. Memorandum by the War Office, 26 June 1935.

34 PRO OS 1/114. MacLeod to Maj.-Gen. A. F. Brooke, Directorate of Military Training, War Office, 14 Dec. 1936.

35 *Report of a Committee on Government Printing Establishments*, p. 125: PP 1927, Cd. 2828, IX.

36 PRO OS 1/113. Memorandum on Ordnance Survey policy, [Sept.] 1935.

37 PRO OS 1/117. Memorandum by MacLeod, 30 Dec. 1935.

38 PRO OS 1/114. MacLeod's comments on the *Final Report*, 12 April 1938.

39 PRO OS 1/114. MacLeod to Colbeck, 25 Nov. 1936.

40 PRO OS 1/114. MacLeod to Toye, 2 June 1938.

41 PRO OS 1/117. Undated memorandum.

42 PRO OS 1/117.

43 PRO OS 1/97. Draft of the OSR for 1939–40 (unpublished).

27
The
Retriangulation
1935-1939

The Need for a New Triangulation

MacLeod's decision to retriangulate Great Britain was crucial for the Ordnance Survey, as the work of overhauling the national plans would be heavily dependent upon both the timely completion and the quality of the new triangulation. The man charged with this onerous responsibility was Major Martin Hotine; the Retriangulation was in large part his creation and his were the methods employed.

The need for a new triangulation did not arise from deficiencies of the Principal Triangulation which was comparable in accuracy to much later work. The deficiencies were in the secondary and lower orders which had been carried out on a county basis to control the large-scale surveys so that, for modern practical purposes, there was 'no consistent National Triangulation, but only a large number of semi-independent triangulations which [could not] be brought into sympathy'.[1]

A new secondary triangulation was therefore essential to enable new large-scale surveys to be carried out according to the Davidson recommendation that 'the 1:2500 survey should be recast on National instead of county sheet lines on a National projection'. The Principal Triangulation would probably have been accurate enough to serve as the controlling framework for the new secondary, but it was doubtful if sufficient of the old stations could have been recovered with certainty for this to have been satisfactory. Moreover the cost of a primary triangulation, with 30 mile sides, was but a small fraction of the cost of the secondary with 4 mile sides, and well worth while in order to ensure a sound foundation for the new work.

THE NATIONAL GRID

The Davidson Committee's recommendations made it necessary also for a new projection to be adopted. The old Cassini projection, in spite of its merit of simplicity, would have been unsuitable; it had been applied to relatively small areas – a single county or small groups of counties – and would not have been satisfactory if used to cover the whole of Great Britain because it is not 'orthomorphic'; away from the central meridian the scale in the north to south direction increases, whereas the scale in the east to west direction remains nearly constant. Except in the region of the central meridian, shapes are distorted and the directions and distances between points, even if they are close together, are not consistently represented. The further from the central meridian the worse these effects: if a single Cassini belt had been used to cover Great Britain the angular distortion would have amounted in some areas to nearly four minutes of arc.[2] Such distortions might have been acceptable for mapping – even large-scale mapping – but would have introduced intolerable complications in minor instrumental surveys calculated upon the projection.

The projection chosen instead was the Transverse Mercator, first employed by the German geodesist Gauss in 1821. It may be simply represented as the projection of the surface from the centre of the Earth onto a cylinder in contact along the central meridian, and is similar to the Cassini in that along that meridian scale remains almost constant. But it is an orthomorphic projection in which the east to west scale is arranged to increase away from the central meridian so that at any point it is exactly equal to the north to south scale at that point. Within a limited area in any part of the projection, angles remain true and distances consistent for most practical purposes, irrespective of the direction of measurement. The scale of course increases with the departure from the central meridian but this can be easily allowed for if necessary by the application of a scale factor.

The projection forms the basis of the rectangular grid system of the National Grid. The true origin is at latitude 49° north and longitude 2° west of Greenwich and the false origin, adopted to ensure that all grid eastings are positive and that grid northings on the mainland of Britain do not exceed one million metres, is 400 km west and 100 km north of the true origin. The scale is 1:2500 too small on the central meridian and about 1:2500 too large at the outer limits.

The Primary Triangulation (Plate 18)

The orthodox way to have carried out the new primary triangulation would have been to have measured its angles by theodolite, the lengths of selected sides by base measurement and extension, and azimuth by astronomical observation. All this work would have been done more or less concurrently and the results would have been incorporated into the computation of the triangulation. However, not for the first time in the history of the Ordnance Survey, circumstances prevented the adoption of an entirely orthodox method. During the first season of observation, between April and October 1936, angular observations of a belt of triangulation, roughly 50 miles wide running along the spine of England from the Isle of Wight to the Tyne, were completed. This belt comprised adjustment Figures 1 and 2 of the triangulation. Eleven of the stations observed were identical in location with Clarke's Principal Triangulation. They were:

Bardon Hill	(58)*
Beacon Hill	(15)
Butser	(9)
Coringdon	(11)
Dunnose	(10)
Great Whernside	(7)
Holme Moss	(26)
Inkpen	(33)
Malvern	(79)
Rombalds Moor	(70)
White Horse Hill	(34)

A preliminary computation of the combined Figures 1 and 2 was made, accepting the former side length Dunnose–Beacon Hill and the direction Butser–Beacon Hill; then the whole combined figure was readjusted in position, scale and direction so as to give a best mean (least squares) fit with the Principal Triangulation co-ordinates at the eleven points, the shape of the combined figure remaining undisturbed. This readjusted figure was then accepted as final and hence as determining the scale and orientation of the rest of the triangulation.

It seems probable that at the root of this decision lay Hotine's mistrust of adjusting triangulation to fixed bases and azimuths, which he believed might do harm rather than good to a network by introducing local inconsistency and distortion, especially when the extension of the measured base was unsound. He wrote:

> Although adjustment to fixed bases and Laplace azimuths has become an article of faith in the modern school of geodesy, there can be no doubt that a comprehensive net adjustment is the better answer to the particular problem of Great Britain, both as regards local geometrical consistency and the avoidance of large over-all cumulative error.[3]

But the actual reason he gave was somewhat different, namely: 'to avoid disturbing the graticule on published large scale maps and coastal charts'.[4] It is not altogether clear what he meant by this: there was obvious merit in a procedure which, while internally consistent, would minimize the differences between geographical co-ordinates of identical points on old and new maps and charts, and it seems probable that this is what was really intended. It would obviously have been too much to expect both the old and the new triangulations to have produced co-ordinates which were identical within plottable limits, and some change in the position of points with reference to large-scale map graticules was inevitable. There was, however, a great practical advantage, which must have been in the minds of Hotine and others responsible, although he does not appear to have acknowledged it specifically.

By effectively fixing the position, scale, and orientation of the triangulation at an early stage of the proceedings, very much greater flexibility was achieved for succeeding phases, and those parts of the triangulation which were most urgently needed for the provision of lower order control for the new mapping could be given priority, less urgent blocks being left meanwhile. With the orthodox procedure neither scale, position nor orientation could have been determined finally for any part of the

---

* The numbers in brackets are the serial reference numbers of the primary triangulation stations.

triangulation until all the angles and bases considered necessary had been measured and the astronomical azimuths observed and computed.

The method chosen implied that the new work was computed upon the same fundamental basis as that of Clarke, the reference being Airy's spheroid defined as follows:

major semi-axis (a) 20 923 713 feet of bar O_1

major semi-axis (b) 20 853 810 feet of bar O_1

But to reduce the likelihood of confusion and ambiguity in the future, all distances were calculated in terms of an unequivocal standard, the international metre, the factor used to convert feet of bar O_1 to international metres being the logarithm $\bar{1}.484\,016\,83$ or in natural terms $0.304\,800\,749\,1$ . . . This ratio was derived from the comparison between the intermediate bar $O1_1$ and the international metre by Benoit and Johnston in 1906 and the comparison between bar $O1_1$ and bar O_1 by Clarke in 1864.[5]

It was always Hotine's intention, at some later stage, 'to fix the scale of the new triangulation afresh from two new base lines directly related to modern length standards in International Metres'.[6] He envisaged applying to the triangulation a weighted mean scale derived from these bases, much as Clarke had done. This however would have meant changing all the co-ordinates of the triangulation stations and other work derived from them and so, to avoid this, he proposed instead 'adopting a new value for the major axis of Airy's spheroid and . . . a fresh table of scale 'errors' for the Transverse Mercator Projection'.[7] In retrospect this proposal seems fraught with many possibilities for subsequent confusion and it is perhaps as well that it was never put into effect. It seems to have been quietly forgotten during the Second World War which was soon to break out, and in the aftermath when demands for control for post-war surveys became pressing. The publication of the projection tables for the National Grid in 1950[8] finally settled the matter. The bases were measured in 1937–8 (and indeed remeasured) as were the lengths and azimuths of many triangulation sides, but these determinations were permitted to affect neither the National Grid nor the published results of the retriangulation in any way. They were used in the first place simply for the purposes of checking but were later incorporated into new adjustments carried out for essentially scientific purposes.

EXECUTION OF THE TRIANGULATION

The first step in the execution of the Primary Triangulation was to draw up a 'paper scheme' with the aid of maps. At this stage the division of the work into blocks of a convenient size was determined, size being governed by the largest number of observations that the computing organization was thought capable of dealing with in a simultaneous least squares adjustment. Before the advent of electronic computing there was no possibility of adjusting the entire triangulation as one block. However the Ordnance Survey in 1935 possessed calculating machines and other facilities not available to Clarke a hundred years earlier and was able to cover the country with fewer but larger blocks. Hotine's original plan made use of six blocks or figures to cover Great Britain; Figure 7 was added several years later. The paper scheme was verified in the field using small ($3\frac{1}{2}$-inch circle) Tavistock theodolites to confirm the intervisibility of the selected stations, and modifications were made where necessary. In areas liable to land subsidence, especially mining areas, stable sites were always chosen if possible – stations were often located on winding-gear towers – but, if an unstable location could not be avoided, or if disturbance for some other reason was likely, for example by roof repairs on buildings, additional 'substitute stations' were selected on stable sites near by, from which the position of the unstable station could be re-established if necessary. Reconnaissance was started in 1935, before observing equipment became available, and Figures 1 and 2 were reconnoitred during that year; by 1937 Figures 1, 2, 3, 4 and 5 had been dealt with.

MARKING OF STATIONS

A matter that received particular care and thought was the marking of stations. In the old triangulation this had usually been done by some form of buried marker giving no surface indication of its location. This led to much trouble, through the difficulty of finding the old stations when they were needed for further survey work; sometimes they had been inadvertently disturbed by builders or archaeologists and, in one instance, by searchers for Zeppelin bombs.[9] A standard pillar marker was therefore designed which would guard against these troubles in the future. This was particularly important because the Retriangulation was only the start of a chain of survey operations that would continue for a long time – indeed indefinitely – into the future. The pillar was in the shape of a truncated concrete pyramid, 4 feet high and 2 feet square at the base. It incorporated a brass 'spider' with three arms 120° apart upon which the instrument was mounted and automatically centred. Vertically below were two mark bolts, one at surface level and the other below ground, both set in separate and mutually isolated concrete blocks. A brass flush bracket affixed to the side provided a bench-mark for heighting by spirit-levelling.

Since 1935 these pillars, some 6500 of them in all, sited on the tops of mountains and in other prominent locations throughout the country, have become one of the most familiar evidences of the Ordnance Survey and its work. To the surveyor they proved a great boon, saving him the trouble of carrying the theodolite legs to the station and providing instead a mount upon which the instrument, beacon, lamp or other observing target could be quickly affixed and automatically centred and one which was so firm that it enabled several of the usual precautions to be dispensed with. The robustness of the design rendered the pillar relatively immune to damage by nature or vandals – even explosives – and, if it was knocked down or tilted, the isolated lower mark was likely to survive and provide for accurate re-establishment. The design of a number of these pillars was modified to suit local conditions: some were built of local stone to harmonize with their surroundings, some served also as collecting boxes for the National Trust, or as topographs at scenic viewpoints; later some were constructed in lighter cylindrical form so that the necessary materials could be carried more cheaply by helicopter to mountain tops. Some carried commemorative plaques, as did the pillar at Miltonhead near Lanark, the birthplace of General Roy.* The Survey Act of 1841 had conferred on the Ordnance Survey the power to establish permanent 'marks, stones or posts', without consent of the owners of the land, but this was used only as a last resort, persuasion having failed. Only fourteen times was this compulsory power invoked.

OBSERVATION OF THE ANGLES OF THE TRIANGULATION

Observation of the triangulation started in April 1936. The theodolite used was the large (5 or 5½-inch) Tavistock made by Cooke, Troughton and Simms, an instrument which had lately thoroughly proved itself on geodetic triangulation abroad, notably the triangulation of the arc of the 30th meridian in Africa. All observations were made during the night to electric beacon lamps, also made by Cooke, Troughton and Simms. For some stations, particularly in the flat East Anglian country, steel towers had to be used as observing platforms. These were portable 103-foot Bilby towers designed by the United States Coast and Geodetic Survey; a practised team could unload and erect one of them on previously prepared foundations in ten hours. All angles were measured on sixteen zeros, the observer having discretion to add to this number if he was dissatisfied with his results.[10] The observers, all of whom were or had been non-commissioned officers of the Survey Battalion, Royal Engineers, had received thorough training and some had experience of triangulation overseas, but few of geodetic triangulation. The first year's work, when the main English chain, Figures 1 and 2, was observed, provided an opportunity for familiarization and settling down. Three observing parties, working independently in the south, centre and north, were employed. A party consisted of an observer, two senior assistants and nine light-keepers. Each light-keeper worked on his own, controlled by the observer using light signals or, if necessary, telegrams or personal visits. Of the two senior assistants, one acted as booker and occasionally as observer; the other was a general factotum with the additional responsibility of supervising the light-keepers. Official transport consisted of nine small vans, a fleet which was supplemented by a variety of powered (and unpowered) wheeled transport owned by the light-keepers. In spite of these rather primitive arrangements, the programme was completed by mid October, almost as planned; 56 primary stations had been occupied and 447 directions observed.

In subsequent seasons observing parties were modified to suit the changing nature of the country traversed. The Highlands of Scotland and other mountainous areas called for an organization which would minimize the number of visits to the less accessible mountain-top stations. The use of independent parties was not appropriate and instead a centralized organization was adopted, with three observing sections of three men each, and twenty light-keeping sections, numbering one to three men each and working according to a co-ordinated programme. This provided for light-keepers to remain in position until all observations to the station concerned had been completed. The operations were physically arduous, the weather often causing not only discomfort, but also exasperation as

* Among other pillars bearing plaques were the first to be observed, Cold Ashby in April 1936, and the last, Thorny Gale in May 1962.

persistent cloud shrouded some mountain tops, notably Ben Macdhui (4301 feet) and the notorious Black Combe in the Lake District, the mountain that had given so much trouble to Mudge in the early nineteenth century that Wordsworth was inspired to write a poem about his experience.

By the end of 1937 Figures 3 and 4 had been completed; Figure 3 to the shores of the Moray Firth by way of the Lake District, the Borders, the Southern Uplands of Scotland and the Grampians; and Figure 4 covering Wales and south-west England; 91 stations had been occupied and 642 directions observed.

The 1938 season was devoted mainly to the observation of Figure 5 covering East Anglia. Towers were required for thirty-four primary stations and for a number of secondary stations as well; as much secondary work as possible was completed around primary stations while the primary towers were still in position. The organization was again modified to include a tower-erection section and the stock of Bilby steel towers was boosted from nine to eleven by the loan of two from the Geodetic Survey of Denmark. By the end of the season 87 primary stations had been occupied and 634 primary directions observed. In addition 302 secondary stations had been occupied, 47 of them steel tower stations, and 2199 directions observed.

The Ridge Way and Lossiemouth Bases

Upon the completion of Figures 1 to 5, the observation of the primary retriangulation was suspended and work was switched to the secondary. Before this, and before war intervened to call a halt to operations, the two base lines which Hotine had envisaged were measured, the first in 1937 along the ancient Ridge Way between White Horse Hill and Liddington Castle in Wiltshire, and the second in 1938 near Lossiemouth on the Moray Firth, the pre-war northern limit of the retriangulation.[11] Before the Ridge Way was selected as the site for the southern base line, the old Salisbury Plain base line was considered; a remeasurement might have thrown interesting light on the relationship between the Ordnance Survey's length standards of Clarke's day and the modern metre; but it was found that the terminals were not intervisible at ground level and, even if towers had been used, grazing rays would have resulted, with the likelihood of lateral refraction occurring and vitiating the base extension. Moreover, the base line was by then obstructed in several places. The Lossiemouth Base was the same as that measured in 1909 in connection with the test of the Principal Triangulation. Both bases were measured with Invar tapes in catenary using the procedures worked out by Hotine in the measurement of the Kate Base of the triangulation of the East African arc of the 30th meridian in 1931–3.

The Ridge Way Base was measured between 10 November and 7 December 1937 – not the most comfortable time of the year for an operation such as this – and the Lossiemouth Base between 19 July and 4 August 1938. The finally accepted length of the Ridge Way Base was 11 260.19308 m, and that of the Lossiemouth Base 7 170.72340 m, the latter differing from the 1909 measure by about 10 mm – a good agreement. The Ridge Way Base reproduced through the adjusted triangulation upon Lossiemouth with an accuracy of 13 parts per million (ppm). For points 700 km apart this was considered satisfactory. Hotine, however, suspected the accuracy of his Lossiemouth base extension, which consisted of a rather complex chain of small triangles situated asymmetrically on the landward side of the base, a layout which introduced the strong possibility of lateral refraction errors. He believed that the 1910–11 extension, observed over a longer period in which lateral refraction errors would tend to mean out, might be more accurate. The two extensions differed from each other by 14 ppm, and if the 1910–11 extension was used with the 1938 measurement the agreement between the 1938 base length and the length carried through the triangulation from Ridge Way was even better – 1 ppm.

Computation of the Primary Triangulation

With the completion of observations in Figures 1 to 5 and the measurement of the two base lines, field work for the Primary Triangulation was suspended. Computation and adjustment of figures had been proceeding as observations became available. For the least squares adjustment of the Principal Triangulation, Clarke had used the method of adjustment by condition equations but during the early twentieth century an alternative was developed called adjustment by 'variation of co-ordinates'. For this, approximate or 'provisional' co-ordinates of all points are first calculated by the simplest possible means. From these co-ordinates the directions of all points observed from each station are deduced together with the lengths of any base lines or other previously fixed sides. The deduced directions and lengths will not, of course, agree with their 'observed' counterparts, and the adjustment process consists in varying the co-ordinates in such a manner that the sum of the squares of the differences between deduced values and observed values is a minimum, suitable weighting being applied to the different types of observation to make them mutually compatible. In both methods the adjustment of one block determines the lengths and directions of sides common to the next block taken up.

The method of condition equations was still the most commonly used in the 1930s. Accordingly it was adopted for Figures 1, 2, 3, and 4, which were adjusted in that order before the war, all calculations being in spheroidal terms, that is, in terms of latitude and longitude; conversion to National Grid co-ordinates was made subsequently. But variation of co-ordinates is much less laborious for large blocks, and incidentally is particularly suited to the electronic computer. It was therefore used for all primary adjustments after the war and, at the same time, the change was made to computation in plane co-ordinates upon the National Grid. The computation of Figure 5 was a case on its own: it was started in 1939 using condition equations and was continued intermittently until 1943, by which time post-war planning had begun. It was clear that an early requirement would be for control in the London area which fell in the southern half of the Figure. This half was therefore completed first, the northern half following later. The discrepancies in co-ordinates along the junction were removed by a second, semigraphic, adjustment and the readjusted co-ordinates issued. These were later checked by a second readjustment of the Figure as a single block by variation of co-ordinates. The discrepancies nowhere exceeded 2 metres and the original co-ordinates were therefore adhered to; all lower order survey work was based on them.

Notes

1 M. Hotine, 'The Retriangulation of Great Britain', *Empire Survey Review* vol. IV, nos. 25, 26 (1937), 29 (1938) (Reprinted as a single volume). See also, throughout, *The History of the Retriangulation of Great Britain* (HMSO 1967).

2 *Constants, Formulae and Methods used in the Transverse Mercator Projection* (HMSO 1950).

3 Hotine, 'Base Measurement', *Empire Survey Review*, 1939, vol. IV, no. 34.

4 Hotine, 'Retriangulation'.

5 E. H. Thompson, 'The Ordnance Survey foot/metre conversion ratio', *Empire Survey Review* 1952, vol. IX, no. 84.

6 Hotine, 'Retriangulation'.

7 *Ibid*.

8 *Projection Tables for the Transverse Mercator Projection of Great Britain* (HMSO 1950).

9 Hotine, 'Retriangulation'.

10 *Ibid*.

11 Hotine, 'Base Measurement'.

28
The
Second
World
War
1939–1945

The Ordnance Survey at Southampton 1939–40

The economies imposed upon the Ordnance Survey between the two world wars had made it incapable of providing an efficient service in a time of rapid topographic change, although the Davidson Committee had made recommendations designed to build up its depleted staff, reform its revision procedures and introduce new map scales. The buildings it occupied at Southampton had long been cramped and obsolete; better housing was promised by the acquisition of the Crabwood House estate on the north-western outskirts of the town. But the first stage of the implementation of these plans took place under the rapidly expanding shadow of Nazi Germany.

The overriding fact about the Ordnance Survey in 1939 was that it had not yet had time to recover from the effects of the lean years between 1922 and 1935. The main task in the previous two or three years had been to carry out the rapid expansion recommended by the Davidson Report. This included the recruitment and training of a large number of men, most of whom were young and therefore of military age.

The London Road office continued to be the Ordnance Survey's focal point, but as an interim measure other premises were secured in and around Southampton, most of them far from suitable for the specialized work which now went on at an increasing pace. At the outbreak of war London Road housed the headquarters and administrative staff, a detachment of Royal Engineers, the Drawing and Reproduction Division, Triangulation and Levelling Division, Archaeology Branch, Workshops and Building Division and the appropriate stores. A lease was taken of a section of the rolling mills at Woolston on the east side of the town, to cope with the great demand for enamel-coated zinc, the new drawing medium both for the Ordnance Survey and for other government departments, and a drawing office occupied part of the same building until, in January 1940, it was moved into the old Central Library near the London Road office. The Central Library was also used as a store for a considerable part of the Department's basic records on glass negatives, and housed two prototype stereogonio-meters and a Wild stereoplotting machine.

Some of the new draughtsmen were accommodated in Hanover Buildings and East Bargate in the centre of the town. Other drawing staff were at Highfield and elsewhere but the most significant development for the future was the increasing use of the new property at Crabwood House, where the formation of a complete reproduction unit was begun in June 1940, under the command of Colonel J. D. Campbell, a recently retired Director of the Survey of India.

But the whole arrangement of the Survey at Southampton, both permanent and improvised, was basically unsatisfactory even for normal peace-time work. Considered as a centre from which to operate a vital war effort it was much worse; it was dangerously sited in a large population centre which was a major port containing an aircraft factory, and only a short distance from a naval base.

The Davidson Committee had not been required to resolve the rather anomalous arrangement whereby the Ordnance Survey contained the bulk of the military surveying man-power and was directed by military officers, while being under the control of the civilian Ministry of Agriculture and Fisheries, and having a numerically preponderant civilian staff. With another major war plainly impending, the war-time responsibilities of the Department were far from clear. It would certainly function as a producer of maps for the use of the Forces as it had done in the Boer War and in the war of 1914–18 but its capacity to provide trained military survey units for a war of movement was doubtful.

With the outbreak of war the mobilization scheme applicable to the Ordnance Survey came into force at once. It had been under review for some years but had not been changed because of uncertainty at the War Office and the probability that any proposed change would lead to long discussions with the civilian ministry which controlled the Ordnance Survey.

Mobilization affected the Survey in two ways. Firstly, it almost at once removed a large part of the Survey Battalion, amounting to seventeen Royal Engineer officers and five hundred other ranks. The loss of these trained men was made good as far as possible by former staff coming out of retirement. Secondly, civilians were now liable to be called up for military service. Nearly two-thirds of the whole civilian strength had joined the Survey only since the beginning of 1936 so that there had been no opportunity for the age pattern of the staff to adjust itself with the passage of time. No specific provision had been made for reservation[1]* and in the first six months of the war 675 of the 2495 Civil Assistants had been called up. The need to retain a nucleus of more experienced staff was only established after prolonged arguments with the War Office. From February 1940 women were trained and employed on production work in increasing numbers, but by this time women were also under conscription for service with the Forces, and War Office consent had to be got for their recruitment and subsequent reservation. The Ordnance Survey was allowed to continue to engage Junior Temporary Civil Assistants aged sixteen to seventeen years who were then trained as 'map constructors'. These young men were enlisted into military survey units when they reached military age.

In the spring of 1940 it was still uncertain how the war would develop, and the future military role of the Ordnance Survey had not been decided when disaster struck in May, with the defeat of the British and French armies and the evacuation from Dunkirk, but the part to be played by Publication Division was clear enough. During the next four years its work was to be the Department's main contribution to the war effort; in 1940 it was already compelled to recruit civilians from the printing trade as it was still expected to supply the whole map requirements of the Army and Royal Air Force. As pressures built up and the war took on a global character, civilian firms were increasingly drawn in and the Ordnance Survey assumed the form of a great map-producing centre, supplying reproduction material to many other printers.

The Ordnance Survey and the War Office

At the outbreak of war three survey companies for service overseas were provided under the mobilization scheme, and two survey training units were made up from the training elements of the 19th Field Survey Company. The departure of the three companies seriously reduced the strength of the Survey Battalion and also removed a lot of equipment which had to be borrowed from the Ordnance Survey to make up deficiencies. Much of this became a permanent loss when it was left behind at Dunkirk. Meanwhile the training units, under the command of Majors E. B. Elkington and H. A. Bazley RE, were housed in Fort Southwick and Fort Widley at Portsmouth. They had difficulty in getting down to effective training because the War Office directed a large number of recruits to them straight from civil life, and it was some time before the flow was reduced to a manageable size.

During the winter of 1939–40 experience showed that the pre-war mobilization scheme which provided for two training units was unworkable in practice and steps were taken towards the creation of a single survey training establishment. These moves were assisted by the active support of Lord Davidson, whose recent part in the reorganization of the Ordnance Survey had given him an understanding of its workings. A new establishment was approved and became the Survey Training Centre RE in April 1940 under the control of the War Office and with Lieutenant-Colonel Elkington as Commandant.

This rationalization had hardly been achieved when the military disaster of May occurred and the survey organization of the field army was completely disrupted. The units were fragmented and dispersed and most of the equipment lost. The stragglers from the survey directorates and the field units gathered at Fort Southwick because the new Survey Training Centre was for the moment the only element of the military survey service remaining intact. Here they were interviewed, re-equipped and posted to units. But Portsmouth was no place for a training centre in the summer of 1940. The new military situation made the place a prime and easy target for enemy air attacks, and the danger of

---

* Those in 'reserved occupations' were exempt from call-up into the armed forces.

invasion compelled GOC Portsmouth to take over the Centre for a while as part of a hastily improvised defence force. This, and heavy air attacks on Portsmouth, interfered to some extent with training, and in January 1941 the Centre was removed to Ruabon in North Wales, where it operated successfully from Wynnstay Park for the rest of the war.

These changes in the organization of military survey training were the outcome of a troublesome dispute between the Ordnance Survey and the War Office. The military body responsible to the General Staff for the provision of maps and advice on all military survey matters was the Geographical Section of the General Staff (MI 4), directed in 1939 by Colonel P. K. Boulnois. GSGS was badly understaffed, and as the prospect of war increased only two more officers were added to its establishment to supervise the map production in hand and to deal with stores, equipment and the war-time survey organization. At the outbreak of war communication was not improved by the removal of GSGS to Cheltenham. Here it was away from close contact with the General Staff, isolated from the main map depot at Alperton near London, and also from the Air Ministry Map Section at Harrow. In addition it was not well sited for working with the Ordnance Survey at Southampton, with whom relations were often difficult.

The Director General, Major-General MacLeod, was a man of strongly held opinions backed by eminent professional skill. No one had questioned his responsibility for training in peace time, but Boulnois now claimed that, as head of GSGS, he should take charge of all military survey training as soon as mobilization was complete. The obsolescent mobilization scheme did not specifically cover this point; moreover, MacLeod was well aware that in the 1914–18 war the Ordnance Survey had continued to be responsible for military survey training throughout its course and he believed there were good reasons for retaining this arrangement. On the other hand, in 1939 the Survey training unit was not a part of the Ordnance Survey establishment, which lent support to Boulnois's claim. The issue was complicated because Boulnois was junior in rank to MacLeod and the Ordnance Survey was under the control of a civilian ministry. On 19 December 1939, in an over-optimistic attempt to resolve the problem, the Director General was put in charge of training all new recruits under the direction of Southern Command, with the title of Inspector of Survey Units RE. It was probably fortunate that these difficulties were quickly resolved by the events of 1940; after the formation of the Survey Training Centre, the Ordnance Survey ceased to have any responsibility for military survey training.

Another bone of contention was the question of map production in the early days of the war, and here MacLeod's anxieties and interventions were entirely justified. The Ordnance Survey was already engaged with heavy map production programmes for both military and civil authorities in the autumn of 1939. The establishment at Southampton had become a map-producing factory working to the requirements of the Forces, and it was necessary to have clear direction on its task since it was now producing nine-tenths of the maps used by them. This led to more friction between the Ordnance Survey and GSGS because the latter, having moved to Cheltenham, was now having a large map-printing works installed there.

Boulnois was either unable or unwilling to give any forecast of probable requirements or of the degree of employment which might be expected at Southampton. The Director General made representations to the Inspector of Royal Engineers, Major-General G. H. Addison, about the new factory, but Addison had already been shown the new plant at Cheltenham and took no action. This turned out to be right, because the need for map-producing capacity was soon to become very great, but at the time MacLeod's desire to clarify the map production policy was entirely appropriate.

The question of the scale of maps to be used by the Army was also urgent in the summer of 1940. It was apparent that GSGS was committed to a policy based mainly on the issue of small-scale maps, a procedure economical in the use of resources but highly dangerous if the production of gridded large-scale maps should suddenly become necessary. This point was brought home with great emphasis by the collapse of France, the Dunkirk evacuation, and the strong probability that the next phase of the war would be fought on British soil. An emergency of this kind had clearly not been allowed for in pre-war planning by the War Office, and the stocks of gridded maps in Command stores and in the Ordnance Survey only covered training areas and almost none of those coastal tracts where invasion might be expected.[2] The immediate need was for at least 50 000 gridded copies of about 150 one-inch sheets of Great Britain printed in a priority based on a forecast of the most likely points of invasion, as well as gridded cover on the 1:25 000 scale. The Ordnance Survey was the only body capable of even attempting to carry out this task and a list of priorities was urgently needed, but no instructions could be obtained from GSGS. Facilities for the transport and storage of the maps were also meagre or non-existent.

It was then that Lieutenant-Colonel Hotine, Assistant Director of Survey at HQ IV Corps, made a vital intervention. He had been with the field survey units in France as deputy to Brigadier Clough, and he now managed to secure a 'first phase' printing order as a result of a visit to Major-General E. C. T. Paget, Chief of the General Staff at GHQ Home Forces. Every printing firm capable of producing maps was now drawn in to help, with the Ordnance Survey providing the plates and the paper. By prodigious efforts the map programme was completed before the expected time of invasion. Hotine also drew up plans for Command depots and arranged for storage space at York; in addition he examined the survey requirements for coastal and anti-aircraft batteries as well as for airfield and radar station construction.[3]

GHQ Home Forces was now charged with the defence of the country, but it had no proper survey organization. From GSGS Boulnois tried to get a Director of Survey posted to GHQ but the Commander-in-Chief, General Sir William Ironside, would not accept this on the grounds that a liaison officer from GSGS would suffice. This refusal was a measure of the lack of appreciation among staff officers of the part to be played by an effective survey headquarters. The situation was made worse by the issue of an Army Order mobilizing twelve divisions ('less Legal, Postal and Survey branches') for the defence of Great Britain.

At this point MacLeod made contact with the Director of Military Operations, Major-General R. H. Dewing, urging the need for a survey directorate at GHQ because without it there was no way of controlling map production to conform with a changing military situation. This led to an interview next day with a committee under the chairmanship of Brigadier O. Lund, Deputy Director of Military Operations, and including Brigadier A. E. Nye (Staff Duties, War Office). MacLeod explained the gravity of the position and it was agreed that there should be a Director of Survey at GHQ, an Assistant Director at each Command HQ, and a field survey unit in each Command.[4]

The need for a highly qualified and determined Director had to be met at once. Brigadier Clough had been Director of Survey with GHQ in France and had temporarily resumed his former post of Deputy Director General at Southampton after his return from Dunkirk. He now stood down on the grounds of ill health and by the end of June Hotine had taken over the duties of Director of Survey, Home Forces, a post which he held through the rest of the dangerous summer of 1940. In October he was suddenly transferred to East Africa, where preparations were being made for the war against the Italians, and Colonel R. E. Fryer succeeded him as Director of Survey.

Serious and avoidable delays in map production still occurred and the supply of maps for the Royal Air Force was unsatisfactory. An attempt was made to remove the obstacles by getting the Ministry of Agriculture and Fisheries to suggest that MacLeod should be put in charge of all production and survey work, answerable for this to the Army Council but remaining under ministerial control for all the civil work of the Ordnance Survey. This was refused by the War Office and no further progress was made until Boulnois left GSGS in September 1941. The whole business of military survey and map production was then placed under a new and centralized control. GSGS was brought back from Cheltenham to a new site at Eastcote on the north-west side of London, and in 1943 was reorganized as the Directorate of Military Survey with an integrated staff to serve the needs of both Army and Air Force in a war which had become world wide. Its drawing and printing establishment was set up in the requisitioned Hygrade factory at Hanwell close by and its success was assured by the appointment of Brigadier Hotine, first as head of GSGS and later as Director of Military Survey. Closely co-ordinated effort in the fields of survey and map production was now ensured.

The Blitz at Southampton in 1940

MacLeod was to remain in post as Director General until July 1943, when he was succeeded by Major-General G. Cheetham, with Brigadier E. R. L. Peake as Deputy. But the last years of his directorate were not to be undisturbed by further trials because the full force of enemy air attack was to fall on his own establishment at Southampton in the latter part of 1940. In 1841 the Ordnance Survey had been uprooted from London and moved to Southampton as a result of the fire at the Tower of London, and almost a century later it was brought very near to complete destruction by enemy attack on its second home.

In the summer months of 1939 precautionary measures against the effects of air raids were taken at Southampton. The organization was voluntary and at first consisted of two fire-fighting crews, two rescue parties, two material decontamination squads and four first-aid parties with all necessary equipment; later many fire-watchers and a bomb disposal squad were added as the need arose. It was centred in the South Range at London Road, where a large air-raid shelter was constructed with an equipment store and provision for dealing with gas contamination.

Little beyond occasional alerts occurred in the first nine months of the war, but the events of May and June 1940 exposed the whole of southern England to short-range enemy attack and Southampton moved into the front line as a prime target. The first phase of enemy assault was aimed at making a quick end by massive attacks on the south-east and London, and by the elimination of the Royal Air Force, but at the end of September the Battle of Britain had been won. The Southampton area was on the side lines at this stage although, in August, staff at Crabwood were witnesses of an action overhead in which the only fighter Victoria Cross of the war was won by Flight-Lieutenant J. B. Nicolson.

There were many alerts by day and night. At first much time was spent in shelters during office hours but this was reduced by the introduction of 'roof spotters' who decided if there was actual danger and if the staff should take shelter. Night alerts seldom led to any attack on Southampton but there was a great deal of heavy gunfire as planes passed overhead to and from other targets. These weighed heavily on the staff working seven days a week, and it was difficult to maintain full working hours especially now that women, most of whom had domestic responsibilities, formed a large element in it.

With the autumn the second phase of the assault began with widespread attacks, chiefly by night, all over the country. The first important event at Southampton occurred in the lunch hour of 24 September when bombs fell close to London Road, and many sappers had a narrow escape when St Barnabas Hall in Lodge Road received a direct hit. The South Range was then camouflaged to give the impression of damage, and so deceive aerial reconnaissance. The enemy build-up continued with attacks on 18 and 23 November during which a Royal Engineer boy was wounded and fire bombs were successfully put out. In the second of these raids damage to water mains in the town pointed to future disaster for there was no independent water supply at London Road and static water tanks were still things of the future. It is interesting to recall that a similar water shortage owing to low tide in the Thames had contributed to the severity of the fire in the Tower of London in 1841.

The great attacks came on the nights of 30 November and 1 December.[5] They were massive and disastrous; 1650 high explosive and 13 000 fire bombs reduced a large part of the town to rubble. The London Road Office was severely damaged. On the first night there were direct hits on the South Range and the North-West Block, and the Barrack Block was set on fire. The Headquarters Office, Cashier's Department, Library, Telephone Exchange, Air Raid Precaution (ARP) Control Room and First Aid Station, Manuscript Store and Large Scale Negative Store were all destroyed, partly by the explosions and then by the fires which could not be controlled for lack of water. Drawing Offices were also lost in the North-West Block. On the second night a high explosive bomb which penetrated to the ground floor of the Jubilee Block started a fire which destroyed the whole building, and at the same time the North Range and the East Pavilion were gutted. This accounted for a map store and the Plan Examination, Boundary and Area Computation and Stores Departments as well as materials and drawings for the one-inch (New Popular) Series. Many valuable documents were lost including some levelling records and almost all the Name Books for England and Wales, those for the extreme north of England alone surviving. Fortunately in all this there were only minor injuries to persons and no bombs fell on the Printing, Proving, Helio and Photo Sections, so that production for war purposes was not directly impeded. The ARP staff could do nothing to save the burning buildings but they made every effort to rescue what they could from the flames, though often in great danger and exhausted from lack of sleep. The good work done on these grim nights was recognized by the award of the George Medal to Lieutenant Jack Keleher RE and Boy N. S. Thompson RE for conspicuous bravery, initiative and devotion to duty.[6] It should also be put on record that, in spite of the fearful state of the town, cleaners arrived for work as usual on these bleak mornings.

It was the civil and not the military side of the Survey's current work which stood to lose most by this attack, but in fact the nine months respite at the beginning of the war had given time to safeguard much of the original material relating to the survey of Great Britain. This was in various forms on paper, copper, glass negatives and zinc plates, and covered all scales. The Photo, Helio, Proving and Photowriter staff had strained to the utmost to duplicate these records which were then sent for storage underground in the Cotswolds and other less-threatened areas. But in spite of all these efforts, which provided a basis for the post-war resumption of normal work, the attack on London Road found the duplication still incomplete and much valuable material was lost, including many glass negatives stored in the old Central Library where they were reduced to a molten mass. The Library in the South Range was completely destroyed. Here, besides a great deal of technical material, perished many valuable books on local topography and history which had been gathered during work in all parts of Great Britain during the nineteenth century. A distressing and unnecessary loss was the great three-foot Ramsden theodolite used by General Roy in the earliest days of the Ordnance Survey. Before the war it stood in the Library and there had been a whole year in which it could have been taken to a place of safety. Instead it had been removed to the basement of Jubilee Block where it found itself among stores, some of them highly inflammable, and shared their fate. Here again there was a parallel with the 1841 fire when Ramsden's zenith sector was lost. More fortunately, on the initiative of Mr B. Watts, Chief Superintendent in the Triangulation and Levelling Division, most of the other historical instruments had been moved from the Bar Room and Long Standard Room to the Ordnance Depot at Wellington in Shropshire.

Another loss was particularly grave under the conditions of 1940. A Wild A5 Autograph and two prototype stereoplotting machines were ruined in the fire. The Wild machine was one of the only two in Britain and as it was a Swiss product it could not easily be replaced. After its remains had been consigned to the scrap-heap, the Air Ministry recovered the main frame and the Cambridge Instrument Company reconstituted the machine using as a pattern the survivor which was with the Central Interpretation Unit of the Royal Air Force at Medmenham.

No time was lost in making it possible to resume work. The Headquarters Office moved into 45 Westwood Road where, shortly afterwards, a bomb fell into the garden and sent the Office into temporary refuge at Crabwood House, but after about a fortnight it was able to return to Westwood Road where it remained until the move to Chessington in 1943. Two other houses in the same road, along with Oakmount School, were occupied by Triangulation and Levelling Division, Boundary Section and displaced drawing sections. More draughtsmen worked above Burton's the tailors in Bargate Circus; part of the map store went to garage premises in Winchester Road. Areas and Plan Examination were housed in Carlton Crescent.

At London Road rubble was cleared from the west end of South Range basement and the Telephone Exchange and ARP control were re-established there; later there was to be a general repair of burnt-out buildings in basement and ground-floor levels. A vivid memory of the early days of recovery was the lighting of open fires on the sacrosanct lawn in front of South Range. These were fed with wreckage from the destroyed buildings and became open-air kitchens for the canteens. Regular fire-watching was now undertaken and 350 of the staff volunteered for this duty, but there were no further serious attacks on Southampton except for a stick of bombs which straddled London Road on the night of 7 July 1941 with more, but this time slight, damage to the South Range.

The Dispersal 1941–3

Despite the recognition of the dangers of over-concentration which followed the bombing of Southampton, fully eighteen months were to pass before any major changes could be made. The danger from air attack remained and wide dispersal into self-contained map production units was the obvious safeguard. Meanwhile the war extended its range into Russia and the Far East and the demand for maps greatly increased.

The immediate measures taken did not extend outside the Southampton area. The growing establishment at Crabwood had fortunately escaped damage and it was now further expanded by more temporary buildings, which housed drawing and reproduction sections. At London Road draughtsmen were packed into surviving accommodation under uncomfortable conditions while some degree of rebuilding took place. Basement and ground floors were made usable in the Jubilee Block, the Barrack Block and the eastern part of the South Range. But though scattered accommodation in and around Southampton was in use as far afield as Causton's printing works in Eastleigh where an instructional drawing centre was set up, another severe attack would probably have brought the whole Survey to a standstill.

Since 1940 Forman's of Nottingham had been printing maps for the Ordnance Survey at their well-equipped factory and this was regarded as a reserve in case Southampton should be overrun. A small detachment was sent from Southampton on 30 September 1941 to occupy a complete section of the premises and to set up and operate a reproduction unit capable of quick expansion at need; a few months earlier, Derby Grammar School had been taken over for a Drawing Division. These dispersed units became known as OND (Offices at Nottingham and Derby); they were under the command of Lieutenant-Colonel C. L. Y. Parker till early in 1943 when Mr W. E. Wilde took over. The combination soon proved its value, and printed large quantities of maps, chiefly of Italy, North Africa, Egypt and, after D-day, of the European theatre of war, often under conditions of great pressure. After the removal of much of the Southampton establishment to Hinchley Wood, Waddon and

Chessington in 1942–3, the importance of OND declined and it was finally closed down in September 1945.

In January 1942 the Ordnance Survey was given two new military establishments to replace that of the Survey Battalion which had been a casualty of 1940. The first of these was a Military Headquarters Staff, which provided the officers, warrant officers, and non-commissioned officers required for the direction of the Ordnance Survey and for certain key posts.[7] The second, known as 522 (Ordnance Survey) Company RE, under the command of Major A. R. Martin, supplied regular tradesmen to assist the civilian technical staff. Its establishment was nine officers and 250 other ranks, but later a varying number of men unfit for field duties were posted to it, sometimes doubling the authorized number. The Company was particularly useful in the dismantling of printing, photographic and other equipment in preparation for the move out of Southampton.

The main stage of dispersal led to the south-western outskirts of London where temporary office buildings were under construction at Hinchley Wood and Chessington. The first of these was occupied on 24 August 1942, when the Special Services Drawing Section and small units of revision and reproduction sections moved in, later followed by staff working on one-inch and 1:25 000 maps. By March 1943 Triangulation and Levelling Division had also moved to Hinchley Wood. The buildings were still unfinished at the time of first occupation and structural alterations had to be made before printing machinery could be moved in, so that for some months staff worked under great inconvenience.

Meanwhile the Britannica Works at Waddon near Croydon had been taken over and modified to take map-printing machinery which began production by the end of July. Two miles from Hinchley Wood, at Chessington, the other temporary office was under urgent construction in the winter of 1942–3. This was specially designed for the Survey, but the building was still unfinished when the first eight spurs were occupied on 1 April 1943. The new Waddon reproduction unit, as well as the printing done by the many outside firms, now came under the control of Chessington.

Thus by March 1943 a headquarters establishment had come into being away from Southampton, which transferred the centre of gravity of the Survey back to the London area; in the course of the year the Maps Branch also left Southampton for the Directorate of Military Survey at Eastcote, moving thence to Osterley Park and finally coming to rest in Chessington when the buildings were completed in December. 522 Company RE, whose headquarters and main body were by this time accommodated at Devonshire House, Ditton Hill, Surbiton, was again able to do much to smooth the passage of these moves. It manned the Waddon printing works and also administered a variety of other small units, including three Royal Engineer drawing sections in Hinchley Wood and Southampton as well as Auxiliary Territorial Service sections working with the civilian air survey unit at Hinchley Wood. Early in 1943 the refurbished and temporary arrangements at Southampton became fully effective in drawing and reproduction work. There was a short break in occupancy at London Road from 1 May 1944, when the site was officially relinquished, but it was reoccupied in January 1946.

The various moves imposed many sacrifices on the staff. They had undergone the trials of enemy attack on homes and offices at Southampton and life was difficult enough without the separation from home which now ensued for many. The widespread compulsory billeting in the Surrey area was not popular with those who had to take in strangers at short notice and there was also fear that the new 'Ordnance factory' might attract enemy attack. But after some difficult preliminaries the newcomers settled down. Many staff were now recruited with no Southampton connections and, as the Chessington Office was to have a life of nearly a quarter of a century, this was to create problems for the future when stakes were pulled up once more for the return to Southampton.

A final enemy threat came when the flying bomb and rocket attacks began after the June landings in 1944. In view of all the trouble taken with dispersal this was an ironical situation. All three of the new Survey establishments were directly in the danger zone but, although considerable damage was done in the district, the main delivery line passed east of the Chessington office, and the only near miss was a flying bomb which fell in the neighbouring zoo, singeing a polar bear and breaking some of the office windows. There was also some roof damage at Waddon but this did not halt production.

Map Production 1936–45[8]

PRE-WAR MILITARY MAPPING

The Ordnance Survey's contribution to war-time military mapping began well before the start of hostilities. From the beginning of 1936 the Survey's programme included the preparation and production for GSGS of map series covering northern France and Belgium, the expected seat of the probable war. Work was at first concentrated on two 1:250 000 series (GSGS 2738, 4042); two at 1:50 000 (GSGS 4040, 4040a) and one at 1:25 000 (GSGS 4041) were put in hand later. All these were collectively known as the 'Rearmament' series. Progress was hampered by the varying quality of the material from which the series were compiled and by changes in War Office thinking which altered the areas to be covered and also the colours to be used on the maps and the amount of generalization. Liaison with the *Services Géographiques* of the countries concerned was through GSGS. This procedure created some friction between GSGS and the Ordnance Survey which was ominous for the future, but perhaps the whole pre-war experience was a useful introduction to the repeated changes in plan and priority which were to follow.

At home there was an urgent task arising from the unrevised state of many of the large-scale plans. Early in 1938 the national organization for air raid precautions asked for a rapid revision of all urban and built-up areas at the six-inch scale. This 'Special Emergency Edition' was carried through with unprecedented speed and was completed with the stocks in store by November 1939. It was made by reducing all available large-scale revision material by pantograph and by duffing out necessary deletions on existing six-inch negatives. It was below normal standards of accuracy and appearance, but, in spite of these defects, it was later useful in the production of the post-war six-inch Provisional Edition.

MAPS FOR THE EXPANDING THEATRE OF WAR

At the beginning of 1940 most of the expansion lay in the future but a first taste of the difficulties of war-time map production was experienced when the forlorn British attempt to hold some parts of Norway against Nazi invasion demanded almost instant production of a stock of maps directly from coloured originals, which were often defective in detail and heavily creased. The few which were produced (GSGS 4090, 4091) before the early collapse of the Norwegian venture were not a success.

From this time the demands for maps of all kinds in large numbers covering most parts of the world increased until the peak was reached in 1944. Problems similar to those presented by the Norwegian maps had often to be faced. Again and again time was too short for making more than a monochrome map by direct photography from coloured originals, although sometimes it became necessary to use colour filters, followed by manipulation and combination of the resulting negatives. These recurring tribulations may, from time to time, have led to a lack of alertness in other directions. European countries seldom showed detail which was outside their own national frontiers on their large- and medium-scale maps, and care had to be taken to ensure that such areas were not treated as sea and printed in blue. One sheet of the Spanish 1:50 000 series showed a blank white space beyond the boundary between Gibraltar and Spain; the Rock had been omitted on the new map and its area included in the sea. This error went uncorrected through all the checking stages, but some time later the Hydrographer of the Navy wrote a letter congratulating the Survey on having sunk the Rock of Gibraltar.

In the early part of the war the reproduction material, which the Ordnance Survey made in large quantities for distribution at home and overseas, consisted of duplicate printing plates or black impressions on enamelled zinc plates. These were much too bulky and heavy for convenience and, apart from the plates supplied to the trade for immediate printing, were superseded by 'black pulls' on paper, taken from the printing plates. In their turn these were not satisfactory and were given up in favour of contact positives or negatives on film. These were known as 'kodalines' because Kodaline film was the first brand used, but the name persisted long after that film had been superseded. Production of kodalines became very large when, for world-wide distribution, up to fifteen sets were required of each map, and special equipment had to be procured for processing and drying them.

MAPS FOR THE INVASION OF EUROPE 1944–5

In preparation for the invasion of continental Europe GSGS directed a large amount of cartographic work to the Ordnance Survey as well as to many military units, British, Canadian and American. The revision of old maps of Europe and the compilation of new ones were difficult tasks for an inexperienced staff, the more so because of the ever-prevailing urgency, the uncertainty of obtaining air photographs, the unfamiliarity of foreign place-names and, as a constant background, the stresses of war-time life in Southampton. GSGS was responsible for producing the specifications for the new maps and these were designed with an eye to rapid production by inexperienced draughtsmen. The results had no pretensions to cartographic beauty and it is not surprising that early editions contained many errors.

One of the first of the cartographic tasks given to the Ordnance Survey in 1941 was the revision of the War Office 1:50 000 map of north-eastern France and Belgium (GSGS 4040), which was to include a reduction in the sheet size. The work was much hampered by delays in obtaining suitable air photographs, and many sheets of the series underwent three or four revisions as new material became available. Later in the same year the Ordnance Survey was directed to compile a new contoured 1:50 000 map of north-western and western France (GSGS 4250) from the French hachured 1:80 000, with revision from air photographs. It was a particularly large and difficult assignment; the maps were of vital importance but the supply of photographs was long delayed, and the sheets of Normandy were completed only just in time for D-day. Subsequently both the design and the execution came in for a good deal of criticism but, taking all the circumstances into account, the map was a creditable production.

While this work was going on, instructions came to prepare a 1:100 000 map of the northern part of France (GSGS 4249), which was intended for the use of armoured forces in a war of rapid movement. In order to save time GSGS 4250 and GSGS 4249 were produced from a common set of drawings made at an intermediate scale. Predictably the 1:100 000, which was a reduction of the drawings, turned out to be overcrowded and difficult to read, features which tended to make the map unsuitable for use in a tank on the move. A special gridded edition of the Ordnance Survey half-inch was printed for the armoured forces training in England before the invasion, to familiarize them with maps at about the 1:100 000 scale.

In May 1942 the Ordnance Survey was given the 1:25 000 map of north-eastern France and Belgium (GSGS 4041) to revise from air photographs, but the Department took almost no part in the production of the new 'Benson' 1:25 000 series covering the invasion area. This project was allotted to the Director of Surveys, Home Forces, and was executed by the military survey units under his command over which he was able to exercise a close and continuous control.

Germany was covered by good quality 1:25 000 maps produced by the various German State survey departments, and large quantities of kodaline negatives of these were needed for the field survey units. In November 1943 Southampton was given the job of producing kodalines from some three thousand monochrome sheets, at the same time removing the German grid and substituting the British. This was virtually completed by October 1944 but not without difficulty. Some of the sheets of Baden and Wurttemburg had not been converted to the Prussian datum and there were discontinuities along the junctions between the State systems, which caused much trouble and confusion. Many sheets of this series (GSGS 4414) were later revised from air photographs. In the summer of 1944 the Ordnance Survey began work on a new 1:50 000 of Germany (GSGS 4507) based on the 1:25 000. The lessons learnt with the earlier 1:50 000 series of France were not forgotten, and the result was a simple, clear map once the specification had been amended to eliminate a proliferation of minor tracks. One of the last cartographic tasks in the final months of the war was the compilation of a 1:25 000 map of Denmark (GSGS 4554) from the 1:20 000 Danish originals. Again, sets of kodalines were produced for distribution to field formations.

Many special maps were prepared for the air arm, each in its turn bringing its own problems which were solved with a speed rarely met with in peace time. The most used single series was the 1:1 million Plotting Chart (GSGS 4080) which covered most of the world. The quantities printed and the number of editions were prodigious, with some sheets running into more than a million copies. Radar lattice charts (GSGS 4153 and 4392–7)* with very tight registration were made of continually expanding target areas in Europe, and there was close liaison with the United States Air Force for the production of target maps** under strict conditions of security. These conditions also attended the preparation of maps for use in commando operations and other secret activity. Finally there was the novel task of printing maps on silk to be sewn into clothing to aid the escape of airman landing in enemy territory and of prisoners of war; the silk had to be mounted on paper before it could go through the printing machines.

The mere recital of these details tends to obscure their full implication in terms of human effort.

---

* A series of air maps at a scale of 1:500 000 with superimposed parabolic curves relating to radar aids used by Bomber and Coastal Commands and photo-reconnaissance units of Fighter Command. First produced early in 1942.

** Maps of special design and colouring for use in night bombing, normally at one-inch scale.

During the preparations for the 1944 landings, and the European campaign which followed, pressure on reproduction staff was enormous. There were dramatic times when the demand for maps in France as the forces fanned out became more than urgent. All ordinary modes of transport by road and rail were too slow and often, in the early hours of the morning, staff were packing maps as they came off the machines while lorries waited to rush them to near-by airfields for direct flight to the seat of war. To meet the challenge shift work went on continually twenty-four hours a day and seven days a week. It was at such times that the staff got an unforgettable impression of the real importance of their work as a contribution to victory. The text of a telegram received at GHQ from one of the American Army Commanders read: 'Nothing matters now but ammunition and maps'.

MAP PRINTINGS 1938–47

Years	OS 'normal' work		OS for the forces		Firms		Totals	
	Maps	Cylinder revolutions	Maps	Cylinder revolutions	Maps	Cylinder revolutions	Maps	Cylinder revolutions
1938–9	2 189 009	7 136 625	3 603 803	15 359 819	–	–	5 789 812	22 496 444
39–40	2 064 118	6 303 832	8 782 035	30 446 208	3 995 314	21 767 721	14 841 567	58 517 761
40–1	2 541 185	9 673 420	16 856 156	72 941 802	10 475 572	54 070 255	29 872 813	136 685 477
41–2	1 706 135	2 847 979	16 630 414	68 811 869	5 074 639	22 313 719	23 411 188	93 973 567
42–3	847 927	1 454 883	31 286 308	122 826 814	14 142 297	43 700 646	46 276 532	197 992 343
43–4	833 830	1 260 734	48 289 934	220 991 869	61 635 031	147 174 804	110 758 795	369 427 407
44–5	1 204 736	2 095 480	65 553 907	296 119 982	52 180 230	247 042 067	118 938 873	545 257 529
45–6	1 184 952	5 033 882	17 946 764	73 448 416	5 392 158	28 596 884	24 523 874	107 079 182
46–7	3 684 457	18 520 655	1 355 484	4 785 738	–	–	5 039 941	23 306 393

The table shows the growth of map-printing to its climax in 1944. In the early years of the war the limiting factor was equipment rather than man-power, but by 1943 much new printing equipment from British firms and process cameras from America had been installed. Commercial firms were used to the limit. Since few of them were capable of extensive plate-making, all plates were made by the Ordnance Survey and supplied with the printing orders.[9]

Other War-Time Work in Great Britain 1939–45

WORK IN THE FIELD

At the outbreak of war there were four field division offices, No. 2 in Bristol, No. 3 in Tunbridge Wells, No. 4 in London and No. 5 in Edinburgh, with another under formation centred at Harrogate but abandoned at once. Divisions fell to a care and maintenance basis with occasional spurts of local activity, usually connected with some war project, but very little of the normal programme could be attempted. This state of affairs continued until late in 1944 when there was an increase in staff as men returned from war service.

Field and office revision of the 1:2500 plans continued when staff could be spared, mostly on priorities set by the Ministry of Town and Country Planning, and an average of nearly two hundred new and revised sheets were published each year. Some experimental work on 1:1250 resurvey and 1:2500 overhaul was also undertaken in preparation for the post-war era. The Air Survey Section, which had been working on 1:2500 revision before the war, turned its reduced staff to the training of new recruits. The Section was expanded to a strength of 120 between 1942 and 1945 and was divided about equally between Crabwood and Hinchley Wood. It was almost exclusively occupied on map revision for the War Office.

Work for the Land Registry continued at a reduced rate. There was an annual average of about 1150 special surveys and about 1650 printing orders; in addition, 1:2500 map sections and parcel books were prepared for compulsory land registration in Surrey.

The Triangulation and Levelling Division, which was much reduced by the loss of its high proportion of Royal Engineers, also had to abandon its usual programme. But all through the war there was much survey and levelling work to be done in advance of airfield and other military construction in many parts of the country, and the Division was also employed in survey and computations for fixing anti-aircraft and coastal battery positions. At the height of the post-Dunkirk crisis a nucleus of staff, complete with computing and field equipment, was secretly held ready to act with the army if there were an invasion. A party also went to the Dover area to fix spotting points for counter-battery work, and to compute co-ordinates and spotters' charts on the Nord de Guerre grid for the heavy guns covering the Straits. With the rapid production of the new gridded 1:25 000 maps for home defence it was urgently necessary to convert all old tertiary triangulation values from feet to metres, and by the end of 1940 the Division had prepared and published the new lists totalling about 21 000 points in Great Britain. Radio location sites were also surveyed and co-ordinated. The production of many GSGS maps gave continuous employment to a grid-computing section which investigated origins and projections and prepared grid-plotting data for some twenty countries and thirty map series.

The amount of civil work done was minimal. No primary triangulation was carried out and other trigonometrical work was confined to the occupation of some 550 secondary and 1400 tertiary stations, usually in connection with surveys for the War Office and Air Ministry. The Levelling Branch, though depleted, was not reduced as much as the triangulation side and a modified programme went on throughout the war whenever staff were available. The Second Geodetic Levelling of Scotland was continued and about a thousand miles of levelling was completed including crossings of the Firths of Forth and Tay. Some secondary and tertiary levelling was undertaken to replace records destroyed at London Road and some work was done on normal programmes including contouring for six-inch and 1:25 000 maps. A special levelling project in the Fens was completed in the second half of 1941 for the Great Ouse Catchment Board. This consisted of a precise level network covering an area of about 820 square miles, which took in a number of fen wastage reference points established by the Board, and required 395 miles of levelling. Fen wastage points are fixed metal standards driven through the superficial deposits into the solid strata below. These deposits often consist largely of peat which, when under cultivation, wastes rapidly, producing a drop in surface level.

Tidal observations continued at Dunbar and Newlyn with minor breaks at Dunbar for repair work.

MAPS FOR THE PUBLIC

During the war the number of maps available for sale to the public was greatly reduced. The drawing of the one-inch New Popular Edition had been in progress until all drawings, field sheets and other relevant documents were destroyed at London Road in 1940. On the same occasion large stocks of maps were lost, particularly of the larger scales, and to replace these, six-inch and 1:2500 maps and plans were printed mainly by private firms under contract, the plates (which had been made for 'direct' printing on flatbed machines) coming from the Ordnance Survey, but the continuous employment of the offset printing machine on war work made it impossible to restore the stocks of one-inch and quarter-inch maps by normal means. To meet the difficulty, in 1943 the War Office agreed to permit the sale of the military editions of these maps to the public; this applied in particular to the war revisions of the one-inch series which covered the whole country.

Early in 1941 the premises of Edward Stanford Limited were damaged by enemy action and many maps were destroyed. To these losses was added the decrease in map sales consequent on the war, the reduction of income being so severe that the amount earned was not enough to meet the expenses of running the agency. Stanford's current contract expired on 31 March 1942 and the opportunity was taken, when preparing a new contract, to enlarge the scope of the agent's business to include issues of maps of Great Britain to government departments and to the Services. Stanford's also became responsible in 1943 for the distribution of maps to the retail trade, apart from Ordnance Survey provincial agents, a function which the firm retained until 1971.

THE HEATHROW CANNON

Finally, in the summer of 1944, the Ordnance Survey harked back for a moment to its origins. Work on the runways of the future Heathrow Airport made it necessary to remove the north-west terminal of General Roy's Hounslow Heath Base of 1784. This had been marked by a partly buried 32-pounder cannon when the base was remeasured in 1791; the cannon was now removed under the supervision of the Chief Superintendent, Triangulation and Levelling, and the Assistant Archaeology

Officer. As an act of piety it was erected on a concrete base with an explanatory plaque in front of the temporary Headquarters at Chessington. When the Ordnance Survey moved to its new Headquarters in 1968 the cannon was returned to the British Airports Authority at Heathrow. On 21 June 1972 it was carefully replaced in its original position where it remains on permanent display.[10]

Notes

1 OSR 1939–40 (unpublished), Foreword.

2 *The Second World War 1939–1945: Army. Maps and Survey* (War Office 1952), pp. 35–6.

3 *Ibid.* p. 36.

4 M. N. MacLeod, 'Autobiographical Notes', OS Library; *Maps and Survey* (1952), p. 35.

5 For statement of damage at London Road see OSR 1940–41 (unpublished), pp. 6–8.

6 *London Gazette* 11 March 1941; *Royal Engineers Journal* Dec. 1964, pp. 440–4.

7 Minute by Director of Military Survey on control of Ordnance Survey, 100/Engrs/2706, 19d, OS Library G 5128.

8 The material for this section is taken mainly from *Maps and Survey* (1952).

9 The table was compiled from unpublished war-time OSRs.

10 OS Bulletin May 1973, no. 2, pp. 1–3, and photograph.

29
The
Restoration
of the Survey –
Expansion 1945–1950

Planning for the Post-War Period 1941–5

The pattern for the future had been set by the Davidson Committee and the expansion of the staff was well under way when the war put an end to all immediate plans for the restoration of the national survey. But the effects of the war itself gave a new urgency to the need for up-to-date large-scale maps, and it was clearly imperative that everything possible should be done so that the work could go ahead with the utmost speed when peace returned and man-power flowed back into the Ordnance Survey.

So, while the war was still in its darkest days, and with the most meagre resources, preparation for the post-war era began. One of the first matters to be tackled was the procedure to be used for 'overhauling' the out-of-date 1:2500 plans in dense urban areas; in 1941, with a very small staff, an attempt was made in Bournemouth to recompile the old County Series plans to fit a network of new control points within the framework of the National Grid, but by 1943 it had been established conclusively that the old urban plans could not be reliably fitted to the new control and that the effort of trying to do so was incommensurate with the dubious quality of the results.[1] It became clear that it was not possible to comply with the Davidson Committee's recommendation that the overhaul of the 1:2500 plans of the whole country should be completed before attention was turned to the question of surveying the urban areas at a larger scale; a resurvey of the towns, preferably at 1:1250, was now becoming unavoidable. The most promising method of doing this appeared to be a combination of skeleton chain survey and graphical completion; both were techniques of which the Survey had almost unlimited experience and with which all the pre-war staff were familiar. A programme of resurvey on these lines could be launched with the minimum of preparatory training – in the circumstances, an overwhelming advantage. By September 1943 four 1:1250 plans of Bournemouth had been surveyed and were ready for drawing.

Major-General Geoffrey Cheetham, who had become Director General on the retirement of MacLeod in April 1943, had many other problems to contend with. The Bournemouth experiment had shown that 1:1250 resurvey of major built-up areas would have to be added to the programme outlined by the Davidson Committee but the method to be used for the overhaul of the rural plans still had to be worked out. Furthermore, the lower order triangulation was very far from being complete, although the resurvey of the towns depended on it; however, the order of tackling the secondary blocks of triangulation depended on the priority given to the various towns, which was not yet settled. The resurvey and overhaul were both long-term projects but Cheetham had also to provide for the immediate needs of the post-war period. Added to the problems of mapping were those of administration: the recruitment and training of large numbers of surveyors in the shortest possible time and the creation of a departmental organization which would enable the mapping programme to be tackled effectively.

Cheetham's own professional staff was very weak in 1943, particularly at Headquarters, where he was supported only by Brigadier E. R. L. Peake and Lieutenant-Colonel C. L. Y. Parker. However, he was still able to discuss the many major issues with MacLeod in retirement and also with the formidable Director of Military Survey, Brigadier Martin Hotine, whose penetrating intellect did not prevent him from adopting a directness of speech and writing which sometimes could only very charitably be described as brusque. Cheetham does not appear to have been deterred either by the size of the task he was facing or by the asperity of his colleague at the War Office. In the next year or so Hotine was to put forward a number of extremely important proposals and it is greatly to Cheetham's credit that he recognized their merit and adopted them.

The Cheetham plan for the post-war programme of the Ordnance Survey formed the subject of a memorandum sent in October 1943 to the Permanent Secretary, Ministry of Agriculture and Fisheries.[2] It set out Cheetham's long-term proposals – based on the Davidson Report – and the measures he recommended for dealing with immediate post-war needs. The importance of early demobilization of pre-war Ordnance surveyors and the early release of survey officers from war-time duties was emphasized; this was to lead, a year later, to a rather acrimonious correspondence with Hotine on civil and military priorities. Finally, the memorandum included a table showing the proposed post-war organization of the Ordnance Survey.

Authority to go ahead with planning on the lines of the memorandum was given by the Ministry in November 1943, subject to reservations on timing and to Treasury approval of the draft establishment. A minor objection referred to Cheetham's wish to introduce metric contours: there would be no metric contours. Another more important condition was that there was to be no transfer to the War Office, either then or at any time.[3]

Cheetham, Hotine and MacLeod had for some time been considering the future relationship between the Ordnance Survey, the Military Survey organization and the proposed Central Organization for Surveys in the Colonial Empire. Both Cheetham and MacLeod saw the possibility of creating a central national surveying department incorporating all three elements under the Director General Ordnance Survey. In some strongly-worded correspondence, the difficulties of creating what Hotine called the 'super-dooper' organization were recognized, and the proposal was dropped. Hotine argued that neither the War Office, not the Colonial Office, nor the Ministry of Agriculture, would be prepared to subordinate their own interests in an organization controlled by one of the other two. He proposed that all three should remain independently sponsored and that they should be linked by a Survey Board to advise on common problems; this Cheetham accepted as a joint policy early in 1944,[4] a decision which marked another step towards the civilianization of the Ordnance Survey.

Cheetham had sent Hotine a copy of his memorandum, including the proposed management structure which was based on the pre-war model greatly enlarged. The post of Deputy Director General was to be retained and the old system, whereby all the senior officers of the Survey answered to him, preserved. In a typically outspoken reply, Hotine severely criticized this on the grounds that, with eleven officers answering to him, the Deputy Director General would constitute an impossible bottle-neck and, together with the Establishment and Finance Officer, would have enormous obstructive power without any defined responsibility for getting the work done.[5] Hotine was not merely critical; he put forward a plan for a new top-level organization in which the Director General had three direct subordinates, responsible respectively for surveying, map production and administration, competent to settle between themselves any overlapping issues. Hotine's letter was dated 8 May 1944; on the 20th Cheetham wrote to the Ministry amending his original proposal to conform with the structure suggested by Hotine.[6]

As the war approached its end, subjects of contention resulting from a clash of interests were not hard to find. The realization that man-power and mapping resources would be needed after the end of the European War, both for 'occupational purposes' and also for the continuing war in the Far East, cut across the Cheetham plan for an early start on the restoration of the national mapping. Cheetham saw this work being postponed for 'an indefinite period' and referred the matter to his Ministry so that the disagreement could be resolved with the War Office at a high level. In the end he had to accept that the requirements of the fighting services had absolute priority, and that the details would have to be settled between Hotine and himself, not at a 'high level' in their respective ministries.[7] Hotine, however, agreed to recommend that men who could be released should be posted to 522 (OS) Company RE, primarily for the purpose of completing the triangulation framework. In the event, the Ordnance Survey had to deal with an increase in mapping for the War Office in August 1945 but by the end of the year this was greatly reduced and in 1946 it had little effect on domestic work.

Within the Department, the first meeting of the Director General's Post-War Planning Conference was held in June 1943.[8] The meeting was composed of the Director General, the Deputy Director General and a group of superintendents, reflecting the extent to which the Ordnance Survey had been denuded of professional staff. One of its most important actions was to initiate the 'Shadow Programme' which enabled the draughtsmen to take up domestic mapping whenever a temporary lull occurred in the flow of work from the War Office.

By the end of the war the lower order triangulation in the secondary blocks covering Bath, Bristol, Birmingham, Hull, London, South Wales and the Firth of Forth had been completed in addition to the Bournemouth area.[9] Ninety 1:1250 plans of Bournemouth and thirty-one of Edinburgh were in hand by the middle of 1944 and much preparatory work had been completed under the Shadow Programme for the new 1:25 000 series.[10] The Treasury had endorsed the Cheetham plan in substance, and in July 1945 it agreed to the proposed management structure including the new civilian officer grades of Division Officer and Assistant Division Officer.[11] The Government declared its acceptance of the programme itself in a written answer in the House of Commons on 20 April 1945.[12]

A great deal had been accomplished, but through no fault of those in charge the Ordnance Survey was in poor shape to embark on the biggest mapping programme it had ever tackled. Its offices were scattered and inadequate for a major expansion, the London Road office in Southampton had been given up in May 1944 and only three field divisional offices existed – in Bristol, Edinburgh and London; in 1944 the London Office had no professional direction. Severe losses in records and reproduction material had been sustained and it was uncertain how much had survived, although it was known that many levelling records had been lost, and that all the quarter-inch Fourth Edition negatives had been destroyed.

On the credit side the drawing and reproduction divisions at Chessington, Esher and Crabwood, and the similar units at Waddon and Nottingham, formed a scattered but powerful and well-equipped force, although much of the printing machinery had been operating for many years at high pressure and would soon need replacement. To the great relief of the hard-pressed Headquarters, the small professional staff was augmented in 1945 by four experienced Royal Engineer officers.

PLANNING FOR AIR PHOTOGRAPHY

Hotine recognized before the end of the war that his future department (the Central Organization for Surveys in the Colonial Empire), and probably the Ordnance Survey as well, would be dependent on adequate arrangements being made for obtaining aerial photographs in large quantities.

Both Cheetham and Hotine strongly supported the conclusion in Recommendation 17 of the Davidson Committee's Report that contracts with civil firms for aerial photography should be avoided. But the creation of a special air survey unit, as recommended by Davidson, must have seemed unnecessary when the enormous resources of the Royal Air Force, released from military operations, would be conveniently to hand. So in December 1944 it was decided that the Royal Air Force would provide the photographs, both in the colonies and in Great Britain.[13] The private air survey industry immediately objected, but at a meeting held at the Ministry of Civil Aviation in December 1945 the decision was upheld. Unfortunately this did not mean that all was to be plain sailing in the future and it was soon realized that although the course chosen was probably the only one open at the time, it was very far from being wholly satisfactory. The run-down of the Royal Air Force and the consequent changes of air-crew, the unsuitability of high speed photo-reconnaissance aircraft for large-scale survey photography, the lack of suitable air cameras and of any control over the photographic operations were factors which, in the following five years, gradually caused so many difficulties that it became imperative to make a change. Nevertheless, great efforts had been made during these years to provide what was wanted, including the formation at Benson in 1947 of a flight of four Anson aircraft equipped for large-scale photography. But the main current of photo-reconnaissance development ran in a different direction and in 1950 the Anson flight was reduced. Attempts were made during this period to design and produce a survey air camera for the Royal Air Force but the prototypes all failed to meet the specified requirements when tested in the air. The Ordnance Survey had to rely for many years on the obsolescent F49 (Williamson Eagle IX) and Fairchild K17 cameras for its photography.

The Administrative Background 1945–50

The short-term elements of the Cheetham plan were mainly tasks for the drawing and reproduction divisions. On 31 March 1945 their combined strength including Royal Engineers was 1924[14] so that, on the face of it, little needed to be done except to switch over fully to the Shadow Programme. However, very few of the staff had any recent experience of drawing to Ordnance Survey peace-time standards, and many had none at all.

On the other hand, the initial demands on the surveyors were mainly for the long-term plan; the strength of Field Division and Triangulation and Levelling Division were 262 and 233 respectively in March 1945, the latter figure including 61 Royal Engineers,[15] some of whom were assisting with the lower order triangulation. The Cheetham plan specified a field strength of over three thousand and although about nine hundred of these posts might be expected to be filled by ex-Ordnance surveyors returning from the Forces, there remained a very large gap to be filled by recruitment.

A Treasury memorandum issued in 1944 had placed considerable emphasis on the importance of quality in the post-war Civil Service, and on careful and centralized recruitment,[16] but such considerations were deferred in order to meet the immediate needs of the Ordnance Survey. The intention was to appoint about 750 Technical Civil Assistants between the ages of twenty and thirty-three, in the first twelve months, from men just demobilized from the Army and seeking work. Recruitment opened in the latter part of January 1946, but the method of selection left much to be desired. Applications were made at local Offices of the Ministry of Labour and National Service, the forms were forwarded to the Ordnance Survey for scrutiny, and applicants thought to be suitable were instructed by post to report to one or other of the field division offices. These appointments were by their nature 'temporary' in Civil Service terms, although there was no reference to this in the recruiting literature; but the possibility of 'pensionable establishment after 15 years service' was mentioned in the Conditions of Employment sent to each man accepted. Candidates were required to be educated 'to School Certificate standard but applicants of lower educational standards would be acceptable . . .'[17] No enquiries were made of previous employers; in fact none of the particulars on the application forms seem to have been verified.

The scramble for man-power (other Civil Service Departments were doing the same thing) appears to have been rather unnecessary. In the first three weeks 250 applicants were accepted so that the flow had to be turned off in February, although it was resumed later in the year. The Treasury was far from satisfied with what was being done and in the middle of 1947 a much more inquisitive form of 'Application for Temporary Employment in the Government Service' was introduced, and references had to be taken up. But otherwise the system remained unchanged for several years.[18]

This indiscrimate recruitment undoubtedly had detrimental results, both immediately and in the longer term. Field Division officers complained of the unsuitability of some of the new men and recommended that all applicants should be interviewed as they had been before the war, but the complaints were not strong enough to bring about any change. Initially progress in the field was much slower than had been hoped and much bad work was found at the checking stages. A strong echo of the first years of the Irish survey between 1825 and 1830 can surely be detected; once again the Survey had committed itself to a large craft-based operation and again it took several years to get the interlocking machinery running smoothly.

However, in 1946 the military rank-and-file element was disappearing and the civilian technical staff, freed to a large extent from military dominance, began to think about its own position and the rewards which were attached to it. There began a long struggle, conducted by the Staff Associations, for higher status defined in terms of parity with other Civil Service technical classes. The insecurity of the base from which the case for parity had to be argued was to some extent the result of the first five years of post-war recruiting, although the roots of the problem went further into the past. Throughout the history of the Ordnance Survey the relation of the military and civilian staff had constituted a powerful undercurrent. Since the mid nineteenth century the civilians had had two main grievances: they were brought into the craft system invented for Colby's sappers and consequently entered the Civil Service by an unusual procedure and without any qualifying examination,[19] which placed them at a permanent disadvantage compared with other Civil Servants both in pay and conditions of service; they also resented the firm hold of the military on the 'superintendence' of the work. The military for their part regretted the necessity of having to employ civilians (except, of course, retired sappers) regarding the Civil Assistants as a lower stratum of employee; as late as 1944 the Director General was hoping for an all-Royal-Engineer Ordnance Survey to emerge from the war.[20] In 1946 the grip of the military on the superintendence was greatly loosened, especially at the supervisory level, but at that very time the recruiting system became more undiscriminating than it had ever been before, with the result that, in later years, it proved difficult to fill satisfactorily some of the more senior management posts open to the non-professional staff. Another effect of the sudden large increase in numbers was to create an unbalanced age structure which led to troublesome promotion blockages and much discontent.

The new entrants of 1946 were ordered to report to field division offices (Bristol, London, Edinburgh or Kidderminster) if they were surveyors and to Southampton or Chessington if they were draughtsmen; the field men were employed on various unskilled duties whilst awaiting their initial training course. To begin with, these courses were held at several centres including Bristol, Catford, Bournemouth, Coventry, and Edinburgh, as well as Southampton, the first three detail-survey courses being planned to start on 1 February 1946. Separate courses were held for those destined for triangulation, traversing or levelling sections, so that at this time there was virtually no common training: the craft elements were completely separated, providing a far greater degree of specialization than the more widely based military survey training of the pre-war years. Juniors were recruited quite differently, in the manner of the pre-war army 'boys'. These youths, aged sixteen and a half, were selected by interview, often locally, and were given some training before joining the army for national service. They were classed as JTCAs – Junior Temporary Civil Assistants – and were sent to field division offices where, among other things, they were taught to draw.

The need to regularize these 'stop-gap recruiting measures designed to augment the staff of the Ordnance Survey by the quickest possible means' was becoming a pressing matter both for the staff themselves and for the Treasury.[21] In 1948–9 an agreement was negotiated between the Department, the technical staff associations and the Treasury resulting in the creation of a Cartographic Draughtsman Class (which included the surveyors) and a Reproduction Class (which included all the printing and reproduction grades). These were national classes, not merely peculiar to the Ordnance Survey, and were subject to national agreements on pay and conditions of service. There followed the assimilation of the old Ordnance Survey grades into the new grades of the Cartographic Draughtsman Class by means of a 'Reconstruction Competition' carried out by interview, through which most of the new staff were able to qualify for establishment as Civil Servants. At the same time permanent and proper arrangements had to be made for recruiting in the 'post-reconstruction' period; in 1948 an Inter-Departmental Committee under the chairmanship of Mr George Brown MP was set up to examine this and other matters, particularly the extent to which the 'Royal Engineer connection . . . should continue', if at all. The Committee with its assessors and secretariat numbered thirteen and, of these, five were senior military survey officers. In spite of this it was not very well informed on matters of historical fact; for example, the Report gives the impression that before 1936 'recruitment to the Ordnance Survey was almost exclusively through the Army', whereas this had been true only for the years between 1928 and 1934. What is perhaps more surprising is to find the following passage in a memorandum submitted to the Committee by the staff associations representing the technical grades: '. . . with few exceptions, recruitment into the Ordnance Survey was via the Corps of Royal Engineers until 1935'.[22]

The Report of the Brown Committee,[23] which was not published until 1950, recommended that staff should in future be appointed by competitive examination and that the Royal Engineer officers should be retained in the Department but limited to thirty-five; in fact the number never exceeded twenty-seven. Among the fifteen recommendations was the suggestion that, subject to the need to preserve posts for the thirty-five Royal Engineers, the higher positions should be filled by the most suitable persons, whether military or civilian, and that members of the technical grades should not be ruled out. Furthermore, a special avenue of promotion to the higher posts should be open to exceptionally promising young members of the technical grades. Neither of the last two recommendations had borne any fruit when the matter was again considered by the Estimates Committee in 1962.

By the end of the 1940s the recruiting of technical staff was becoming increasingly difficult. The overwhelming flow of applicants which had continued throughout 1946 and 1947 had largely dried up, partly because the level of pay was still unattractive despite the new class structure and conditions of service. The end of the reconstruction period should properly have coincided with the introduction of the new regular recruiting but, largely because of the delay in publishing the Report of the Brown Committee, it was not possible for the Civil Service to hold the first competitive examination until the autumn of 1951. So in order to meet urgent needs for more staff the old scheme, now heavily labelled 'temporary' had with reluctance to be reintroduced both for adults and juniors.[24] The fall in new entrants enabled the Divisional training schools to be closed and from 1950 onwards trainee surveyors were sent directly to the Basic Training Wing then situated in Elmsleigh, a large and inconvenient house on the outskirts of Southampton.

Cheetham's post-war programme was based on expanding the staff from its war-time level of about 2300 to 6000, which he thought could be accomplished within two years of demobilization. Whether this could have been achieved was never determined because in December 1946 a Ministerial Committee was appointed by the Prime Minister to control the size of the non-industrial Civil Service, and the growth of the Ordnance Survey was thereafter limited by successive annual man-power ceilings.[25] On 1 April 1947 the figure was 4000; this was increased annually until March 1951 when the authorized non-industrial man-power reached 4800, corresponding to a total staff of about 5500. On the face of it, this was within striking distance of Cheetham's planning figure, but it is doubtful, in view of the difficulty of recruitment and the high rate of resignation, if the number could have been increased much more. In fact, the strength of the non-industrial staff actually in post reached its maximum – nearly 4700 – in the latter part of 1948;[26] after 1951 the man-power ceiling was reduced.

By the end of 1946, apart from the Royal Engineer officers, no soldiers remained in the Ordnance Survey. 522 (Ordnance Survey) Company RE and other RE Survey units had worked for the Department while awaiting demobilization; Royal Engineer drawing sections had been temporarily accommodated at Kidderminster and Waddon in the autumn of 1945 and the topographical section of 523 Field Survey Company RE had worked briefly on one-inch revision.[27] The disbandment of the Ordnance Survey Company in December 1946 brought to an end an era that had begun with the formation of the first survey company of sappers over one hundred and twenty years before. But the army had one more legacy to bestow on the Ordnance Survey. Many pre-war regular sappers were reabsorbed as civilians over the next few years; collectively they had seen war-time service all over the world on surveying and mapping operations of great variety, encompassing a breadth of experience they would never have otherwise obtained. Many had held responsible positions as officers, warrant officers and senior non-commissioned officers. This injection of experience was to carry the Ordnance Survey through the difficult period of technical change in the middle 1950s, but it also delayed the realization that in a technological age a narrow craft training was inadequate as a preparation for filling the non-professional management posts.

The Short-Term Plan

Cheetham's short-term plan consisted broadly of two elements: to prepare for the expansion and the initiation of the long-term plan, and to produce new and revised medium and small-scale maps and air-photo mosaics to meet the immediate needs of planners and other users.

The short-term mapping programme was in five parts, the first four to be completed within two years:

1 The production of a new 1:25 000 series on National Grid sheet-lines.
2 The production of a revised and gridded six-inch map on the old sheet-lines.
3 The production of a new gridded one-inch map on new standard National Grid sheet-lines in England and Wales, and in Scotland by gridding the Scottish Popular Edition.
4 The completion of the 1:2500 County Series revision started before the war, using pre-war revision material.
5 As a stop-gap measure in large towns, the production of air-photo mosaics at approximately 1:1250 scale.

In Appendix 4 of his Memorandum Cheetham wrote: 'It is understood that the production of a good 1:25 000 map at a very early date is considered to be of great importance to planners'. When approval in principle was given to the programme in November 1943, the Permanent Secretary affirmed that it was 'of the utmost importance that the immediate needs of the planners should be met'. The new Provisional 1:25 000 map, to be completed in two years, was therefore given the highest priority. At first the drawing of the map was carried out not only in the drawing offices of both Large Scales and Small Scales Divisions at Southampton and Esher, but also at Waddon and at Field Division offices where JTCAs and Royal Engineer draughtsmen were employed. In 1947, after the withdrawal of the Royal Engineers on demobilization, the work was gradually concentrated in the drawing divisions. By January 1948, at the end of two full years, only 516 sheets had been published out of roughly 1850,[28] and it was not until 1956 that the series was completed. In 1949 the Department of Health for Scotland complained that the 1:25 000 map of Edinburgh was 'twenty years out of date'[29] and in the same year the representative of the Ministry of Town and Country Planning, Dr E. C. Willatts, at a meeting in the Ordnance Survey, pointed out that the 1:25 000 map was not an official planning map under the regulations of the National Parks and Access to the Countryside Act of 1949.[30] As early as September 1946 a London County Council representative had said that the scale was too small for work in towns. The complaints about the out-of-dateness led to a start being made on a revised edition in 1950, using, for the most part, revision material collected for the one-inch map.

The underestimation of the time needed to produce the Provisional 1:25 000 map, making non-sense of its intended function of meeting immediate needs, was an error of judgment reflecting, perhaps, the weakness of Cheetham's Headquarters staff in 1943. It remains something of a mystery why the series was ever made at all. Many of the planners working during the war on post-war reconstruction had certainly found the War Office 1:25 000 (GSGS 3906) very useful. This map, being a photographic reduction of the six-inch, was very difficult to read, but a good deal of revision had been added during the war and Cheetham referred to it as being 'nearly up to date'[31] (which it certainly was not); the wish for a 'good 1:25 000 map' might have been an acknowledgement of the value of the War Office map and an expression of the planners' hope for a more legible version of it. The Davidson Committee had recommended that 1:25 000 sheets should be produced only of selected areas as an experiment, but MacLeod had a particular interest in the series and was prepared to go ahead with it when opportunity offered and to adopt it as the basic scale in mountainous areas. In 1940 he had decided that 'a reasonable block of sheets' on 10 km × 10 km sheet-lines should be produced by draughtsmen who were temporarily spare from war work. He recorded that 'the demand for the 1:25 000 series was for education, engineering and for military training'; it seems that at this early date the principal officers of the Ordnance Survey were committed in their minds to a new 1:25 000 series long before the planning justification emerged.[32]

The next series in the programme for meeting immediate needs was the Provisional six-inch, to be published on the old sheet-lines with revision and with the National Grid added. The plan again proved to be a miscalculation; in fact the series was abandoned in 1953, when 7000 out of 16 000 sheets had been published, and the effort was transferred to the National Grid Provisional six-inch on 5 km × 5 km sheet-lines, and to the Regular series. With the advantage of hindsight, it seems a pity that the whole effort (1:25 000 and six-inch) was not applied to the six-inch map on National Grid sheet-lines in the first place.

The National Grid one-inch map was to be a new Sixth Edition for England and Wales on standard sheet-lines 40 km × 45 km. Fifth Edition material was 'reconstituted' for the southern part of the country but in the north of England the series had to be in provisional form because it was based on the old Popular Edition; in Scotland, where the Popular Edition was a more recent map, it was thought to be sufficient to add the National Grid without changing the sheet-lines. Eleven sheets of the Sixth Edition in England had been printed during the war but had not been issued to avoid confusion with maps carrying the military grid; with this flying start the programme was completed to time at the end of 1947 but not without set-backs and difficulties. The quality of the Sixth Edition maps, both reconstituted and provisional, was disappointingly low, partly because the standards in the drawing office had not yet recovered to their peace-time level, but also because it proved difficult to obtain high quality chemicals and materials for the various drawing and reproduction processes. An inordinate amount of time and effort was spent 'improving' the work by touching-up imperfections and, after much heart-searching, Cheetham decided that only certain particularly bad sheets were to be improved and the rest left as they were.[33] He also believed that the Sixth Edition would have to last several years before it could be replaced and decided that every effort should be made to produce a really good new half-inch map as soon as possible. So, in 1946, the small-scales revisers were set to work within the sheet-lines of the half-inch map; but nothing came of this venture for many years. These stop-gap activities give a strong impression that a good deal of effort was being wasted in the drawing offices. If this was so, it was also not surprising. Cheetham had plenty of draughtsmen at his disposal; what he lacked was up-to-date survey information for revision, and for this reason the short-term programme could not possibly have wholly succeeded. Hundreds of surveyors were being recruited but they were nearly all put to work on the 1:1250 survey of the major towns, an effort which produced very small returns in area covered. In 1947 it was already recognized by the Ordnance Survey that the Sixth Edition badly needed revising.[34]

The 1:2500 revision of 1938–40 had not all been incorporated in published maps and there remained about three thousand unrevised sheets for most of which revision material existed. The drawing for these was partly carried out in field division offices by JTCAs during their first two years of service and partly in the drawing divisions; it was completed in 1947, well within two years of the start of the post-war programme. The revised sheets were standard County Series sheets; no grid was added.

The short-term programme included an excursion into an entirely new field – the production of air-photo mosaics; these were intended, in Cheetham's words, to 'do something to fill the gap until the new survey at 1:1250 scale can be published'. Towards the end of 1945 the work of producing mosaics was taken over by a new unit, the Air Photo Division, located at Esher. The main tasks of this Division were liaison with the Royal Air Force, the maintenance of records of air-photo cover and the production of prints, enlargements, rectifications and mosaics from the air film. The mosaics were made from rectified air photographs on 1:1250 sheet-lines and later at six-inch scale on 5 km × 5 km sheet-lines. Their quality was generally very good, but they were expensive and sales were low. Regular production was brought to an end in 1951 and the Air Photo Division was absorbed into the Triangulation and Levelling Division by the end of the year.

The Long-Term Plan

In Cheetham's long-term plan the 1:1250 resurvey of the major towns was to be completed in ten years and the overhaul and reconstitution on National Grid sheet-lines of the 1:2500 was to take five years longer. These estimates – they were little more than guesses – were very over-optimistic, and the work took well over twice as long. When the estimates were made, the method of 1:1250 resurvey had hardly been decided, the extent of the 1:1250 programme had not been worked out, the overhaul method for the 1:2500 maps had not been formulated and it was uncertain how much 1:2500 resurvey would be necessary. Moreover, the impact of continuous revision on field resources had certainly never been studied. Cheetham's guess erred towards optimism in the same way as most of his other planning estimates, but it would have been impossible to make an accurate predition with so many of the factors unquantified. Field man-power never reached the figure on which Cheetham based his plan, but on the other hand improved methods were eventually adopted which largely compensated for this. The estimates in the 1943 Memorandum were clearly intended to imply that there was a very large amount of work to be done, but that this would not stretch too far into the future.

One of the unresolved problems of preparing for the new large-scale surveys was where to start, and here the Ordnance Survey had to be guided primarily by the Ministry of Town and Country Planning, which in August 1944 provided a list of ten priority towns – Bristol, Coventry, Exeter, Liverpool, Manchester, Plymouth, Portsmouth, Southampton, Swansea and London. The Ministry continued to give this kind of advice for many years, but it soon became evident that for some purposes – for instance, special official requirements – wider consultation was needed, and to provide this, the Inter-Departmental Committee on Repayment Services was formed. Representatives of five departments attended its first meeting in September 1946, but surprisingly there was no-one from the Ministry of Agriculture, HM Land Registry or the National Coal Board. In 1949, because of the known attitude of the Brown Committee to wider consultation, the membership was enlarged to include the British Electricity Authority, the Post Office, the Coal Board and the British Transport Commission, and the title was changed to the Advisory Committee on Ordnance Survey Services.[35] The possibility of meetings with local authority associations was discussed at this time but no permanent arrangement was made for many years. The Committee was further enlarged in 1951 and again retitled, becoming the Advisory Committee on Surveying and Mapping.

FIELD-WORK

The start of the resurvey was in fact discouragingly slow: the average annual production in the first five years was only 939 plans at 1:1250 and 156 square kilometres of 1:2500. This must have made the size of the task appear dauntingly large and accounts for the inward-looking attitude that developed in these early years as the Ordnance Survey turned its back firmly on distractions from the main programme such as any kind of response to local and immediate needs. In 1948 the 1:1250 task was assessed as comprising 37 000 plans; in 1949 a formula was devised, taking into account area, population and rateable value, for deciding which towns should be included; the task was thereby reduced to 30 000 plans.[36] However, the rigidity and complication of such a formula soon led to its abandonment and in 1951 the total was given as 34 000.

The threat to the lasting value of a well-executed large-scale survey posed by manuscript documents that were not dimensionally stable was well understood in the nineteenth century although no solution then existed. The enamel-coated metal sheets introduced for drawing in the 1930s seemed to offer a way out for the surveyor, and much of the early experimental work was done on enamels. In 1944 Mr Charles Emery of the Field Division devised a more sophisticated alternative in the form of anodized aluminium plates, 20cm square, four of which could be mounted together in a sketching case.[37] This important invention also solved one of the perennial problems of the surveyors – that of carrying work across the edges of field sheets. Successful field trials were completed in 1944 but in the immediate post-war years great difficulty was experienced in getting the 'butt-joint' plates manufactured to the required tolerances, thus adding another uncertainty to the worries of the Ordnance Survey management.

Once the method of 1:1250 resurvey – a succession of stages, linking minor triangulation, traverse, chain survey and graphical detail survey – was settled, the Department's main problem was to get the surveying and drawing operations working smoothly in balance. In the first two or three years the planning of the programme was very much a hand-to-mouth affair. The Director General himself decided, in direct consultation with the planners, which towns were to be next in the programme, but sometimes necessity dictated otherwise as in September 1947 when the Triangulation and Levelling Division had to insist that the lower Clyde towns could not be included in the immediate programme because the tertiary triangulation had not yet been done.[38] Field planning was obviously at a very immature stage at this time and the same was true of the field organization. In step with the expansion, new Field Division offices were opened at Kidderminster in 1946, Nottingham in 1947, and Harrogate in 1948. The Field Division forces were organized in Town Groups, which carried out the lower-order traverses to which the chain lines were connected, the chain survey and the detail survey; the main and secondary traverses were the responsibility of the Triangulation and Levelling Division. It was proposed in due course to form Rural Groups, without the traversing staff, to deal with the 1:2500, but it was obvious that there would be small towns in a Rural Group area that would have to be surveyed at 1:1250 scale, which led to the concept of the Mixed Group. The inconvenience of splitting the traversing between two divisions was soon apparent and the entire traversing operation was handed over to Triangulation and Levelling Division in 1947.

The field organization was complicated further by the housing difficulties that confronted staff who had to move frequently from place to place. In April 1950 the Director General (now Major-General R. Ll. Brown) asked his advisers whether the policy of putting comparatively large numbers of men into a given town so as to finish the work quickly was justified.[39] Would it not be better, he asked, to use smaller units in a larger number of towns which would then all be completed at about the same time but would leave the field staff undisturbed for a much longer period? With the same object in mind, would it not be better, after completing the 1:1250, to move outward into the immediately surrounding 1:2500 rural area rather than a much greater distance to a new town? The housing shortages at this time were such that in the compromise policy that was eventually agreed upon, the staff stability element was recognized as an important factor to be taken into account. Such variations of the field programme would have produced corresponding variations in the flow of work to the drawing office, but the rate of 1:1250 progress was so slow at this time – in October 1949 the rate of detail survey was 4.0 plans per surveyor/year[40] – that the main worry of the Director of Map Publication, Brigadier F. O. Metford, was about what would happen in the drawing office when eventually all the towns were finished and field output suddenly increased as the bulk of the effort was transferred to the rural areas. In November 1949 the Director of Establishment and Finance, Mr F. G. C. Bentley, pointed out the need for a co-ordinated plan in both production directorates.[41] The making of such a plan, which would accurately predict the output in the field and the drawing office, was to become a major preoccupation in the years ahead, but in 1949 it was concluded that the drawing office would have no difficulty in keeping pace for the next five years.

The war-time air survey section was greatly reduced after the end of 1945 and in March 1947 consisted of twenty-six staff belonging to Field Division, located at Esher. Experiments with urban resurvey from air photographs were carried out without any very widespread faith in the adequacy of the method. The manual technique used had much in common with graphical survey on the ground and was almost as slow. Experiment followed experiment – in Bournemouth, Hull (where the Decca system of navigation was used for the first time) and in the rural area surrounding Bristol; eventually, in 1947, a graphical method based on rectified enlargements was applied with much greater success for the resurvey of Southend. The 1:1250 air survey programme was then extended to Bath, Southport, part of London, and half a dozen other towns.

The 1:2500 overhaul stood initially below the 1:1250 in order of importance, but several circumstances were to modify this distinction. In 1947 the National Coal Board asked for precedence to be given to the coalfield areas both for resurvey and overhaul. This request was unhesitatingly supported by the Ministry of Town and Country Planning and the Department of Health for Scotland, who said that their own priority areas were practically the same.[42] From this time it was accepted that rural areas in the coalfields would have to be tackled at an early date. The NCB defined their priorities in 1947 and again in revised form in 1950 although at this time no new maps had been produced in the coalfields outside the large towns. Another development which changed the outlook on the overhaul came from HM Land Registry, which in the early 1950s began to discuss the possible extension of compulsory registration of title to the counties of Essex, Sussex and Kent.[43]

After a number of experiments two methods for the 1:2500 overhaul were tentatively formulated in 1948; the plan was to deal with the areas round the large towns and in the coalfields by 'Chelmsford' partial resurvey and with the more rural areas by 'Cotswold' overhaul.[44] The Chelmsford method, which was surprisingly sophisticated for a Department generally unenthusiastic about air survey, made use of aerial triangulation as well as graphical air survey. Air photographs of Essex were obtained in 1947 and 1948 (hence the name 'Chelmsford'), the Nottingham and Durham coalfield areas were put in the flying programmes for 1949 and 1950 and the stereocomparators used for the analytical aerial triangulation were programmed to take up the two coalfields after the completion of Essex in 1954. The shift of attention to large blocks of 1:2500 mapping was welcome news to the drawing divisions for which the scattered patches of 1:1250 resurvey seemed to defer almost indefinitely the prospects of starting on the Regular derived six-inch. At the end of 1949, the Director of Field Survey, Brigadier R. P. Wheeler (who was not a great air survey enthusiast) began to have well-founded doubts about the Chelmsford method largely because 'we were not our own master'; he was referring to the uncertainty of being able to obtain air photographs because of weather and the difficulties with aircraft and cameras. On the other hand, progressive developments of the Cotswold method of overhaul, which was entirely a ground survey operation at this time, were giving very promising results. But these doubts were not yet to result in any change of policy; indeed it was decided in 1949 to decentralize air survey to field divisions, partly to carry out the 1:1250 programme but also to prepare for the extension of the Chelmsford method. Air survey units were accordingly set up in London and Nottingham and later in Harrogate. A similar section was prepared for in Bristol but never actually formed. The combined 'Chelmsford-Cotswold' plan was confirmed in January 1950 and again in May 1951.[45]

Systematic continuous revision represented largely unexplored territory for the Ordnance Survey and throughout this period the underlying principles remained undefined, and the necessary organization and methods undecided. However, some of the problems were identified: the provision of a suitable field document for continuous revision and the prevention of the deterioration caused by repeated cycles of reproduction. Continuous revision started in Bournemouth in 1946 and in Swansea, Portsmouth and Plymouth in the autumn of 1947. From the first, continuous revision posts were much sought after by field staff, because such appointments largely eliminated the threat of frequent moves; a special selection procedure, in which the candidate's domestic responsibilities were taken into account, had to be instituted for dealing with applications.

PUBLICATION

Besides the basic large-scale surveys, the long-term programme included derived 1:2500 mapping of the large towns, a new Regular six-inch map made from the larger scales, a new Regular 1:25 000 produced from the same source (except in the Scottish Highlands where at this time it was regarded as the future basic scale), a redrawn one-inch map and new half-inch and quarter-inch series.

In the drawing offices the short-term programme was in full swing, but the provisional six-inch on the old County sheet-lines was far from being a distinguished product, and in October 1947 it was decided to compile a few sheets in selected areas on National Grid sheet-lines.[46] It happened that some of these sheets were partly covered by new survey and the opportunity was taken to practice Regular six-inch drawing where this occurred, giving rise to the 'part and part' sheet with some square kilometres derived from the old map and some redrawn from the new survey. A National Grid Regular six-inch pilot sheet was produced in 1950 and pilot designs were also prepared for a Regular 1:25 000 although it was recognized that the publication of this series would not begin for many years. The possibility of producing the 1:25 000 and the six-inch from a common drawing was first mentioned in March 1950.[47]

The derived 1:2500 map in areas of 1:1250 survey was also slow in making its appearance, although at this time each sheet consisted of only four 1:1250 components. In 1948 the first sheets were made by redrawing the 1:1250 at the smaller scale, but the drawing office could not be convinced that it was necessary to draw the same plan twice and at the end of 1949 the Director General agreed that the 1:2500 should be produced by direct photographic reduction from the 1:1250.[48]

Because of the imperfections of the Sixth Edition, the Department decided in the latter part of 1947 to make an entirely new one-inch map without further delay: the Seventh Edition, later to be known as the Seventh Series.* At the same time the small-scales revisers were transferred from the control of Small Scales Division to Field Division and in January 1948 they set to work in South Wales in the area of the Seventh Edition pilot sheet – sheet 142. When the first proofs of the map appeared in the

---

* The following terms and definition came into use in 1955:
'series': a number of sheets having a common design or specification.
'edition': a version of a published map. The original version is the A Edition. For subsequent versions (e.g. after full revision), the Edition letter is advanced by one.

autumn of 1949, they were sent to many interested persons and organizations, and the final modifications to the specification were made on the basis of the comments received.

In the early years after the war, map issues increased steadily from a total of just over one million in 1946 to just under two million in 1949 but thereafter there was a decline. The main increases were with the large and medium scales, although unfortunately the medium scale records did not distinguish between the six-inch and the 1:25 000.[49] In October 1947, Cheetham commented on the 'disappointing sales' of the 1:25 000 for which the printing orders – intended to provide for a two-year period – ranged from only 125 to 1000 copies of each sheet.[50] The wholesale distribution of maps in England and Wales, apart from the supply to Ordnance Survey provincial agents, remained in the hands of Edward Stanford Ltd, but in 1949 the Scottish wholesale agency was transferred from W. and A. K. Johnston to Thomas Nelson and Sons.

Science and Research

H. L. P. Jolly, the Research Officer, was seconded to the Control Commission for Germany in 1946 and did not return to the Ordnance Survey. Before the war some doubts about the role of the Research Officer had been felt in Triangulation and Levelling Division because it had led to a divided responsibility for geodetic work; it was argued that the Ordnance Survey needed a scientist primarily to advise on fundamental scientific and mathematical problems. So a new post – the Scientific Adviser – was created and Mr Thomas O'Beirne was appointed to it in 1947. The experiment was not a success. The Scientific Adviser was without any scientific staff and found that he was expected to function as a walking encyclopaedia, answering intermittent questions about unconnected details. When he had to have assistance it was loaned to him from the technical staff whose craft background prevented them from doing anything 'other than rule of thumb routine tasks'. He resigned in August 1949 but before leaving he produced a report in which he drew attention to the weakness of the Ordnance Survey on the mathematical and scientific side, citing the general ignorance of photogrammetric and geodetic theory.[51] Everywhere, he said, routine and traditional practice held the field. That these strictures were generally true was admitted in later years. At the time the Director General concluded that if the Ordnance Survey wanted any research done, it was best carried out as sponsored research at one of the universities.

Notes

1 Ordnance Survey Central Registry file 11398. Henceforward such files are indicated by the letters CR.
2 PRO OS 1/170.
3 *Ibid.*
4 Papers on the organization and control of Survey Departments, post-war; OS Library G5128.
5 Papers on the post-war organization of the Ordnance Survey; OS Library G5126.
6 PRO OS 1/170.
7 *Ibid.*
8 PRO OS 1/192.
9 OSR 1944–6 (unpublished); OS Library.
10 Post-war Planning Conference No. 10; OS Library.
11 PRO OS 1/170.
12 *Hansard*, 410, House of Commons, 20 April 1945, col. 838.
13 CR 14784.
14 OSR 1944–5 (unpublished).
15 *Ibid.*
16 CR 14767.
17 *Ibid.*
18 *Ibid.*

19 See the *Report of Departmental Committee on Pay and Classification of Ordnance Survey Staff, 1911*, p. 5: PP 1911, Cd. 5825, XXXVII.
20 Papers on the organization and control of Survey Departments, post-war; OS Library G5128.
21 OSR 1954–5, p. 15. No annual reports exist for the years 1947–8 to 1953–4.
22 Joint Statement to the Brown Committee by AGGAT and IPCS, p. 11.
23 *Report of the Inter-Departmental Committee on Survey Staffs* (HMSO 1950).
24 CR 14767/1.
25 OSR 1954–5, p. 15.
26 CR 15075.
27 Director-General's Conference Minutes, November 1945; OS Library.
28 CR 15036. Minutes of Inter-Departmental Committee on Repayment Services, January 1948.
29 CR 15036/1. Minutes of Committee on Repayment Services, November 1949.
30 *Ibid.* July 1949. Verbatim text.
31 PRO OS 1/170. Appendix 4 to Cheetham's memorandum.
32 PRO OS 1/383. Minute 15. CR 11896.
33 PRO OS 1/198.
34 Director General's Conference Minutes, September 1947; OS Library.
35 CR 15036/1. Minutes of Committee on Repayment Services, July 1949.
36 CR 14643.
37 CR 14542.
38 CR 14643.
39 *Ibid.*
40 *Ibid.*
41 *Ibid.*
42 CR 15036. Minutes of Committee on Repayment Services, October 1947.
43 PRO OS 1/239.
44 CR 14643. See also Ch. 33, and Ordnance Survey Professional Paper, no. 25, '*The Overhaul of the 1:2500 County Series Maps*'.
45 Director General's Conference Minutes, January 1950, May 1951; OS Library.
46 Director General's Conference Minutes, October 1947; OS Library.
47 Director General's Conference Minutes, March 1950; OS Library.
48 Director General's Conference Minutes, December 1949; OS Library.
49 OSR 1954–5, p. 14.
50 PRO OS 1/383.
51 T. O'Beirne, *Scientific Research, the Scientific Adviser and the Ordnance Survey*, January 1949; OS Library.

30
The
Restoration
of the Survey—
Consolidation
and Recession
1950–1960

Staffing and Accommodation

Two events took place within roughly a year of each other which were instrumental in setting the pattern for the 1950s. In June 1949 Major-General R. Ll. Brown succeeded Cheetham, and the financial year 1950–51 marked the end of the expansion. Brown imposed order and coherence on the somewhat confused activities of the expansion era, but the reduction in man-power and resources was the theme that characterized the decade as a whole.

The Ordnance Survey's non-industrial man-power complement in March 1951 was 4800; in the following ten years it was progressively reduced to 3803. The losses were necessarily borne largely by the technical staff, and led to a search for economies and expedients and to the adoption of new and more productive technical methods. At first the decrease in nominal man-power was made irrelevant by the difficulty of attracting new staff and by a high rate of resignation; the latter provided a quick and natural way of reducing numbers but it also tended to dilute the technical staff as experienced men were replaced by inexperienced. Recruiting by competitive examination, as recommended by the Brown Committee, was started in 1951, but was not altogether successful in providing the numbers needed to counteract the resignations, and the long interval between examinations only resulted in an intermittent flow. This particular inconvenience reached an unacceptable level in June 1954 when the Civil Service Commission found itself unable to hold another examination until March 1955. The Ordnance Survey therefore sought a more flexible procedure and it was eventually agreed that the examination should be replaced by a continuous interview competition which, when introduced in 1956, immediately gave much better results. As it happened, improved recruiting was accompanied by a drop in resignations following a substantial increase of pay. This was the outcome of a claim put forward by the staff association, the Institution of Professional Civil Servants (IPCS) and taken before the Civil Service Arbitration Tribunal in October 1957, when it was largely conceded.

Meanwhile another matter which affected every member of the staff was settled. It had been recognized in 1938 that a new office would be needed to house the expanded Department, and the Crabwood site at Maybush on the outskirts of Southampton had been purchased. In 1947 the need to concentrate in one location was even more pressing, but strategic considerations were thought to rule out Southampton. A site at Wellingborough was considered and in 1950 was declared to be 'suitable'. In 1955 tentative dates for the move were announced: building was to begin in September 1957 and the move itself was to start in 1959. This immediately produced strong opposition from the Southampton staff, supported widely by the people of Southampton and the surrounding area, leading to questions in the House of Commons (notably on 15–16 November 1955) by local members of Parliament; but the Government held firm. However, early in 1956 it emerged that the strategic outlook had changed and that there was no longer any military objection to concentrating the Ordnance Survey at Southampton provided that 'any plan for the Department's evacuation should be phased so as to allow the Services to make the fullest use of its resources in a warning period'. Other factors which certainly affected the decision were the state of the national economy and the consequent reductions in Government and local authority expenditure, as well as the pressure from the staff and public in Southampton. The Wellingborough project was officially abandoned in January 1956, but more than eight years were to pass before a start was made on the building of a new Headquarters at Southampton.[1]

From 1950 onwards the role of the staff associations became increasingly important in Ordnance Survey affairs. The technical staff had previously been represented by two associations, the Association of Government Geographers and Allied Technicians for the lower grades, and the Institution of Professional Civil Servants for the supervisors, but in 1950 AGGAT was absorbed into the IPCS and thereafter the technical staff, which included most of those employed in the reproduction sections, were represented by the one association. The growth of an effective Whitley system in which the Staff Side played an important, positive and independent part was a feature of the 1950 decade.

Consolidation

The lack of coherence which persisted throughout the expansion and characterized the short-term programme was one of the first matters to be attended to during the Brown regime. The principles underlying the way the various post-war objectives were to be attained had never been formally specified, and Brown immediately set about defining Ordnance Survey policy in relation to all its activities. Ordnance Survey 'policy' statements were really a mixture of objectives, policy and operating instructions; they served a valuable purpose and became in effect the standing orders on which all detailed instructions were based. Policy statements were reviewed not less often than once each year; they were never regarded as immutable documents and practice sometimes changed before policy was altered to conform, but they gave a direction to Ordnance Survey affairs which was lacking in the previous period. Brown also sought to control the Department's private language by the elimination of 'esoteric terms' without, it must be admitted, complete success.[2]

The short-term programme – a title becoming increasingly inappropriate – was closed down or continued only in modified form. Regular mosaic production was stopped in 1951, the bulk of the effort on the Provisional 1:25 000 Series was transferred to the revised edition after 1950, and in 1953 work was stopped on the Provisional (County Series) gridded six-inch map in favour of the Provisional and Regular Series on National Grid sheet-lines.

There were many other loose ends. The arrangement with the Royal Air Force for air photography was becoming more and more unsatisfactory and was recognized by both sides as being a post-war expedient which had served its purpose. In 1951 an agreement was made with the Ministry of Transport and Civil Aviation (MTCA) for some of the flying to be undertaken by the MTCA flying unit, whose primary function was the monitoring of airway navigational systems. The new arrangement enabled the Ordnance Survey to purchase its own air cameras and to operate them in the air with its own staff; the aircraft used by the MTCA unit were quite suitable for Ordnance Survey air photography and were likely to remain so. By 1956 the MTCA was providing nearly all the flying, although the Royal Air Force continued to fly some sorties for tidal photography until 1963.[3] But the change did nothing to remove one major disadvantage: the Ordnance Survey remained dependent on an organization which existed for a different purpose; and eventually the arrangement with the MTCA failed for the same reason as that with the Royal Air Force: the development of the flying unit's primary function led to the exclusion of the contingent air survey.

The decision to use both Chelmsford and Cotswold methods for the 1:2500 revision was never very secure, and when the success of the latter was confirmed, the value of the slower and more costly Chelmsford method became doubtful. It proved very difficult to obtain satisfactory air photographs in the two coalfield areas which were next in the Chelmsford programme and it seemed unlikely that the more expensive method would give better results. So the work in Essex was curtailed early in 1953 and the coalfields were programmed for what became known as 'normal Cotswold' overhaul.[4] The air survey sections in some field divisions were run down, and by 1955 all were finally disbanded. One or two experimental variants of the overhaul, made obsolete and uneconomical by the Cotswold method, were also abandoned.[5] These changes greatly simplified the planning and execution of the survey, but towards the end of the decade so much reliance was being placed on the universal efficacy of the Cotswold method that it was sometimes used in circumstances where a full resurvey would have been the proper course.

Perhaps the main contribution of the Brown era to the process of consolidation was in the organization of continuous revision and the clarifying of some of its principles. Brown was convinced of the primary importance of continuous revision and he set out to improve and standardize the somewhat *ad hoc* arrangements that had existed for controlling revision sections and defining section areas. The Treasury Organization and Methods Unit was called in to give advice on the maintenance of revision records, and in 1953 it recommended the Kardex card index system for recording the amount of revision outstanding on each large-scale plan. This was a step in the right direction, but the card index was not wholly effective because it failed to locate each of the elements to be surveyed, and early in the 1960s it was superseded.

Brown was determined to solve the two outstanding problems of revision: the preservation of quality from one edition to the next and the making of a suitable, stable field document.[6] The first was successfully dealt with by using a combination of photographic processes, but no satisfactory way could be found for transferring the image from a new edition to four butt-joint plates for the succeeding stage of field revision. In June 1952 all butt-joint plate experiments were ended[7] and the astrafoil sheet, which was neither stable nor robust, became the standard continuous revision document; this was a disappointing end to several years of experiment which should, perhaps, have had a different result. But in 1952 the continuous revision organization was expanding so rapidly that a decisive step had to be taken.

The reform of the planning and recording process for the resurvey and overhaul was also overdue. The area covered by each task had to be defined, the various stages fitted into a time framework, and the man-power and other resources allocated. Accommodation for field parties had to be ear-marked and the field staff kept informed about future moves. A fairly sophisticated system was needed, stretching for some five years ahead, which could be operated at a routine level within the guidelines of an annual planning directive. During Brown's directorship such a system was developed, reaching its final form in about 1954.

The somewhat unwieldy field organization remained to be rationalized. The Town Group as a unit was over-large, especially for work in the middle-sized 1:1250 towns, and the Rural Group needed some capability for 1:1250 resurvey. At the end of 1952 a simplification into one type of sub-unit – the Field Survey Group – was decided upon. This was smaller than the Town Group and was made up of self-contained sections which could be employed independently on any of the detail survey tasks. The term 'Division', hitherto used to describe the main elements in the Ordnance Survey and also, by long-established custom, the subordinate units of the field survey organization, was from 1953 reserved for the former. The 'field division offices' became 'region offices' and were renamed geographically; at about the same time Triangulation and Levelling Division was transformed into Geodetic Control Division.[8]

Another change which might be regarded as part of the general tidying-up operation, although it did not take place until 1956, concerned the scale of the basic survey in the Highlands of Scotland. The obsession with the 1:25 000 map, started by MacLeod before the war, was reinforced for a time by Cheetham's 'planning requirement', but lingered on after this had been forgotten. The choice of the 1:25 000 as a basic scale had been made within the Department rather than through consultation and, after the views of Scottish users had been canvassed in February 1956, the scale for the Highlands was changed to the six-inch.[9]

COPYRIGHT

The provisions of the Copyright Act of 1956 enabled the Ordnance Survey to revise its copyright regulations in 1958 and to increase its charges. With the coming into force of the new rules the Director General assumed responsibility, delegated to him by the Controller of HM Stationery Office, for the administration of the Crown copyright subsisting in every Ordnance Survey map for a period of fifty years from the end of the calendar month in which it was made. The delegated authority was limited to routine cases; out-of-the-ordinary requests to reproduce official material still had to be referred to the Controller.

Pressure on Resources

EXPEDIENTS

The pressure on resources brought about by economic recession and man-power reductions gave an impetus to widespread technical changes which resulted generally in higher productivity and helped to prevent what would otherwise have been a serious decline in output. But the consequences were not so satisfactory when the pressures led to the adoption of expedients and restrictive regulations.

At the end of 1953 the Director General and his principal advisers were forced to consider possible economies.[10] Referring to the 1:25 000 map the Director of Field Survey, Brigadier A. H. Dowson, wrote: 'Except for the [military need] . . . it might be better to drop this scale altogether . . .', thereby demonstrating how far the 'planning requirement' had evaporated. There were, however, other more important matters under scrutiny.

In July 1953 Major-General J. C. T. Willis had succeeded Brown. He was a gifted man with a clear and logical mind and a sharp and ready wit, but he lacked some of Brown's infectious enthusiasm and his dedication to continuous revision. Willis saw that in its heyday under Brown some rather wasteful practices had grown up, particularly in the production of too frequent 1:1250 new editions. In January 1954 he was prepared to sanction a change in the yardstick for generating new editions – which would have roughly halved their frequency – provided that revision in the field was kept up to date and that some arrangement existed for releasing up-to-date information.[11] This decision was beyond criticism, because no principle was sacrificed and there was a promise of worth-while savings. Practice, however, did not conform to principle for very long. In 1956 modified rules were published, one of which fixed the minimum interval between editions at five years; this had the effect of delaying the execution of the revision survey until the time came for a new edition to be made, thus breaching Willis's first safeguarding condition. The second was also sacrificed. In October 1954 it was decided that Advance Revision Information (up-to-date copies made directly from the continuous revision field sheets) was not to be publicized or encouraged, on the argument that it diverted resources and delayed publication.[12] Willis must have changed his mind in a very short time, perhaps by being persuaded that, in the circumstances, expediency overruled principle. In 1958, after Major-General L. F. de Vic Carey had taken over from Willis, a directive on continuous revision was issued to Field Division, containing the objective: 'To keep the continuous revision effort to a minimum consistent with not falling unduly into arrears'. It was difficult to quantify 'unduly' and there was a large increase in the backlog of unsurveyed new detail, a deterioration which at this time went on insidiously because changes in the total amount of unsurveyed work were not being accurately recorded. Finally, in 1958, it was decided to restrict continuous revision to part of the country only and to deal with the remainder on the cyclic principle. This new system, referred to as 'block revision' was never put fully into operation.

Another attempt to save effort in the field was by 'by-passing'. This dubious practice, which consisted of producing a new 1:2500 overhaul plan on National Grid sheet-lines without revising it, was first suggested in 1948,[13] but it was not until July 1952 that a large number of plans in the county of Devon thought to contain less than ten units of change[14] were selected for by-passing.[15] This was later to become a great nuisance, because it emerged that the amount of change was often much greater than supposed and the by-passed plans became an inconveniently scattered, but nevertheless large, task that had somehow to be tackled after the main body of surveyors had moved on.

The staff reductions had led to a drop in field output by the middle 1950s and this was made worse by two other factors. The Ordnance Survey had committed itself in 1947 to give priority to the resurvey and overhaul of the coalfield areas, and between 1952 and 1954 was repeatedly reminded by the National Coal Board that underground workings had to be related to surface features by December 1962 in order to comply with the Coal Mines (Surveyors and Plans) General Regulations 1952.[16] In the Department it became a generally held belief that the Ordnance Survey itself was under a statutory obligation to complete the coalfield plans by this date. In fact the obligation was with the NCB; the Ordnance Survey's commitment was merely based on an agreement which at the outset was in very general terms. Nevertheless a large proportion of the field effort was concentrated in areas of special difficulty, such as South Wales, where the output rates were, from the nature of the work, particularly low. This transfer of surveyors delayed the survey in populated and developing areas outside the coalfields and drew off man-power from continuous revision.

Resources were further stretched by the introduction of compulsory land registration in Surrey in 1952, the city of Oxford in 1954, Oldham in 1956 and Kent beginning in 1957. Very little Overhaul had been completed in the rural areas, the County Series maps were out of date, and a large number of special surveys had to be carried out for the Land Registry although these were of no permanent value to the Ordnance Survey. More man-power had therefore to be diverted from the main task, particularly from the already hard-pressed continuous revision sections in the near-by towns. An indication of the increase in Land Registry work is given by the average annual number of special registration surveys or survey 'cases'. For the period 1946–50 this was 2934, but in 1955–60 it had risen to 8131.[17] Because of the drop in field output the large-scales draughtsmen began to run out of work. The number of plans reaching the drawing office in 1955–6 was five hundred short of the planned figure and many draughtsmen were transferred to drawing the Provisional six-inch on National Grid sheet-lines, with the incidental benefit that the production of this long-overdue map went up significantly.[18]

Field output rose between 1958 and 1960, partly because of better recruiting after the pay award and partly through the introduction of improved methods. By the end of the decade the field/drawing imbalance had been reversed, and surveyors were being offered transfers to drawing. Work on tourist maps, the half-inch and the Regular 1:25 000 was virtually halted but in spite of this the backlog of large-scale plans awaiting drawing continued to increase. The possibility of producing the six-inch and the 1:25 000 map from one set of drawings had been briefly considered several years before, but now this proposition took on a new attraction. Experiments were put in hand and were soon giving hopeful results. In 1959 Regular six-inch maps, drawn to a new specification, began to appear. The baleful influence of the 1:25 000 continued to make itself felt, this time on the six-inch, which became greatly over-generalized (Plate 19).

In 1958 the Ordnance Survey finally gave way to pressure from the Ministry of Housing and Local Government to show rights of way (as defined under the National Parks and Access to the Countryside Act 1949) on its maps, but it limited the agreement to the one-inch Seventh Series and the 1:25 000 Second Series. At Southampton the news was received with mixed feelings as it was foreseen that, apart from the extra work, there would be many complications. The nature of a 'right of way' was the main source of confusion, for if a 'right' was not exercised for any length of time, the corresponding visible feature on the ground probably disappeared, and the 'way' ceased to exist except as an abstraction. The Act provided for rights of way to be defined, in the first instance, on 1:25 000 or six-inch maps on the basis of surveys carried out by parish councils. They were therefore added to maps which were often obsolescent by people who were not surveyors, so that the relationship of a right of way to a visible footpath or other feature was often uncertain; nevertheless, the rights of way as shown on these 'Definitive Maps' had legal authority under the Act. Also they were extinguished and created by various authorities at irregular intervals and these changes could not possibly be put on the maps as they occurred. At first the Ordnance Survey believed it should show only those rights of way which existed as topographical features,[19] but it soon realized that it could not make this kind of distinction. The solution eventually adopted was to show, within the limitations of scale, all the rights of way that were included on Definitive Maps of a stated date.[20] The first one-inch map to show rights of way was sheet 180, published in 1959.

NEW METHODS

In the first decade after the war, the Ordnance Survey was often accused of technical conservatism in its attitude to photogrammetry, an accusation that was in some ways well founded. Looking back on this period, a later Director General said in his evidence to the Estimates Committee in 1963: 'We did not, I think, fully appreciate the potentialities of [air survey] . . . until a few years ago'. He explained this attitude as 'cautiousness'; but there was also a deep-seated unwillingness to exchange the chain, which had been used effectively for well over a century, for any untried, newfangled system. Before the war and in the years immediately following it, the Ordnance Survey was content to apply its own graphical ground survey techniques, based on intersections and alignments, to air photographs, with moderate success both for revision and for resurvey. But the potentialities had remained unexplored. The Ordnance Survey had one first-order stereoplotting machine, a Wild A5; this had been damaged and hastily repaired during the war and had been sent at the beginning of 1948 to Wild in Switzerland for a complete overhaul. Yet it was not until 1953 that this excellent machine was used for a comprehensive experiment on 1:1250 resurvey.[21] In the intervening years air-graphic resurvey and the Chelmsford method continued, without any striking advantages emerging for either.

The conservative attitude was not confined to air survey. In 1950 the Ordnance Survey became interested in the self-reducing tacheometer, an instrument combining a theodolite with an optical distance-measuring device, and in January 1950 an experimental field trial was started at Banstead. Three years later the trial was still going on[22] and the provisional conclusion reached in December 1952 was that the tacheometer had no 'particular' advantage over the chain for 1:1250 work in places like Banstead, but might be useful for resurvey in South Wales, where the topography favoured optical measurement. It was considered that chain survey should remain the standard method. The final report on the experiment was not produced until August 1954, by which time the verdict on

1:1250 tacheometric survey had been revised. It eventually emerged that, apart from the initial expense, the tacheometer was superior to the chain in every way, strikingly so in accuracy and production costs. Yet after three years of trials a wrong conclusion had been reached. The explanation can only be found in the operation of the Ordnance Survey craft system, and in the professional weakness pointed out by O'Beirne. Because the number of professional officers was so small and because they changed so frequently, the conduct of trials such as this was largely in the hands of craftsmen, often directed by craftsmen promoted into positions of considerable responsibility and authority. No strong scientifically-oriented guidance came from the professional side. There may have been no actual prejudice against the tacheometer, but it appears to have been used in the earlier trials as if it had been a chain, paralleling the application of graphic ground survey to graphic air survey. A craft upbringing made it difficult for a surveyor to perceive the entirely new way of executing the survey made possible by a new instrument such as the stereoplotting machine or the tacheometer.

On the air survey side there were other difficulties, mainly with flying and photography. In December 1952 the Deputy Director Field Division concluded that air photography was uneconomic north of a line from the Wash to the Severn;[23] this was another conclusion that proved to be false although it could not this time be held against the craft system.

Suddenly the inertia seems to have been overcome; in 1954–5 the experimental resurvey at Oxford with the A5 began to show startling economies amounting to fifty per cent on the standard method, and there was talk of a thirty to forty per cent improvement with the tacheometer.[24] Some of these early estimates turned out to be over-optimistic when a fair comparison was made, but the savings remained very large. For the management they pointed one way of escape from the pressure on resources, but the moment was an unfavourable one for embarking on a programme of heavy capital expenditure. However, the prize was obviously so great that it was worth fighting for and in November and December 1955 Willis addressed two papers to the Permanent Secretary of the Ministry. The first was a restatement of the tasks facing the Ordnance Survey and a review of the progress that had been made in the ten years since the war; it concluded with a plea, in general terms, for more man-power and money. The second was an appeal for support in obtaining approval for specific capital expenditure on plotting machines and tacheometers. He wrote:

> A large proportion of the field survey of the Ordnance Survey is being carried out by methods which are completely out of date and which have long been abandoned by all major overseas organizations and by all civilian survey undertakings. Indeed, on two occasions in the last six months the Department has been held up to public ridicule before an informed international audience for this very reason.[25]

Willis's arguments were accepted and the Department was given authority to purchase the necessary instruments.

At about this time a British firm, Hilger and Watts, produced a first-order plotting machine designed by Professor E. H. Thompson of University College, London, who had served as a Royal Engineer officer in the Ordnance Survey in two assistant director posts before his retirement from the army in April 1951. The development of this instrument and the promised support given to the manufacturers by the Department undoubtedly stimulated interest in photogrammetric methods in general and particularly in stereoplotting machines. The prototype was sent to Chessington for user trials in 1955 and the Ordnance Survey was able to specify this machine as part of its capital equipment programme, so reducing the sum that would have to be paid in foreign currency. In the three financial years from 1955 the Department acquired twelve plotting machines, including five Thompson-Watts, four Santoni Stereosimplex and three Wild A8s, the latter being primarily intended for the six-inch resurvey of Scotland. In the next three years seven more were purchased making a total of twenty-five machines which included the A5 and two old second-order Wild A6 plotters obtained from the Air Ministry. In 1955 and 1956 the Thompson-Watts plotters were plagued by teething troubles, but the photogrammetric staff were left in no doubt that they had to succeed (Plate 20).

The air-graphic method was not finally abandoned despite these successes. The weather was not particularly favourable for air photography in 1957 but most of the 1:1250 photographic programme was completed, providing a quantity of photographs that outran the capacity of the new plotting machines. So the graphic method was reintroduced for four towns, partly to keep the method in existence, but it soon entered on a new lease of life as a result of an experiment in 'air assisted overhaul',[26] which was aimed at assisting the surveyors in 1:2500 areas of special difficulty – for instance where extensive developments had almost totally obliterated the old features – by carrying out a preliminary revision from air photographs at Headquarters before the plans were sent to the field. In the same year Willis issued a new policy statement which laid down that air survey methods should be used 'whenever they could be employed with economy and efficiency'. After many years in the wilderness, if this expression can be used to describe the decentralized air survey sections, the air surveyors found themselves concentrated at Chessington, using expensive new equipment and working on a full programme of 1:1250 and six-inch resurvey, overhaul revision, and contouring. The importance and diversity of these tasks led in 1958 to reorganization and the formation of Air Survey Branch within Geodetic Control Division, which had for some time been responsible for contouring (either by 'stereo-sketching' or with the Wild A6 plotting machines) and aerial triangulation.[27]

Once the hesitations of Banstead were past the surveyors rapidly became converted to the tacheometric method; as more instruments were purchased and issued to the various regions the enthusiasm for 'tachy' grew, partly because it proved to be the most accurate of all the 1:1250 methods. In 1960–1 the 2348 plans completed in the field were made up of the following:[28]

Stereoplotting machine	467
Air-graphic	195
Tacheometer	1362
Chain	324

The rapid extension of the tacheometric method is evident from these figures; some chain survey remained, largely because it had been programmed many years previously and the minor control points had been surveyed on the chain survey pattern, However, the full economies of plotting-machine survey were obviously still not being realized.

An important consequence of the experimental 1:1250 survey of Oxford with the A5 plotting machine was the introduction of standard accuracy tests. The first group of these tests carried out in 1957 confirmed that the A5 produced large-scale surveys at least as accurately as the chain. Subsequently, accuracy testing became a matter of routine within the responsibility of Geodetic Control Division; tests of the 1:2500 were started in 1959 and of the six-inch in 1961.

The possibility of making further economies in man-power by adopting mechanized systems for other processes was not overlooked. In 1953 the Treasury undertook a study of punched card machinery for some survey computations. The report was not encouraging, but the Ordnance Survey did not accept its conclusions and set about modifying the form of the computations to suit the punched card equipment. In March 1954 the Treasury was asked to re-examine the question, and in November it recommended a punched card system for levelling and some traverse computations. By the following autumn an IBM 626 calculator had been installed at Chessington. In this instance the pace of change was remarkably rapid, contrasting with the story of the tacheometer and the stereo-plotting machine, but the grip of the craft system was much less strong in the Computing Section to which the more mathematically minded and sometimes better qualified surveyors tended to gravitate. In 1958 additional equipment was bought, enabling computations for levelling and traversing, tacheometric survey, some photogrammetric and triangulation calculations, and the processing of field statistics to be carried out with substantial savings.[29] The complex computations for determining the positions of control points photogrammetrically from stereocomparator observations were beyond the capacity of this relatively simple installation and, because they took a great deal of time to do manually, programs were developed, with the co-operation of the National Physical Laboratory, for transferring part of the computations to their ACE computer. In 1954 the method was successfully tested and, a year later, was applied to the six-inch resurvey of the Highlands.

Measurement of parcel areas on the 1:2500 plans by the time-honoured scale and trace method* took up such a disproportionate amount of time that it also seemed a suitable subject for automation. A research project was initiated and by 1957 it had been demonstrated that an automated planimeter was more likely to be practicable than devices based on the scanning principle.[30] Accordingly a specification for a planimeter with an electronic head was prepared in April 1958 and by the end of 1959 it was undergoing user trials which led to its adoption. At about this time a new system of numbering parcels cut by sheet edges was brought into use and areas were published to two decimal places of an acre instead of three. This last change was made to suit the new equipment, although the value of the third figure had always been doubtful.

The draughtsmen, like their colleagues in the field, were to find a partial solution to the man-power shortage in new labour-saving methods. The technique of scribing as an alternative to pen-and-ink drawing had been successful on plastic materials, but the glass used in Ordnance Survey drawing

---

* The scale and trace method, invented by a sapper before 1850 (who received a reward of sixpence a day extra pay) uses a sort of slide rule which totals the number of squares printed on a sheet of tracing paper. The tracing paper is laid over the map, covering the parcel being measured.

offices damaged the scribing points, and this was something that had to be overcome within the Department itself. New scribing tools were designed and scribing on coated glass was begun for the 1:2500 scale in 1956.[31] Within a year the changeover to scribing for this scale was almost complete, with a gratifying saving in time of twenty-seven per cent over conventional drawing.[32] This was just as well, in view of the increase in field output that was to take place in the following two or three years.

NEW MAPS, A RETREAT FROM AUSTERITY

The new 1:2500 plans were now reaching the map-using public in substantial numbers, but the small square sheets were generally received with disfavour, partly no doubt because of the inconvenience of replacing County Series by others on different sheet-lines. In August 1959 the Ordnance Survey responded to the pressure of opinion by changing the format of the 1:2500; pairs of sheets were combined to give a sheet size of 2 km from east to west by 1 km from north to south. The change greatly added to the difficulty of producing revised 1:2500 plans in areas where these were derived from the 1:1250, because the eight component sheets which had to be combined rarely had the same date of revision.

The new Seventh Edition of the one-inch began to appear in 1952 and unlike its predecessor was praised on all sides (Plate 21). The map was designed in a simple, open style and was very well drawn and printed, and it was certainly not an austerity product, having initially ten colours. Here at last was something that the drawing office could be proud of, but before it was published there was an internal disagreement on publication policy. The financial management was anxious not to waste the substantial stocks of some sheets of the Sixth Edition and wanted to delay the publication of the Seventh. In the field and in the drawing office it was generally held that new editions should be published as early as possible; the technical staff were, after all, working to produce up-to-date maps, and the withholding of information for commercial reasons was a practice they found hard to understand.[33] A second round of small-scales revision for the one-inch map began in 1958 and from this time onward regular revised editions were published* but the argument on marketing policy continued.

The publication of the new quarter-inch Fifth Series (the scale was actually 1:250 000) started in 1957. The design had two features which, from the point of view of legibility, were rather contradictory: a reduction in content compared with the earlier series, and yet heavier relief depiction by layers and hill shading (Plate 22). The first of these was 'justified by the forthcoming production of the Half-Inch to One Mile Series',[34] but as the half-inch never materialized, it must be assumed that the content reduction turned out to be a mistake. The road system was strongly emphasized and the map laid some claim to being classed as a motorists' road map, but the heavy layers and hill shading obscured some of the names, and the elimination of many minor roads reduced the value of the map for this purpose. This combination of design features raises doubts about the role the map was intended to fill. The answer appears to lie in the Ordnance Survey's traditional inclination towards the general map; the Fifth Series probably succeeded reasonably well in being all things to all men without being a notable success for any particular purpose.

In the 1950s very little Regular medium-scale mapping was published – merely a few hundred derived six-inch sheets. For the six-inch resurvey it had long been the intention to add a new style of rock drawing to the maps of the more mountainous areas of the Highlands; rock depiction had been studied for many years, and various possibilities had been tried and rejected. In January 1957 the Director General ordered that 'the most economic method was to be used for this somewhat valueless feature'.[35] Yet in the same year, perhaps after Willis's departure at the end of May, the draughtsmen produced a pilot six-inch sheet covering part of Foinavon in Sutherland, very heavily laden with rock drawing, which became the model for subsequent sheets. Here again austerity seems to have fought a losing battle.

The difficulties of the early part of the decade had been successfully countered by radical changes in methods, but in its last two years a pause occurred in the forward movement. Costs were rising, largely as a result of the pay award of 1957, more staff reductions were necessary, and the Ordnance Survey, now under Major-General L. F. de Vic Carey – who had succeeded Willis in June 1957 – again had to turn to restrictions and expedients. Carey was a man of great personal charm and if he appeared to lack some of the dynamic qualities of his precedessors, it was perhaps because it fell to him to preside over this uneventful and negative period in the affairs of the Department.

---

* Sheets of the one-inch Seventh Series were revised at cyclic intervals of seven, fifteen or twenty-five years depending on the likelihood of change within each sheet.

Notes

1 PRO OS 1/390.
2 Director General's Conference Minutes, May 1951; OS Library.
3 OSR 1963–4, Appendix 6.
4 Director General's Conference Minutes, January 1953; OS Library.
5 See Ordnance Survey Professional Papers, no. 25, *The Overhaul of the 1:2500 County Series Maps* (1972).
6 Director General's Conference Minutes, May 1950, June 1950, April 1952.
7 Director General's Conference Minutes, June 1952.
8 Director General's Conference Minutes, February 1953.
9 OSR 1955–6, p. 9.
10 CR 14640/1.
11 *Ibid.*
12 Director General's Conference Minutes, October 1954.
13 Director General's Conference Minutes, December 1948.
14 For 'units of change' see p. 338.
15 Director General's Conference Minutes, July 1952.
16 PRO OS 1/225.
17 OSR 1961–2, Appendix 6.
18 CR 14643/2.
19 Director General's Conference Minutes, February 1956.
20 Ordnance Survey Policy Statement no. 55, December 1959.
21 Director General's Conference Minutes, January 1953.
22 Director General's Conference Minutes, October 1952.
23 Minutes of Field Conference, December 1952.
24 Minutes of Field Conference, July 1954.
25 Willis Papers, OS Library G 7057. Also in CR 17570.
26 Ordnance Survey Field Experiment FE 202.
27 OSR 1957–8, p. 8.
28 OSR 1960–1, p. 9.
29 CR 17324/1, /2.
30 Director General's Conference Minutes, November 1957.
31 Director General's Conference Minutes, January 1956; and OSR 1956–7.
32 OSR 1957–8, p. 13.
33 PRO OS 1/470. Minute 33 and others.
34 OSR 1956–7, p. 12.
35 Director General's Conference Minutes, January 1957.

31
The Post-War
Trigonometrical Survey
and the
Third Geodetic Levelling
1945–1960

Post-War Triangulation

PRIMARY TRIANGULATION

After the Second World War the most urgent trigonometrical task was to provide secondary, tertiary and lower order control for the large-scale surveys. However, by 1949 it was possible to resume observations to complete the primary retriangulation of Great Britain by observing Figure 6, which included the rest of Scotland, the Western Isles, the Orkneys and the Shetlands. Two observing parties, operating independently, were used, the northern section working northwards from Caithness through the Orkneys and Shetlands, and the southern starting from the boundary of Figure 3 in Argyllshire. Observations started on 11 May and, for the southern party at least, the difficulties of triangulation in the Highlands soon made themselves felt. On his first night the senior observer fell waist-deep into a bog, and the elements, as usual, took a hand. Observations on Ben Nevis started on 21 May, but were not completed until 11 June, twenty-two nights later, most of which were spent by the observing party on the summit at temperatures well below freezing, waiting for gaps in the clouds. There were strong winds and snow fell frequently, often lying on the summit to a depth of five or six feet. The northern party also had difficulties: there was the problem of transportation from island to island and one observer dislocated his shoulder beating off an attack by Arctic skuas, whose nesting he had inadvertently disturbed. But on the whole the problems were less than in the south and by the end of June the northern chain had been completed although, unfortunately, it was later found that the average misclosure of the triangles was somewhat high, probably because of lateral refraction. The southern section finished its programme later, reaching the lower hills of Caithness by 24 July.

During 1950 the triangulation effort was again switched to secondary and lower order work, except for one small party which successfully reobserved the unsatisfactory Shetland work in spite of bad weather. To obtain the requisite two nights' observations, Foula (461) and Monas Hill (462) were continuously occupied for twenty-two and twenty-one nights respectively.

The year 1951 was something of an *annus mirabilis* for geodetic work by the Ordnance Survey. The whole of the remainder of Figure 6 was observed, including much difficult country in the Western Highlands and the Western Isles, and a new Figure 7 was added making connection with the Isle of Man. These tasks were completed between 26 April and 4 November by a party of forty-six men made up of four observing sections and seventeen light-keeping sections. In addition a new connection with France across the Strait of Dover was observed jointly with the Institut Géographique National between 2 May and 31 July; and finally the Ridge Way Base was remeasured between 4 and 25 October.

THE SECONDARY AND LOWER ORDER TRIANGULATION

The observations of 1951 completed the basic primary retriangulation framework of Great Britain and thereafter the main effort was on secondary and lower order work. The country had been split up into 147 secondary blocks, each bounded by sides of the primary triangulation. Hotine's original intention had been to have a secondary triangulation with the relatively short ruling side-length of

4 miles (7 km) in order to avoid the need for a complete tertiary network in addition. Secondary observations had started concurrently with the primary in 1936 and by 1938 twenty-one blocks had been completed. By this time, however, it had become evident that the policy was mistaken: not only was it found difficult to site stations that would be intervisible but – and this was more serious – the labour of rigorously adjusting by least squares each block of sixty or so stations was prohibitive. Hotine had therefore decided to change to a more orthodox secondary network with a 13 km ruling side-length, which would itself be used to control a tertiary triangulation with 7 km sides. In this way the number of secondary stations in a block was roughly halved, greatly easing the tasks of siting and observing stations and of adjusting the blocks. The tertiary stations were not calculated as part of a network but were fixed individually by the most convenient means and computed semigraphically.

Observations upon this basis continued until 1950, by which time all but the mountain areas of the country had been completed. Tertiary triangulation was not thought necessary for these areas where, in general, the largest scale of mapping would be the six-inch (or 1:10 000). These were to be surveyed from air photographs and controlled by aerial triangulation for which the secondary triangulation was adequate. Later, in 1958, a practical method of adjusting a complete block of aerial triangulation by least squares became available for the first time in the shape of the Jerie[1] Analogue Computer, enabling the control to be reduced still further. Round a 48 km × 48 km block all that was required were points about 13 km apart along the perimeter and these could be quickly provided by means of a traverse using the recently invented Tellurometer to measure the distances between stations. The work was further accelerated by the use of a helicopter to assist in the building of station pillars and also to convey the observing party from one station to another. This proved to be a very rapid and economical method of providing control but, unluckily, it could only be applied to the last three secondary blocks in the Highlands because, by then, the secondary task elsewhere was almost complete.

Control of a lower order than tertiary was only provided in areas where it was needed for the large scale – generally 1:1250 – surveys of built-up areas. Such 'town control' was always based on a fourth order triangulation and traverse until the advent of short range electromagnetic distance-measuring equipment in 1964 enabled it to be provided very much more quickly and cheaply by bearing and distance measurements.

ANCILLARY OPERATIONS

With the virtual completion of the angular measurements for the primary retriangulation of Great Britain it was natural to consider the employment of geodetic resources on ancillary operations. One of the first to receive attention was base measurement. Hotine had not been entirely satisfied with his 1937–8 Lossiemouth Base, mainly because the terrain covered by the extension was unsuitable. In 1939 he had stated the intention of eventually measuring one or two more base lines and had reconnoitred one such line running between Warth Hill and Spital Hill in the north-eastern corner of Caithness, which the triangulation had not then reached. He was well aware that the measurement of this or any other such base line was 'not an immediate practical necessity for the triangulation of the country', for which the location, scale and orientation had already been determined, but he believed that 'it may well serve a purpose of general geodetic research valuable to larger countries where linear measurements are of greater necessity in arriving at definitive results'.[2] In a more cost-conscious age this altruistic purpose might have appeared a slim justification for a fairly expensive geodetic operation. However, the proposal survived the period of the war and the departure of Hotine; indeed it seems to have gathered strength with the years for, by 1951–2, it was stated categorically that 'a second base in the North of Scotland was required to hold the triangulation of Great Britain', although it was not made clear why a retriangulation which was already firmly and irrevocably fixed needed to be 'held'. At any rate the decision was taken to measure the Caithness Base and this in turn led to the remeasurement of the Ridge Way Base, partly in order to give the base-measurement team practice and experience in easier country before they tackled the more rugged terrain of Caithness; and partly because of some minor defects of procedure which Hotine had noted in the 1937 measurement.

The remeasurement of the Ridge Way Base by a party of forty men in all took place from 4 to 25 October 1951, the officer in charge being Major M. H. Cobb. The equipment and methods were essentially those of 1937 but a number of refinements were introduced in the light of earlier experience, including the use of 4½-foot drums for storing the Invar tapes, as a precaution against

over-stressing them while winding onto the smaller drums originally provided with the Macca*
equipment. The procedure for crossing a three-hundred-foot wide, fifty-foot deep ravine was also
changed. Hotine had avoided it by an offset but Cobb made two direct measurements, one with the aid
of three steel towers and the other at ground level. The finally accepted length of the base was
11 260.18650 m, which differed by 6.6 mm from the 1937 measure, a very satisfactory agreement.[3]

The Caithness Base was measured between 20 April and 11 June 1952, using a slightly larger party,
with Major Cobb again in charge. The base was long – nearly 25 km – and had other unusual features
which complicated the task of measurement, including terminals erected on hills about 400 and 500
feet above the lower sections of the base, and a 1.5 km stretch crossing a deep and soft peat bog. But in
spite of these and other difficulties a very good result was obtained, the standard error of the whole
base, calculated from the forward and back differences for sections, being ±20 mm.

ELECTROMAGNETIC DISTANCE-MEASUREMENTS AND THE SCALE OF THE TRIANGULATION

Whatever the validity of the original justification for measuring these two base lines, events soon
demonstrated their great value, both to the Ordnance Survey and to the surveying profession at large.
The Ridge Way Base, measured twice in recent years with great care, was established as probably the
most accurate long base line in the world. The accepted weighted mean length, 11 260.1887 m, is
almost certainly within 5 mm of the truth, giving an accuracy of better than one part in two million.
The Caithness Base, although somewhat less accurate, is longer, and this, with its elevated terminals,
makes it unique. Both base lines were to serve a most useful purpose in the revolution in surveying
methods which was about to occur with the advent of electromagnetic distance-measuring instruments. These instruments make use of the very great accuracy with which the frequency of an electric
oscillation can be measured (about one part in 10^{11} or better is obtainable) in order to time the journey
out and back of light or other electromagnetic pulses and so, knowing the speed of light, determine the
distance traversed. The first such instrument to be produced for geodetic purposes was the Geodimeter, invented by Dr Erik Bergstrand of Sweden in 1947. An early model had been acquired by the
United States Army Map Service who were anxious to test it over an accurately measured base of
length comparable to that of a primary triangulation side. No such length was to be found in the
United States, but the long Ridge Way Base and even longer Caithness Base were ideal for the
purpose. The instrument was therefore brought across the Atlantic in 1953 and used to measure both
bases as well as a side Saxavord (463) to Fetlar (459), at the extreme north of the triangulation. An
unexpected difficulty was encountered at the outset in operating this novel equipment: the Geodimeter works by means of light-pulses reflected from the farther end of the base and, at that time, could for
this reason only be used during darkness. It was taken hopefully to Caithness early in June, but the
twilight which, at this latitude and in this month, persists all night, made successful observation
impossible. So the equipment was moved south to the Ridge Way Base, where it worked satisfactorily,
and later, in the middle of August, moved back to the north by which time the nights were dark
enough. The Ridge Way Base was measured between 5 and 30 July, the Caithness Base from 13 to 20
August and from 20 September to 5 October and the side Saxavord–Fetlar between 4 and 12
September.

The results achieved were remarkable: the measurement of the Ridge Way Base differed by only 26
mm (2.3 ppm) and the Caithness Base by 71 mm (2.9 ppm) from the taped lengths, the Geodimeter
length being the greater in each case.[4] So consistent were the results that it was thought more likely
that the velocity of light *in vacuo*, upon which they were based, (299 793.1 km/s), was in need of
revision than that the Geodimeter measurements themselves were appreciably in error. The Ridge
Way result, if accepted as correct, gave a velocity of 299 792.4 km/s and Caithness 0.2 km/s less.
These values were published in a letter to *Nature* and were in due course confirmed as very near to the
truth, especially the stronger Ridge Way determination.[5]

The Geodimeter measurements (and the Invar tape base measurements that preceded them) were
not, however, of much practical use to the Ordnance Survey. They seemed to show that the adopted
scale of the triangulation was somewhat too large, by 7 ppm at Ridge Way, by 20 ppm at Lossiemouth,
by 17 ppm in Caithness and by 6 ppm at the northern tip of Shetland; but there was nothing at that
time that could be done about these errors which were, in any case, not serious. They did not warrant
further checks by Geodimeter which, in those days, was a bulky instrument and fairly laborious to use.

* The Macca Base Equipment was designed by, and named after, Captain G. T. McCaw. The manufacturers were Cooke,
Troughton and Simms.

Its range was also limited; the 25 km of the Caithness Base was about as much as it could achieve, considerably less than the average primary triangle side. The United States instrument was therefore returned and no replacement acquired. However, the case was very different with the next contender in this new field, the Tellurometer (Plate 23). This instrument, which was invented by Dr T. L. Wadley of South Africa and first described in 1956, used radio microwave pulses instead of light and could therefore be employed as effectively by day as by night.[6] It also had much greater range (50 km or more), and was considerably lighter and more compact, portable and convenient in use, even though similar instruments were needed at each end of a line rather than an instrument at one end and merely a reflector at the other. An early objective of Dr Wadley's was to test a production model on the Ridge Way Base and in April 1957 this was done with the co-operation of the Ordnance Survey. Once again the results were remarkable. Both the base itself and the sides of the base extension figure were measured, the whole operation taking only a few days, and the results were extremely consistent. They yielded a new value for the velocity of light of 299 792.5 ±0.3 km/s which, later in the same year, was reported to the 11th General Assembly of the International Union of Geodesy and Geophysics.[7] This figure, which agreed closely with the results of other determinations, including one by an entirely different method at the National Physical Laboratory, played its part in the international adoption during the year of an almost identical value, 299 792.5 ±0.4 km/s. Advances in the realm of physics have made possible even more precise determinations and in 1974 a final and definitive value of 299 792.458 ±1.2 m/s was internationally agreed. To the decimal places then given, the 1957 value agreed exactly with this.

The Tellurometer had proved such a success that the Ordnance Survey acquired a set of instruments and trials were extended, mainly with secondary and lower order work in view. But the instrument was so quick and easy to use that the opportunity was taken during the course of this work in the next few years to measure several primary sides, revealing a disquieting – or, at least, disappointing – state of affairs. The scale errors of the primary triangulation were found to be much larger in certain areas than had been supposed and the variation from area to area was also considerable. The scale was everywhere too large but, whereas in the south of England and in the extreme north of Shetland the error was small – about 5 ppm – elsewhere it was much larger and reached a maximum of about 45 ppm (or about one part in 22 000) in south-west Scotland, an accuracy very much inferior to that with which the first order triangulation was then generally credited, and which Hotine evidently expected. The Department, with commendable honesty and frankness, lost little time in publicizing its findings in a paper presented to the Commonwealth Survey Officers Conference in 1959[8] and continued with its checks of triangulation scale.

The Ordnance Survey's experience led other countries to check their triangulations with this new instrument and it was soon discovered that Britain was by no means alone in possessing a framework less solid than previously supposed, similar – indeed worse – results being found in several instances. The truth was that the advent of the Tellurometer had made it possible for the first time to check the scale of triangulation effectively and, not surprisingly, this revealed a general tendency towards over-optimism.

AZIMUTH OBSERVATIONS

Hotine was evidently even less convinced of the use, for the triangulation, of astronomically observed azimuths than he had been of measured base lines, for he does not seem to have proposed that such observations should ever be carried out. However, if checking – or 'holding' – of scale was necessary, the same applied to the orientation of the triangulation. Accordingly the decision of the Ordnance Survey to observe a programme of 'Laplace Azimuths' in 1953 was logical. A Laplace Azimuth is an astronomical observation of direction, corrected for the difference between astronomical longitude and geodetic longitude due to deviation of the vertical at the point of observation. The usual method is to make observations for astronomical azimuth and longitude and to correct for the difference from geodetic longitude which the latter reveals. However, this had disadvantages in high latitudes and the Ordnance Survey preferred a method devised by Professor A. N. Black, then Professor of Mechanical Engineering at Southampton University, which gave geodetic azimuth directly, using low altitude stars.[9] Stations were observed in pairs at each end of a triangulation side in order to eliminate as far as possible the effects of lateral refraction. Pairs of stations were sited at the Ridge Way and Caithness base lines and at Fetlar (459) and Saxavord (463) where the distance had been measured by Geodimeter.

Pairs were also sited at the south-western extremities of Cornwall (St Agnes Beacon (175) and Tragonning Hill (181)) and Scotland (Cairn Pat (360) and Inshanks (361)). The observer used a Wild T4 astronomical theodolite lent by Oxford University. The results gave differences with the triangulation (observed minus triangulation) varying between +2″.18 at Cairn Pat–Inshanks, and −1″.48 at Fetlar–Saxavord, a total range of 3″.66 or about 17 ppm. This satisfactory agreement, which was confirmed by the observation of further pairs of stations in 1967–9, indicated that, for some reason not clear, direction had been maintained considerably better than scale in the retriangulation.

OTHER SUPPLEMENTARY WORK

While the operations concerned with the scale and orientation of the triangulation were proceeding, the network itself was being extended and supplemented in various ways. Some of this work consisted of extensions to make connections with other countries; some was more in the nature of tidying up. Inconsistencies noted while lower order work was being done led to the reobservation of the primary triangulation in South Wales in 1955–6.[10] This revealed that two stations, Llangeinor (89) and Mynidd Maen (73) had moved, one by half a metre, possibly owing to subsidence, and as a result some of the lower order work had to be corrected. The Royal Greenwich Observatory at Herstmonceux was brought into the triangulation in 1953 and its parent installation at Greenwich in 1954. In 1957 an interesting operation took place to extend the triangulation to St Kilda, uninhabited for many years but shortly to become an important observation post for the rocket range in the Outer Hebrides.

The object of the connections with Herstmonceux and Greenwich was to establish geodetic position and azimuth in order to obtain comparisons with the very accurate astronomic positions and azimuths derived from their own observations. Laplace azimuth stations were established at the two observatories, at the meridian transit telescopes. At Herstmonceux the observatory azimuth mark was only three miles distant, at Pevensey, and it was impossible to determine the position in the horizontal plane of the optical centre of the Cooke Transit Circle accurately enough to ensure that the centring error would not appreciably affect the azimuth connection; an unusual type of observation was therefore made from the azimuth mark back into the eyepiece of the transit telescope. At Greenwich the geodetic connection resulted in a remarkable discovery. It was found that the Airy Transit Circle which, since 1850, had been internationally accepted as defining the zero meridian of longitude, was about 8m east of the meridian in terms of the triangulation. Since the latter had been fitted to Clarke's Principal Triangulation, which was supposed to have been based on the zero meridian of longitude as so defined, such a large discrepancy was very surprising. Investigations by the Chief Assistant at the Royal Observatory, Dr R. d'E. Atkinson, revealed that the Airy Transit Circle, which had been installed by the Astronomer Royal, Sir George Airy, in 1850, had been sited 5.79 m to the east of the old Pond Transit which was the instrument to which Clarke had referred his work and which had formerly defined the zero meridian. Extraordinary though it may seem, this shift of the zero meridian had been completely lost sight of. It is also extraordinary that Clarke made no mention of the shift in his *Account of the Principal Triangulation*, although clearly he must have been aware of it. The 5.79 m shift did not of course account completely for the longitude discrepancy, but the residual of 2.29 m was typical of the discrepancies between the old and new triangulations in this area.

COMPARISON WITH THE PRINCIPAL TRIANGULATION

As the retriangulation progressed a record was kept of the positions, in the new system, of stations of the old Principal Triangulation which had been positively identified and recoordinated. Over the greater part of Britain the discrepancies were small, 1–2 metres or less; but they naturally increased with the distance from the eleven points in Figures 1 and 2 to which the retriangulation was fitted, reaching about 5 m in Northern Ireland and the Hebrides and attaining a maximum of 18 m in the Shetlands. Such discrepancies were only to be expected, especially in the Shetlands, where the Principal Triangulation was less strongly observed than elsewhere. A group of rather surprisingly large discrepancy vectors in East Anglia, radiating to east and north and progressively reaching a maximum at the coast of about 6 m, at first sight seemed to suggest that East Anglia might have been slipping off into the North Sea, but closer examination made it clear that these differences also were due to the triangulation rather than to land movement. They amounted to no more than 20 ppm of the distance from the fitted common points and, in general, the agreement between the two triangulations was good.

As the triangulation of the mainland neared completion the Ordnance Survey gave attention to connections with other countries and, not unnaturally, the first to be dealt with were those that had been included in the Principal Triangulation: with France across the Strait of Dover, and with Ireland.

For the 1951 Anglo-French connection there were separate teams from the two countries, each observing at its own stations. On the British side these were Beachy Head (194), Fairlight Down (193), Paddlesworth (190) and Rumfields Water Tower (201), and in France La Canche, Montlambert, St Inglevert and Gravelines Water Tower. The results were good, the average triangular misclosure being 1″.00. As, however, the French and British datums were different, the co-ordinates in the two systems were not directly comparable. In the following year the connection was made with Ireland. All observations on the mainland and in Northern Ireland were made by personnel of the Ordnance Survey of Great Britain, and those in Southern Ireland by observers from the Ordnance Survey of the Republic of Ireland, the latter being first attached for training to the British parties. The joint observations took place between 19 April and 8 October 1952; during this period the Ordnance Survey, at the request of the Ordnance Survey of Northern Ireland, also carried out a primary triangulation of their territory. At the same time some additional observations were made on the mainland to strengthen the base of the Irish connection. Once again, in spite of some very long rays – that between Prescelly (107) and Ballycreen in Southern Ireland was 98 miles in length – a good result was obtained with an average triangular misclosure of 1″.16.

At about this time positional relationships within and between the continents were becoming of increasing importance from the military standpoint. The development of long-range rockets was proceeding apace, as was the technique of accurately measuring long distances over the Earth's surface by electromagnetic means. Shortly after the war the United States had carried out a readjustment of all the triangulations of continental Europe in order to produce a single system (the European Datum) upon a uniform projection (the Universal Transverse Mercator projection) to be used as the basis of all NATO military map grids.

There was an evident need for the United States to relate its own geodetic system to this European Datum more precisely than in the past, and in 1953 the United States Air Force (USAF) set about connecting the two continents by means of a chain of SHORAN trilateration.* SHORAN was able to measure distances between points as much as 800 km apart. In the system a transmitter was carried in an aircraft flying across the line to be measured, at the terminals of which two transponder stations were located. The distance between the two stations was derived from the minimum sum of the signal transit times from the aircraft to each terminal and back. A chain of triangles with measured sides was set up between Canada and Norway proceeding via Greenland, Iceland, the Faroes, the Shetlands and Scotland. The first link to be measured by the USAF, in September 1953, was that between three stations in the Shetlands and the north of Scotland: Saxavord, Warth Hill and Mormond, and three in southern Norway: Skibmannshei, Eigeberg and Helliso-Fyr. This was an interesting and, on the whole, successful operation although not of a primary geodetic standard, and marred by a 12 m discrepancy in the SHORAN and triangulation measurements between the Norwegian stations, which was too great to be reasonably ascribed to the triangulation.

Post-War Levelling

THE SECOND GEODETIC LEVELLING OF SCOTLAND

The interruption caused by the First World War led to the curtailment of the Second Geodetic Levelling which, apart from the connection with the tide gauge at Dunbar, covered only the greater part of England and an area in South Wales. There was a proposal in 1926 to carry out a second geodetic levelling of Scotland, in conformity with what had been done in the south, but this was a time of increasing financial stringency and the project was deferred. It was resurrected in 1935 when expansion was once again in the air and levelling started in 1936. The network was designed to cover the whole of the mainland of Scotland, with the exception of the coastal areas of Argyll and Inverness-shire where the necessary water crossings would have created difficulty. The work was to have been done to the same standards as in England and Wales but with British levelling instruments

---

* SHORAN = Short Range Aids to Navigation. The system actually used was a slightly modified version which the USAF called 'HIRAN'.

manufactured by Cooke, Troughton and Simms in place of the Zeiss levels formerly used. However, by 1939, the levelling had only progressed northward as far as the Forth and Clyde when, once again, war intervened.[11] Nevertheless, it was not stopped; Scotland was virtually without reliable height information and it was apparent that the post-war large-scale programme would be seriously handicapped if this situation still existed when the new surveys were taken up. The levelling was therefore continued spasmodically, using whatever staff there were, including men not fit for active service as well as those whom the vagaries of the military machine happened to make temporarily available.

The field-work was eventually completed in 1952, computation and adjustment being carried out in four successive blocks as observations were completed. The final block was dealt with in 1953, but analysis of the results showed that the levelling, unlike that of England and Wales, could not be classed as 'levelling of high precision'; the 'probable total error' calculated from circuit misclosures, was 2.17 mm per $\sqrt{km}$, which exceeded the new limit of 2.00 mm set in 1948 by the IAG for the highest class of levelling. This failure to meet the standard was not surprising, bearing in mind the conditions in which the field-work had been carried out. Levelling is, superficially, one of the simplest and most straightforward of surveying operations and when accuracy is not of great importance it is, in practice, simple and straightforward. But this is certainly not so when, as in geodetic or high precision levelling over long distances, great accuracy is sought. The operation itself remains simple, indeed monotonously simple, but because the end result is the algebraic sum of a very large number of small measured differences of height, very stringent precautions have to be taken to eliminate errors which are systematic; that is, errors which are not random and to some extent self-cancelling as observations are multiplied, but which are cumulative roughly in proportion to the number of observations or the distance levelled. In this context even the most minute errors, quite undetectable in single observations, are of great importance. There are many ways in which such errors may arise unless suitable precautions are taken. For example, the ground might progressively yield under the weight of the observer and his instrument between his first levelling sight in the backward direction and his second levelling sight in the forward direction, thus slightly exaggerating the height rise in the space levelled. The necessary precautions are many in number and often tedious in application. The reasons for them are not readily appreciated by the ordinary leveller who may often find that his work satisfies the simple checks he is able to apply himself even if he ignores the less obvious precautions. If standards of training and supervision are relaxed at all, or if a desire to accelerate output is allowed to influence standards, as occurred in the later stages of the Scottish levelling, the accuracy attained is liable to fall off sharply.

It was recognized that the second geodetic levelling of Scotland could not be accepted as satisfying scientific requirements in such questions as the rate of uplift or subsidence of the land, or long-term changes in sea-level. It was however quite adequate to control the lower order levelling required for practical purposes, and was used to provide heights for the post-war surveys.

THE THIRD GEODETIC LEVELLING

In 1950, while the work in Scotland was still proceeding, an appreciation was made of the situation in England and Wales. The Second Geodetic Levelling had a number of deficiencies; it did not cover East Anglia and Kent and the network in northern England was sparse; in Wales there was only a single circuit through Abergavenny and Brecon, with a branch to Carmarthen. There were a number of branch lines not forming parts of closed circuits, including the lines to the three Ordnance Survey tide gauges at Newlyn, Felixstowe and Dunbar, and the lines to Liverpool and Carmarthen; some lines were poorly sited and the layout of circuits left something to be desired. It would have been possible to supplement the network by levelling additional circuits, but it is unsatisfactory to carry out geodetic levelling piecemeal over a long period because it is difficult or impossible to use such levelling to detect, still less measure, long-term vertical movement of the Earth's crust. Moreover, if such movement does occur, it introduces inconsistency into the network.

The only practicable way of providing England and Wales with a more satisfactory geodetic network was to carry out a complete relevelling. From the scientific viewpoint also, this was clearly desirable as a means of investigating vertical movement of the Earth's crust. After a lapse of almost forty years since the epoch of the Second Geodetic Levelling, it was by no means unlikely that measurable vertical movement had occurred. It was also desirable to determine whether the rather surprising 0.8 feet rise of sea-level between Newlyn and Dunbar which Wolff and Jolly had found from their analysis of the earlier levelling[12] was confirmed by relevelling.

It was therefore decided that a third geodetic levelling should be carried out. For this a revised network was designed which covered almost the whole of England and Wales. The advice of the Geological Survey was taken as to the stability of the proposed routes, and some badly sited lines from the Second Geodetic Levelling were eliminated, as were some uneconomically small circuits. But all the former fundamental bench-marks were included and some new ones added in areas to which the levelling had been extended. The total length of the lines in the network was increased from 2989 miles to 4530 miles, and the only substantial area not well served was the coastal land northward from the Wash. To have included satisfactory circuits here would have entailed a level transfer across the Humber, which was more than could be achieved with the transfer technique then in use.

These measures to improve the network were, unfortunately, not matched by steps to improve upon the equipment or techniques of earlier years and there was little or no preliminary research to this end. The levelling instruments were those that had been employed on the levelling of Scotland; the levelling staves were the same Cambridge Invar staves with engraved graduations that had been used for the Second Geodetic Levelling of England and Wales, and in general the field procedures were the same.

Field-work started in November 1951 and the new levelling was accomplished in stages. The first, which was completed by December 1953, consisted of four lines from Newlyn, Felixstowe, Dunbar and Aberystwyth, all converging on Warwick in the centre of England. The second stage, completed by April 1955, linked up the outer ends of these, and the third broke down into smaller circuits the levelling in the four quadrants thus delineated. This was completed by March 1956 and some supplementary lines were levelled in the fourth stage by October the same year.

As the field-work was nearing completion, it was decided that a third geodetic levelling of Scotland should be carried out to the same standards as that of England and Wales so that the whole of Great Britain might be covered with levelling of a uniformly high quality. The Scottish network was revised and the layout of circuits improved, advantage being taken of a much better method that had recently been devised for transferring levels across water gaps. This was based on simultaneous vertical angular observations by theodolite from each side and was capable of giving level transfers of geodetic accuracy across gaps of as much as 8 km. The earlier method, which depended on the use of the gradienter screw of the level, was very much less accurate and limited to gaps of 200 m. Consequently lines crossing estuaries had generally been excluded, a restriction that was particularly cramping along the coasts of Scotland. The new levelling in Scotland started in 1956 as that in England and Wales was concluded. It was eventually completed at the end of 1958.

Computation of the levelling of England and Wales had proceeded as the field-work progressed, but final analysis had to await the completion of all observations. The method of computation and the various corrections applied were identical with those used formerly. Only in the assessment of the accuracy of the levelling was a different method employed. For the Second Geodetic Levelling the Lallemand formulae, adopted by the IAG in 1912,[13] had been used, but for the new levelling a system devised by J. Vignal of the French Levelling Service, recommended in a resolution of the General Assembly in 1948, was introduced.[14] This differed from the earlier system chiefly in being based on the more logical assumption that systematic error would not persist as truly systematic beyond a certain limiting length of line. Thereafter it would vary and, for sections of line of length greater than the limit, it would display the character of a random or accidental error. The Ordnance Survey's analysis, however, did not support this latter assumption and no limiting length could be determined. It seemed that a small and nearly uniform systematic error persisted whatever the length of line. Nevertheless, an analysis of the circuit closures indicated a high degree of accuracy, the total assessed error being 1.13 mm per $\sqrt{\text{km}}$ or 0.00469 feet per $\sqrt{\text{mile}}$. For the whole net between Newlyn and Dunbar the probable total error was 0.12 foot.

These assessments had been made entirely on the basis of internal evidence – circuit misclosures and the differences between forward and back levelling. It was when the levels from the adjusted network were compared with independent quantities that some surprising results emerged. The levelling gave a height for the tidal observatory bench-mark at Dunbar almost 0.6 foot higher above the Newlyn datum than it had been in 1918 and, when the results were related to a level representing the trend of mean sea-level at Newlyn and Dunbar, they indicated that sea-level was now almost 1.3 feet higher at the latter place than the former, or, in other words, that the northward rise in sea-level between the two ports had increased by about 0.5 foot since 1918. Both these results were difficult to accept. Some upward movement of the land in northern Europe, probably due to delayed recovery from downward displacement under its burden of ice during the last glaciation, was known to have taken place, but differential upward movement between Newlyn and Dunbar of as much as 0.6 foot in forty years would be most unlikely. As regards sea-level it was known that this was slowly rising around Britain but it was impossible to explain satisfactorily why it should rise 0.5 foot more at Dunbar that at Newlyn. The records of the Newlyn tide gauge showed a mean sea-level rise there, relative to the land, of about 0.2 foot between 1918 and 1950; the Dunbar gauge however indicated a relative rise of only 0.06 foot. If the assumption were made that the absolute rise of sea-level had been uniform round the coast (as seems most likely), this would indicate that the land at Dunbar rose about 0.14 foot during the period. Such a rise would be readily acceptable although, of course, it would not be compatible with the levelling.

Comparison between the levelling and the tide gauge records at Felixstowe on the East coast showed a rise of sea-level relative to the land similar to that at Newlyn, and negligible change in the land level. It seemed therefore that the levelling must be burdened with a systematic error which affected the north to south direction but not the east to west and experiments at Chessington provided the most likely explanation. It was found, by making repeated readings of the levelling staff in sunlight and in shade, that illumination by direct sunlight had the effect of lowering the reading by between one and two ten-thousandths of a foot. When levelling in a north to south direction, the northerly (or south-facing) stave in each levelling space would tend to be directly illuminated by the sun more often than the southerly (or north-facing) stave. This would have the effect of introducing an apparent rise as the levelling was extended northwards which could well amount to something like half a foot between Newlyn and Dunbar. The trouble was evidently that the graduations on the Invar levelling staff were engraved; no such effect was observed with a stave having a completely smooth surface with painted graduations. Error due to this cause might have been eliminated if there had been more preliminary research but this is not certain. Many countries used staves with engraved graduations but none had ever reported a similar experience.

The outcome of the Third Geodetic Levelling of England and Wales was something of a disappointment. The strong possibility that it was appreciably affected by systematic error made it impossible to base firm conclusions about land and sea levels upon it or to confirm or controvert the northward rise of sea-level which the Second Geodetic Levelling had appeared to establish. The same staves had been used for both levellings and if they had contributed to systematic error in one it was most likely that they had done so in the other. However, one beneficial result was the re-stimulation of interest in precise levelling and the associated subject of mean sea-level. Since 1918 this interest had waned with a number of unfortunate consequences. Of the three tidal observatories set up by the Ordnance Survey between 1913 and 1917 only that at Newlyn had continued in satisfactory operation without a break. The Ordnance Survey had handed over its responsibility for the Felixstowe Observatory to the Harbour Board in 1930, but the Harbour Master continued to send the tidal records to the Ordnance Survey until January 1951, when this arrangement was brought to an end by the Department. Dunbar remained in operation until 1950 but by then silting-up of the harbour was resulting in failure to register the lowest tides and the station was abandoned. There were many other tide gauges operating in Britain but they had never been connected to a geodetic levelling network. In fact the Ordnance Survey had, over the years, virtually ceased to concern itself with the behaviour of sea-level, a regrettable state of affairs which was evidenced by the omission of the Department from the long list of authorities consulted by the Departmental Committee under Lord Waverley's chairmanship, which enquired into the disastrous East Coast floods of 1953.[15] Now, however, there was a marked change: a joint investigation by the Ordnance Survey and the Hydrographic Department of the Admiralty revealed the existence of several well-maintained tide gauges, operated by various authorities, which could with advantage be connected to the geodetic levelling network. To these were shortly added a number of additional gauges recommended by the Waverley Committee, which had recognized the important part which relatively small changes in mean sea-level could play in determining the liability to disastrous flood. Together these gauges covered the whole coastline with the exception of the north-west coast of Scotland. The Advisory Committee for Oceanographical and Meteorological Research, set up as a result of the Waverley Report, accepted the suggestion of the Ordnance Survey that a tide gauge be sited at Ullapool to fill this gap.

All these tide gauges were in due course rigorously connected to the geodetic levelling; for this some additional circuits were required, the largest extension being along the east coast of England north of the Wash. Arrangements were also made to check the heights of the tide gauges twice a year as a precaution against local movement. During the visits made by Ordnance Survey staff for this purpose the opportunity was taken to check that the gauges were being operated correctly and that the necessary meteorological and other observations were being made. In this way thirty-five reliable tide gauges were eventually linked to the levelling network in Great Britain, ensuring that in the future there would be an adequate supply of data about mean sea-level and a much better prospect of drawing reliable conclusions from the analysis of it.

When the field-work of the Scottish levelling was completed it was computed and separately adjusted as an extension to the English network. This work revealed some rather large differences with the earlier levelling, amounting to almost a foot in places but, since there had been no previous rigorous connection to any tide gauge, there was no further problem of reconciling the results of levelling and mean sea-level observations. Nevertheless connection with the Aberdeen tide gauge seemed to show that the remarkable upward slope of sea-level towards the north was maintained.

In addition to the problem of interpreting the results of the Third Geodetic Levelling, there arose a very practical problem of how, if at all, to apply these results to the Ordnance Survey's published bench-mark heights. Because the reality of the changes was by no means established it was clearly inadvisable to adopt the new height values *in toto*; this would have introduced changes of about half a foot in places in England, and even more in Scotland, and would certainly have created difficulties for engineers, especially during the transition period. On the other hand, the more recent levelling was certainly more consistent with the present heights of bench-marks relative to each other locally. A compromise was therefore adopted: in England and Wales the old heights of the fundamental bench-marks were maintained and the new levelling was adjusted to these for the purpose of controlling lower order levelling. In this way large changes were avoided but local changes which were more likely to have reality were taken into account. In Scotland, the results of the relatively recent Second Geodetic Levelling were accepted as they stood. Thus, for the levelling as for the triangulation, the concept of separate systems for practical and scientific purposes was introduced.

LOWER ORDER LEVELLING

Upon the completion of the Second Geodetic Levelling, it had been decided, quite rightly, that the lower order levelling should be reobserved and recalculated on the basis of the new network which was more accurate and more consistent than the Initial Levelling and related to a more realistic view of mean sea-level than the old Liverpool datum. But this lower order relevelling was not, at first, done in a very satisfactory manner. Some secondary levelling was carried out as supplementary control for the tertiary levelling from which the bulk of the bench-marks were heighted; but there was not much system about this nor any consistent method of adjustment. Very often new lines of tertiary levelling were simply 'strung in' by adjustment of the terminals to other tertiary levelling. The result was to produce inconsistency between bench-mark heights on adjacent sheets of large-scale mapping and sometimes between adjacent areas in the same sheet. When the decision was taken in 1951 to carry out a third geodetic levelling, about half of the tertiary levelling had been reobserved and transferred to the Newlyn Datum but from then onwards the lower order levelling was done consistently, each area enclosed by a primary circuit of the Third Geodetic Levelling being broken down by secondary double levelling into five to ten tertiary blocks. Within the latter, bench-marks at a minimum density of four per mile in the country and eight per mile in towns were provided by tertiary single levelling along most of the roads. The secondary lines were adjusted by least squares to the geodetic circuit bounding each block, and the tertiary levelling was adjusted to the secondary by a simpler, but nevertheless rigorous, system using weighted mean heights of junction points. In this way local consistency was ensured. The Second Geodetic FBM heights were preserved in the practical readjustment of the Third Geodetic Levelling and therefore it was a relatively straightforward matter to continue with the new lower order procedure when the new and slightly altered heights along geodetic lines became available in 1956.

The transference of all tertiary levelling to the Newlyn Datum was completed in June 1956.[16] By March of the same year a programme of cyclic relevelling had been initiated under which all tertiary blocks were to be completely relevelled after the following approximate periods:

Normal areas	20 years
Mountain and moorland areas	40 years
Fenland subsidence areas	10 years
Mining subsidence areas	5 years

Provision was also made for 'out of cycle' relevelling to deal with new development.

An important departure of the 1950s was the decision in 1954 to publish levelling information primarily in the form of typed lists of bench-marks covering 1 km squares rather than as heights shown on large-scale plans. In this way the latest height information became much more readily available:

the new system was also much better suited to electro-mechanical and electronic computing, the first regular use of which in the Ordnance Survey in 1954 was for levelling and traverse computations. The new method was easily programmed to print out directly bench-mark lists in the form desired which could be reproduced on demand by a dyeline process.

Notes

1 Dr Hans G. Jerie of I. T. C. Delft. See *Photogrammetria* 1957–8, XIV, p. 161.
2 M. Hotine, 'Base Measurement', *Empire Survey Review* 1939, IV, no. 34.
3 M. H. Cobb, *The Measurement of the Ridge Way and Caithness Bases 1951–52*, Ordnance Survey Professional Papers New Series, no. 18. (HMSO 1953).
4 I. C. C. Mackensie, *The Geodimeter Measurement of the Ridge Way and Caithness Bases 1953*, OS Professional Papers New Series, no. 19 (HMSO 1954).
5 R. C. A. Edge, 'New Determination of the Velocity of Light', *Nature* 1956, 177, no. 4509.
6 T. L. Wadley, 'The Tellurometer System of Distance Measurement', *Empire Survey Review* 1956, XIV, nos. 105, 106.
7 J. Kelsey and R. C. A. Edge, 'Trials of the Tellurometer carried out jointly by the Ordnance Survey of Great Britain and the South African Council for Scientific and Industrial Research'. Paper presented at 11th General Assembly of IAG, Toronto 1957.
8 J. Kelsey, 'The Use of the Tellurometer by the Ordnance Survey in 1957 and 1958'. Commonwealth Survey Officers Conference Paper, no. 26, Cambridge 1959.
9 A. N. Black, 'Laplace points in moderate and high latitudes', *Empire Survey Review* 1951, XI, no. 82.
10 OSR 1955–6, p. 6.
11 'Third Geodetic Levelling', Unpublished draft of Professional Paper. Ordnance Survey, Southampton.
12 A. J. Wolff and H. L. P. Jolly, *The Second Geodetic Levelling of England and Wales 1912–1921* (Ordnance Survey 1921).
13 *Ibid.*
14 'Note on the Evaluation of the Precision of Levelling', *Bulletin Géodésique* no. 18, Dec. 1950.
15 *Report of the Departmental Committee on Coastal Flooding 1953*: PP 1953–4, Cmnd. 9165, XIII.
16 OSR 1956–7, p. 7.

32
The Restoration of the Survey – The Reappraisal 1961–1968

Revision

The staff reductions of the 1950s and the expedients that were adopted to counteract them soon began to have damaging consequences, and by the beginning of the following decade the time was ripe for a critical re-examination of many Ordnance Survey practices and attitudes. The first matter that demanded attention was the state of the continuous revision system which, by 1960, was showing signs of considerable strain. The statistical returns from the revision sections, although inadequate in many ways, confirmed that the amount of unsurveyed development was rapidly getting larger and that the surveyors were being overwhelmed as the backlog accumulated and as the area under continuous revision increased with the publication of new 1:1250 plans.

The first necessity was to find a reliable way for estimating the changing man-power needs of continuous revision, which were entirely outside the Department's control, being dictated by the amount of construction taking place on the ground. Such estimates could be made by keeping a total, in some suitable unit, of the amount of change that was occurring and comparing it periodically with the total surveyed; if all was well, the amount of unsurveyed change would remain constant, indicating that the revisers were keeping pace. Following this principle, new statistical returns were devised and, as the extent of the undermanning was revealed, surveyors were transferred to continuous revision from the resurvey and overhaul programmes. A substantial reduction in the flow of new surveys to the drawing office naturally followed this withdrawal of man-power; the number of overhauled 1:2500 plans sent forward dropped from 5096 in the financial year 1961–2 to 3200 two years later. The accumulation of undrawn plans awaiting attention in the drawing office, which had grown very large in the last few years, stopped increasing, to everyone's relief, but the sensitive balance between survey and drawing had been disturbed, and it only needed one more adverse circumstance in the field to upset it completely; the severe winter of 1962–3 provided just such an additional check. In a normal year over the greater part of the country the winter season had very little effect on the survey and any drop in field output was mostly accounted for by the shorter length of day. But in the winter of 1962–3 the surveyors had to contend not only with prolonged difficulty of movement but also with the cover of hard snow which concealed kerbs and similar features as well as large numbers of control points in the shape of pipenails driven into roadways and pavements. In the drawing office relief was suddenly replaced by alarm as the stockpile of work rapidly diminished, and by the early autumn of 1963 it was clear that measures such as the switching of emphasis in recruiting from draughtsmen to surveyors were quite inadequate and that something drastic had to be done.

In Field Headquarters the programme of overhaul and resurvey was re-assessed, taking into account the newly-determined needs of continuous revision which, it now appeared, would absorb the whole of the man-power provisionally allotted to Field Division before the overhaul programme could be completed; even assuming a further redistribution of man-power between drawing and surveying, the restoration of the survey was likely to be delayed until the last decade of the century. The Ordnance Survey would have to have a substantial increase in its technical staff if it was to complete the tasks laid upon it by the Davidson Committee within a reasonable time. These facts and arguments were put to the Ministry and to the Treasury where they were critically received,[1] particularly by the Treasury where officials were for a time unconvinced of the need to revise plans that had only just been published. They suggested that continuous revision might be halted for ten years while the remainder of the Overhaul was polished off, but the Ordnance Survey rejected this misguided proposition. The Director General, Major-General A. H. Dowson, who had succeeded Carey in 1961, made it known that the inviolability of continuous revision was a matter on which he could not compromise; this degree of firmness, coupled with the strength of the arguments, convinced the authorities in Whitehall. In February 1966, the Minister for Land and Natural Resources (into whose hands the control of the Department had passed in April 1965) announced in Parliament the Government's approval of a twenty per cent increase in Ordnance Survey staff, spread over the next ten years, to enable the restoration of the survey to be completed by 1980.[2]* The qualification was added that the extra cost would have to be met by increased revenue. However, a primary tenet of Ordnance Survey policy – that continuous revision had the first call on man-power – had been affirmed and recognized.

In the 1950s the rules governing the revision of derived maps had done little to ensure that they were kept up to date. One such rule had prohibited the incorporation of revision material into a derived map until after it had been published at the basic scale. Brown was unconvinced about this, and had looked forward to a free flow of information into all scales of maps. In 1961, and again in 1964, successive Directors of Map Publication pointed out the absurdity of the rule. Dowson compromised in 1961 by agreeing that it should not be applied to roads on the Regular derived six-inch, but the change was not put fully into effect until 1966 when a new statement of policy abolished the old rule.[3]

The Department's response to public needs was at last changing. Hitherto the convenience and the economy of its internal operations had dominated its attitude to short-term demands, but now the recognition of the value of maps in a changing world, not as an intermittent historical record but as a means of providing information that had to be in time if it was to be of any use, carried with it the obligation to do everything possible to provide what was wanted when it was wanted. The realization that up-to-date information must flow without impediment into the hands of users was perhaps the most important aspect of the reappraisal.

The Estimates Committee 1962–3

The Estimates Committee of the House of Commons examined the affairs of the Ordnance Survey during the winter of 1962–3, and its criticisms and recommendations provided a strong stimulus to self-examination. Dowson, who had been Director General for about a year when he faced the Committee, was a man of great personal integrity who was disinclined to political manoeuvring; his answers to the Committee's questions were impressively frank and unbiased. He did not try to conceal the Ordnance Survey's scientific shortcomings or its slowness in adopting air survey methods. He also acknowledged 'that in time a suitable arrangement could be made by which the organization could become [wholly] civilian without detriment to its efficiency',[4] although he saw nothing seriously wrong with the existing system. Nevertheless, he appreciated 'that there may be a feeling in some minds that it is an incongruity that a large civilian organization should be managed by soldiers'. The Institution of Professional Civil Servants, in its evidence to the Committee, also displayed notable open-mindedness. The General Secretary Designate of the Institution, Mr W. McCall, declared: '. . . one should give full credit to the military organization in the matter of survey. Their survey training course is superlative . . .' At a later point in the proceedings he added '. . . we are more than anxious not to make adverse reflections on the military officers for whom we have a high regard'.[5] These fair and balanced judgments must have impressed the Committee very favourably because while recommending several changes to the system it warmly commended the 'dedication, devotion and enthusiasm of those members of the staff whom they [had] met'.[6]

The Committee's ten main recommendations dealt with the need to improve liaison with local authorities, the question of staffing at the professional level and various ways of securing economy and increasing the Department's revenue. It also had something to say about ministerial responsibility for the Ordnance Survey.

STAFFING

Probably the most important recommendations were those which concerned the professional staff.[7] They repeated several of the conclusions of the Brown Committee – that all posts should be open to

---

* 1980 was the estimated date for finishing the Overhaul if the extra man-power was granted, allowing for normal expansion and rundown. It had no other significance, but it came to be regarded as a target set by Parliament.

suitably qualified members of the technical staff and that exceptionally promising young members should be selected for professional training – but also asked that defence needs should be reviewed with the object of establishing the 'minimum requirement of military officers in the Ordnance Survey'. The use of the word 'minimum' suggested that the Committee agreed that the existing situation was 'incongruous' and had accepted the Director General's belief that it would be possible to civilianize the professional staff 'without detriment to efficiency'.

The Ministry of Defence immediately announced a reduction in the number of military posts from twenty-seven to eighteen and, as recommended by the Estimates Committee, an Inter-Departmental Committee on Survey Staffs was set up under the chairmanship of Mr S. P. Osmond, a Treasury official, to carry out a general review of Ordnance Survey professional posts. This Committee did not report until August 1965 when it proposed, among other things, a further reduction to eleven in the number of military posts. Its recommendations were accepted by the Ministers concerned and another body, the Inter-Departmental Working Party on Survey Staffs, chaired by the Director General, now Major-General R. C. A. Edge, was formed to decide in detail how the decisions should be implemented. The Working Party began its deliberations in June 1966 and reported in the following January. It proposed that the rundown of military posts from twenty-seven to eleven should be spread over ten years and that the civilian professionals should form a joint staff to be shared by the Ordnance Survey, the Directorate of Military Survey and the Directorate of Overseas Surveys. Civilian professional vacancies were 'in the main to be filled by graduate entrants'. The Working Party made a clear distinction between professional surveying staff and promoted technicians and forecast a reduction in the number of management posts open to the technical staff; this apparently ran contrary to Recommendation 3 of the Estimates Committee, which said that all posts should be open to them. In the event, the number of non-professional management posts filled from the technical staff actually rose from fifteen in 1962 to twenty-two in 1974, partly as a result of increases in establishment.

The integration of the civilian professional staff was aimed at providing a reasonable career structure as well as a varied experience for the professional officers. But integration was not a straightforward matter. The Directorate of Overseas Surveys was not craft-based; in it much of the practical surveying, which the Ordnance Survey left in the hands of its technical staff, was carried out by the junior professional officers. This meant that nearly all the basic grade civilian professionals would be employed in the Directorate of Overseas Surveys and that the young professional, although benefiting from experience in an undeveloped country, would have little or no knowledge of a large structured Civil Service Department until after he was promoted.

The Working Party proposals were agreed to by the Treasury in April 1967. The Joint Survey Service – the title given to the integrated civilian professional staff – came into being, and a Joint Management Committee, with the Director General and the Director of Overseas Surveys alternating as chairman, was set up to oversee the arrangements for recruitment, training and career planning, posting and promotion. The first appointments of Joint Survey Service officers to posts in the Ordnance Survey were made early in 1969.

In 1950 the Brown Committee had recommended that the 'minimum academic qualification' for professional surveying staff 'might be taken as the equivalent of that set for entry to the Royal Institution of Chartered Surveyors' and following this, many Royal Engineer Officers joined the Institution's newly formed Land Surveying Division. However, the link with the RICS was nearly severed when the heads of the three survey departments withdrew from membership because of differences with the Institution on matters of policy. In 1967 this link was restored and strengthened when associate membership of the RICS in the Land Surveying Division became the qualifying standard for entry to the Joint Survey Service. Similarly, full membership of the Institute of Printing became the standard for professional Map Reproduction officers, but there was one notable difference. The Working Party proposed that appointments into this professional class should be made from the technical staff, as it believed that the Ordnance Survey could not attract experienced professional men from the printing trade.

The news that the replacement of the military officers by civilian professionals would probably lead to a reduction in the number of senior posts open to the members of the technical staff came as a considerable shock to most of them, and when it became known in 1968 that promotion boards for filling vacancies at Assistant Division Officer and Division Officer level were having some difficulty in finding suitable candidates from among the technical staff, this was seen as a device for releasing more posts for the new professionals. In order to clear up this point beyond doubt an IPCS nominee, a professional officer from outside the Department, was invited to become a member of the appropriate Ordnance Survey boards in 1969. His report to the IPCS confirmed the conclusion already reached by the promotion boards: the technical staff were too narrow in their knowledge and their outlook, although this was considered to be a defect in the system rather than in the candidates themselves.

The Ordnance Survey was faced with two conflicting circumstances. The new professional structure with its emphasis on early service with the Directorate of Overseas Surveys made it even more important to fill some of the lower management posts with promoted technical staff, but it seemed impossible to fill these posts adequately. By 1968 the most widely experienced among the technical staff – those who had served in responsible positions during the war – had already been promoted and the Ordnance Survey was having to draw on its immediate post-war recruits, whose educational qualifications were generally rather low and whose training in the Ordnance Survey had been particularly narrow. Moreover, the demands on management, especially in a technological sense, had greatly widened. So it had to be recognized that craft training superimposed on education barely to 'O' level standard was not an adequate preparation for management and that a higher level of education and training would have to be introduced for selected members of the technical staff, if effective non-professional managers were to be forthcoming in the future.

As an aftermath of the 1957 pay awards a Treasury Working Party was set up in 1961 to review the cartographic class and to carry out a post-by-post inspection. This rearguard action by the Treasury resulted in 1962 in the creation of an Assistant Cartographic grade for the more routine type of work, particularly in large-scales drawing. The new class had a two 'O' level entry and its members were supposed to be unable to undertake the more skilled drawing operations. Craft skill, however, was not related to the possession of one extra 'O' level, and the division of the work between the assistants and the cartographic draughtsmen produced some absurdities. The Institution of Professional Civil Servants opposed the introduction of the new grade, not because it objected to assistants but because it wanted them to be an integral part of the cartographic class, not separated from it by a different level of entry and an independent pay structure.

The relations between the Staff and Official Sides in the Ordnance Survey were not often coloured by conflict or differences of opinion. The usual pattern was one of a good working relationship which dealt successfully and unobtrusively with day-to-day problems and reached acceptable joint solutions. The Staff Side was always ready to recognize management problems connected with the technical work of the Survey, and to assist in devising solutions and in recommending them. Many suggestions initiated by the Staff Side were readily complied with; one major and most successful joint exercise in 1964 was the negotiation of two new promotion agreements, one for the technical classes and one for the Executive-Clerical group, which was described as 'a model of Whitley co-operation'.

Nearly all training ventures, such as the integration of staff training in the 1960s, received full Staff Side support. There were already field and drawing schools, both in Southampton, but these were the separate responsibilities of Field and Large Scales Divisions; no other formal organization existed. The increasing emphasis being given in the Civil Service to training, together with the forthcoming move to the new building under construction in Southampton, were propitious circumstances for the formation of a unified training division, which came into existence at the end of 1965 in time for it to take part in planning its accommodation in the new Headquarters. The division was responsible for conducting or arranging all internal and external training, and one of its important tasks in the early years of its existence was to foster the development of advanced technician courses in surveying, cartography and printing. It had the additional function of providing information services, including contacts with the broadcasting authorities and the Press.

CONSULTATION

Another of the main recommendations of the Estimates Committee stressed the importance of good liaison with local authorities.[8] The Ordnance Survey had always been aware of the need to maintain close contact with a group which was perhaps its principal customer, but the practice was full of difficulty. Local authorities were to a certain extent autonomous, their organizations varied considerably, and it was almost impossible to penetrate the whole of an authority from a single point of contact. Engineers, surveyors, planners, architects, all used maps but they were not always alive to each other's needs or to what was being done to meet them. Regular annual conferences with representatives of local authority associations had already begun in January 1962, over a year before the Estimates Committee reported, and at about the same time regional contacts had been intensified. In 1961, in accordance with the changing outlook on local and immediate needs, region officers were encouraged to make minor adjustments to their programmes if this would help local authorities, and a round of regional conferences was arranged. At the first of these, held at Birmingham in 1963, a suggestion from one of the delegates that each authority should nominate an Ordnance Survey liaison officer from among its staff, to act as a two-way collecting and distributing point for information, received general support. In the next year or two liaison officers were nominated in all the large and many of the smaller authorities and thereafter the system was applied with some success, but as there were great variations in the status of the individuals nominated, there were wide differences in their usefulness.

In October 1962 the Ordnance Survey started another series of annual meetings, this time with an all-embracing title – the Map Users' Conference. Any society, institution or association which could claim to represent a class of map-user not already provided for was entitled to send a representative. So ramblers, motorists, horsemen, farmers, country gentlemen, university geographers, publishers, teachers, members of learned societies, chartered surveyors, architects and planners all sat down together. Not surprisingly these meetings sometimes became very lively as conflicting outlooks were revealed, and it was rare for the conference to provide any advice that could be regarded as a consensus of opinion. The range of interests was too wide and the conference was later divided into two sections.

The lack of effective liaison was nowhere felt more strongly than in the Advisory Committee, the oldest of the consultative bodies. Of the three departments that had been responsible for the Ordnance Survey since the war, the Ministry of Land and Natural Resources and the Ministry of Housing and Local Government* showed greater interest and took a larger part in the Advisory Committee meetings than had the Ministry of Agriculture. In May 1967 the latter was actually sponsoring a number of mapping projects using Ordnance Survey material as a base without any previous consultation, without acknowledgement and without regard to copyright rules.[9] There was an exchange of letters between the Director General and the Permanent Secretary, Ministry of Agriculture, and an agreement was reached to regulate future activities of this sort. The incident raised a wider issue – the effectiveness or otherwise of the consultative arrangement with government departments. Doubts were felt in the Ordnance Survey about the ability of some of the Advisory Committee members to provide the kind of liaison intended; when asked to produce a note 'on the extent to which they were in a position to represent their departments and associated organisations', most members replied that they only came to listen. It had to be concluded that the annual meetings were not a very effective way of providing forward-looking and authoritative guidance to the map-makers.

Although the Estimates Committee's recommendations on consultation with local authorities were anticipated by the Ordnance Survey by over a year, the adequacy of the measures taken left something to be desired. The Committee's belief that 'more could be achieved'[10] was not accompanied by any practical advice on how this should be done; and the annual meetings at Headquarters with the associations continued to be too remote and the contacts at regional level continued to lack authority.

MARKETING AND REVENUE

Evidence put before the Estimates Committee disclosed that in the previous ten years receipts from the sale of maps had risen by 150 per cent, but 'map issues', which included issues to government departments, increased by only 64 per cent, the higher revenue being largely attributable to increased prices which the Director General put at sixty per cent. The Department was unable to tell the Committee how many maps had actually been sold, a state of affairs which the Report described as 'most unsatisfactory'.[11] These were certainly the harshest words in the Report and to some extent they applied to the whole field of sales accounting, publicity, marketing and copyright; they marked the beginning of the end of the Survey's hitherto rather complacent attitude towards raising its revenue.

Since 1866 the prices charged for Ordnance Survey maps had been based on the cost of printing and did not include the cost of surveying and drawing, a principle that was endorsed by the Treasury in 1931 and again in 1950. The cost-accounting system brought into use in the 1930s had as its object the determination of the costs of the various stages of printing, folding and mounting the maps of each series. Additions were made to cover storage, distribution, overheads including administrative office costs, traders' discounts, and a margin of profit, in order to arrive at the selling prices. This arrangement certainly did not encourage an enterprising policy on prices.

The Estimates Committee recommended that Ordnance Survey services should be provided as

---

* The Ordnance Survey passed into the care of the Ministry of Housing and Local Government in February 1967 when the Ministry of Land and Natural Resources was abolished.

economically as possible, which was taken to mean that the gap between expenditure and revenue should be minimized. The Committee proposed that a sales manager with recent experience, preferably in a commercial undertaking, should be appointed without delay and that expenditure on sales promotion should be increased; ways were also to be sought for preventing future infringement of copyright. In the final paragraph of the Report, the Committee remarked that 'dedication to the ideal of public service tends to result in a stifling of the commercial spirit'.

A civilian sales manager (Miss B. D. Drewitt, a Civil Servant) was appointed, but not until May 1966. In the meantime a modest effort had been made in introducing measures to increase revenue. A new scale of royalty charges, operating from 1 January 1965, and new efforts in sales publicity, gave evidence of a developing commercial consciousness. Early in 1966, following the Government's decision that the expansion of the Ordnance Survey would have to be paid for out of increased revenue, substantial increases in the prices of large-scale maps and a 25 per cent rise in royalty charges for the reproduction of large-scale material were announced. Mainly as a result of the higher prices, issues of large-scale maps fell from 988 000 in 1964–5 to 623 000 in 1970–1, but thereafter there was some recovery;[12] however, income from map sales continued to rise throughout. Royalty revenue rose from £164 000 in 1964–5 to £610 000 in 1968–9, partly due to the higher charges and partly because of a comprehensive review of the terms of compounded-fee licences* which was begun in 1966.

The events leading to the price increases of 1966 were the means of establishing a new criterion for pricing Ordnance Survey products: the simple system of covering the cost of printing was replaced by charging as much for a product as the market would bear, which implied transferring as much as possible of the financial burden from the taxpayer to the actual users of the maps. At a time of rising costs and price restraints the increases in revenue failed to improve the ratio of receipts to total expenditure, which remained at about 33 per cent.

There was still much to be done and in 1968 the Ordnance Survey began a review of its marketing system. A Treasury paper on *Arrangements for Marketing Maps*, produced in 1963, had made no definite recommendations for a change although various possibilities were considered. The paper recognized the importance of facilities in London for inspection and immediate purchase of all Ordnance Survey maps of England and Wales – the 'London shop window' – but this was a somewhat costly service because of the space required for the maps, and the staff to advise enquirers; nevertheless the Treasury considered the service essential, particularly to meet the day-to-day needs of government departments. The immediate cause of the review of 1968 was the approach of the date for the renewal of the contract with Edward Stanford Ltd. Since 1943, besides providing the London shop window, the firm had acted as wholesale agents for the distribution of Ordnance Survey maps to the retail trade in England and Wales. The outcome of the marketing review was that Stanford's ceased to be main agents and the Ordnance Survey resumed responsibility for the distribution of maps to retailers in England and Wales, but these new arrangements did not come into force until 1971.

MINISTERIAL RESPONSIBILITY FOR THE ORDNANCE SURVEY

When an Establishment and Finance Officer was first appointed to the Ordnance Survey in 1938, the Treasury commented:

> My Lords note that the Chief Staff Officer who will act as Establishment and Finance Officer will in effect be the representative of the Principal Establishment Officer of the Ministry.[13]

Successive Ordnance Survey Directors of Establishment and Finance, notably Mr F. G. C. Bentley in 1958, achieved a much higher degree of independence than was implied by the Treasury comment, on the basis that Establishment functions, apart from important matters of general policy, were very largely delegated; in such matters, major and minor, the Ordnance Survey dealt directly with the Treasury, Staff Associations etc. 'with [the Ministry's] full knowledge that this was being done'.

It was not easy to put these arrangements precisely into words, but an attempt was sometimes made, as in October 1960:

> The Ordnance Survey is responsible to the Minister who is advised by the Permanent Secretary of any new or out of the ordinary occurrences concerning it. The day-to-day affairs are administered by the Director General who consults the Ministry when any major changes of administrative or technical policy are proposed or when senior civilian vacancies have to be filled . . . The Ordnance Survey has its own parliamentary vote for which the Director General is the accounting officer.

* A compounded-fee licence was a licence to reproduce Ordnance Survey maps issued on payment of an annual fee.

In paragraph 11 of the Report of the Estimates Committee, this degree of independence was endorsed together with the companion doctrine that the Ordnance Survey should not be placed within the responsibility of a Ministry 'which might be tempted to put pressure on the Survey to give priority to work in which they have a special interest'. Thus the Ordnance Survey enjoyed considerable freedom in the exercise of its functions both technical and administrative; but it remained fully subject to the constraints on man-power and other resources applied by the Government through the Treasury and, after it was set up in 1968, the Civil Service Department.

The principles enunciated by the Committee were applied when, in January 1965, the transfer of the Ordnance Survey to the Ministry of Land and Natural Resources was under discussion. The Principal Establishment Officer of the Ministry of Agriculture wrote:

> . . . at the time of the Estimates Committee there was no Ministry of Land and Natural Resources. And the comments of the Committee . . . could not apply to a statement of case from the Ministry of Land and Natural Resources, based on the following points:
> (i) They are responsible for acquiring and holding the Government's corpus of knowledge on land.
> (ii) They are a disinterested Department with no axe to grind and could be held to be more dispassionate than we are.

The Minute went on:

> Against the change one can only advance the pragmatic argument. The present arrangements work well; there seems to be little point in disturbing them; the future and functions of the new Ministry are so uncertain that a change might be followed by a further change in the future.[14]

Commenting on this Minute, the Director General summed up the arguments from the Ordnance Survey's point of view:

> The most important point is that the Survey's resources should be adequate to the real needs of the nation and should be deployed to the best national advantage: therefore the Ordnance Survey should be under the control of the Minister best able to ensure that these desiderata are fully met.[15]

The Ordnance Survey remained under the department broadly responsible for 'holding the Government's corpus of knowledge on land' when ministerial responsibilities were reshuffled in subsequent years, but retained the degree of independence defined by the Estimates Committee in 1963.

Field Survey – a Reappraisal

In spite of Willis's decision in 1957 to use air survey whenever it was advantageous to do so, the extension of its application seemed to have lost impetus in the first few years of the next decade. In 1962–3, out of 1977 completed 1:1250 plans, only 559 were based on air survey. When a review of the future 1:1250 programme was carried out in 1962, some 1800 new plans were added, all of which were at first planned for tacheometric survey, the argument being that the plotting machines were already fully committed on resurvey and contouring, but the Director of Field Surveys was able to demonstrate that there were financial advantages to be gained by purchasing more plotting machines. Four more first-order machines were therefore obtained and much of the 1:1250 work remaining to be done was transferred to the air survey programme with the result that the proportion based on air survey rose to about one-half of the total. This could have been increased further, but the main 1:1250 programme had only about five years to run and there were financial objections to a still larger investment.

The Ordnance Survey's arrangements for obtaining air photographs now underwent another change. Experience had shown that the only way of being reasonably sure of getting the air photographs needed in any year was to have aircraft standing by, ready to take advantage of short spells of clear weather. Because of its primary task, the Ministry of Transport and Civil Aviation Flying Unit was unable to meet this requirement although for a time one aircraft was allocated on stand-by. As the possibility of forming an Ordnance Survey flight was virtually non-existent, the only course that remained open was to contract with civil air survey firms. A start was made in 1963 when one aircraft was hired to supplement the resources of the MTCA Unit; from 1966 all the flying was by civil contract.

The application of air survey to the Overhaul, which started with the Air Assisted Overhaul experiment in 1957, was at first a headquarters operation. Its advantages were soon apparent, particularly in areas where overhaul by ground survey was difficult, and the number of air-revised plans sent to the field for completion rose from 300 in 1961–2 to 1500 in 1962–3.[16] In 1961 the Overhaul was begun in rural areas of Aberdeenshire; in this part of Scotland winter work was frequently interrupted by snow, and the Region Officer for Scotland, Major A. C. Marles, suggested that field surveyors might carry out graphical air revision on their own plans during the winter months. A field trial, carried out in 1962, was immediately successful, so much so that the wider possibilities of this idea were at once recognized and surveyors were trained to use the photographs throughout the year, not merely as a winter expedient. In this way the 'air/ground' method was born and by 1966 all the remaining Overhaul plans, 120 000 in number, were scheduled either for air/ground or for air revision at Headquarters. The rapidity with which these techniques were introduced was a convincing indication that 'professional conservatism', which the Estimates Committee had seen in some Ordnance Survey attitudes, was a thing of the past. The same conclusion could be drawn from the speedy adoption of electromagnetic distance-measuring instruments of various kinds and from the willingness to abandon time-honoured procedures when these had outlived their usefulness.

The spirit of innovation soon extended to the six-inch resurvey of the mountain and moorland areas of Scotland, which had been started in the middle 1950s. Initially the whole survey was carried out by Air Survey Branch but in 1959 the completion of the maps on the ground was transferred to the Field Division. When the survey began in the north-west Highlands, the ground completion was very slow because of sparse communications and the necessity for covering long distances on foot to make minor additions to the map. A few years previously helicopters had been used successfully during the secondary triangulation of Scotland (1957–61) for transporting pillar-building materials and observation parties to the tops of mountains, and in 1964 the idea was adapted to the detail survey. The helicopters did not reduce the cost of the survey but enabled a great deal more to be accomplished in each season, a considerable gain in an area where it was not possible to work in winter and where there were often other restrictions such as those imposed by grouse shooting and deer stalking.

The Ordnance Survey was able to make use of its new versatility after the colliery tip disaster at Aberfan on 21 October 1966. Air photographs of the area were taken on 25 October and the necessary extra control points were surveyed by Geodimeter in the next few days. The plotting and contouring by stereoplotting machine of an area 2km × 1km at 1:1250 scale with contours at five-foot vertical intervals were completed by 11 November and on the same day advance copies of the map were in the hands of the Tribunal conducting the Inquiry.

The survey of the coalfields was duly completed in 1962 and field effort was redeployed into the remaining 1:1250 towns and the rural areas. In the latter, attention was first concentrated on the minor towns, and the 'progress' maps soon broke out into a rash of small patches of completed Overhaul, which did not suit the derived mapping sections in the drawing office. Progress in these towns was at first slow, which helped to cause the balance-of-work crisis in 1963, but once the air/ground method got under way, field output began to increase rapidly. The surveyors' rate of progress improved generally by 30 per cent, often by 50 per cent, and in some places by as much as 100 per cent, which was fortunate because the progressive man-power increases promised by the Government in 1966 did not survive the financial year 1968–9; the strength of the non-industrial staff rose from 4008 on 31 March 1966 to 4252 on 31 March 1968, and afterwards it remained at about this level.

In 1967 the rising field output, combined with difficulty in recruiting draughtsmen, was responsible for another crisis of balance; the number of surveyed plans awaiting drawing once again increased and the delay between survey and publication became unacceptably large. The drawing office began to work overtime and many field surveyors were transferred from Overhaul to continuous revision. Towards the end of 1968 an unprecedented step was taken; surveyors were compulsorily transferred to Southampton for periods of six months where they were given short scribing courses and put to work on the 1:2500.[17] Finally in 1969 an agreement was made with the Ordnance Survey of Northern Ireland for a drawing unit about fifty strong to be recruited and trained in Belfast for scribing the 1:2500 plans.[18] These measures, taken together, proved adequate and the emergency arrangements at Southampton were soon discontinued, although the Northern Ireland drawing section was retained.

A critical eye was directed at the Ordnance Survey's cyclic tertiary relevelling programme, introduced in 1956, which included a relevelling of subsidence areas at five-yearly intervals. But this frequency of relevelling proved to be wasteful because subsidence could take place at any time and the shortness of the cycle was no guarantee of accuracy. Instead, it was proposed to fix bench-marks in positions that were known to be stable so that reliable subsidiary levelling by local authorities and others could be carried out from these bench-marks whenever required. After consultation, the five-year cycle was abandoned in 1966 and in the same year a reduction in the density of bench-marks in urban areas was announced after it had been agreed that a density of sixteen per square kilometre would meet users' requirements.[19]

From 1964 onwards officers of the Ordnance Survey began to play a much larger part in the deliberations of international scientific organizations such as the International Association of Geodesy and the International Cartographic Association, marking an improvement in the scientific reputation of the Department which, since the war, had stood at a rather low level. Much of the credit for the revival must go to Brigadier R. C. A. Edge who was Director of Field Surveys from 1962–5 before becoming Director General.

PLACE-NAMES

Between the world wars the Place-Names Committee of the Royal Scottish Geographical Society had again lapsed,[20] but in 1938 it was revived with the primary object of carrying out research similar to the work of the English Place-Names Society;* however, one of its members, Mr George Dot, continued to advise the Ordnance Survey until his death in 1959. The functions of this Committee relating to the Ordnance Survey were then transferred to the School of Scottish Studies, University of Edinburgh. But before this change occurred, the Ordnance Survey was having trouble with place-names everywhere, in a way that was completely new.

During the straitened 1950s, the principles underlying the practice of place-names collection had been relaxed. The gathering of evidence for a new or changed place-name was often time-consuming, and the new generation of surveyors found it particularly difficult and frustrating. It was felt that, if an absolute authority could be identified for each category of place-name, the work of the surveyor would be greatly simplified; he would merely have to consult the 'competent authority' and could at once accept the version he was given. The competent-authority principle was thereupon incorporated into the surveyor's instructions mainly as a means of saving time and effort. Among the authorities to be referred to were the Board of Celtic Studies and the Royal Scottish Geographical Society for Welsh and Gaelic names respectively: the opinion of these bodies was to be taken as mandatory for all natural features not falling within direct ownership. The version given by the owner of a property was mandatory for that property and local authorities were the competent bodies for the names of towns and villages. Unfortunately the competent-authority doctrine was ill-founded and the Ordnance Survey soon began to be harassed by its own rules. The name Plynlimon, long in common use, was replaced by Pumlumon; Njugals Water was adopted for a lake in the Shetlands *against* the advice of the School of Scottish Studies because the owner had to be accepted as the authority. Forest names given by the Forestry Commission displaced the ancient names of woods.

These unforeseen absurdities led in 1964 to the re-establishment of customary usage over all other forms of authority, restoring to the surveyors the task of having to find out what customary usage was. As a basis for revised instructions for the surveyors, a new statement of policy was written by the Director of Field Surveys:

> In Great Britain, except for certain administrative names, there exists no national body or group of bodies responsible for laying down for official use the names and spellings of places appearing on official maps or in other official documents. The Ordnance Survey has always therefore itself assumed the responsibility of deciding what place-names are to appear on the maps and how they are to be spelt. In making its decision the Department is guided primarily by local usage and custom and makes such enquiries and consults such authorities as appear appropriate in order to establish with as much authority as possible the most suitable name, form and spelling for all places shown. Evidence tendered as a result of such enquiries is never in principle mandatory although it is frequently accepted. Any conflict is resolved by the Ordnance Survey itself.

Later in the same document the objective was summarized:

> . . . to find out and adopt the recognised names of all surveyed features . . . a recognised name is defined as that form of name and spelling which at the date of survey is most generally useful and acceptable in the locality concerned.[21]

LAND REGISTRATION

In the half century before the Second World War the Ordnance Survey's relations with the Land Registry had not been very harmonious, but after the war continuous revision, by providing up-to-date

---

* The English Place-Names Society was founded in 1923 to carry out a study of the etymology of English place-names.

maps, seemed to have removed the chief cause of friction. When in 1964 the Land Registry announced an expansion of compulsory registration of title aimed to cover all the built-up areas of the country by 1974,[22] their programme conformed well with the planned progress of the 1:1250 survey and the corresponding extension of continuous revision; but in other ways the situation was not so satisfactory.

Land Registry map sections were made by tracing from the 1:1250 plans in a special drawing and printing section controlled by Field Division, located in its South-East Region Office in London. The preparation and maintenance of these were slow and laborious and involved the transmission of revision material, including field documents, between the other regions and the London office. As the Land Registry expansion got under way, the flow of work increased, but any substantial enlargement of the London drawing office was out of the question because draughtsmen were almost unobtainable in London. In 1965 the work began to accumulate and the Land Registry complained about the delays. Help was sought the next year from the large-scales drawing sections at Southampton, but it was obvious that some more radical solution was needed. The Organization and Methods Division of the Treasury was consulted in September 1965 and six months later it submitted proposals for reorganizing the work in the two Departments.[23] Trials followed and the new procedures were agreed to in principle in January 1967; a pilot scheme was started in June and the new system was brought into use in the following year. The Ordnance Survey still produced the map sections but they were now in the form of extracts of published plans, not tracings of selected detail. Land Registry region offices kept the master map sections and became responsible for printing the copies needed for individual registrations of title. When a map section needed revision the master was sent directly to the appropriate Ordnance Survey continuous revision office where the new detail was added. The London drawing and printing office was closed and the initial map-section preparation was transferred to Southampton.

Metric Maps

Post-war Ordnance Survey maps were produced in a metric format, as recommended by the Davidson Committee, and all carried a metric grid; moreover, the linear measurements by field surveyors were made in metres so that the full adoption of the metric system was a change towards which the Ordnance Survey was already predisposed. However, the Minister had rejected Cheetham's proposal for metric contours in 1943, so that height-information continued to be shown in feet. Areas were given in acres and the distances to the nearest towns in the margins of the maps were in miles. In 1961, the implications of complete metrication were examined and a paper was prepared in 1963 for submission to the Minister of Agriculture, but the Ordnance Survey was told to wait. The Government eventually announced its support for the adoption of the metric system by British Industry in 1965 and soon afterwards the Minister of Technology set up a Joint Standing Committee, composed of representatives of government and industry, to exercise a general surveillance over the change. At its first meeting the Director General presented a paper setting out the Ordnance Survey's proposals for metric maps, including a reference to the decimal scales needed to replace the six-inch and the one-inch.[24] The proposals affecting the large-scale maps were immediately endorsed, largely to conform with the plan for an early change to the metric system by the Construction Industry, and the Ordnance Survey was authorized to consult with interested bodies. In the light of their comments and suggestions, the original plan was modified to include the immediate adoption of the 1:10 000 scale and, at the insistence of the Ministry of Agriculture, the retention of the acre, although hectare values were to be given as well; the agricultural industry was apparently not at that time ready for metric units of area. In March 1969 these proposals, which related only to maps at 1:25 000 and larger scales, were approved by Ministers and by the end of the year the first fully metric 1:1250, 1:2500 and 1:10 000 maps had been published.[25] No changes were made to the popular one-inch and smaller scale maps at this stage although the replacement of the one-inch map received intensive study within the Ordnance Survey. For the time being, the general change to metric units remained a subject of controversy in Parliament and in the country.

Map Production and Publication

The reappraisal did not lead to such dramatic changes in the Drawing and Printing Divisions as elsewhere. Once a map series was in the course of publication it exercised a powerful stabilizing influence which tended to inhibit the introduction of radical changes especially in the absence of public demand. The Regular six-inch map in its inferior over-generalized form was generally disliked, but there it was – in the map stores and in the shops – and there seemed to be no alternative to going on with it. The long-awaited Second Series 1:25 000 map reduced from eight six-inch components made its appearance in December 1965 when the first fourteen sheets were published (Plate 24). It was immediately acclaimed as a fine cartographic production, going some way towards compensating for the failings of the six-inch. But it soon became apparent that in developing areas the map was going to be very expensive to produce because the six-inch components were usually several years out of date, which meant calling for continuous revision information. At first, unfortunately, this was not done, with the embarrassing sequel that one of the early Second Series 1:25 000 sheets was found to be more out of date in some respects than the Provisional map it replaced. To make matters worse, sales of the map remained obstinately low and the Ordnance Survey felt obliged to warn map users at the consultative meetings in 1969 and 1970 that it was doubtful if production could be continued, an announcement which at the time gave rise to no more than a murmur of dissent.

The half-inch map which Cheetham had once looked upon as a cartographic face-saver made an appearance in 1958, when sheet 36 covering Birmingham was published. It was headed, rather obscurely, 'Second Series', although there had already been three quite distinct versions. In the next two or three years, work on the half-inch slowed down, until in 1961 the series was abandoned on the grounds of economy, a recognition perhaps that scanty resources were not being used to the best advantage on a map scale that was well provided for by a commercial publisher. Three sheets, Snowdon, Norwich, and Greater London, were retained for a time, but all were eventually withdrawn except Snowdon, which was enlarged to include the whole of the Snowdonia National Park, and classified as a tourist map.

Between 1958 and 1967 several one-inch tourist maps were published, some of which incorporated refinements in hill-shading and others the results of experiments in colour printing, either by half-tone or with percentage-dot screens. The first of these, a new edition of *Lake District*, was published in 1958 and proved to be a best-seller. It introduced a yellow 'sunny-side' tint above the 500 foot contour to complement the purple-grey shading on the shadow side; below this level there was a pale green layer. A similar system was adopted for the two Scottish sheets, *Ben Nevis and Glencoe* (1959) and *Loch Lomond and the Trossachs* (1961), where it was particularly successful in depicting the relief, mainly because these sheets were uncluttered with other detail. In the *Cairngorms* tourist map (1964) the continuous colour variation from light green to purple, giving an effect similar to conventional layers, was produced by a trichromatic half-tone process, thereby reducing the number of colour printings. The half-tone method was also employed for the *New Forest* (1966) although on this sheet the colour shades were used to distinguish the various landscape types, relief being shown solely by hill-shading. The map was not a cartographic success but, like *Lake District*, it became a best-seller. Two tourist maps, *Dartmoor* and *Exmoor*, were published in 1967, using percentage-dot screens for the layer tints, which again reduced the number of printings. The last three sheets followed from the advice of the Estimates Committee on 'the possibility of extending the range of tourist maps to cover . . . the New Forest and Devon'.

A new kind of archaeological map appeared in 1964, showing the whole length of *Hadrian's Wall* in great detail at a scale of two inches to one mile on a single sheet. This successful production was followed in 1969 by a similar map of the *Antonine Wall*. New editions of two of Crawford's period maps, *Roman Britain (AD43–410)* and *Britain in the Dark Ages (AD410–871)*, were brought out in 1956 and 1966 respectively, and three new maps were published – *Monastic Britain* in 1950, *Ancient Britain* in 1951 and *Southern Britain in the Iron Age* in 1962. The map coverage of the period from the Roman occupation to the Norman Conquest was completed with *Britain before the Norman Conquest (AD871–1066)* in 1974.

The large-scale maps had always contained a pictorial element known in the Ordnance Survey as 'ornament', but this often had little planimetric significance although it added substantially to the cost of drawing. In 1962 a start was made towards greater simplicity by discontinuing the ornamental depiction of spoil heaps and refuse tips and replacing with annotations. The depiction of coastal rocks and slopes and other comparable features inland came under similar scrutiny a few years later. On the old County maps the coastal rock had been drawn from nature but this did not fit the new tide lines on the overhauled 1:2500; it had therefore been replaced by symbolized rock 'drawing' stuck on by the draughtsman which, though much less costly than a new survey, bore little or no relation to nature. The proposal to substitute annotations for the rock and slope symbols was supported at the round of consultative meetings in 1966, and a combined field and drawing trial was put in hand. The results were conclusive: an over-all saving of 10 per cent in drawing costs was realized, rising to as much as 50 per cent on sheets containing a large amount of ornament.[26]

A perennial worry in the Map Publication Directorate was the delay between the survey and publication of the large-scale maps, which at times amounted to over a year. The mass-production methods employed in the Drawing and Reproduction offices were themselves partly responsible because the production flowline was subdivided into a number of stages each of which had to have its own head of work so that no-one would have to wait for the next job to arrive. The time spent actually working on the map was only a small fraction – between one-third and one-fifth – of the total production time, and it seemed impossible to improve on this to any extent. The delay was a serious and in some ways an intolerable inconvenience to many users of large-scale maps; their needs were partly met by Advance Revision Information, but this was, unfortunately, not easy to obtain once a revised field sheet had entered the production flowline in the drawing office. Some entirely new way of publishing large-scale mapping information seemed to be called for, but the problem was so radical and touched on so many interests that for a time it was shelved.

Lithographic printing had never been a particularly suitable way of reproducing the single colour large-scale plans for which the print runs were in the order of fifty to one hundred copies of each sheet, but no satisfactory alternative had been found. Moreover, because the number of different maps was very large – about 150 000 – much expensive storage space was needed both in the Ordnance Survey itself and in the shops of its large-scale agents. The Treasury paper of 1963 on marketing mentioned the possibility of making enlarged prints from microfilm and in 1964 the practicability of this means of reproduction was put to the test. With such a system, single copies could easily be made without waste of time, individual orders could be dealt with through the post on demand, and the map store could be dispensed with, all of which appeared to offer a large saving which was very attractive to the Publication Division. It was found that a 35mm system would not give the required resolution and efforts were concentrated on 70mm microfilm combined with electro-photographic print-making. Reasonable quality was soon obtained with the 1:1250 scale maps but the greater reduction and enlargement needed for the 2km × 1km 1:2500 sheets led to a loss in quality. A slight touch of fantasy was given to these experiments because it appeared that the only difficulty lay in reproducing the stipple used to symbolize roofed buildings, but a new 70mm camera with higher resolving power, purchased in 1968, was able to cope successfully with the stipple. In spite of this, the reactions of users of the trial copies were disappointing, not because of the quality of the prints, but because the zinc-oxide-covered paper marked easily and was very unsatisfactory in damp conditions.[27] The microfilm story was to take a new turn in the next decade, but for the time being there was no further significant progress with printing on demand and the large-scale plans continued to be produced by lithography.

Advances in the technology of map reproduction did not depend to the same extent as in surveying and drawing on initiative from within the Ordnance Survey itself. The large commercial printing industry in Great Britain was backed by a correspondingly large number of equipment and material manufacturers. It had its own research organization and it supported several trade journals. Generally the Ordnance Survey adapted and adopted the equipment and processes of the commercial world so that changes within the Department were to some extent a reflection of the continuous development going on outside. In the period 1961–8, the main innovation was probably the replacement of letterpress by photo type-setting for the names and numbers on maps; after 1964, this was done almost entirely by Monotype film-setters. The introduction of a map-folding machine in 1961 was a first step towards the mechanization of map finishing which had hitherto been almost entirely a manual operation; a laminating machine, and a casing machine which put the covers on the folded maps, were added in 1968 and 1969, virtually eliminating manual finishing.

REPAYMENT WORK

From the middle of the nineteenth century the Ordnance Survey categorized one section of its work as 'repayment work' or sometimes as 'special services', making a distinction which was, for the most part, rather unreal. A 'repayment service' was one that was individually costed and was paid for by the sponsoring department instead of being financed out of the Vote; however, repayment services for the Land Registry, the Institute of Geological Sciences, the Ministry of Defence and other government departments fell as firmly within the responsibilities of the National Survey as the standard map series themselves, in that they were tasks which the Ordnance Survey executed at the behest and with the authority of the Government. Distinguished from repayment work of this kind was a fringe of discretionary activity undertaken by the Department for individuals and organizations, subject to resources being available.

The commitments to the War Department, the Land Registry and the Geological Survey were of long standing. Throughout the post-war period the Ordnance Survey allocated a part of its cartographic and printing resources to repayment work for the Ministry of Defence, and a similar if rather less clearly defined arrangement existed with the Institute of Geological Sciences for Drawing and printing geological maps. Cartographic work for the Land Registry consisted mainly in the production of map sections from the standard large-scale maps, some drawing done in the field region offices and a large amount of survey. The charges levied were calculated from the number of special surveys undertaken.

Other large regular commitments included map-printing for the Directorate of Overseas Surveys and for the Ordnance Survey of Northern Ireland, while in smaller quantities maps were prepared for the Boundary Commissions, the National Parks Commission, the Soil Survey, the Land Use Survey, in map-extract form for Examination Boards, and intermittently for many other bodies.[28] In 1967–8 it was estimated that repayment services absorbed about 17 per cent of the Department's map production capacity.

Basic Ordnance Survey Policy

The concept of the Department's role which had been built up during the years of reappraisal were embodied in six short paragraphs by Major-General Edge in his statement of *Basic Ordnance Survey Policy*, written in 1967:

1 To provide and maintain as a national service the surveys and maps of Great Britain required for scientific, military and general use by Her Majesty's Government and the public as a whole. This includes:
 (a) Geodetic surveys and associated work.
 (b) Basic scale topographical surveys.
 (c) An archaeologcial reconnaissance survey.
 (d) The production from these surveys of maps at appropriate scales.
2 Subject to 6 below, to undertake special services for official and private users where the Department is, by reason of its main activities, the most appropriate agency to do so, and provided its function as a national service is not jeopardized.
3 To undertake or promote such research as is necessary to ensure the efficiency of its operations.
4 To carry out its task as economically as possible, using either its own staff, agents, or contractors, whichever is advantageous.
5 To secure the maximum return from sales, royalties and charges and from exploitation of the by-products of its normal activities, provided such exploitation is appropriate for the Department and does not lead to undue dispersion of effort.
6 Not to engage in additional activities purely for the sake of profit nor to compete with other organizations offering satisfactory service to the public in similar fields, but to co-operate with such organizations, both governmental and commercial, provided the Department's own commercial position is not thereby compromised.

This important document – the aims had never before been specifically stated – was offered to Central Government for endorsement, but without result. Whitehall did not object to the Ordnance Survey using it internally, but preferred to preserve its own freedom of action in defining the functions of the Department. Six years later, the responsible Minister was to produce his own version of the aims of the Ordnance Survey.

Notes

1 Director General's Committee Minutes, December 1964.
2 *Hansard* 725, House of Commons, 23 Feb. 1966, cols. 118–20.
3 OS Policy Statement 17, 1966.
4 *Eighth Report from the Estimates Committee 1962–63*. Evidence para. 238: PP 1962–63 (239) V.
5 *Ibid.* paras. 333 and 341.
6 *Ibid.* para. 52.
7 *Eighth Report*, Summary of Recommendations, para. 53 (2)–(5).
8 *Ibid.* para. 53 (1).
9 Director General's Committee Minutes, July 1967.
10 *Eighth Report*, para. 9.
11 *Ibid.* paras. 44 and 45.
12 OSR 1968–9 and 1970–1, App. 4
13 CR 19138.
14 *Ibid.*
15 *Ibid.*
16 OSR 1962–3, p. 6.
17 Director General's Committee Minutes, August 1968.
18 Director General's Committee Minutes, June 1969.
19 OSR 1966–7, p. 2.
20 *Scottish Geographical Magazine*, 1938, LIV, p. 148.
21 OS Policy Statement 54.
22 Director General's Committee Minutes, July 1964.
23 Director General's Committee Minutes, March 1966.
24 Director General's Committee Minutes, May 1966.
25 OSR 1969–70, p. 1.
26 Director General's Committee Minutes, September 1968.
27 OSR 1969–70, p. 9.
28 *Eighth Report*, p. 19, Table B.

33
The Topographical Survey after the Second World War

New Methods

1:1250 RESURVEY

The uncompromising chain survey of the mid nineteenth century, by which almost all the ground detail was fixed by chain and offset, was relaxed for commonsense reasons of economy once revision became the main occupation of the surveyors. Instead of having to survey all the new features by chain, they were allowed, in suitable circumstances, to add them directly to the old map by 'examination', that is, by graphical alignments, prolongations and intersections within the framework of remaining detail. Towards the end of the century the rigidity of the chain triangulation was eroded further by the introduction of traversing for fixing the control from which the chain lines could be measured. When after the Second World War the 1:1250 urban resurvey became the main task, it was planned as an amalgam of all three procedures: traverse for providing control in the form of 'revision points' (RPs), chain survey for a detail framework with the main chain lines running between the RPs, and a final stage of graphical completion in which the remaining detail was fixed by graphical alignments and short linear measurements within the chain survey. The chained detail was penned in red and was known as 'red detail'; the graphical work was in black and was called 'black detail'. The old term 'examination' was misleadingly retained for the graphic survey, whilst the chain survey was called 'detail survey' – an anachronism that persisted until the early 1960s.

The new chain survey provided more opportunities for individual judgment than had the system devised by Colby, particularly in deciding the balance between the red detail and the graphical infilling. This freedom had its dangers as Colby would certainly have predicted. The temptation to reduce the chain framework still further and to rely on the skill of the more experienced surveyors to fill in 80 or 90 per cent by graphical survey, proved to be irresistible in the early post-war years, but 'skeleton chain' was not a success largely because the bulk of the surveyors were new recruits who lacked the uncanny skill of the older Ordnance Survey men in building up a complete map from a vestigial framework. When new methods, replacing the chain, were eventually brought into use, the three stages – traverse control, red detail and black detail – were retained; all that was altered was the way of surveying the red detail, although the density of the control required varied widely between one method and another.

In the first few years after the war the 1:1250 resurvey was carried out mainly with the chain, but the Ordnance Survey did not ignore air survey altogether; it devised a method which drew on pre-war revision experience and which could be regarded as an extension of its traditional graphical field survey to the air photograph.[1] After several experiments a technique was used for the resurvey of Southend which gave satisfactory results. The air photographs were taken with a twenty-inch-lens Williamson F49 camera at a scale of 1:2500; but 'air-graphic' was very extravagant in photography, requiring an overlap of 60 per cent in the fore-and-aft direction and 55 per cent laterally, and a correspondingly large number of rectifications enlarged to map scale were used by the plotters. Enough control had to be provided so that the plumb point of each photograph could be reseted accurately onto the plot; this amounted to nine points per photograph on alternate strips, the intermediate strips being covered by the large lateral overlaps. Thereafter a complex pattern of intersections was constructed, based on the radial line principle, with at least four rays through each detail point. The work was slow and called for meticulous care, but when done by experts the results were good and comparable in accuracy with the chain survey, although it took a long time to convince some of the more senior surveyors that this was so. In less skilled hands, especially in hilly towns like Bath, the air-graphic survey was sometimes below the standard which was later defined as acceptable.

Improved ways of surveying the red framework, by tacheometer and stereoplotting machine, were adopted in the mid 1950s but only after prolonged hesitation. Once in the hands of the surveyors the Kern DK-RT self-reducing tacheometer was a great success. The density of permanently marked control points was much reduced, and this control was intensified by the Field Division men themselves by means of tacheometric traverses, providing perhaps one hundred tacheometric stations per square kilometre, from which the red detail was fixed by direction and distance. Computing the co-ordinates of the tacheometric stations, plotting them by rectangular co-ordinatograph on the butt-joint plates, and plotting the red detail by polar co-ordinatograph were all done at headquarters. Unlike other forms of red detail, that produced by the tacheometer was virtually free from plottable error so that when the surveyors undertook the final stage of field completion they were able to work from a comparatively sparse but very accurate skeleton with great confidence. Once again, in the late 1950s when the demands on the small number of tacheometers were many, there was an unfortunate tendency to reduce the skeleton, but this had the effect of increasing the cost, and a proper balance had to be kept. Such was the enthusiasm generated by the new instrument that the various field region offices began to develop their own proprietorial styles, whose effectiveness or otherwise was eventually revealed in the cost statistics. The office responsible for the London area believed that buildings were the most suitable feature for the tacheometric framework, forming the best basis for graphic survey. They also became aware of the power of the instrument when used in a housing estate under construction when the walls were about at waist height. In these circumstances it was possible to survey nearly all the detail by tacheometer very quickly, but the surveyors had to recognize that the cost of the headquarters operations had also to be considered in order to arrive at an optimum balance between the instrumental and graphical phases.

Once it was accepted, the stereoplotting machine (initially the Wild A5) proved itself capable of producing the cheapest 1:1250 survey, taking into account the cost of the photographs, the control survey and the ground completion. Its economy depended on using high quality photographs of the smallest scale that would give the required accuracy and on plotting the maximum amount of detail from the photographs. Unfortunately not all the detail to be shown on the maps was visible from the air. In open modern housing estates where the properties were separated by fences, a very high proportion could be taken from the photographs, although this did not include the whole outline of buildings because of the overhang of the eaves and the dead ground produced by the buildings themselves away from the centres of the photographs. When they could not see the ground lines, the air plotters put in the roof outlines in pencil, leaving the field men with a very easy task. In fact in some areas it was too easy, with little to do beyond fitting the ground plans of the houses inside the roof outline and collecting names and house numbers, which some surveyors found rather dull compared with the completion stage of a tacheometric survey.

At the opposite end of the urban landscape where trees and hedges concealed fences, paths, roads and buildings, there was a great deal to be added, but the problem was very different from that of filling in a tacheometric framework, which, though sparse, had been positioned to meet the needs of the surveyor completing the map. The plotting machine 'red' consisted of those fortuitous scraps that did not happen to be hidden by the trees; these were often fragments of linear features and not well-defined points. Moreover, the air survey was not free from plottable errors, there being frequently a discrepancy of about 0.2m–0.3m between the length of any line measured on the ground and the corresponding distance on the plot. The error did not accumulate away from control, as in a chain survey, but remained the same over the whole of the map sheet, and was caused by the inherent uncertainty in making a pointing in the plotting machine from photographs at the chosen scale. In open areas this shortcoming was not of great importance, but beneath the trees where so much less was visible it merely added to the uncertainties of identification. So in some wooded areas, such as Fleet in Hampshire, additional control points and tacheometric survey had to be provided to supplement the air-photo red detail. 'Tachy infilling' entirely eliminated the savings expected from the air survey but, once the lesson had been learnt, care was taken to exclude such areas from the air survey programme.

The accuracies of the completed 1:1250 maps of open areas made by tacheometer and by stereoplotting machine were about the same. The tacheometric detail generally had a standard error in position that was better than 0.2m, but the extensive graphical infilling increased the over-all error to about 0.4m which was roughly the same as for the completed air survey plans, although with these the amount of graphical work was very much less (Plate 25).

The photographs for 1:1250 plotting machine resurvey were taken with a twelve-inch-lens F49 camera from about 4000 feet until 1964 when the Ordnance Survey bought a modern Zeiss 30/23RMK camera which gave a picture of improved quality, enabling a reduction in scale to about 1:5000 to be made. Most of the plotting was done on Thompson-Watts instruments fitted with twelve-inch goniometers. The Wild A8 machines were less suitable for this work because the photographs had to be reduced in size in order to accommodate the principal-distance limitations of the A8.

For several years before and after 1960 all four methods of 1:1250 resurvey were in use simultaneously, partly because the various stages of planning and executing a field survey task took several years to complete, perhaps as many as five or six. Resources were committed during planning, and control points were provided to suit the projected method of detail survey, so that any change, even to one nominally more economical, always resulted in delay and sometimes waste. And, before the cost of any new method could be reliably assessed, a reasonably large sample of completed maps had to be examined. Even so, cost comparisons were never straightforward, because of variation in the density of the detail, and in the difficulty of survey of one map sheet compared with another. To overcome this, all the completed 1:1250 maps were examined and given a numerical rating known as the Plan Assessment Rating, which took the factors of density and difficulty into account and which could therefore be used to establish a basis of comparison between different 1:1250 maps and different methods of survey. The existence of serviceable old equipment and the need to retrain staff were other factors that delayed the discarding of methods which were recognized to be obsolescent. However, by 1960, the last of the chain-survey towns, apart from extensions, had been completed and by 1965 the last air-graphic town had been finished, although air-graphic survived and flourished in the 1:2500 Overhaul.

SIX-INCH RESURVEY

The resurvey of the basic six-inch areas of Scotland, begun in 1956, provided a complete break with tradition. Not only were the lower order control, the outline detail and the contours surveyed by photogrammetry, but in the final stage of ground completion much use was made of the plane-table. At first the photographs, scale 1:24 000 1:27 000, were taken with six-inch-lens Fairchild K17 and Williamson F49 cameras, and the plotting machines used were the Wild A6 transferred from contouring and the Santoni Stereosimplex.

The resurvey was begun at about the same time in the Southern Uplands and in the north-west Highlands.* In the Southern Uplands it had been intended to compile the new map from a combination of the old County six-inch detail and new air-surveyed contours but the discrepancies between the old and the new led to the immediate abandonment of this plan and the decision to resurvey. Here the new map was based entirely on control fixed on the ground, but in the Highlands the whitewashed pillars of the secondary triangulation provided the framework for analytical aerial triangulation by stereocomparator. The calculations for the formation of strip and block co-ordinates were carried out at the National Physical Laboratory, at first on the ACE and, from 1956, on the DEUCE computers. There remained the tying down of these arbitrary block co-ordinates to planimetric ground control and at the beginning this was done by a semigraphic adjustment which was not entirely satisfactory. In 1958 a mechanical analogue known as the Jerie Analogue Computer[2] was successfully tested on the block adjustment; this device continued to be used with good results until 1962, by which time computer developments enabled a wholly numerical adjustment to be substituted.

Tests of the accuracy of the six-inch resurvey which were concluded in 1962 showed not only that the semigraphic adjustment was a source of significant error but also that the A6 plotting machines and to some extent the Stereosimplex were not altogether suitable for this exacting task. The A6 machines had already been transferred back to the contouring of derived maps and in the early 1960s the resurvey work was taken over completely by more modern instruments such as the Wild A8 and the Thompson-Watts with six-inch goniometers. For the 1964 flying season a modern Wild RC8R camera was purchased to replace the much-used F49, giving a great improvement in photographic quality.

The nineteenth-century uncontoured six-inch maps of the north-west Highlands of Scotland were sometimes little more than sheets of rough pasture symbols with the watercourses added, but the

* The north-west Highlands were selected as being suitable for an experimental survey because of their remoteness from other areas of work.

mid-twentieth-century versions were dominated by the contours.* The outline detail was often scanty and the plotting-machine operators found that some of it was difficult to see on the photographs; wire fences were important features which were frequently impossible to follow; the pattern of ground surface vegetation and rock, though usually visible on the photographs, was not easy to classify.

But the men in the field had their troubles too. The Six-inch Group worked intensively for seven days a week in the summer season only and, because of the sparse road pattern in the Highlands, did a great deal of walking with usually only a little to show for it. The missing fences created many time-consuming problems, especially when the landscape lacked any precisely defined plotted detail, as it frequently did. Fortunately the air surveyors were able to help. They could often see traces of the fence line and find identifiable objects in the neighbourhood, such as large boulders, which they could plot and which the ground surveyors could work from. The waste of time spent in walking long distances was eventually eliminated by using helicopters to transport the surveyors to their places of work and to collect them later, and it was also found to be possible to classify the surface vegetation whilst in flight.

The plane-table was an obvious choice for surveying scattered detail in mountain and moorland areas where well-defined points fixed in the stereoplotter were very few. The six-inch sketching board had an attachment for fixing to a plane-table tripod and the Six-inch Group had at its disposal a number of telescopic alidades** whose vertical circles carried Beaman scales so that horizontal distances and height differences could be rapidly calculated from stadia readings on a vertical staff without using tables. The alidades were extensively used both for making normal resections and intersections, as distant objects were not always easy to pick out with the eye in the Highland landscape, and for plane-table traversing when the facility for making optical distance-measurements saved time and effort. In areas of closer detail the surveyors used traditional graphical methods, sometimes with the assistance of the box sextant. However, the long-delayed adoption by the Ordnance Survey of the plane-table was not a complete success. An accuracy test made in 1974 disclosed that features fixed with it in the test area did not conform to six-inch accuracy standards – in other words, the standard error of position was greater than 3.5m. This disappointing result might be attributed in part to the relative inexperience of Ordnance surveyors with the plane-table and to the fact that the area of work was not confined to the central part of the plane-table as is the normal practice.

CONTOURS

In the early 1960s the surveyors were expected to carry out a visual check of contours and to add any that had been omitted because of shadow or cloud on the photographs, but a visual check of plotting-machine contours was of little practical value, because any errors that existed could not be reliably detected by eye. When omitted contours had to be supplied, which was not very often, the surveyors used the plane-table with the telescopic alidade for running height traverses. As most of the shadow areas were on north-facing precipices, the plotting machines, even with the handicap of shadow, usually gave results superior to anything the plane-tablers could accomplish.

The programme of stereoplotting-machine contouring also included the derived six-inch maps, for which the Wild A6 instruments were used at first and later the four Santoni Stereosimplex plotters. It proved to be impossible to keep the production of new derived six-inch maps in step with any rational contouring programme, because the former tended to be made in small scattered patches, as the major and minor towns were surveyed at the larger scales, whereas the latter was necessarily linked to substantial blocks of contouring photography. Where no Regular six-inch maps existed, the contouring was fitted to the detail of the Provisional Series, it being accepted that occasional adjustments would have to be made to fit the Regular maps when they appeared. These adjustments were carried out in the drawing office.

In nearly flat areas, such as the Fens, contours were not meaningful unless surveyed to an accuracy attainable only by instrumental methods on the ground. Between about 1960 and 1972 ground spot-heighting and contouring in flat areas for the derived six-inch maps were done with the telescopic alidade. For surveying contours the alidade was used on the plane-table with the telescope in the

---

* At 25-foot vertical interval until 1969. Thereafter throughout Great Britain at 10m vertical interval in mountainous areas and 5m vertical interval elsewhere.

** The telescopic alidades were a legacy from stereo-sketching; they had been used to provide extra height control for the stereo-sketchers.

horizontal position, serving as a level; the distances to the various staff positions were determined by stadia readings. Below the twenty-five-foot contour a mesh of spot heights 300m–700m apart was fixed, usually by height traversing; for this it was the practice to detach the alidade blade from the instrument, which was then mounted on a tripod. The traverses were run from bench-mark to bench-mark through the selected positions where spot heights were required, a method of height fixing also used for contour accuracy testing. After 1972 ground contouring and spot heighting were abandoned and the work was transferred to the air surveyors, but in flat areas no attempt was made to follow and plot a contour directly in the plotting machine; instead a large number of deliberate height pointings were made and, where possible, the contour interpolated.

The accuracy standard for stereoplotting-machine contours required that the standard error should not exceed ±6 feet in areas of medium relief. Except in mountainous districts this limit was rarely approached and never exceeded. The standard error of plotting-machine spot heights was probably about half that of the contours. Up to the end of 1974 no accuracy tests of plotting-machine spot heights and contours in flat areas had been carried out, so that their value remained somewhat in doubt.

Revision

It is an axiom of revision that no two independent surveys, however good, can be expected to agree precisely at every point. When the quality of a 'good' survey is diluted by a measure of human fallibility, perhaps through haste or carelessness, the ground begins almost literally to shift under the revisers' feet. Herein lies the intractable problem of revision survey. New work will never fit precisely into old. But how should these discrepancies be reconciled? With a map that is less than 'good' how and when should a process of equation be abandoned in favour of new survey? If the latter choice is made, how far should the new work extend and how should it be linked to the areas of old maps where equation is acceptable?

In nineteenth-century Ireland Leach had realized that the trouble did not merely spring from inferior work or distortion but was fundamental to all measurement and applied to maps with particular force when the dimensions of objects were arrived at by different physical routes or by different measurement methods. In the 1960s and 1970s, although the problem was better understood it was still the principal difficulty in revision survey. When 1:1250 town surveys produced by stereoplotting-machine were revised by tacheometer, the new and the old work sat uncomfortably together even though each conformed to the standards of accuracy laid down for it. But it did become possible to determine statistically the errors which were inherent in each of the methods used and to give some guidance to the surveyors in identifying those which were outside the acceptable limits.

THE OVERHAUL REVISION

The practice of 'coaxing' or 'humouring' (as old as the Survey itself) by altering the position of the detail of the old map so that the new work could be fitted in, was one to be undertaken only with the utmost reluctance. Although a local problem might appear to have been resolved in this way, there was always a strong possibility that others had been created and that the accuracy of the map overall might have been worsened rather than improved. These considerations certainly applied in the 'Cotswold' Overhaul of the 1:2500 County Series.

The Cotswold Overhaul consisted of two stages. The old maps had to be recompiled to remove the distortion in the size and shape of the old sheets, and to bring them into conformity with the new projection and the new retriangulation control; then the map detail, which sometimes had remained unamended since the revision of 1891–1914, had to be revised. The first stage could be described as a rather sophisticated application of the old restorative device of 'shining-up'; in the process the new triangulation stations were inserted on the old map in sympathy with surrounding local detail, and then made to coincide with their correct co-ordinated grid positions. There was thus a possibility that any local error in the detail near a new triangulation station would be spread into a much larger area of the map. Further, the causes of the distortion of the old paper documents, particularly the bowed sheet edges, were not completely understood; the distortion was complex in origin and irregular in occurrence. Consequently the shining-up process, although reducing some of the errors, left others unchanged and probably introduced some that were new.

In carrying out the revision, the surveyors were compelled to move some of the old detail, if only to remove the discontinuities caused by shining-up, but they had to decide which way to make the shifts and where to stop. In the early days of the Overhaul they sometimes found themselves entangled in wholesale shifts of the old map as the need to resolve one discrepancy led to the creation of another, which in turn had to be dealt with. The execution of this kind of revision called for much skill and judgment which sometimes seemed out of proportion to the mediocre standard of accuracy that could be attained. When very little of the old map was 'laid down with perfect correctness' the revision had necessarily to take on the same quality. For many surveyors the urge to try to improve on this state of affairs was almost irresistible, but if the framework of the old map was disregarded, the new survey was likely to be no better if not worse than the old.

When the detail of the old map did not provide a usable framework for revision, the proper course was resurvey, but the Ordnance Survey was always reluctant to abandon an old survey. As in the days of Leach and Yolland, expedients were devised in the 1960 decade to avoid as far as possible the expense and delay of resurvey. However, the latter-day surveyors had a new tool – the air photograph – which enabled them to delimit the faulty areas and to add patches of new work which were not linked to rigid control, but were fitted as closely as possible to the surrounding detail of the old map.* Patches of resurvey, based on proper control, were no answer in these circumstances; as when mending an old garment with new cloth, the old and the new would never hold together round the edges.

The success of the Cotswold Overhaul depended on the injection of just enough National Grid control to enable the old plans to be fitted to the new triangulation; significantly more than the minimum would distort the old detail to an extent that would make revision impossible. This delicate balance proved to be attainable in those parts of the country where a high proportion of the new triangulation stations could be plotted on the County Series maps in correct relationship with the old detail. Where the County Series detail was very sparse, as in some of the more open rural areas, the positioning of the triangulation stations within the detail framework was uncertain, and the method began to fail; tests conducted in the early 1970s revealed that the accuracy standard for the Cotswold (± 2.5m standard error) was not being met in these conditions. Two solutions were possible: one was a complete resurvey which was bound to be expensive; the other was to fix and incorporate additional control in such a way that the Overhaul accuracy standard was restored, which would cost significantly less.

One of the early experimental Overhaul techniques, the 'Chelmsford' method, was a novel combination of stereocomparator control, graphical air survey, compilation of material taken from the County Series plans and graphical field completion. It had not survived long in competition with the much simpler and cheaper Cotswold method, but in the 1970s many of its weaknesses had been overcome by technological advances. The uncertainty of obtaining air photographs had greatly diminished and the computation of aerial triangulation had been fully computerized. It was therefore possible to resurrect the Chelmsford idea in a modified form, and in 1974 trials were initiated of a method which was based on exactly the same elements as Chelmsford, the main differences being that butt-joint plates were not used and the graphical air survey was done, not at Headquarters, but in the field. First conclusions were that the accuracy needed could be attained without difficulty, but that some uncertainty about comparative cost remained. Cost comparisons later led to the conclusion that, in most circumstances, a resurvey was preferable.

THE REVISION OF THE NATIONAL GRID PLANS

Revision by examination** continued to be the normal method for the National Grid plans, with the constraint that, where it did not already exist, a framework of instrumentally-fixed detail had to be provided in areas of new development at the appropriate density for the instrument employed, which was usually the tacheometer. When adding infilling detail by examination, the surveyors preferred to base their construction lines on old instrumentally-fixed features rather than on old graphical work, particularly where the tacheometer had been used. Accuracy tests had shown that tacheometric

---

* Rectified enlargements of the photographs were widely employed especially for the air/ground method (see Ch. 32). A simple instrument designed by W. J. C. Blogg, a member of the cartographic staff, was regularly used to determine the tilts of the photographs before rectification. This device gave substantial economies compared with other methods, and in 1972, under the Staff Suggestion Scheme, Mr Blogg received an award of £1500 for his invention.

** In the early 1960s the terminology was changed. 'Examination' became 'detail survey'; and 'detail survey' became 'chain survey', 'tacheometric survey' etc. or collectively 'instrumental detail survey'.

survey had a standard error of position of less than 0.2m whereas with the graphically-fixed points the error was twice as large.

The instrumental framework itself had to be supported by some form of accurate control and there were obvious advantages to be gained if permanent control points were put in at the time of the original survey. The chain survey for the 1:1250 plans depended on Revision Points fixed by traverse at a density of about forty pairs of points per square kilometre. They were usually on well-defined permanent detail features and photographs were included in the records so that the position of each could be identified later with certainty. The two RPs in a pair were placed so that a chain line could be started from a point on the line joining them. Revision by chain survey was thus well catered for, but the change to tacheometric methods in the mid 1950s made such a dense network unnecessary. Instead, Permanent Traverse Stations were positioned at a density of one or two per square kilometre; as the name indicates, these were permanently marked points, usually rivets or pipenails, fixed from the main traverses.

Some 1:1250 plans surveyed from air photographs were based on control points obtained by aerial triangulation. These 'air-trig' points were used for setting up the stereoscopic models in the plotting machines and had merely to be well defined on the photographs and not necessarily detail features that could be recognized on the ground. The needs of revision were for a time forgotten, and a small number of towns surveyed by this method were left without adequate revision control which had later to be provided by normal ground traversing, nullifying the savings of the air-trig. Such omissions were later avoided by including a number of extra points in the aerial triangulation, clearly identifiable on the photographs and on the ground, situated where they would be of most use to the revisers.

The enormous advantages, both in speed and economy, of using air photographs for the resurvey inevitably raised the question of whether similar benefits were to be gained for the revision of the new plans. But because the economy of air survey was partly dependent on being able to procure the maximum number of photographs from each sortie, small and scattered areas which had to be surveyed at short notice were not the most suitable subjects. Furthermore, the weather made it often impossible to respond quickly even in the summer. But when a delayed response was acceptable and the development to be surveyed was large or could be photographed on the way to or from a main target, the advantages of air survey were realizable, and many such areas were photographed for continuous revision from the late 1960s onwards. Some developments were particularly suited to air survey, such as large and complex industrial installations and linear features like motorways. An immediate response was not usually necessary for revision of this sort so that air survey became the normal way of dealing with these often inaccessible features.

THE CONTROL OF CONTINUOUS REVISION

When the resurvey was planned it had been possible to lay down a programme, covering the work of a known number of men over a known number of years, with a predictable output of new plans. No such programme could be devised for continuous revision because Headquarters had no control over the amount of new construction to be surveyed or its location. It was therefore not possible to plan in advance where the surveyors would be needed or in what numbers. Yet the system had to be able to respond to changes which could only be detected by the man on the spot.

A means of regulating the size of the organization in order to ensure that the survey kept pace with the change had to be found. Clearly such a state of balance would exist if the amount of unsurveyed change stayed at the same level. If this unsurveyed work could be measured in a suitable work unit, the sum of all such units would provide a national total; one total could then be compared with another of a later date. As it happened, there was a ready-made system in use which, although defective in one respect, was easily adapted for providing head-of-work statistics: this was the 'house-unit' method of assessing the amount of change on a plan in order to determine when a new edition should be made. One new house equated to one house-unit and other categories of detail were given house-unit values. The house-unit was, however, an element of change on a map and not a measure of the effort required to survey it. This inequality was probably not very significant when house-units were considered in bulk and so, in default of anything better, the house-unit was adopted for measuring revision work. Statistics were collected every six months; any increase in the amount of unsurveyed change was converted into a deficiency of man-power and the organization was reinforced accordingly.

It was clearly desirable to keep the head of work as small as possible consistent with economic operation. The economic rules were divided into two categories; both were aimed at minimizing non-productive overheads and maximizing the time spent actually surveying in the field. The first category dealt with intelligence and the need to obtain information about development without the surveyors' having to carry out time-consuming ground reconnaissance. The local authorities became the main source of this information which they provided with unfailing willingness, although in a variety of different ways, most commonly in the form of lists of completed buildings. The larger authorities supplied the revision sections with layout plans of forthcoming developments such as new roads and housing estates. Other undertakings such as Electricity Boards, Water Boards and the Forestry Commission contributed information about their present and future programmes. The surveyors on their part kept all these organizations informed of the progress of the revision and of the services offered by the Ordnance Survey. The second group of economic rules was directed to the control of the work itself and the regulation of the amount of unsurveyed change. The surveyors were instructed not to undertake revision surveys in normal circumstances unless there was at least one day's work for a surveyor in a locality. Accumulations of three days' work had normally to be attended to unless continuing development in the locality made this wasteful.

The day-to-day planning and supervision of continuous revision had to be primarily the responsibility of the lowest levels of management, and in the absence of a programme and a regular output of work, the upper levels were always conscious of the lack of a means for monitoring performance. The defects of the house-unit system, the local variations in the complexity of the survey and the incidence of uneconomic work such as land registration cases made it difficult to get the control information needed for evaluating the efficiency of individual sections; in the 1970s this problem still remained to be solved.

FIELD METHODS FOR ONE-INCH REVISION

The surveyors' traditional means of transport for one-inch revision was the bicycle, at first because of the greater mobility it provided. However, allegiance to the bicycle persisted long after the motor-car had come into general use, and in the 1970s the 'curved bicycle level' for attachment to the horizontal bar of a bicycle still remained the standard device for measuring road gradients on steep hills.

Until the introduction of the 1:50 000 series, the small-scale revisers used the six-inch map as a field document,* adding new features normally by graphical intersections and alignments, but resorting to prismatic compass traverses where detail was sparse, and occasionally to the plane-table in areas of dense revision such as new housing estates. Distances were usually paced, each surveyor having determined the number of his paces equivalent to a chain, or later to 20m.

Only a small minority of Ordnance surveyors were attracted to one-inch revision, partly owing to its nomadic character but also because many found it difficult to widen their topographical horizons, having been brought up on 1:1250 or 1:2500 surveys. Actually the six-inch framework was usually so dense that the work was straightforward; occasionally when large reafforested areas had to be tackled, such as Kielder Forest in the early 1960s, ground survey proved to be too slow and recourse had to be made to air survey. The small-scales reviser carried out no more field revision than was absolutely necessary, drawing as much as possible on later large-scale surveys, either published or held in continuous revision section offices, and on air photographs. Some information had always to be gathered on the ground, notably the road classification used on the one-inch, the road gradients, and the spires and towers of churches for which there were special symbols.

Tide Lines

The surveying of tide lines on the ground has always been a tricky job for the surveyor. Both high and low water marks are of legal significance, as defining the foreshore, but these lines have no permanent topographical reality, especially in England and Wales where mean high and mean low water represent the levels of a medium tide; in Scotland the corresponding high and low tide lines are those of mean spring tides. On rocky coasts the levels so defined have some degree of permanence, but on shores of sand, mud or shingle, small changes can occur from day to day, and after storms the changes may be extensive. The times of high and low water at any point on the coast may be easily predicted

---

* For the 1:50 000 the revisers' field document was changed. A 1:25 000 scale enlargement of a portion of the 1:50 000 was printed on transparent material and a paper copy of the 1:25 000 map was fitted beneath it. The reviser became responsible for much of the generalization, a task previously undertaken in the drawing office.

from Admiralty Tide Tables and the prediction verified afterwards by reference to the nearest Standard Port, but the ground survey itself, particularly of the low water mark on flat shores and estuaries, is always difficult and sometimes hazardous.

Shortly after the Second World War it was decided to use air photographs for mapping the low water mark and in 1947 tide photography with infra-red film was included in the flying programme, a length of coastline near Bournemouth being the first to be photographed. The first camera to be used was the six-inch-lens K17, and the scale of the photographs was usually 1:20 000. On the infra-red film the water's edge is sharply distinguished, as infra-red light is absorbed by water but strongly reflected from the land surface. The photographs included enough of the coast to enable the tide line to be plotted by graphical air survey; in some extensive areas of very shallow coastal water the photo scale had to be reduced to make this possible.

The way of dealing with the high water mark changed over the years. At first ground methods were generally used but from the early 1960s air survey from infra-red photography was preferred when the nature of the foreshore made work on the ground difficult. Later, when the surveyors employed on the Overhaul were provided with normal panchromatic photographs for the air-ground method, they transferred the tide lines first to the photographs by visual sketching and then graphically to the field sheet. Finally, in areas being resurveyed by stereoplotting machine – mainly those for the basic six-inch – the height of the high water mark was calculated from the tide tables and plotted as a contour* from the normal six-inch resurvey photography. In particularly awkward places, such as the island of St Kilda, the resurvey photographs were taken at low water so that both tide lines could be plotted as contours.

It very often happened that the high and low water marks on a particular sheet were plotted from surveys made at different times, and this occasionally produced some surprising results. When in 1962 the high water mark in the River Mersey at Runcorn was resurveyed by ground methods, it was found at one point to intersect the low water mark,** which had been plotted some time before from air photographs, at right angles. This was caused by the piers of a new bridge which had changed the flow of the river and the tidal currents. The anomaly had, of course, to be put right, but many minor discrepancies of the same sort must exist, and it is hard to see, with a feature of such impermanence, how they can be avoided.

Archaeology and the Post-War Survey

With the return of peace in 1945 came great changes in the organization and conduct of the archaeological survey. The post-war programme of resurvey, Overhaul and continuous revision gave an opportunity to plan and carry out a truly effective presentation of archaeology and history on maps of all scales.

Crawford retired in 1945 and Grimes, his natural successor, was soon afterwards appointed as Director of the London Museum. There followed a long delay in which the Treasury meditated such matters as the conditions which would apply to a woman archaeology officer, but eventually, in January 1947, Mr C. W. Phillips was appointed to succeed him.

Phillips had known Crawford since 1927 and had assisted him unofficially in his work at the Ordnance Survey, becoming one of the early 'honorary correspondents'. When a Fellow of Selwyn College, Cambridge, he became secretary of the Prehistoric Society in 1935 and was associated with several major archaeological operations, notably in 1939 when he undertook the excavation of the Sutton Hoo burial ship. In 1939 Crawford had suggested that Phillips might be interested in the post of Assistant Archaeology Officer in the Ordnance Survey but at that time he was prevented from accepting by other commitments. When Grimes left, however, he was free to succeed him and he remained with the Ordnance Survey for nearly twenty years. It is to Phillips that credit must be given for the creation of an effective archaeological surveying and recording organization within the Ordnance Survey.

After the war archaeology quickly became interesting to a much wider public mainly through its skilled presentation on radio and television programmes. The techniques of air photography, field reconnaissance and excavation had all made great progress and the opportunities given by war damage started many excavations which kept the subject in the public eye. But for the Survey,

---

* The height of the high or low water mark, in relation to Ordnance Survey Datum, varies from place to place; these lines cannot therefore be regarded as contours in any strict sense.

** Actually the line defining the channel of the river at low water, above the level of Low Water but below High Water.

concerned with the presentation of archaeology on its maps, the accelerating destruction of archaeological sites and features was a serious matter. This had begun with the ploughing-up campaign of the First World War and although it had slackened after 1920 it returned with increasing vigour after 1939. The second attack was continued after 1945 by the encouragement of ploughing of marginal lands for grants, thus threatening the areas where many antiquities still survived. The building of all kinds of service installations during the war was followed by the development of new towns, housing estates and various public services, the whole process being strongly reinforced by the use of earth-moving machinery which made the levelling of a large site the work of an hour. The Forestry Commission also added its quota of destruction by breaking up moorland areas for planting and by masking the surface detail of large areas under dense stands of conifers. All this taken together suggested that before the opening of the twenty-first century most of the less important features of field archaeology would be doubly things of the past.

It was a matter of public concern that, even though this destruction might be inevitable, it should not take place without some record of what was swept away. The Ordnance Survey was the only organization likely to move quickly enough across the country to make such a record in a comparatively short time, and its current revision programme, planned to end before the century, provided just the opportunity needed. The Survey's archaeological section was therefore reorganized and expanded.

Crawford had foreseen some of the future needs of the Branch in a memorandum which he submitted in 1944, but the post-war developments exceeded even his expectations. After 1947 the Branch was gradually enlarged as the general revision got into its stride, and it acquired the status of a Division. This expansion was not easy, as none of the small number of pre-war staff had returned, and the only field of recruitment was the Ordnance Survey itself; the number of men likely to be fully capable of specialized archaeological work was inevitably small. However, under its new Archaeology Officer, who took over a staff of four, the Branch increased until, on his retirement, Phillips was able to hand over to his successor, Mr R. W. de F. Feachem, an Archaeology Division with a strength of sixty-five.

RESEARCH AND RECORDING

The treatment of field archaeology demanded the co-ordination of three stages: the gathering of accurate information, careful field reconnaissance and survey (which did not include the detailed study or excavation of sites), and the correct insertion of the results on the published maps and plans.

The first of these required research into sources, which meant that the whole literature of the subject since the late seventeenth century had to be examined, including the large number of local publications as well as those of national scope. All available air photographs had to be scrutinized, the contents of museums reviewed and local organizations consulted. Field reconnaissance had to proceed well in advance of the Survey's revision programme. The field staff were briefed on the possibilities of each area and made their own contacts with local informants. They had to be competent to examine literary sources at need and to maintain good relations and an exchange of information with local museums. The results of their investigations, along with the surveys, were then returned to the office staff who sent them, with the necessary instructions, to the appropriate part of the Field Division's regional organization, for incorporation in the new map. It was the responsibility of the office staff to see that all had been interpreted and positioned correctly and that descriptions were accurate. In the final publication they had to make sure that the material was appropriate to the scale of map and that correct type faces and sizes had been used. This system proved itself to be so efficient that the field divisions were prepared to accept the work of the Archaeology Division in all matters including the detail survey of the site.

The county in Britain has been an entity for over a thousand years and experience had shown that it formed the most convenient base for assembling information about antiquities. Counties are not archaeological regions in their own right but, south of the Border at least, many of them have possessed a local archaeological society for more than a century. In the first ten years after the war the priority given to the 1:1250 urban survey, with its limited number of antiquities, made it possible to complete the recording of a number of counties before the 1:2500 Overhaul, with its much greater demands on the archaeological surveyors, got properly under way. Between 1953 and 1960 the county system had to be temporarily abandoned because the Overhaul was going on in so many areas at the same time, but it became possible to revert to county recording in 1961, after a big effort had been made by the archaeologists to get well ahead of the Field Division surveyors.

Access to the necessary books was a continuing problem. The Ordnance Survey library of the inter-war period was inadequate – in any case it was entirely destroyed in 1940 – and Crawford worked from his own books or from external libraries, most of them a long distance from Southampton; but the post–1947 programme could only be worked easily if a library was quickly built up in the office. As in Crawford's day the personal library of the Archaeological Officer bore the brunt for a long time, but it was soon recognized that there must be easy access to books and for a while in 1948 it looked as though one of the suggestions made in Crawford's memorandum of 1944 would be realized by setting up the Archaeology Division in Cambridge close to specialized libraries. If this project had materialized it would have created its own problems of communication with the rest of the Ordnance Survey, but it failed through lack of accommodation in Cambridge. Staff now had to be sent every day from Chessington to read in London. By the end of 1950 the costly nature of this proceeding was plain and eventually a general policy of purchase was adopted by which all books were acquired at need.

The main record consisted of a card index based on parishes and originally grouped into counties; this was later reordered into the series of 100-kilometre squares of the National Grid. Each monument, site and archaeological find, with its map reference, received its own card arranged in a National Grid numbering sequence, along with an account of its present state at the time of the field section's visit. Where appropriate a sketch was added and sometimes also a snapshot photograph of quality good enough to aid identification. Any literary references were given, as well as the names of local informants. The contents of a card varied greatly with circumstances, and it was customary to collect all valid field information even though it was not always of sufficient importance to put on a published map. The purpose of this was twofold: to make a record of items which could otherwise escape notice elsewhere and to provide a body of information from which period maps could be compiled or revised. What appeared to be unimportant observations sometimes pointed the way to important sites only found later when the ground was thoroughly searched.

The Division also gathered material about historic sites, continuing a practice long antedating 1920, but it only concerned itself with buildings when they were either ancient ruins or structures of historical or antiquarian importance which should appear on the map. No attempt was made to survey them as buildings except for the basic ground plan but care was taken to describe them accurately.

A secondary record was kept on a complete set of the six-inch maps on which every feature or find was noted as it became known. In a limited number of areas of special density this record was kept on 1:2500 plans, and on one scale or the other it was easy to get a quick visual appreciation of the content of any area.

The Ordnance Survey maintained the contacts with honorary local correspondents so successfully developed by Crawford. With increased direct activity in the field, less emphasis was placed on this source than formerly but the debt which the Ordnance Survey owes to unofficial helpers is very great. It is also impossible to overestimate the value of the work done by the Cambridge University Committee for Air Photography under Professor J. K. S. St Joseph. A close liaison was kept with this body which, while receiving support from the Survey in the form of the necessary maps, provided the Archaeology Division with air photographs whose great fund of information completely transcended anything that could be made out on the ground.

FIELD RECONNAISSANCE AND SURVEY

Great Britain contains a large variety of visible field archaeology covering a period of nearly ten thousand years; more than one hundred and fifty different types have been recognized. The country is naturally divided into highland and lowland zones, roughly along a line from the Humber to the mouth of the Severn, and these two zones required somewhat different treatment from the field investigators. A larger proportion of readily visible features survived in the highland zone and in marginal lands, not because of the former existence of a larger ancient population there, but owing to a wider use of stone for construction and greater freedom from later interference. This is particularly evident in the Orkneys and Shetlands where traces of ancient life are very numerous, all depending on the use of stone where wood has always been a rare commodity. In the lowland zone ancient settlement was much heavier and many important monuments also survive, but the construction materials were usually perishable and where stone was employed it was often pillaged for later use. The true density of lowland settlement only becomes fully apparent on air photographs.

The survey task with extant and measurable features was normally greatest in the highland zone where much of the archaeology was not noted on the nineteenth-century plans. In the lowland zone, owing to the greater destruction of visible features, site antiquities were more common, and much of the field evidence consisted of scatters of pottery and other traces of settlement on land long under cultivation. It was here also that whole ancient landscapes could be seen on air photographs in sharp detail, which had to be recorded even though the complications of some of them were so great that much could not be shown on published large-scale plans whose main purpose would have been defeated by such a degree of encumbrance.

To deal with all this work there was a progressive increase in the staff to provide one field section to work in each of five of the six field regions, with two in the sixth, Scotland. Work in England and Wales progressed smoothly but adequate provision for Scotland was less easy. Much of the country is 500 miles from Headquarters and, while it has its full quota of archaeology, recording was laborious owing to the absence of a strong county interest. The complete resurvey by air methods of the remote and desolate highland areas at six-inch scale posed a new problem, as the population clearances which had continued for more than a century after 1750 created a special kind of recent archaeology requiring record. The ruins of many villages and crofts which are the traces left behind this migration stand desolate all over the Highlands and Islands, as in Sutherland where the pattern of the former settlement was totally disrupted by the clearance of 1814–20, and sites of villages like Grummore, Rodal and Truderscaig became mere heaps of stones.

The need to make a better effort in Scotland generally and to deal with the formidable Highland problem led in 1958 to the establishment of a sub-office in Edinburgh under the Assistant Archaeology Officer, with recording staff and field sections geared to the local need. Close co-operation between this detachment, the Royal Commission on Ancient and Historic Monuments (Scotland), the Inspectorate of the Ministry of Works, and Scottish archaeological interests generally, greatly improved this service in Scotland.

The special effort made by the Ordnance Survey in the general revision of its maps since the Second World War should go a long way towards completing the record of the country's field archaeology before much of it vanishes, and to providing material for the future use of the Royal Commission on Ancient and Historic Monuments. The progress of the Survey's main task also benefited by the better organization of archaeological work. Before 1947 the need for the revisers of the field divisions to pay attention to antiquities often slowed their rate of progress. They had to search for reliable informants, often in vain, and they had no expertise of their own on which to rely. The new organization enabled accurate archaeological surveys and descriptions to be supplied in advance of the post-war survey, correcting past errors and ensuring the authenticity of many new discoveries.

The product of nearly two hundred years of archaeological surveying by the Ordnance Survey was a national record not equalled or even approached by any other national survey. The series of maps published for common use in Great Britain are enriched with an immense amount of accurately sited, surveyed, and described material, which may be used as a firm basis for almost any line of archaeological research which proceeds from a study of the distribution of relics of the past.

Notes

1 H. St J. L. Winterbotham, *The National Plans*, OS Professional Papers, New Series, no. 16 (HMSO 1934) p. 68.
2 See p. 308.

34
Geodetic
Developments
1960–1974

The Readjustment of the Triangulation

As far as the Ordnance Survey's own operations were concerned, the co-ordinates of the stations of the Retriangulation and of lower order work based upon it were settled with virtual immutability in 1951 when the main body of the triangulation was completed, and this meant that, for some years, it was not altogether clear what was to be done about the various base measurements and scale and azimuth checks that had been carried out since then. There could be no question of altering the published co-ordinates or the maps based upon them, even military maps used by NATO. And since the accuracy and consistency of the National Grid co-ordinates, in spite of the recently discovered scale variations, were amply sufficient for practical purposes, both civil and military, to have attempted to revise them would have been most mistaken. The British were, of course, signatories of the NATO Standardization Agreement which adopted the UTM (Universal Transverse Mercator) grid but, characteristically, obtained a dispensation under which, on military maps of Britain, the National Grid would continue to appear but in a slightly modified form which made it acceptable as a 'UTM grid'. Nevertheless, the incompatibility of the National Grid with the European Datum did give rise to difficulties, principally in the military sphere, and in 1955 Brigadier G. Bomford, the Reader in Geodesy and Surveying at Oxford University, made a semigraphic adjustment of the triangulation, using the scale and azimuth data then available, in order to fit it into the European system. He incidentally used this readjustment to assess the misclosure of the USAF's SHORAN connection with Norway when compared with the adjusted British and European triangulations. This put the SHORAN positions of the British stations about 47 feet south and 53 feet west of their triangulation positions.[1]

This readjustment and the circumstances giving rise to it made it apparent that a more rigorous adjustment was desirable, and the *Annual Report* for 1954–5 publicly stated this objective for the first time:

> ... in the interests of geodetic knowledge, a readjustment is being carried out to take account of the measured bases and azimuths, and to convert the triangulation to terms of the new European Datum.

In the following year the *Report* added that the purpose of the readjustment was 'among other things, to obtain a more accurate Figure of the Earth'. Thus was history repeating itself: the main object of Clarke's Principal Triangulation had been precisely the same.[2]

The new policy of having, in addition to the immutable National Grid network, a purely scientific network not bound to serve any particular practical objective, was incorporated in the relevant Policy Statement in 1962. This was an important step: it made possible rational justification of geodetic operations to determine scale, azimuth and geoidal shape and helped to ensure that the Ordnance Survey would continue to have a valid scientific function, the function which gave it birth and which contributed much to its professional vigour but one which was in danger of becoming submerged in the ocean of the Department's increasing practical responsibilities. Developments in the world of science and technology occurring at that time made this change of policy particularly opportune. The importance of accurate knowledge of long distances on the Earth's surface was increasing, not least because of the stringent demands inherent in the accurate tracking of long range rockets and, a little later, of artificial satellites. At the same time the potentialities for adjusting large triangulations had been vastly increased with the advent of electronic computing. By this means not only could the size of an adjustment block be enormously increased but an adjustment could be repeated using the same computer program, at relatively small cost, in order to incorporate new data. Thus the scientific network would by no means be fixed and unalterable: it would evolve more or less continuously to take advantage of later developments.

The change was opportune also in that it coincided with an international move to readjust, in a consistent manner, all the triangulations of Europe. This project was sponsored by the International Association of Geodesy (IAG) and, from 1963 onwards, the objective of the Ordnance Survey to prepare the British network for incorporation in this adjustment assumed increased importance. So that scale might be further strengthened many more sides were measured by Tellurometer and by improved versions of the Geodimeter, more portable than the original and capable of operating over longer distances and in daylight. There was some hesitation at first as to whether these measurements should be arranged to form long continuous traverses across the length and breadth of Britain, or whether it was better to carry them out in groups distributed more or less evenly throughout the country; but the latter concept eventually carried the day.[3] The triangulation was strengthened by the observation of additional angles in areas where the geometry was somewhat weak, notably in the Irish Sea figure and the East Yorkshire figure, and in the general tidying-up some stations were eliminated.

A new connection between France and England exploited the recently discovered potentialities of the Tellurometer. It was between four stations on the Isle of Wight and south coast – Dunnose (10), St Catherine's Hill, Coringdon (11) and The Verne – and three stations of the French primary triangulation on the northern coast of the Cotentin Peninsula near Cherbourg – Digulleville, Flottemanville-Hague, and Mont Etolan. The Verne was sited within the grounds of Portland Prison, an establishment originally used for the incarceration of French prisoners of the Napoleonic War, but this unfortunate association was accepted by the French party with a good grace in the interests of geodesy. The operations took place between 2 May and 19 July 1963, both distance and angular measurements being made on as many cross-Channel lines as possible. Angular measurements were made by teams from each country observing at its own stations. Distance measurements by Tellurometer were made by separate French and British teams, operating their own instruments in pairs, one each side of the Channel. It had originally been supposed that the curvature of the Earth would make it impossible to measure the longest cross-Channel lines by Tellurometer direct, and plans were made to employ a 'line crossing' technique using instruments mounted on a survey ship of the Royal Navy sailing a course near the mid-point of each line. But a trial measurement of the Beachy Head–Dunnose line, 103 km in length, showed that most of the cross-Channel lines should be measurable direct. The line crossing technique was therefore used, with the aid of the survey ship HMS Scott, only for the longest line measured, (Coringdon–Mont Etolan, which was 117 km long) and even for this, direct measurement was also found to be possible.

In spite of the unprecedentedly long rays and other unusual difficulties, the operation was most successful; all ten of the possible cross-Channel lines were measured by the British party and six by the French, angular observations were made by both parties on all nine rays with intervisible terminals (the stations Coringdon and Mont Etolan were 'intervisible' by Tellurometer but not by theodolite because the path curvature for microwaves is considerably greater than for light waves). The observations were found to be very consistent, the greatest standard vector error of position, relative to The Verne, being 0.256 m at the most distant stations, or about $2\frac{1}{2}$ ppm of the distance.[4]

In 1969 the connection to Ireland was reinforced by the measurement of eight lines across the Irish Sea by Tellurometer, one of them 137 km in length, and three lines of the primary triangulation of Ireland by Geodimeter model 8, in co-operation with the Ordnance Survey of the Republic of Ireland.[5] In addition seven further pairs of Laplace azimuths were observed during 1967–8.

The IAG planned to deal with the European triangulation in conveniently laid out blocks, each of which was first to be internally adjusted before all of them were brought into mutual sympathy by a process of fitting by least squares at common stations at the edges. The British triangulation together with that of Ireland, north and south, and including the two connections with France and the SHORAN connection with Norway, formed Block VI. It was the intention eventually to include the observations of all these constituent elements in a single simultaneous adjustment, but this objective had to be approached in stages. The first step was to carry out a 'free' adjustment of the British triangulation, that is, an adjustment making use only of the observed angles and ignoring the measurements of distance and azimuth, in order to enable the geometrical strength of the network to be assessed. This was completed as a single simultaneous adjustment in 1968.[6] The next step was to repeat the readjustment making use of all data available. This was done by the Ordnance Survey in 1970 and repeated independently by Nottingham University. Both adjustments dealt with all observations simultaneously and differed only slightly from each other in the method adopted for weighting.

The free adjustment of 1968 showed a marked improvement over the original adjustment as regards scale variation which was reduced from a range of about 40 ppm to about 15 ppm for the triangulation of the mainland. Some of this improvement must have been due to the geometrical strengthening of the net, but probably most of it derived from the fact that the whole triangulation had been adjusted in a single block rather than as a number of individual figures. The adjustments of 1970, which again dealt with the British triangulation as a single block, made use of 1900 observed directions between 292 stations, 180 measured distances and 15 observed Laplace azimuths, one of which was derived from observations made with the transit circle at Greenwich by the Royal Greenwich Observatory. The Laplace azimuth at the Cooke Transit at Herstmonceux was not used because there was an existing Laplace azimuth for the ray Herstmonceux Pillar–Fairlight Down. The existing value differed by only 0".12 from the Cooke Transit value and was preferred because the latter had to be transferred to a triangulation side via the short ray to Pevensey. The results from Nottingham University and the Ordnance Survey agreed closely with each other: Herstmonceux was taken as the origin for both and the greatest difference in co-ordinates, which occurred at the furthest station, Saxavord (463), 1112 km distant, was only 0.35 m in easting and 0.66 m in northing.[7] The adjustments produced agreement with the measured distances to within 5 ppm and with the measured azimuths to within half a second in the case of the Ordnance Survey and within about one second for Nottingham, the difference being due to the different weightings adopted. The discrepancies with the earlier adjustment were, however, considerable, reaching a maximum (relative to the origin) of about 23 m in northing and 4 m in easting, the earlier value being the greater in each case. The readjusted positions were clearly more accurate than the original and were probably within one or two metres of the truth (or 1–2 ppm of the distance from Herstmonceux).

Satellite Geodesy

The launching of the first artificial Earth satellite, Sputnik I, by Russia in October 1957 was an event of immeasurable significance in many contexts, not least that of geodesy. Within a few weeks of the launching, a most important geodetic quantity, namely the polar flattening of the Earth, which formerly could only be calculated from the results of laborious triangulation and astronomical observations and whose value lay uncertainly somewhere between 1:297 and 1:299 was firmly established as 1:298.3, a figure which has since been refined only by the addition of further decimal places. This was achieved by dynamical consideration of the satellite's orbit; however, it was the geometrical application of the artificial satellite that first interested the Ordnance Survey. In this application the direction of the satellite, photographed by a powerful camera against a background of stars, may be accurately determined. If this is done simultaneously from a number of points, separated by (say) some hundred of kilometres, and if such observations are repeated many times for different satellite positions, a three-dimensional framework of observed directions can be built up, comparable to a terrestrial triangulation, from which relative positions can be calculated, given at least one accurately known distance in the framework, usually the distance between two of the stations.

From the outset the Ordnance Survey took an active part in both national and international studies and projects in this new field. The Royal Radar Establishment at Malvern had developed special cameras for tracking rockets, and the Ordnance Survey, in co-operation with it, carried out trials in 1964 using an experimental model. In December of the same year the IAG set up a West European Sub-Commission for Satellite Triangulation, and the Director of Field Surveys (and Director General designate) Brigadier R. C. A. Edge, was appointed President. In the following year observations continued at Malvern using two large permanently-installed cameras with elaborate timing equipment, recently built to the design of Mr J. Hewitt of the Royal Radar Establishment. The Sub-Commission launched an international project for a satellite triangulation network covering the whole of Europe, with all the principal nations participating. From the outset the observations of the Hewitt camera, operated by personnel of the Ordnance Survey, played an important part. Britain also set up an international satellite-prediction service, operated by the Radio Research Station at Slough, which was an essential element in obtaining the necessary simultaneous observations at widely-separated camera sites. Shortly after this the Ordnance Survey acquired the two Hewitt cameras and formally established a Satellite Tracking Unit of eight surveyors and a scientific officer. One of the cameras remained at Sheriff's Lench, between Pershore and Malvern, and the other was moved to the outskirts of Edinburgh to be operated by the staff of the Royal Observatory there. Mr Hewitt, a Senior Principal Scientific Officer, transferred to the establishment of the Ordnance Survey and continued to give advice and to supervise the operations in the Malvern area until his death in 1975.

Since that time the Ordnance Survey and the Hewitt cameras have taken a prominent part in several other international projects, co-operating with observing stations in many parts of the world, including the United States, Russia, Africa and South America, and progressively contributing to a vastly improved knowledge of the exact size and shape of the Earth, the relation between its continents, the form of its equipotential surface – the 'geoid' – and the nature of its upper atmosphere. This new knowledge has been of cardinal importance in many fields, including space research and the guidance of space vehicles.

In 1975 the results of the Western European satellite triangulation were still being analysed. In order to give reliable scale to the system, accurate measurement of the distance between certain pairs of widely separated stations was necessary. One of these 'base-lines' connected Malvern with the Austrian station at Graz. It consisted of a precise traverse made by measuring contiguous sides of the existing triangulation with a laser Geodimeter, and observing Laplace azimuths at every other station (Plate 23). The Ordnance Survey measured the British section, between Malvern and Calais, during 1970 and 1971. Later, in 1971–2, a similar traverse was provided between Malvern and Edinburgh by measuring the lengths of nine triangulation sides and observing seven additional Laplace azimuths.

Geoidal Sections

In order to obtain the most complete and accurate results from triangulation, including satellite triangulation, it is necessary to know the form of the geoid in the neighbourhood of the observations. The geoid is the equipotential surface of the Earth at 'sea level' or, in other words, the surface of an idealized, unperturbed and uniformly dense ocean with unimpeded access to all parts of the land mass. The general features of the geoid may be determined from satellite observations but its details can only be found by terrestrial surveys. The most usual method is to take a 'geoidal section'. This is done by making astronomical observations for deviation of the vertical at a series of points along the line of the section, whose geodetic positions are accurately known. The profile of the geoid, which is everywhere perpendicular to the local vertical, may thus be drawn, using a method of interpolation to complete it between stations of observation. Since 1945 a number of geoidal sections have been observed in Britain. The first was a section from Tongue, in the extreme north of Scotland, to Dover, observed by Dr A. R. Robbins of Oxford University in 1950–2. Additional sections were taken along the line of the Malvern-Graz and Malvern-Edinburgh base lines in 1970–2 and in subsequent years further sections were added to build up an open framework of north to south and east to west lines. It was the intention, in due course, to incorporate all the work in a long term project to create a unified adjustment of the terrestrial and satellite triangulation frameworks of Europe.

Levelling Connections with Europe

The completion of the levelling of England and Wales occurred shortly after the IAG had resolved to produce a unified levelling network for the whole of Europe,[8] but at that time there was no possibility of incorporating the British levelling because the Channel gap was too wide even for the improved method of level transfer. There were suggestions for making a hydrostatic levelling connection by means of a submerged water-filled pipeline, as had been successfully done in Denmark to carry levelling across the Great Belt,[9] but the cost would have been very great for the wider crossing at the Strait of Dover. Eventually a connection was made by two scientists from the National Institute of Oceanography by means of an analysis of sea levels, currents and meteorological data observed over a continuous period of 723 days, on both sides of the Strait. The results, published in 1963,[10] showed that the Ordnance Survey's Newlyn Datum was 0.226m below Normaal Amsterdam Peil (NAP), the datum adopted for the European levelling. At the same time, and in response to the same resolution, the British levelling was recomputed in terms of geopotential units (GPU). The GPU is a measure of the work done in transferring unit mass from one equipotential surface to another at a different level. The equivalent orthometric height difference therefore depends on the value of gravity at the point of transference or, for practical purposes in terms of a levelling operation, the value at the instrument station. The recomputation gave heights in GPU for a number of recently incorporated tide gauges and, as expected, showed a steady rise in sea-level around Britain from south to north, with the level at Aberdeen the equivalent of about 430mm higher than at Newlyn. This tendency was not however reproduced in the European levelling on the eastern shore of the North Sea, which put sea-level in southern Norway only about 32mm higher than at Ostend.[11]

A readjustment of the whole British levelling network as a single figure was carried out in 1970 and was combined with an analysis of the recent French relevelling and of observations at tide gauges connected to the network of both countries. This showed an apparent rise of sea-level from Marseille to Brest of about 300mm, which gave some confirmation that sea-level did rise quite sharply from south to north.[12] But the whole question remained a doubtful one, the resolution of which would evidently have to await a fourth geodetic levelling of Great Britain in which every possible precaution would be taken against systematic error, especially systematic error affecting the north and south direction of levelling.

The National Gravity Reference Net

When the 1963 adjustment in terms of GPU was made, observed values of gravity along levelling lines were not available, and values dependent upon the latitude and height of each station were derived by means of a standard gravity formula. It was the objective to recompute and readjust the network on the basis of observed gravity values as soon as these were made available. To provide this data an operation was launched in 1964 in co-operation with the Institute for Geological Sciences (IGS). The instruments employed were gravity meters, which make use of a very sensitive spring-balance to compare the force of gravity at one station with that at another, the same instrument or group of instruments being taken to each station. The starting point must be at a place where the absolute value of gravity is accurately known and, in order to calibrate the gravimeters periodically, it is also necessary to have a base with terminals having different, known, gravity values. Provision of these basic requirements was the responsibility of the IGS which had over the years, in co-operation with others, established a number of reliable gravity base stations with values referred to Pendulum House at Cambridge. These were used to provide a Short Calibration Line near Macclesfield. Here a 60 milligal (mgal) difference in gravity between the terminals could be achieved by locating one in Macclesfield itself and the other 1200 feet higher on the Pennine scarp near by. This base was supplemented later by a second between Hatton Heath, near Chester, and Prees in Shropshire, which gave a 55 mgal difference for a much smaller difference in elevation.

The gravity measurements along the lines of the geodetic levelling network were the responsibility of the Ordnance Survey, whose observers used Worden gravity meters provided by the IGS. A characteristic of any gravity meter is a tendency to 'drift' with time, and this had to be allowed for. Measurements were done in two stages: in the first, gravity differences between Fundamental Bench-Marks (FBM) were determined by 'forward looping', differences for a number of intermediate Gravity Base Stations (GBS) being determined in the process; the second stage, described as 'infilling', gave the gravity differences between each GBS and all intermediate Flush Bracket Bench-Marks. Both procedures demanded opening and closing observations at the starting station within two hours, but in forward looping only one new station was observed in each loop whereas for infilling as many new stations were observed as the time limit allowed.

By the winter of 1967–8 all forward looping was completed, giving gravity values for all FBMs. A small calibration discrepancy of 0.1% between this network and the IGS base stations was found, as well as some local discrepancies of a few tenths of a milligal. To provide further control the IGS therefore observed a primary 'airport' net during June 1970, their gravity meters being conveyed by air from station to station. This net was then connected to the levelled network at convenient FBMs by the Ordnance Survey. In the meantime infilling had continued and was eventually completed by the winter of 1970–71, thus providing the Ordnance Survey with reliable gravity values at all its geodetic levelling bench-marks for the recalculation of the network in GPU. At the same time the IGS and the nation at large were provided with a consistent framework of accurate gravity stations much denser than had existed in the past, a facility of great value to geologists and geophysicists.

In June 1972 the IGS observed another network by aircraft, linking the British net to a number of European stations of the IAG International Gravity Standardisation Net 1971. It became possible to recalculate the British gravity and levelling network in terms which were entirely consistent with their European counterparts and to create the National Gravity Reference Net 1973, a system in which the average standard error in gravity at a FBM is 0.047 mgal, a satisfactory figure in comparison with the force of gravity itself, about 981 gals (1 gal = 1cm per sec^2), or the total range throughout Britain, about 750 mgal.[13]

Notes

1 *The History of the Retriangulation of Great Britain* (HMSO 1967).

2 See p. 143 *et seq.*

3 OSR 1966–7, p. 1.

4 *Geodetic Measurements across the English Channel 1963*, OS Professional Paper New Series, no. 21 (Ordnance Survey 1971).

5 OSR 1969–70, p. 2.

6 OSR 1968–9, p. 2.

7 V. Ashkenazi, P. A. Cross, M. J. K. Davies, D. W. Proctor, *The Readjustment of the Retriangulation of Great Britain, and its Relationship to the European and Terrestrial Satellite Networks,* OS Professional Paper New Series, no. 24 (Ordnance Survey 1972).

8 Resolution no. 5 of the 10th General Assembly of the International Union of Geodesy and Geophysics, Rome 1954.

9 N.E. Nörlund, *Hydrostatisk Nivellement over Store Baalt* (Geodaetisk Institut, Köbenhavn 1945).

10 D. E. Cartwright, J. Crease, 'A Comparison of the geodetic reference levels of England and France by means of the sea surface', Proceedings, Royal Society (A) 273, 1963, 558–80.

11 R. C. A. Edge, 'Connection of 3rd Geodetic Levelling to UELN', Paper presented at the 13th General Assembly of the International Association of Geodesy, Berkeley 1963.

12 J. Kelsey, 'Considerations arising from the 1970 Readjustment of the Geodetic Levelling of Great Britain', Symposium on Coastal Geodesy, Munich, July 1970.

13 *The National Gravity Reference Net 1973* (Institute of Geological Sciences and Ordnance Survey 1974).

35
The Restoration
of the
Survey –
A New Home
and New Aims
1968–1978

The New Headquarters Building

The announcement by the Government in 1956 of the abandonment of the Wellingborough project mentioned 'the advantages of retaining the traditional location at Southampton' but did not contain any promise that the whole of the Headquarters would be concentrated there; in fact the Minister refused to commit himself about the future of the staff at Chessington. However, concentration in better accommodation was clearly necessary, and the Wellingborough affair had indicated that this could only be at Southampton, where the Crabwood site was still available although partly occupied by temporary huts.

So in 1960 the first steps were taken to establish the Ordnance Survey in a permanent building designed especially for it – a situation it had never before enjoyed throughout its entire history. Treasury approval to the draft plan prepared by the Ministry of Public Buildings and Works was given in principle in January 1962 and the main features of the design of the building were largely settled in the same year by a team under the senior architect, Mr L. P. Murphy FRIBA. The first sod on the Crabwood site was cut in June 1964 and in April of the next year the Minister of Agriculture, the Right Honourable Frederick Peart MP, laid the foundation stone. This was almost his last act as Minister responsible for the Ordnance Survey, because this function passed soon afterwards to the Minister of Land and Natural Resources. The move of the staff into the new building began in June 1968, and was accompanied by the transfer of a formidable quantity of stores and equipment from the Chessington office and the old offices in Southampton; the only item that appeared to daunt the removers was the large number of glass negatives – about 160 000 – which were not only fragile but very valuable. The final stages of landscaping the surrounding grounds, tree planting, turf laying and the erection of a large sculptured mural, the work of Mr K. I. McCarter, in the space between the three main buildings, were accomplished by the spring of 1969 (Plate 26).

The formal opening of the new Headquarters by Her Majesty the Queen, accompanied by the Duke of Edinburgh, took place on 1 May. The opening ceremony was attended by the Minister of Housing and Local Government, the Right Honourable Anthony Greenwood MP and many other government and local dignitaries, as well as three former Directors General of the Ordnance Survey. After the Queen had unveiled a commemorative plaque, the Director General, Major-General R. C. A. Edge, presented Her Majesty with an album containing maps and aerial photographs of the Royal residences.

The several components of the Ordnance Survey Headquarters staff were now together for the first time in a building that had been specifically designed for them. Besides the administrative and divisional headquarters, the new offices housed all the drawing and reproduction sections, the map finishing sections, the Publication Division, all the various stores including the map store, the air photo plotting machines and other photogrammetric equipment, the Archaeology Division, the library, conference and exhibition rooms, and the computer, together with a staff of about three thousand. This concentration in one group of buildings had some rather paradoxical consequences; staggered hours and the numerous entrances, stairways and lifts had the effect of separating and even isolating different groups of staff who had hitherto seen each other every day, but these were minor matters compared with the splendid working conditions and the administrative convenience which the new surroundings provided.

As a monument to its early history, the Department was able to place on permanent exhibition in the main entrance hall the Ramsden eighteen-inch theodolite, first used for the survey of Kent in 1795. This beautiful instrument, almost as old as the Survey itself, had survived over fifty years of use in the field and every change of location from the Tower of London to its new position of honour at Crabwood.

The new centralization naturally called for some reorganization. In Map Publication Directorate all the drawing elements were now concentrated in one Cartography Division, and all the printing and associated processes in one Reproduction Division. For the reproduction sections the contrasts between the old and new settings were particularly striking: in the new building they had two adjoining working areas, each over an acre in extent, which were made more impressive by a large amount of new equipment; over the previous few years the routine replacement of much of the older printing and processing machinery had been delayed so that each unit could be installed directly into its permanent position. The bringing together of the Survey and Publication headquarters enabled the longer term planning functions, hitherto in two parts, to be combined in a new division which was also given responsibility for development. To succeed the old Chessington punched card unit, a new computer section was formed within the Geodetic Control Division to operate the newly-installed ICL 1902 computer. At about the same time the opportunity was taken to make a number of minor changes in Field Directorate including the decentralization of routine minor-control surveys and levelling to field regions, and the transfer of Air Survey Branch from Geodetic Control Division (now renamed Geodetic Services Division) to Field Division (now renamed Topographic Surveys Division). These changes in organization were completed by October 1970. Early in 1971 Publication Division was expanded to deal with wholesaling, and in the same year Finance Division was enlarged because of the introduction of full accounting. The developments in Publication, Finance and Planning increased the number of administrative and support staff at the expense of surveyors and draughtsmen; in 1955 the ratio of administrative and clerical staff to surveyors and draughtsmen was about 1:10, but by 1974 it had risen to about 1:6. However, some administrative grades were employed in the computer unit where they contributed to the technical work of the Department, so that the figures quoted somewhat overstate the extent of the change.

Staff Affairs and Training

For the Staff Associations the new era started reasonably well. In 1969 the Ordnance Survey Whitley Committee was given the status of a Departmental Whitley Council; in 1970 and 1971 there were satisfactory pay awards in line with the rising rates of pay outside the Civil Service. However, the Report of the Fulton Committee on the Civil Service (1968) introduced a new uncertainty with its proposal for a unified grading structure into which the current multitude of grades and classes would be absorbed,[1] and it was natural that the grading level to be accorded to the cartographic class should become a matter of concern. No easy success attended the efforts of the Institution of Professional Civil Servants on this issue, and by 1975 no decision had been reached. Another cause for anxiety, also born of the Fulton Report, was the question of 'hiving off', since the Ordnance Survey was clearly a possible candidate for conversion into an 'autonomous board or corporation'.[2] In general the Staff Side opposed such a change of status, and in 1969 obtained from the official management an undertaking that, if any positive moves were proposed affecting the Ordnance Survey, it would be consulted.

The efforts of the Department and others to bring into being a technician's qualification in surveying and cartography were at last successful when in 1968 the Department of Education and Science agreed to the introduction of Ordinary and Higher National Certificates in Surveying and Cartography, and to the setting up of a Joint Committee to prepare syllabuses and to administer the courses and examinations. The first ONC courses in these subjects started at the Southampton Technical College in 1970; the Ordnance Survey selected about thirty students each year on the basis of each candidate's possible promotion potential as well as his academic and practical ability. The existence of a genuine technician qualification had little or no effect on the Department's long-established craft training, which continued unchanged, but it offered a means of giving higher education and advanced training to those likely to be in the promotion field in the future. For more senior staff, for whom formal courses and examinations would not have been wholly suitable, a different way had to be found. Here the military connection was able to help, and in 1969 the School of Military Survey at Newbury agreed to run a series of advanced courses designed on very flexible lines so that senior staff with widely different education and experience could all benefit to the limit of their individual abilities. Similar courses for senior staff were started in the North-East London Polytechnic in 1973.

ONC courses for printers had been running for several years and two young members of the reproduction staff began attending classes at the Southampton College of Art in 1964; both of them eventually became professionally qualified and were appointed to professional posts in the Department. The recommendations of the Brown Committee of 1950, and the Estimates Committee of 1963, that there should be 'an avenue of promotion' for the technical staff to professional posts had at last borne fruit.

This overdue event was shortly followed by another of a very different kind which must have given some satisfaction to at least one section of the staff. Although women had worked in the drawing office, in map finishing and in the administration for many years, surveying in the field had always been an exclusively masculine preserve on the grounds that it was 'unsuitable' for women because it was arduous, solitary and took the surveyor into areas that were sometimes remote and occasionally insalubrious. But in 1972 when the recommendations of a Civil Service Committee on the employment of women were accepted by the Civil Service Department, other government departments were advised that 'it should be open to both men and women to be considered for any job in the non-industrial Civil Service and that appointments should be solely on the grounds of suitability and qualifications.' Faced with this edict the Ordnance Survey reconsidered its discriminatory attitude and in the latter part of the year recruitment to surveyor posts was extended to women. As might have been expected, this victory of principle over prejudice did not produce any dramatic changes. Few women were attracted to the field surveyor's life but those that were appointed proved to be entirely capable. During the next five years the number of women in the field never exceeded four.

Mapping

The metrication of the popular small-scale maps was delayed while public opinion was adapting itself to the idea of using metric units, the main point remaining to be settled being the decimal scale to replace the one-inch. One possibility, the 1:50 000, appeared to have more advantages than any of the others. The representatives of map users attending Ordnance Survey consultative meetings showed no nostalgic allegiance to the one-inch (a feeling virtually confined to the Ordnance Survey itself) and urged that the 1:50 000 should be introduced without delay. A review of the map market, carried out in 1970 by a market research agency, showed that public opinion also was generally more favourable towards the 1:50 000 than to any of the alternatives. The Ordnance Survey was anxious to go ahead with the new scale partly because the reproduction material of the one-inch was becoming rather expensive to maintain, but it was not until November 1971 that the Minister gave his approval for the production of a map at 1:50 000. Because the metrication issue was still controversial, he stipulated that imperial units should still be used for heights, contours and distances. By this time metric maps and map extracts were being printed in small numbers to meet the needs of schools; fortunately this confused state of affairs did not last very long and in 1972 authority was given for the new map to be in metric form. The first block of 103 sheets in the southern half of the country was published on 7 March 1974.

The introduction of the metric 1:50 000 did not mean a complete break with the past: the existence of the one-inch material and the need for economy in production led to the new map being a direct offspring of the old. Indeed, the First Series 1:50 000 was merely a photographic enlargement of the one-inch with some colour changes, although ingenious techniques were used to prevent the line thicknesses from becoming correspondingly enlarged. The need to change to the new sheet-lines (which were chosen with great care) as swiftly as possible provided ample justification for making the First Series in this way, but there was some disappointment among cartographers when the first sheets of the Second Series appeared and it was seen that the new map was only a redrawn enlarged one-inch following closely the style of the First Series (Plate 27). The Ordnance Survey certainly departed from tradition when it produced the 1:50 000.[3] Hitherto, changes in the design of the one-inch map, such as for the Fifth Edition and the Seventh Series, had been accompanied by redrawing from larger scale material, but in spite of publicity claims, no general attempt was made to exploit the possibilities of the new scale – indeed, some features previously shown were omitted (for example, tree symbols and parish boundaries). However, market research had revealed an overwhelming approval of the Seventh Series, tempered by the view that it was becoming overcrowded and hard to read, and as it was a primary requirement that the new map should sell well at a reasonably low price and recover the cost of its production, any radical redesign would have been, from a commercial point of view, wasteful and unnecessary. So the 1:50 000 was made to look rather like the one-inch, but sufficiently different to stand on its own feet. All the early indications from the map-buying public showed that this was what it wanted.

When Advance Revision Information was first publicized in 1962 it was regarded by the Publication Directorate as a minor eccentricity of Field Division which was perhaps of limited use to some local authorities. Edge had suggested in 1964 that it should become the main outlet for large-scales mapping information, but this was seen as a more serious threat to established interests and practices, and he was overruled. The notion that the fair-drawn lithographed large-scale map should be the final product of the Survey was very firmly rooted, but such developments as the printing-on-demand experiments, and the introduction in 1966 of an enlargement service both of the finished plans and of the continuous revision field sheets, gradually brought about a change of attitude. In 1969 photographic reductions of 1:1250 maps to 1:2500 were offered to users who wanted more up-to-date versions of the latter scale in town areas,* and in the next year another variation, this time in the form of 35mm film mounted in aperture cards, was put on the market. The choice of 35mm microfilm was, on the face of it, surprising in view of the difficulties encountered with 70mm in the printing-on-demand trials. However, the two were intended to fulfil quite different functions: the 70mm method was designed to replace lithography whereas the 35mm aperture cards merely provided an additional service. The mapping operation began to be seen as the creation of a bank of topographical data which could be stored in different forms and from which information could be drawn off in many different ways. Quite suddenly Advance Revision Information became a respectable marketable product and its handling was transferred to Publication Directorate. To mark this rebirth it acquired a new title – the Supply of Unpublished Survey Information (SUSI) in 1972. Meanwhile the use of microfilm was extended; between 1971 and 1974 several Ordnance Survey agents, first in Plymouth and later in Cardiff, London and elsewhere, were supplied with banks of 35mm microfilm from which they were able to make prints on the spot of any of the large-scale maps within their area. In 1973 microfilms of SUSI documents were added to the agents' microfilm banks so that they were sometimes able to offer more up-to-date information than that shown on the fair-drawn plans; in 1977 the microfilm service was given a separate identity under the title of SIM (Survey Information on Microfilm). Lastly a start was made on providing continuous revision offices with simple copying equipment so that copies of the survey documents, in their most up-to-date form, could be supplied directly to the public.

AUTOMATED CARTOGRAPHY

The adaptation to mapping of automatic drafting machines controlled by information stored on magnetic tape was first studied extensively in this country by the Experimental Cartography Unit (ECU) of the Royal College of Art. From the outset the Ordnance Survey was greatly interested in the possibilities of digital mapping and in 1969 and 1970 the ECU carried out some experimental work on the Department's behalf.[4] But the main interest of the ECU was in mapping at very small scales, primarily of a thematic character, whereas the Ordnance Survey soon turned its attention to the many uses to which a large-scale data bank could be put, both within the Survey itself for map production and as a product in its own right that might be sold to organizations such as large local authorities and public undertakings, who were themselves interested in storing distributional information in digital form. The Ordnance Survey acquired its first digitizing table in April 1970 and also a digital encoder for fitting to the output shafts of a Wild A8 stereoplotting machine. Thenceforward progress was rapid and in October 1970 the digital mapping experiments became the responsibility of the new Planning and Development Division which, although small in size, had a nucleus of professional officers. In the same month a computer-driven drum plotter was purchased and by March 1971 the development of the technique was practically complete.[5]

Major-General B. St G. Irwin, who became Director General in September 1969, was soon faced with the necessity of making several crucial decisions. One of these concerned the extent and the pace

---

* The derived 1:2500 had always been notorious for being out of date. Eventually, in 1973, production of the lithographed derived 1:2500 was suspended.

of the Department's commitment to digital mapping. Great progress had been made but the technique was still in its infancy and the cost of the equipment, which might well have become quickly obsolescent, was very high. On the other hand, if the Ordnance Survey failed to exploit the opportunity offered by digital mapping, others would certainly do so and, once lost, the lead would be difficult to regain. General Irwin rejected a wait-and-see strategy and took a bold and imaginative line. In a policy directive he wrote:

> The full potential of an automated system will not be realised unless and until all the required topographic data is banked in digital form and continually updated . . . [an automated system] is a proper long term objective for the Department . . . In the short term the stage has been reached where further progress can only be made with the aid of a pilot production project. The Department will therefore undertake [this] using automated techniques as soon as circumstances permit.[6]

These 'circumstances' included the purchase and installation of eight more digitizing tables and a precision master plotter, as well as the training of digitizing and editing staff for Cartography Division, which was put in charge of the production project. The trials covered an urban 1:1250 area in Hampshire and a block of rural 1:2500 maps in Herefordshire, the latter being also intended to provide a data bank for experimental 1:10 000 maps. In March 1974 the cost of making large-scale maps by digital methods was found to be rather higher than by conventional techniques, but many probable consequential advantages had not been taken into account. In the financial year 1973–4, ninety-two 1:1250 maps and 179 square kilometres of 1:2500 mapping were produced by digital methods; in the following year, when about seventy draughtsmen and fourteen digitizing tables were employed in the digitizing and editing section, the output rose to about five hundred 1:1250 and nine hundred 1:2500 maps.[7]

Computerized Planning

The ICL 1902 computer installed in the new building in August 1968 undertook all the work of the Chessington punched card equipment and also the photogrammetric computations that had previously been sent to the National Physical Laboratory. To this were soon added further geodetic computations, the pay roll, computer-based planning, digital mapping and map-order processing. By 1970 two shifts were failing to deal with the load of work and in March 1971 the ICL 1902 computer was replaced by a larger machine (an ICL 1904) obtained second-hand from another government department. By the end of the year the ICL 1904 was itself becoming overloaded and in 1972 a study was initiated to assess the Ordnance Survey's future needs and to recommend the best type of computer to deal with them. Preliminary estimates suggested that it would require at least twenty, and perhaps as much as sixty, times the capacity of the ICL 1902. The processing of planning data and management information were to be among its principal tasks.

The ability to make accurate forecasts of output and man-power requirements had long been the Department's most pressing need. Early in 1969 a firm of management consultants, working in conjunction with the Civil Service Department, carried out a feasibility study for a computer-based planning system, on the basis of which it was decided in March to develop a mathematical simulation of the large-scale mapping operation which would enable the management to study the effects of variations in planning strategy quickly and easily. The mathematical model was handed over to Planning and Development Division, and after six months of testing was ready to begin work in January 1971. The 1972–3 version of the long-term plan resulted from the consolidation of thirteen variations and alternatives produced from the model in the computer; this degree of refinement would have been quite impossible in the days of 'manual' planning. The consultants' assignment was extended in 1970 to include a preliminary study for a computer-based short-term planning and control system which could be linked to the long-term planning model.

Marketing

The Ordnance Survey resumed responsibility for the direct distribution of maps to the retail trade in January 1971 and in April the main agency for England and Wales was transferred from Edward Stanford Ltd. to Cook, Hammond and Kell of Caxton Street, London; Stanford's continued to act as an Ordnance Survey agent, concentrating on the sale of prints from microfilm.

Early in the previous year it had been decided to use a computer-based method for processing customers' orders. A system was devised by a firm of consultants and accepted in July 1970; this left far too little time for proving and when put into use in 1971 it was beset with teething troubles. The Post Office dispute added to the difficulties and a substantial backlog of orders accumulated, but by the middle of the year most of the faults in the computer program had been put right, and the planned standard of a forty-eight hour service had been reached. The Ordnance Survey's small force of sales representatives, who previously had dealt only with the provincial agents, was increased from three to seven in March 1971, and an intensive effort was made to diversify and increase the number of sales outlets. Once it was running smoothly the new method of distribution produced gratifying results. Issues of small-scale maps rose from 2.4 million in 1969–70 to 3.02 million and 3.13 million in the two following years.

In the copyright field, too, the drive to increase revenue was much in evidence. Charges were increased by 25 per cent in 1970, 10 per cent in 1972 and 5 per cent in 1973, and the licensing arrangements with various groups of users were reviewed. The aim of these reviews was to relate licence fees as closely as possible to the amount of copying actually done and where necessary to replace the former flat-rate system with a more equitable way of assessing the fees. Between 1970 and 1974 the licences of local authorities, surveyors and estate agents, architects, solicitors, construction engineers, water authorities and printers were reviewed and in 1973 charges to government departments were introduced. The increase in revenue was again gratifying. Royalty revenue in 1969–70 was £628 000; it rose to approximately £1 million in 1972–3 and to over £2 million in 1973–4, although the last figure was inflated by advance payments and by the clearance of arrears.[8]

The review of the map market in 1970 was intended primarily to assist in the formulation of map-marketing policies by determining what the various scales were used for and consequently what information should be shown. Apparently, interest in maps on the part of the general public reached a peak at about age forty-four, was noticeably greater in men than in women and was significantly higher in the south than in the north.[9] An inference drawn from the report of the market survey was that map-makers could easily get out of touch with the preferences of the uncritical map user and that cartographic refinement was not necessarily a selling point when a larger map market was being sought. Nevertheless, many of the professional staff were uneasy about the increasingly commercial attitude of the Department and were inclined to echo Matthew Arnold's belief that it was the Government's duty to provide a good map of its country, not a cheap one.

In 1972 attention was centred on publicizing the Ordnance Survey's services to professional people and particularly the diversifications of its large-scale products, but subsequent advertising campaigns reflected some of the conclusions of the market survey. The launch of the 1:50 000 in 1974 became the focus of a special publicity effort; about 1.25 million copies of the southern block of sheets had been supplied to retailers by the end of the month of March, only three weeks after publication.

The new commercial spirit was soon showing significant results, although to some extent the Department was caught between the crossfire of the Government's call to maximize revenue and its prices and incomes policy. At the beginning of the decade the ratio of revenue to expenditure was about 33 per cent, but in 1972–3 there was a rise to 39 per cent which increased to nearly 47 per cent in the next financial year.*

In order to make its products and activities more easily identifiable by the general public, the Ordnance Survey commissioned the Central Office of Information in 1968 to design a 'house style' for the Department. This consisted of a new Ordnance Survey symbol and a distinctive moss-green colour for publicity material and official vehicles.

Management Accounting and Accountable Management

From March 1970 to August 1971 an inter-departmental committee of officials – the Committee on the Ordnance Survey – met to conduct a 'management review of the organization and operation of the Ordnance Survey'; the activities of the Committee, including its preliminaries and aftermath, formed a background which coloured the life of the Department from 1969 to 1973. While the Committee was still sitting its deliberations encouraged certain enterprises which were consistent with its line of

* The expenditure columns of the financial statement in the annual *Report* for 1974–5 included a new heading: 'Payments from Vote of other Departments' which meant that services provided by the Department of the Environment and HMSO, hitherto ignored in the published figures, were shown as costs incurred by the Ordnance Survey. The new charges were also incorporated retrospectively for the three previous years, introducing discrepancies between the figures in the 1974–5 statement and those published earlier. The percentages quoted here do not take these charges into account.

thought but which it did not necessarily originate. Included in this category were developments in planning, management accounting and information systems, marketing, pricing policy, and the presentation of large-scales information.

The management review had as one of its objects the assessment of 'the extent to which the Survey might be expected to operate in the context of accountable management', and this had the effect of accelerating the movement towards more sophisticated forms of accounting which had been going on slowly for many years. At first the Ordnance Survey was advised by accountants from the Treasury and the Civil Service Department, but in December 1971 it appointed its own professional accountant. Some months before, the Treasury had suggested a framework for a management accounting system, including full cost-accounts, operating accounts, balance sheet and budgeting, and during the latter part of the year a trial of this system was begun. At the same time a start was made with accountable management: each manager was to be held responsible for his performance against budgets, standards of achievement and other tests. Budget centres and cost centres were defined and an immense flood of new jargon passed into the Ordnance Survey vocabulary.

Although the method of providing short-term control data suggested by the consultants in 1970 was not adopted, it was obvious that a computer-based Management Information System, designed to provide managers with statistical information about the work for which they were responsible, had to be developed to complement management accounting and budgeting. Accordingly, in April 1971 a Management Information System Project Team was formed to design such a system in collaboration with the planners, accountants and production managers. All the management systems depended for their effectiveness on the swift processing of a large amount of statistical data and its rapid distribution to managers, but this quick response could only be obtained by full computer processing, and the computer was too small for this to be done. Managers were thus faced with the extra work of providing the data without experiencing the benefits of the system, and they were inclined to withhold judgment, particularly on budgeting where variances between planned and actual performances were revealed several months after the period to which they related.

New Aims

The conclusions of the review undertaken by the Committee on the Ordnance Survey were made public in the form of an announcement in the House of Commons on 19 February 1973 by the Secretary of State for the Environment and in a supplementary statement by the Director General on the Secretary of State's behalf soon afterwards.[10]* This was nearly a year and a half after the Committee had concluded its deliberations but the intervening period had not been without incident. The secrecy of the Committee's proceedings caused great public resentment when it became known in November 1972 that the report itself would not be published; by this time rumours about hiving off were in circulation, and this had led to questions in the House in early February.

The Minister's announcement contained new aims for the Ordnance Survey which appeared to imply that the production of the basic scales and the six-inch map would if necessary receive Exchequer support but that all the other scales would be produced only if the costs were covered by payments from users. The Director General's statement on points of detail included two items which were to start a considerable controversy.[11] The first concerned the 1:25 000 map: if the public sector requirement for this series did not justify its production, the Ordnance Survey was free to publish only those individual sheets which it considered the market could support. The second related to tertiary levelling: after a transition period tertiary levelling would cease except as a repayment service. The fate of the 1:25 000 was a cause for regret within the Ordnance Survey because the Second Series was one of its best cartographic productions; but the need for the scale had always been questionable and it was doubtful if the Department had the resources to maintain the series properly. The loss of tertiary levelling, although it attracted much less public interest, was another matter. It formed the major part of the basic survey of heights and its usefulness, whether in connection with floods, subsidence, disasters like Aberfan, engineering works or just drains, depended to a large extent on the fact that it was in being; many surveyors both inside and outside the Department doubted if it was possible to provide an effective levelling service on a 'you can have it if you pay for it' basis.

Public protest on the apparent intention to abandon the 1:25 000 if no public sector need was found to exist was surprisingly vigorous and sustained. There were many questions in the House in March

* Responsibility for the Ordnance Survey passed to the Department of the Environment when the latter absorbed the Ministry of Housing and Local Government in December 1970.

and April and almost continuous correspondence in *The Times* during July and August. Meanwhile the Ordnance Survey and the Department of the Environment had been carrying out an extensive consultation (as they were charged to do in the Secretary of State's announcement) on several issues: how the repayment levelling service was to be operated, whether the criteria defining 1:10 000 and 1:2500 basic areas should be changed, whether the map content of the three largest scales met the needs of users both public and private and – this was a new development – whether a cheaper 1:25 000 map made by direct photographic reduction would be acceptable to the private sector. The opinions of 2292 organizations were sought mainly by means of questionnaires and as the summer progressed the responses began to come in.

On 31 July the Royal Society sent a letter to the Secretary of State, containing a plea for adequate consultation before decisions were taken affecting the interests of the scientific community, and giving the opinions of scientific bodies on the two proposals under dispute. Several professional organizations also wrote to the Minister opposing the abandonment of the current levelling arrangements. This weight of opinion, combined with the evidence gathered by the questionnaires, convinced the Minister; he made his decisions known, without waiting for the end of the Parliamentary recess, in a letter to the Royal Society, in which he stated that the 1:25 000 map would continue to be produced as a national service with a content similar to the Second Series, and that tertiary levelling on the old basis would be retained with, possibly, some modification in detail.[12]

The Minister's letter also contained two important statements of principle which significantly changed the emphasis of the announcement of February. He wrote:

It is not our intention that products and services should be abandoned altogether if it is in the public interest that they should continue to be available

and elsewhere:

. . . in such cases [when in the public interest] Exchequer support will if necessary continue.

This amounted to a considerable broadening of the terms of the original announcement in which it appeared that Exchequer support would be restricted to the basic scales and the 1:10 000. The second change was, in effect, a broadening of the definition of 'the public interest':

. . . the Government will have regard both to the requirements of the private sector as well as to those of the public sector.

In the original announcement the needs of the private sector were apparently disregarded when the future of the 1:25 000 was made dependent on 'the needs of the public sector'.

The review of basic scale areas led to the confirmation of the existing criteria for defining the boundary between the 1:2500 and 1:10 000 basic scales, and the answers to the questions on map content showed that, in general, current information and forms of presentation met the needs of most map users.

The Ministerial statement of February 1973 had concluded with the words:

. . . but one possibility [for financing] is that the Ordnance Survey might operate as a Government Department with a statutory trading fund.

The Government's Trading Funds Bill, published in May 1973, was an 'enabling' measure and did not in itself institute a change in the financial status of any department; however, several possible candidates were mentioned in the Bill and among them was the Ordnance Survey. When the Bill came before the House of Lords in July[13] and both Houses in October, much of the debate centred on the affairs and the financing of the Ordnance Survey. Eventually a House of Lords' amendment deleting any reference to the Ordnance Survey from the Bill was accepted by the Government,[14] and in two further amendments a safeguard was inserted which dealt with the procedure to be followed if at any time in the future the Ordnance Survey, or any similar department, was considered to be a suitable body for financing by means of a trading fund under the Act. Before an order directing the establishment of such a trading fund could be laid, the Act required the responsible Minister to consult appropriate persons and to lay before Parliament a report on these consultations.[15]

The trading fund issue, considered in isolation, might well have caused little comment inside or outside the Houses of Parliament, but the conclusions of the Committee on the Ordnance Survey, as revealed in the announcements of February, made it only too clear what might happen if commercial considerations were allowed to dominate an organization that was seen as providing a valued national service. Within the Ordnance Survey itself the question of the trading fund did not generate as much concern as the proposals about mapping and levelling. Financing by means of an annual Vote, as well as being in some ways wasteful, was inflexible when it came to planning resources for the longer term, and the prospect of being freed from this constraint had its attractions. But the basic scale mapping of the country was necessarily a national service paid for largely by the Exchequer, so that its financing under a trading fund would presumably have been effected as a notional sale of large-scale maps to, say, the Department of the Environment. To many, including the Director General, this seemed an artificial and needless complication, especially as it would merely have transferred the net cost of the national survey to the Vote of another Department.

The events of 1973, including the announcements of February, the reviews, the Minister's letter to the Royal Society, and the debates on the Trading Funds Bill led to the formulation of principles which were of great significance. One of these emphasized the primary importance of the 'needs of users'. The Royal Society had, in its letter of 31 July, proposed a new way of determining the 'needs of the scientific community', and in his reply the Minister had given it his approval:

> I would like to adopt your suggestion that the Royal Society should sponsor a meeting with representatives of a wide range of scientific disciplines . . . to consider how to improve the arrangements for ensuring that the Ordnance Survey are aware of the scientific interest in their work.[16]

The Ordnance Survey's consultative meetings had previously suffered from the weakness that in general the delegates came to listen and rarely offered any continuous or authoritative guidance. The Department had long been aware of these defects and had already decided in principle that better consultation could only be secured by transferring the initiative and much of the responsibility to groups of users. The Royal Society proposals were timely in that they provided the opportunity for adopting this concept and extending it to other groups of map users. The Ordnance Survey immediately began discussions with professional bodies and with local authority associations with this object in view; by the autumn of 1974 three such consultative committees had been formed, sponsored by the Royal Society, the Royal Institution of Chartered Surveyors and the Association of County Councils. In 1975 a fourth was added to cater for recreational interests, under the sponsorship of the Central Council for Physical Recreation.

The Ordnance Survey emerged from the debates and consultations with its function as the Government's central surveying and mapping organization confirmed; none of its services had been changed in substance. Towards the end of 1973 public controversy died away and the Department gratefully resumed its normal existence.

In January 1974 the Government announced that in future the post of Director General of the Ordnance Survey would no longer be filled by a major-general on the active list. On his retirement from the Army on 6 April 1974 Major-General B. St G. Irwin became the first Director General to be a Civil Servant and so brought to an end the Ordnance Survey's long tradition of military direction.*

One of the less obvious effects of the Committee on the Ordnance Survey was that attention was diverted from the need to re-examine and redefine the Survey's role for the period following the completion of the restoration, something which should, perhaps, have been done early in the 1970s. The Ordnance Survey therefore had to face the economic pressures of the middle seventies before its future functions had been established and endorsed by the Government, and consequently the inevitable measures of economy were applied in ways that sometimes seemed arbitrary and unsupported by any clear objectives. On 6 May 1977, when the Secretary of State for the Environment eventually announced that he proposed to put in hand 'a study . . . of national survey needs',[17] he said that new financial targets had been set for the Survey – to increase from one-fifth to about one-quarter the proportion of costs recovered on large-scale information and on the 1:25 000 series, and to achieve full cost recovery including servicing of capital on the small-scale maps and survey information 'as soon as possible over the next five years'.

This announcement coincided with the retirement of Major-General Irwin; his successor, Mr Walter P. Smith, the Survey's first civilian Director General, found that he was to be immediately faced with the onerous responsibility of guiding the Department through an official review that might well prove to be as significant for the Ordnance Survey as the Dorington inquiry of 1892. As in the late 1880s, when the original survey was nearing its completion but no unequivocal commitment to revision had been made by the Government, so in the 1970s the outlook of the Department was clouded by uncertainty and anxiety. What now appeared to be needed was a new Committee of Inquiry in the Dorington mould, which would be open to receive evidence and would produce an authoritative plan for the future. In January 1978 the Secretary of State announced the appointment

---

* Agreed to by the Secretary of State for the Environment in consultation with the Secretary of State for Defence and the Lord Privy Seal, 22 Jan. 1974.

of a Review Committee, chaired by Sir David Serpell, which appeared to be so constituted that this might be accomplished. Its terms of reference were short but comprehensive:

> Taking into account the views of users and other interested parties, in the context of national surveying and mapping needs, to consider and make recommendations about the longer term policies and activities of the Ordnance Survey and ways of financing them.[18]

Notes

1 *Report of the Committee on the Civil Service 1966–68*, I, paras. 214–43: PP 1967–8, Cmnd. 2638, XVIII.
2 *Ibid.* paras. 188–91.
3 For 1:50 000 revision, see p. 339f.
4 M. St G. Irwin, 'Developments in Automated Cartography at the Ordnance Survey', *Cartographic Journal* 1971, 8, no. 2, pp. 133–8.
5 R. C. Gardiner-Hill, *The Development of Digital Maps*, OS Professional Paper no. 23, 1972.
6 Quoted in *ibid.* paras. 4.2, 4.3.
7 OSR 1974–5, p. 10.
8 OSR 1969–70, App. 7; OSR 1973–4, App. 7.
9 B. Drewitt, 'The Changing Profile of the Map User in Great Britain', *Cartographic Journal* 1973, 10, no. 1.
10 *Hansard*, 851, House of Commons, 19 Feb. 1973, col. 32.
11 J. B. Harley, 'Changing the Minister's Mind', *Area* 1974, 6, no. 3.
12 The Royal Society's letter and the Minister's reply are quoted in *Area,* 1973, 5, no. 4, pp. 268–70.
13 *Hansard*, 344, House of Lords, 26 July 1973, cols 1950 *et seq.*
14 *Hansard*, 345, House of Lords, 17 Oct. 1973, cols 338 *et seq*; and 861, House of Commons, 24 Oct. 1973, cols 1391 *et seq.*
15 *Hansard*, 861, House of Commons, 24 Oct. 1973, cols 1391 *et seq.*
16 *Area*, 1973, 5, no. 4, pp. 268–70.
17 *Hansard*, 931, House of Commons, 6 May 1977, cols 299–300.
18 *Hansard*, 942, House of Commons, 17 Jan. 1978, cols 141–2.

Plates

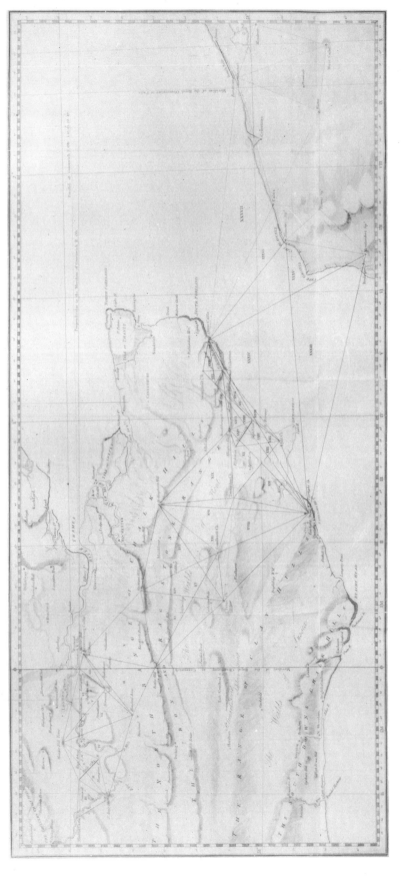

PLATE 1. Roy's Triangulation 1787-8.

Ordnance Survey

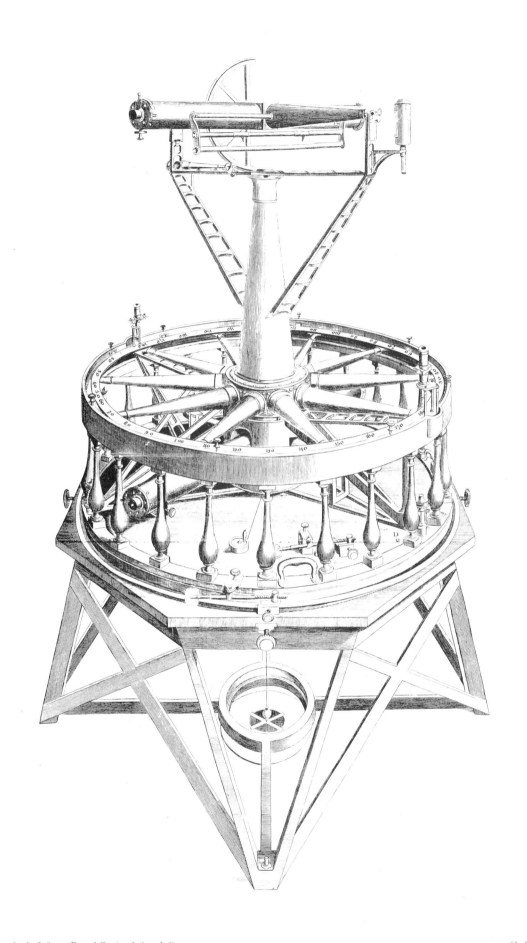

PLATE 2. Ramsden's 3 foot 'Royal Society' theodolite.

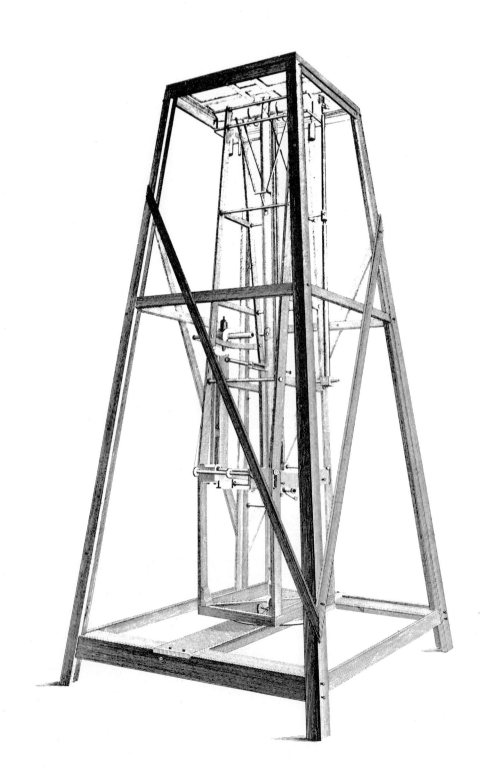

PLATE 3. Ramsden's Zenith Sector.

Ordnance Survey

(b) Old Series one-inch map, part of sheet 1, Essex (1805).

Ordnance Survey

PLATE 4. (a) Part of one-inch map of Kent (1801).

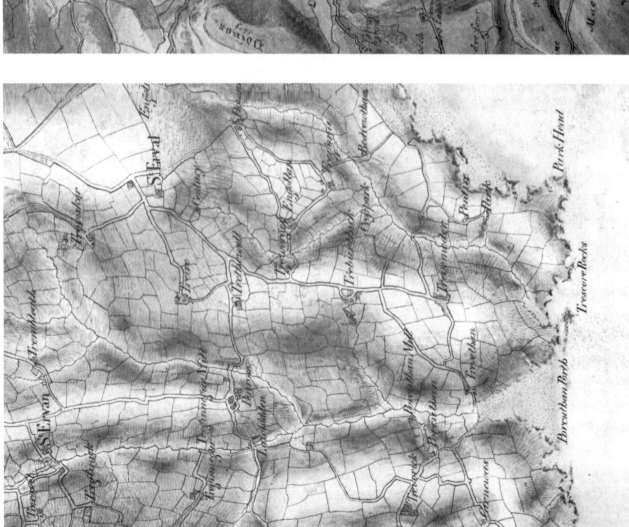
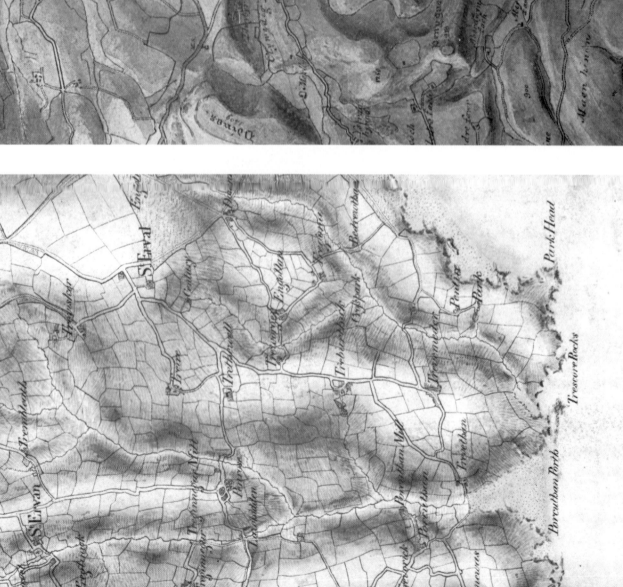

PLATE 5. Surveyors' 2-inch drawings for Old Series: left, sheet 7 (1810), right, sheet 321 (1822).

Courtesy of the British Library.

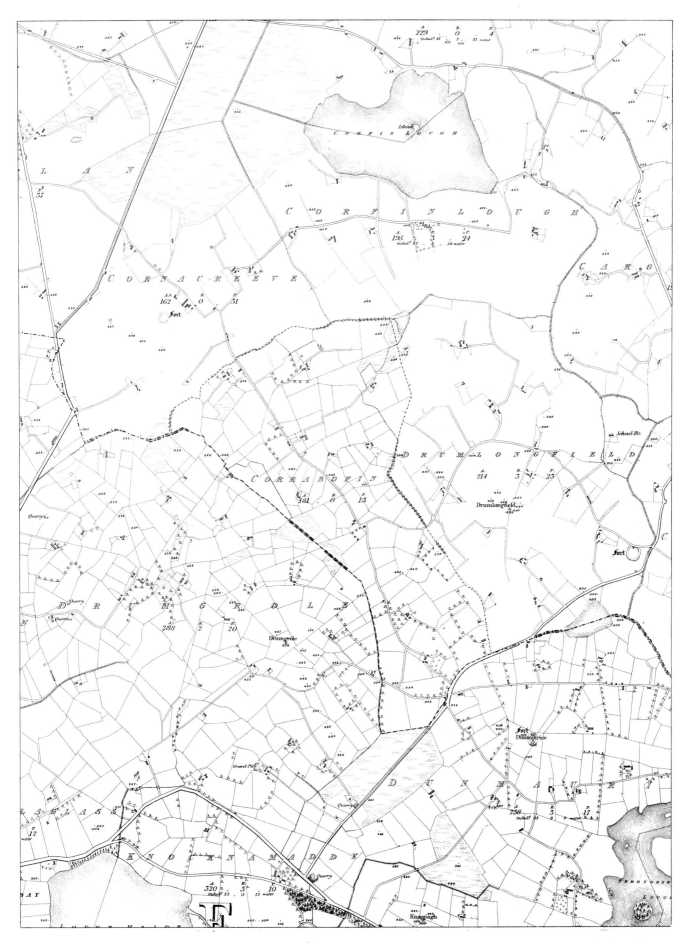

PLATE 6. Six-inch map of Ireland, part of sheet 19, County Monaghan (1836).   Ordnance Survey

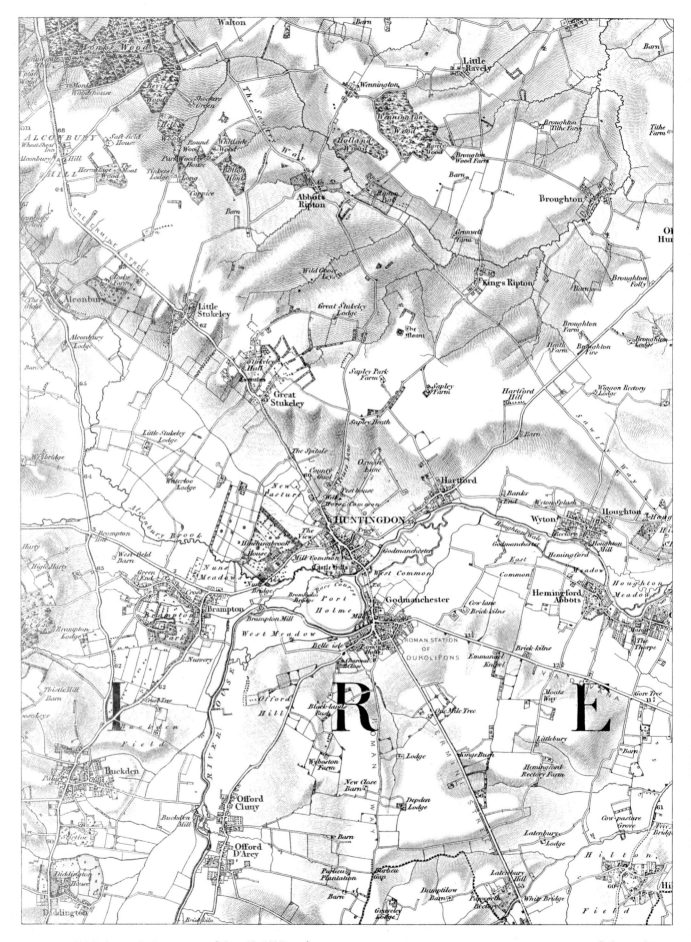

PLATE 7. Old Series one-inch map, part of sheet 52 (1835).

Ordnance Survey

PLATE 8. Part of 1:528 plan of Sunderland (Surveyed 1856).

Ordnance Survey

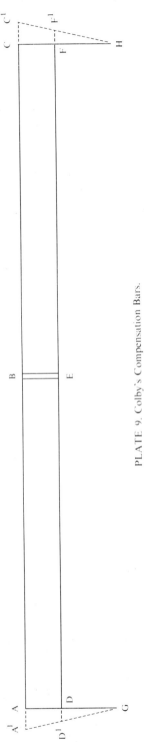

PLATE 9. Colby's Compensation Bars.

ABC and DEF are two metal bars with different coefficients of expansion, ABC having the greater coefficient. They are fixed together at their centres B and E; the ends are free to expand or contract. ADG and CFH are two steel tongues, pivoting at A, C, D and F and carrying the measuring marks G and H. The separation of the two bars ABC and DEF is so selected that, for all reasonable changes of temperature, the length GH remains constant.

The two bars were made 10 feet 1·5 inches long, 0·5 inches broad and 1·5 inches deep, firmly fixed together at their centres. Bar ABC was of

brass, bronzed and lacquered; bar DEF was of iron, browned, lacquered and painted with lampblack, the extent of the lampblack surface being altered as necessary to give a rate of temperature change equal to that of the brass bar. The steel tongues were marked with dots at the compensation points to give a distance between the dots of 10 feet. Microscope bars, (M) constructed on the same principle, were used to measure the 6 inches between the compensation points on adjacent bars.

Ordnance Survey

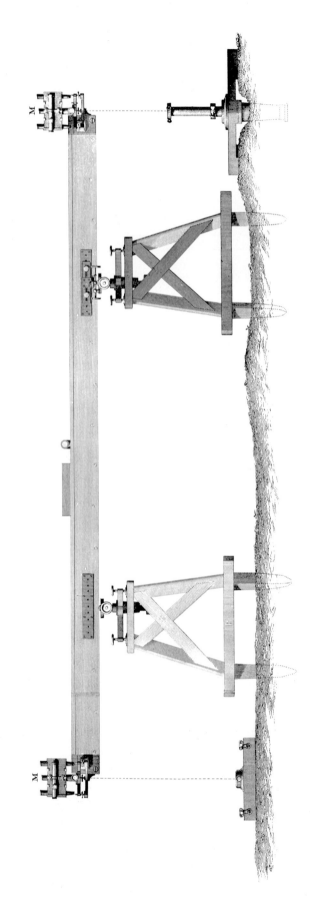

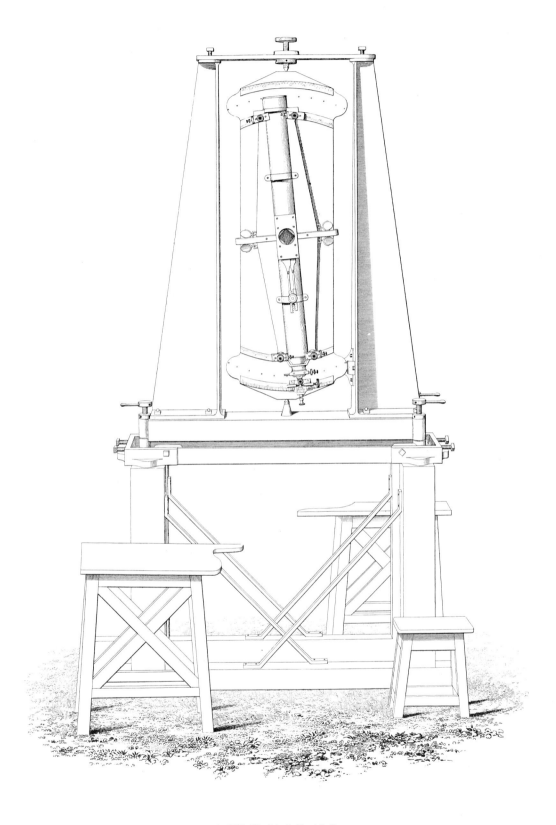

PLATE 10. Airy's Zenith Sector.

The telescope had an object glass of 3·75 inches diameter, and focal length of 46 inches; the eyepiece carried five fixed meridional wires and a single wire at right angles to them, moved by a micrometer screw, one division of which was about 0·4 second. The sector arc was graduated to 5 minutes read by micrometers on which a division of the drum represented about a quarter of a second. The whole instrument weighed about 10 cwt.

Ordnance Survey

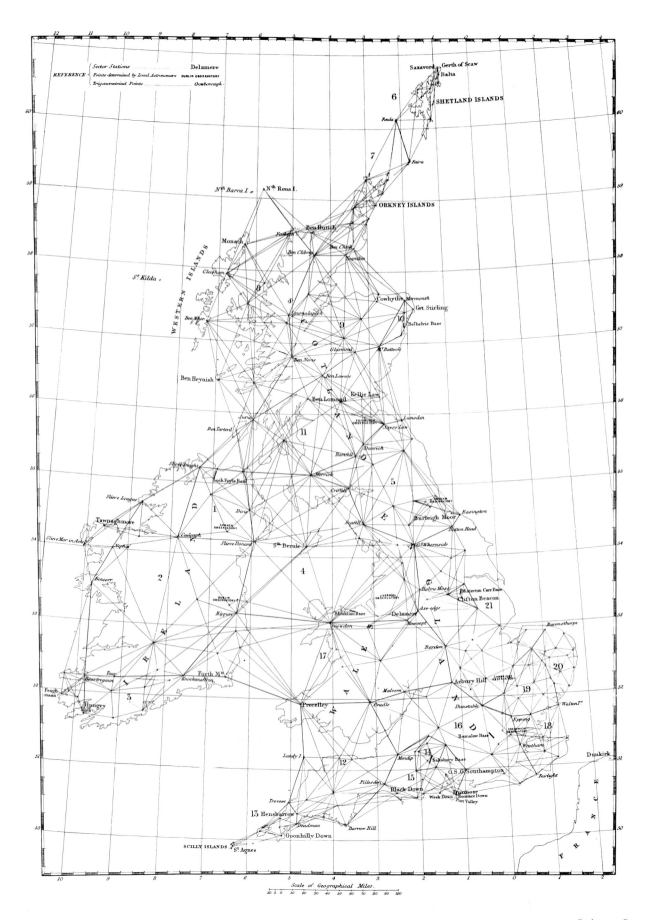

PLATE 11. The Principal Triangulation with adjustment figures.

Ordnance Survey

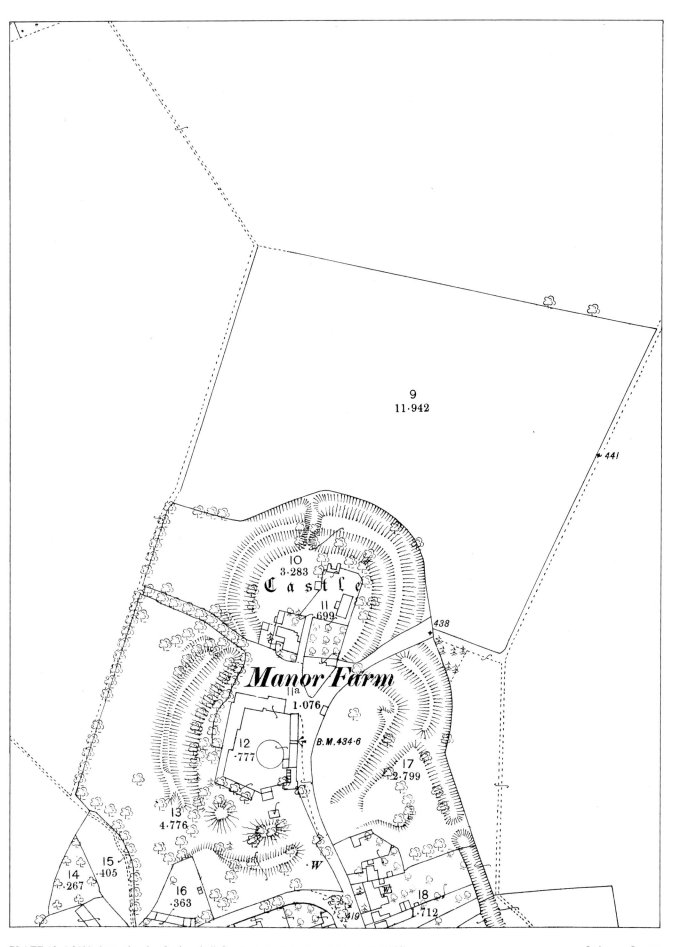

PLATE 12. 1:2500 sheet, showing Ludgershall Castle, part of sheet Wiltshire 48/8 (1880).

Ordnance Survey

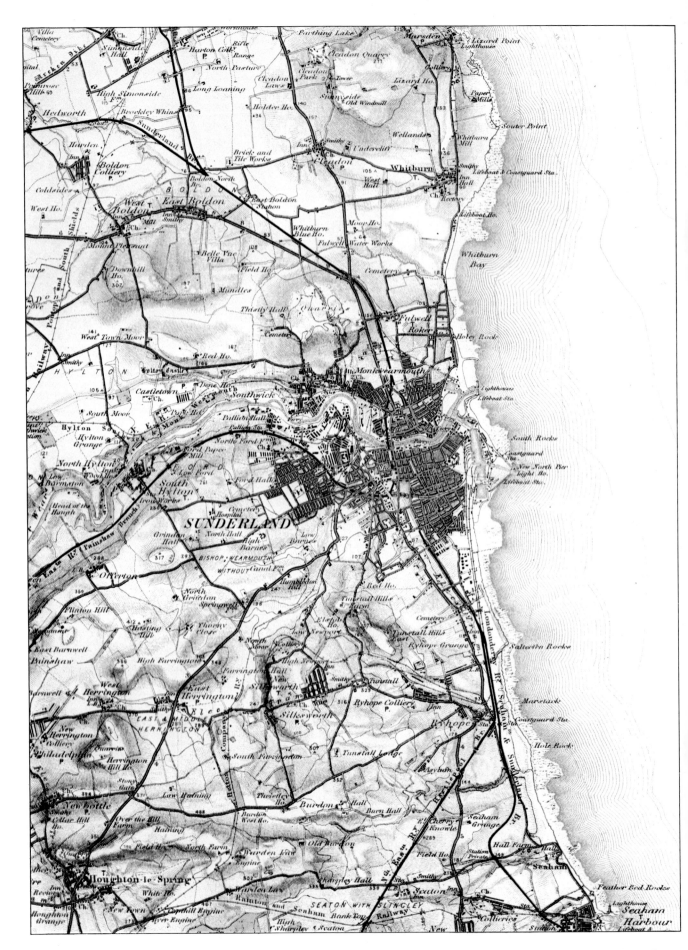

PLATE 13. The one-inch map in colour, part of sheet 21 (1903).

Ordnance Survey

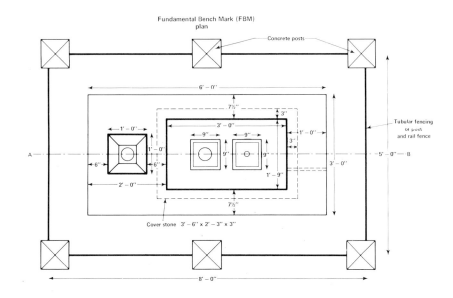

Fundamental Bench Mark (FBM)
plan

Concrete posts

6' – 0''

7½''

3''

3' – 0''

3''

1' – 0''

1' – 0''

9''

9''

1' – 0''

9''

9''

3''

A

5' – 0'' — B

6''

6''

3' – 0''

2' – 0''

1' – 9''

7½''

Tubular fencing
or post
and rail fence

Cover stone 3' – 6'' x 2' – 3'' x 3''

8' – 0''

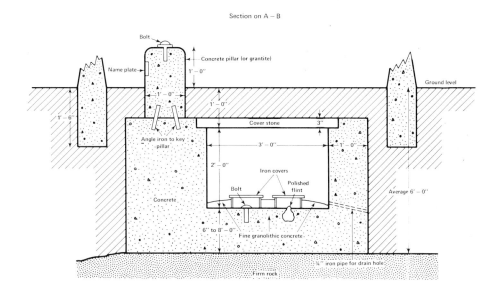

Section on A – B

Bolt

Concrete pillar (or grantite)

Name plate

1' – 0''

Ground level

1' – 0''

1' – 6''

1' – 0''

Cover stone

3''

Angle iron to key
pillar

3' – 0''

1' – 0''

2' – 0''

Iron covers

Average 6' – 0''

Concrete

Bolt

Polished
flint

6'' to 8' – 0''

Fine granolithic concrete

¾'' iron pipe for drain hole

Firm rock

PLATE 14. Fundamental Bench Mark.

Ordnance Survey

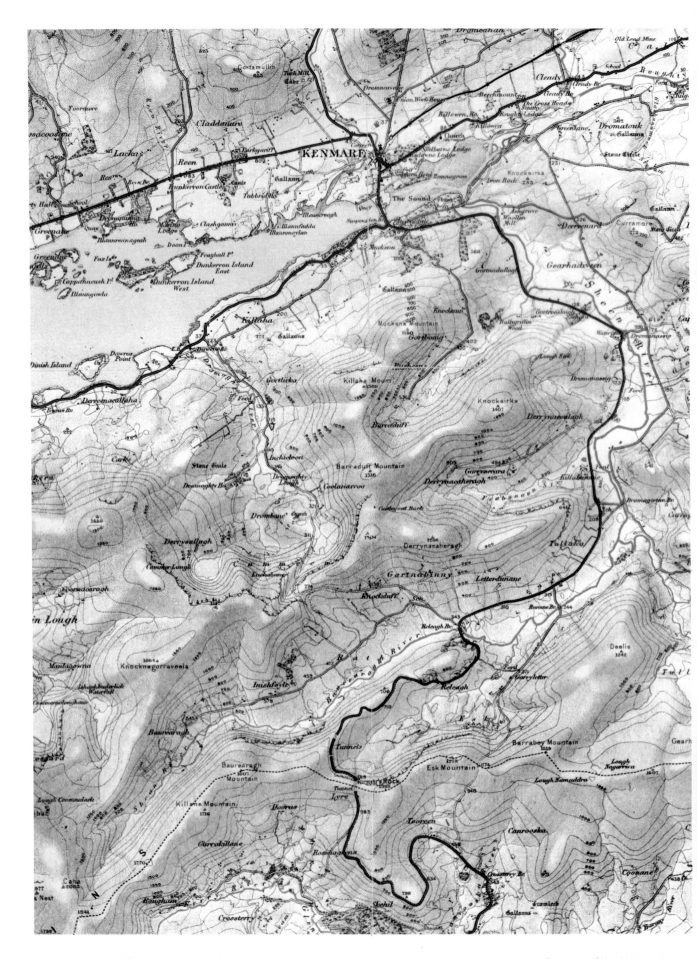

PLATE 15. Part of Killarney tourist sheet (1913).

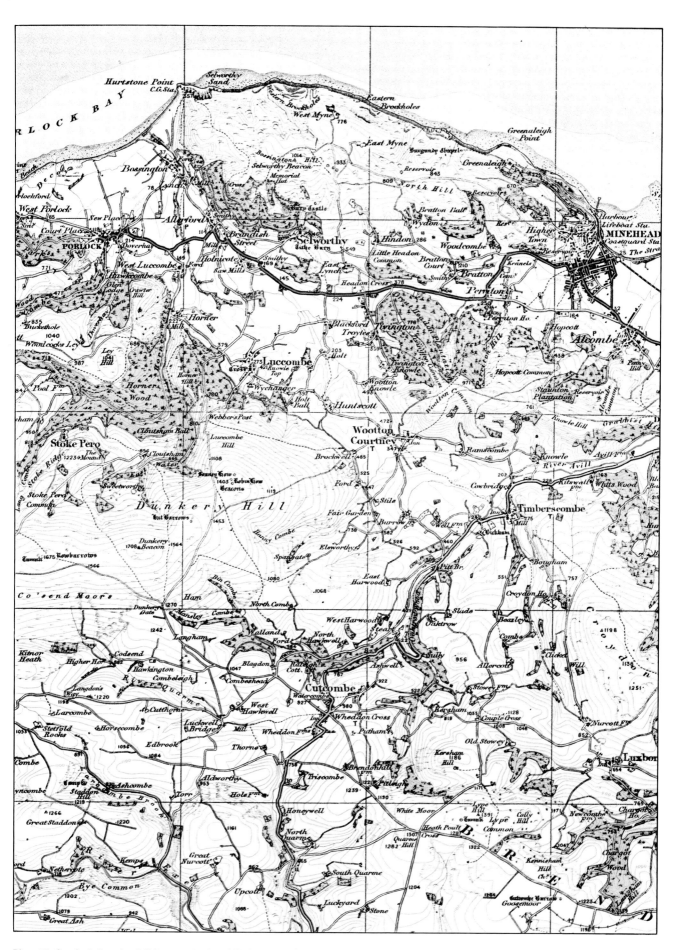

Plate 16. One-inch Popular Edition, England and Wales, part of sheet 119 (1918).

Ordnance Survey

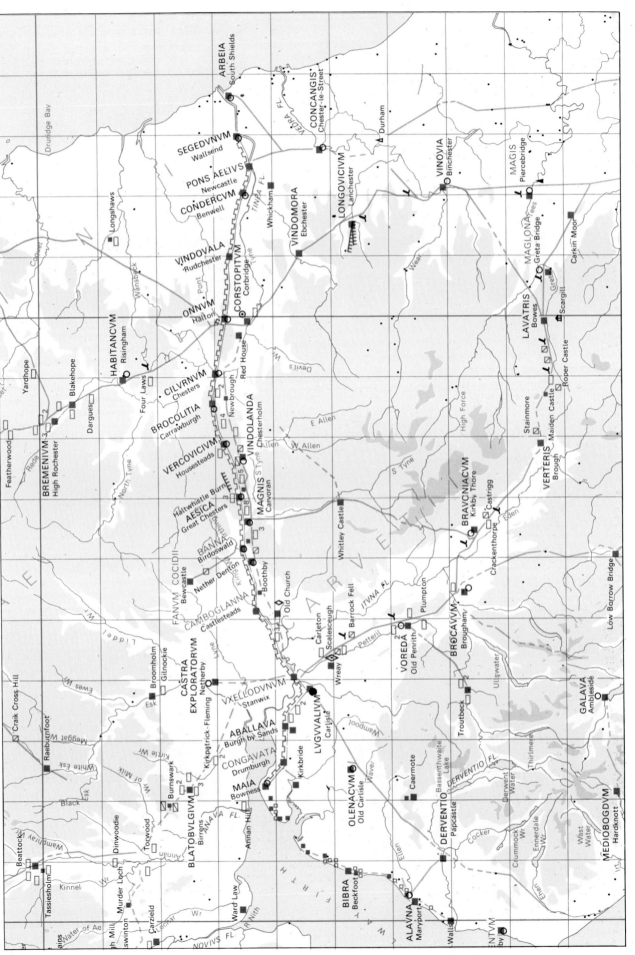

PLATE 17. Part of Map of Roman Britain, 4th edition (1978).

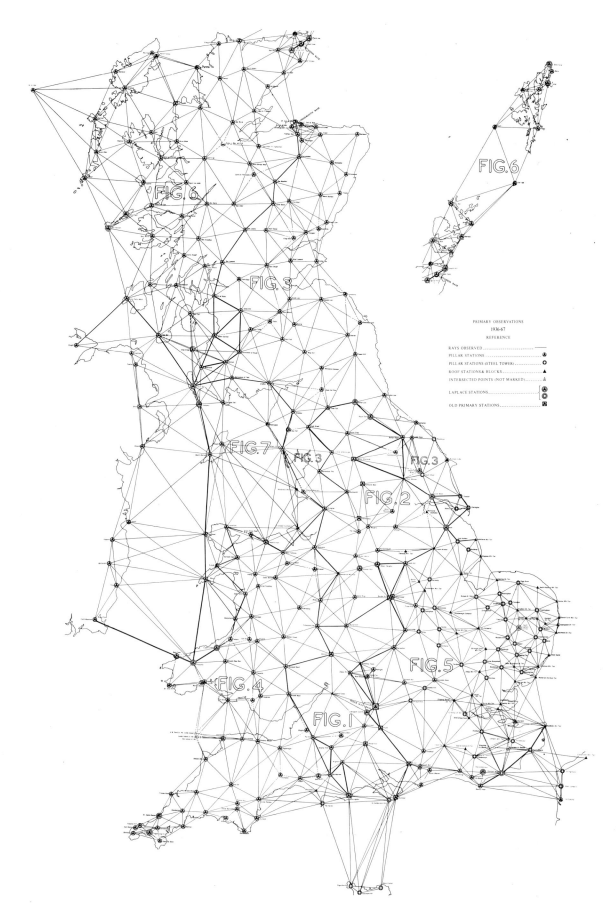

PLATE 18. The Primary Retriangulation with adjustment figures.   Ordnance Survey

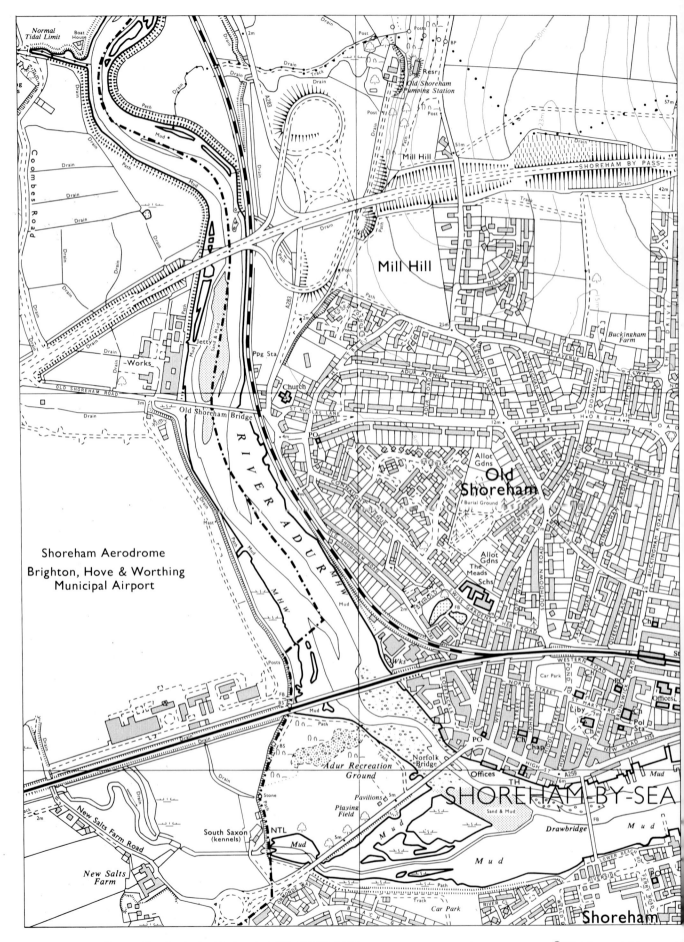

PLATE 19. 1:10 000 map. Regular Derived Series, sheet TQ 20 NW (1972).

PLATE 20. Thompson-Watts stereoplotter, Mark 1.

Ordnance Survey

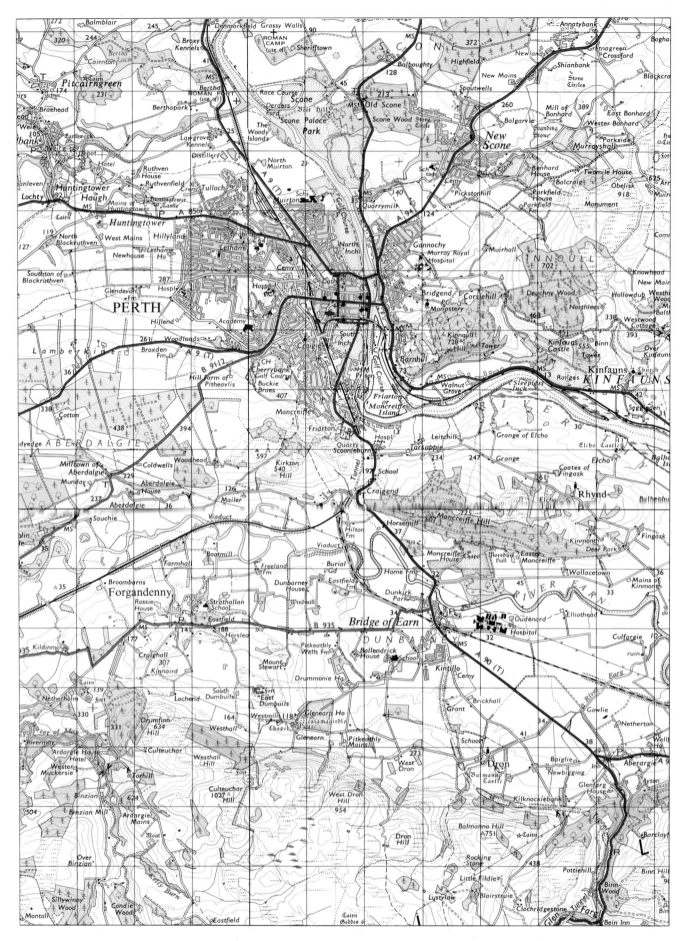

PLATE 21. One-inch Seventh Series, part of sheet 55 (1969).

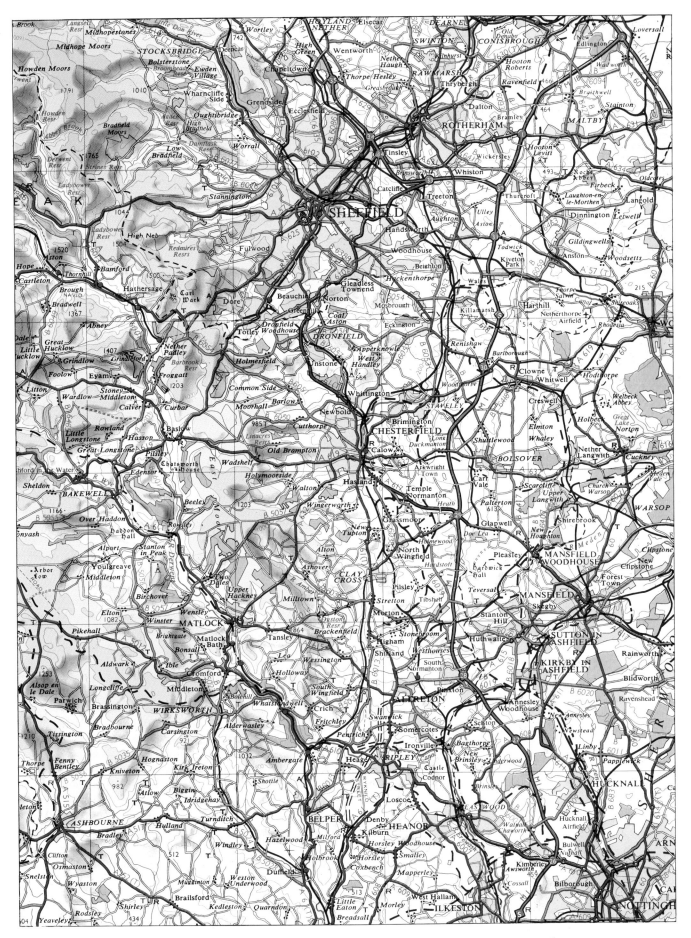

PLATE 22. Quarter-inch Fifth Series, part of sheet 11 (1978).

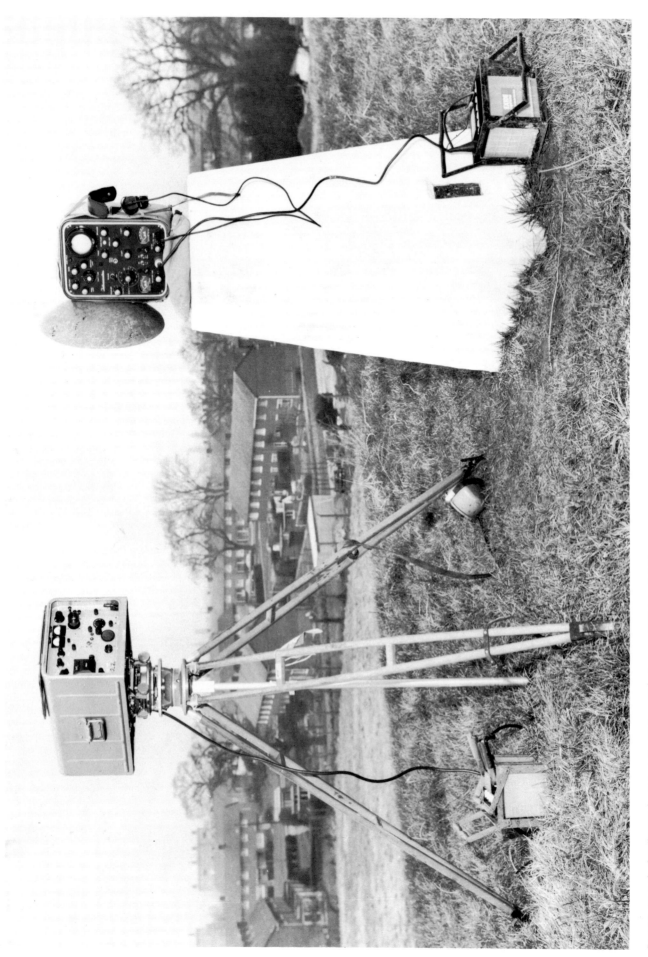

PLATE 23. Left, Geodimeter 8, used on the Malvern-Graz traverse 1970-1, and right. Tellurometer MRA2, used on the cross- Channel connection 1963.

Ordnance Survey

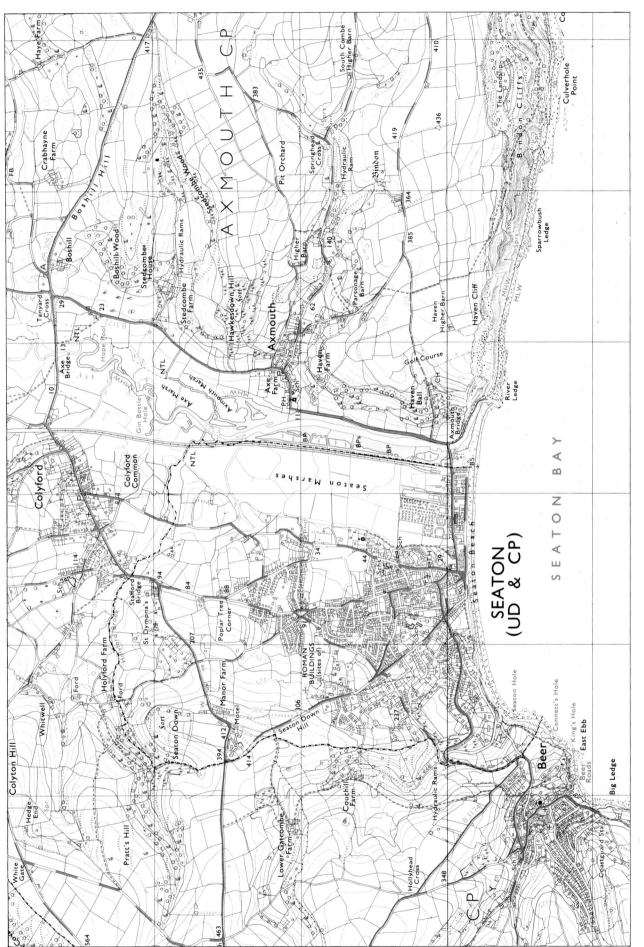

PLATE 24. 1:25 000 Second Series, part of sheet SY 29/39 (1973).

© Crown copyright reserved.

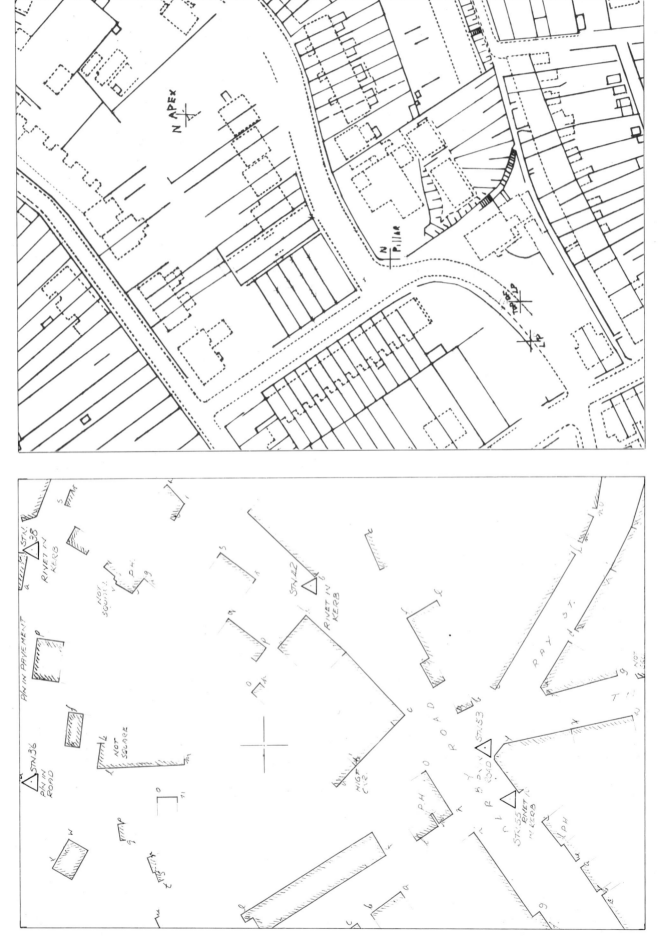

PLATE 25. 1:1250 instrumental survey: left, tacheometric; right, stereoplotted.

Ordnance Survey

PLATE 26. The new building at Maybush, Southampton.

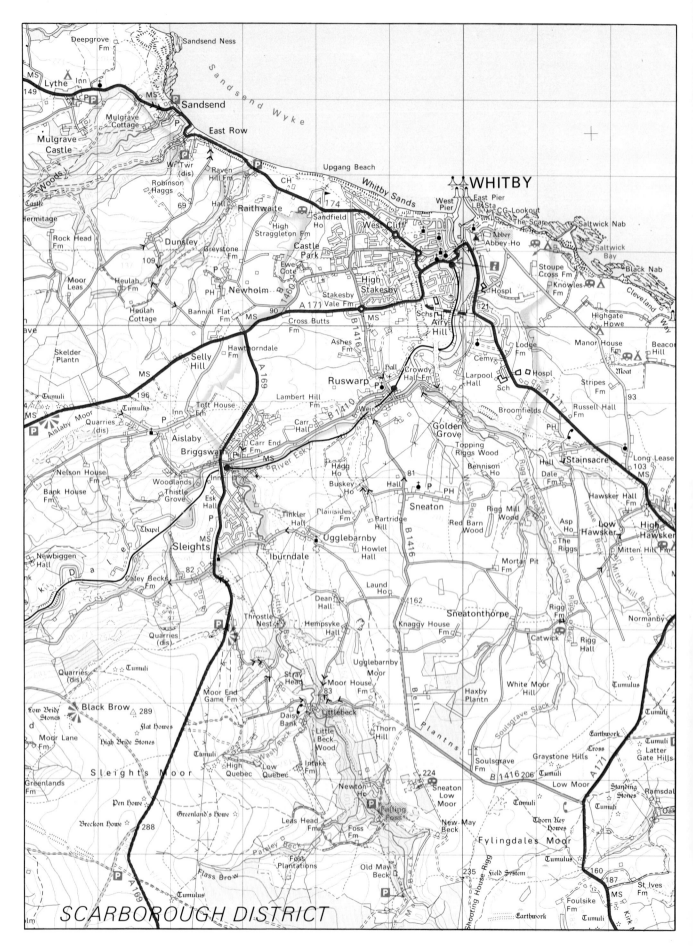

PLATE 27. 1:50 000 Second Series, part of sheet 94 (1976).

Appendices

Appendix I: Roy's General Instructions for the Officers of Engineers employed in Surveying: Appendix containing practical observations on Surveying

General Instructions for the officers of Engineers employed in surveying

In every District to be surveyed, the first thing to be considered will be; What situations are the best, for the Base or Bases to be measured, as the foundation of the work, and for connecting the different Serieses of triangles together?

These Bases should therefore be as long as the circumstances of the ground will permit; not less than a Mile, or a Mile and a half: and as often as possible, they should be measured on the sand of the Sea Shore; because in such cases no Reduction of any kind will be necessary on account of difference of level.–

Every Base should be measured at least twice; and oftner if there should be any remarkable disagreement between the first and second measurement.–For this purpose, one chain should be kept as a standard, with which those in common use will be from time to time compared at least at the beginning and end of any operation, that a true mean may be taken for the ultimate length. And with a view to still greater accuracy it will be proper to observe the heat of the Air, as shown by the Thermometer at stated intervals, while the operation is going on.–

The principal Triangles, connected with the Base or Bases, will be such as are nearly equilateral, formed by the Church Steeples, Windmils, single Trees, or other conspicuous objects and in each of these Triangles all the three Angles should be as often as possible actually observed with the large Theodelet, that the reduction to 180° may be properly made.

In many cases it will be advisable and even necessary, to establish signals by Camp Colours or otherwise on the chief eminences, whose situation being permanently marked on the ground, so as to be referred to occasionally, will form so many auxiliary triangles for connecting the Survey, where other remarkable Objects may be wanting. –

With regard to profil or elevation, the relative heights of the angles of the great triangles, are such, as on all occasions should be first determined: Because these being once settled, the relative heights of all other chief commanding points of any general Range running parallel to the shore, or to a River, such as an Army would occupy to oppose the Descent of an Enemy on the coast, or his penetration into the country after he had effected a Landing, will be subsequently ascertained with respect to the first; and the whole should refer to Low Water Mark at spring Tides, by some permanent Mark, taken on a Quay or Wharff, or some other substantial Building situated near the Shore, to which reference may be had on any future occasion.

In certain cases, the smaller heights near the shore will be best determined by the accurate application of the Telescopic Spirit Level. But in general, the Business will be greatly expedited, by taking the Angles of elevation or depression, with Ramsden's best Theodelet, from some centrical point, whose distance from a number of others has been already ascertained by trigonometrical computation, and from which point all the others can be distinctly seen. –

In levelling, if the Telescopic level be adjusted *by inversion in its Y³* at any intermediate point exactly half way between the two Station Staffs, the relative heights of the vanes, or their distance from the centre of the Earth will be obtained at once, without any allowance for curvature or Refraction. But by the Angles of elevation or depression, allowance, according to the distance, must be made for curvature and Refraction, at the same time, that great accuracy must be observed in adjusting the Instrument, and taking the Angles repeatedly, that a true mean may be obtained for the ultimate Result. –

One method of keeping the Books must be adhered to by all the Engineers, that any one of them may be able to lay easily down the observations of the others. Perhaps for common Surveying, the best kind of Book would be one of the quarto size, with certain Columns ruled on the page towards the left hand to contain the Angles and measured distances of the stations, commencing at the bottom of the page; while the Right hand page, contained the corresponding Sketch or Eye Draught: *or the mode recommended in the Appendix to these Instructions may be made use of and whichever found best in practice will of course be adhered to.*

The Commanding Engineer on the spot will charge himself with the determination of the great triangles, and will register in a Book kept by himself every thing concerning them; as well as what may relate to the relative heights, whether determined by the Level or by the vertical appartus [sic] of the Theodelet.

The filling in or surveying the interior part of the great triangles will [probably] be executed in the common manner by the Junior Engineers, with the small Theodelets and chains provided for the purpose. They will [of course] *consequently* proceed [along] *around* the contours and Creeks of the shore; along the great Roads and lanes; and also along the courses of the Rivers, Rivulets, [and principal Drains or Water-gangs]. The Boundaries of Forests, Woods, Heaths, Commons or Morasses, are to be distinctly surveyed, and in the enclosed parts of the

Country all the hedges, and other Boundaries of Fields are to be *carefully* laid down. *altho' the exact Turn of every one need not be surveyed, if frequent Cuts in different directions are made thro' the inclosures and the direction of the fences laid down where they intersect these cuts, the remainder may generally be taken by the Eye.*

The Risings or irregularities of the ground are every where to be expressed with care; so as to render the plan truly topographical, by preserving that gradation or keeping which should distinguish at first sight the higher part above those that are lower; and these last above such as are quite flat. To do this in the best manner, the plan of the Lines, or great features of the Country, should be first laid down; which being done, the particularities of the surface, will be more readily and truly represented afterwards. –

The first survey will be made from the Magnetick Meridian; But in every district it will be necessary by observation of the Sun or Stars to determine a true Meridian; by ascertaining the Angle that it makes with some one of the longest sides of the great triangles; whence the variation of the Compass will at the same time be determined.

Each Field cannot be represented on less scale than two Inches to a mile; which may be that generally made use of for the [whole] *general* plan [of the Coast]. Particular *Sea* Ports of consequence, such as the Thames and the Medway &c, [would] *will* require a scale of about six Inches to a mile. [But] *These may afterwards be reduced to* a Scale of one Inch to a mile [seems to be sufficient for a whole County; and perhaps] for the Island in general, [half an Inch would suffice]. –

A Book of general *miscellaneous* Remarks should also be kept, wherein may be entered every thing that occurs relative to the nature of the Coast, such as, what parts of it are accessible, and what not; at what distance from the shore, ships of war may come to an Anchor to cover a debarkation from Boats; and what sort of communications there are leading from the Coast to the interior Country, in case an enemy had made his landing good: *also the nature of the soil, how far the clay, chalk, or Gravel country Extends. Whether there is plenty of Timber and of what sort, and size.* And as in every chalk country the Rivulets generally run underground & the Inhabitants are supplied by wells dug to a considerable depth; it will be proper to mention the depths of such wells.

It would also be useful to endeavour to ascertain, what may be the numbers of Horses, Black Cattle and Sheep, in each district, noting the seasons of the year when they are in the Marshes or grazing lands near the Coast; and when not?

When the Engineers have made themselves thoroughly acquainted with any particular district where they may be employed, they will be able to point out the Routes by which the Cattle should be driven back on the landing of an Enemy; and the place of Rendesvous where they would be most secure.

The number of Carriages of different kinds in every district should be estimated noting the distance of their Wheels, and the width of the Tracks in each Parish.

The Collectors of Taxes will be able to give information of the number of Waggons & Carts in each Parish and the Clerks of the Militia Subdivision Meetings will be able to say how many men are on the Lists for Balloting in each Parish.

Appendix Containing practical observations on Surveying

It will be necessary first, that the Men be instructed in setting out the Ground or Roads to be Surveyed, that is to say to put up the Station Sticks in sight of each other and at as great a distance asunder as possible, as short distances not only prolong the Survey, but loss of time in observing with the Theodolet. The sticks may be cut out of the Hedges about 5 or 6 feet long and as straight as they can be got. Each stick should have the bark scraped off about a foot from the ground that the Engineer may the readier see the bottom of the stick when taking his observation; besides this each stick should have a moderate size card put on it the better still to be certain of the object, and it would not be amiss to have printed on these cards in large letters, *Surveying the Roads &* as the Country people are too apt to pull them down not knowing for what purpose they are set up.

When the Men are so far instructed to set out the ground they will receive the Engineers orders over Night what part is to be sett out next morning, and which should not fail of being done by the hour appointed, so that when the Engineer comes on the ground he may not have to wait for that or anything else.

The next thing necessary will be to instruct them in measuring with the chain, and that they strictly observe that no links of it are bent or that the Rings are foul of each other – & and that they very carefully measure the Chain every morning with the ten foot Rod laid out in a Right Line on the ground which should be as plane as they can find. –

There should be at least three Men to each Engineer when Surveying, and they may be employed as follows. They set out in the Morning all together to the place appointed and Prepare their Sticks, leaving one Man at the first Station with the Chain and the instrument whilst the other two are gone forward to set out the ground according to their instructions, which when done they come back to the Man left with the Instrument and wait the Engineer's coming. –

When they begin measuring one Man goes foremost with one end of the Chain who carries ten scewers of about 10 or 12 inches long, when he has got the length, he will be directed by the Engineer in a direct line to the object or Station they are going to, when he puts one of his scewers down perpendicular exactly at the Ring at the extremity of the Chain, which the Man behind observing. He will in future direct the first Man to keep in the Right Line whilst the Engineer is busy in making his Notes in the field Book. –

The third Man is to carry the Instrument only, from Station to Station, and if he could be taught to plant the instrument Horizontally so that the plummet hanging from the center of the Instrument may be exactly over the hole where the Stick stood, a deal of time might be saved for the Engineer, as he then would have nothing to do when he got to the Station but to make observation.

As many different Methods are used for making Notes in the field it is presumed the following is not only the most correct but also the most expeditious, as will be seen by its form, but one thing is first to be presumed, ie you write upwards from the bottom beginning at the last Page of the Book instead of the First, by which means your Book always runs as you go on in the Survey –

[There then follows a drawn example of how a page should be set out.]

Having gone on according to the foregoing Field Book 'till the whole is surveyed and the Close made by the bearing E45 .15, proceed again like manner another District 'til all is done that was set out. –

The work gone on with for 6 or 8 days will begin to make a considerable figure when Plotted, it may then be necessary to make Cuts thro' the Parts already done, which should be in the narrowest places of the Plott, remembering to follow the foot ways if possible as there will be the less Umbrage given to the proprietors of the lands you go thro'.

These cuts may be set out in the same manner as the Roads remembering to go from some Station or other that has been used in Surveying before. It would be advisable not to have the cuts to enclose more than about 100 Acres where the fields run large and not more than 40 or 50 Acres where they run small, as the filling in afterwards will be done with more ease and dispatch. –

The form of the field Book for these cuts may be kept in the same manner as the Roads were done, tho' there will be other occurrences in the offsets which will easily be visible in going along, but great care must be taken not to book an object on the wrong side.

When the cuts are plotted to the Roads & as done before, it will then be necessary to fill them in with the fields and the face of the ground circumscribed by them; for which purpose no method has been found more expeditious and exact than the following.

Trace on a Sheet of Oil'd or transparent Paper the part to be filled in from your Plan, and put it on a drawing board with a frame round it, on a Sheet of White paper of the same size, the Board may be made so as to fix on the top of a strong stick shod with Iron to stick in the ground with the Board on it, then begin at any one Station or part of the cut and sketch in what is seen of the Spot round you, and reserve the next 'till you get to the next Station, the choice of which depends on the Engineer. The Men at the same time may run the distance with the chain or perambulator to the next Station or spot of Sketching remembering if any abuttals of Hedges Buildings & fall in the way that they are immediately laid down by the Scale and Compasses for in filling in they are of the utmost use. – when the Sheet is full it may be taken off and put on the Plan from whence it was traced taking care that every part coincides exactly with the original, which may easily be seen through the Paper, and then traced on it having a Piece of Tracing paper between and drawn in and finished. –

I approve of the above Instructions and desire that the first part of the Survey may be of the Country between the River Thames & Medway East of the Road leading from Gravesend to Chatham and afterwards the Ground south of the Medway extending from Maidstone to the Sea opposite the Isle of Sheppey, and towards Sitting-bourn. The Islands of Shepey and Grain are Surveyed a Weekly Program is to be reported to me and to M General Roy.

        Signed   Richmond etc.
                    Master General
                    July 17th 1785

PRO WO 30/ 115 ff 183–8

Appendix II: Dawson's Course of Instructions in Military Surveying and Plan Drawing

Detailed account of the Studies in each Branch of Instruction

The First Branch, commences with an explanation of the properties, uses, & adjustment, of Instruments for taking Angles; after which, methods of taking horizontal, and vertical Angles, are shewn, with the means of verifying, or correcting the observations in different Cases, and the manner of entering them in the Field Book. An explanation of Instruments for measuring Distances, is next given – the way of using them in different cases is shewn; the Errors which may result from unevenness of Surfaces, or other causes, are pointed out, and means of correcting them proposed. With the measurement of Distances, the manner of entering them in the Field-Book, and of sketching the things to which they relate, is shewn. Then follows an explanation of the properties, use, and adjustment of Instruments for Levelling – and the way is shewn of taking Altitudes, and making sections by the Spirit-Level, and by other Instruments and means. This, appearing to be what is necessary as introductory to Surveying – It is applied to Practice, by performing a Survey of a small quantity of Ground, which, it may be supposed, is to be Fortified, and a Plan of it required proper for an Engineer to project his Designs on. In this Survey, every circumstance of the Ground itself, and whatever occupies or relates to it which is important to be noticed, is surveyed, in the most accurate & complete manner. The distances to neighbouring Heights, Objects, or Passes, at, or within reach of Cannon-Shot, are determined; the Lines of defence & Direction are observed, and proper Altitudes and Sections are taken. When this Survey is completed, the way of plotting or projecting it on Paper is taught, and when the Ground-Plan, is laid down, Methods of determining the Areas of Inclosures etc, on it, will be given. The Plan will then be completed, by lightly shading the varieties of the Ground, and adding Remarks & References in writing, with such indicatory signs as may be necessary to illustrate the Plan, or complete the description it is to convey.

As what has hitherto been laid down, must in a great measure be performed by the Teacher – the Pupil will want more practice under his Eye, than it will afford, to qualify him for beginning to survey by Himself. This Branch of Instruction will therefore be concluded, by, the Pupils accompanying the Teacher on the General Survey, for the purposes of getting a Habitude of using the Instruments, with readiness and accuracy; and of obtaining Information on the Process of conducting a topographical Survey.

Second Branch. The piece of country which is to be chosen as the subject of description in this Branch, may be considered as a military Position which is to be taken up and fortified; and the object of the Survey, is to produce a Plan, on which the disposition of Troops, Works, Intrenchments & obstacles may be projected. It is not supposed necessary to maintain the same degree of accuracy & nicity in this Survey, which was proposed in the particular Survey belonging to the 1st Branch of Instruction, but considerable precision being essential in the determination of general Distances and Heights – these are first ascertained Trigonometrically, which gives an opportunity of explaining the Process, and affording necessary Practice, in Trigonometrical-Surveying. Roads, Rivers, and particular Boundaries, will then be surveyed instrumentally – & these being plotted & copied off – The Accidents of the interior Ground, are filled-in by the Plain-Table.

Third Branch. The Instructions in Reconnoitring, will consist of Sketching Ground, and Positions, by Eye, in the manner practised by the Officers of the Quarter Master General's Staff.

Fourth Branch. The instructions in this Branch are, on the delineation & relief of Surfaces, and the description, & indication of whatever things belonging to them, which are important in military concerns. To facilitate the use of Delineation and Relief in the expressions of Form, and to acquire a power of defining objects by them with sufficient certainty, it is proposed to practice from Models as well as Ground. For this Purpose, Stones may be taken as Models of Hills, their Surfaces being frequently varied by accidental frictions, to a direct similitude of features, with those, which Hills display. Other natural accidents of Country, as Coasts, Rivers, Marshes, etc. together with artificial accidents, as Towns, Villages, Roads, Inclosures, descriptions of Cultivation etc. etc. may be taught in the usual way, by copying from Examples. When the Pupil is able to delineate & shade correctly & readily, any variety of Surface which presents itself – and to draw with necessary precision and dispatch, every other thing which belongs to topographical Plans – and is also able to add, the usual kind of Writing, with sufficient neatness – He makes fair drawings, of the Plans produced from his own Surveys, which, concludes the Instructions.

Appendix III: Colby's Instructions for the Interior Survey of Ireland, 1825

(From the only known copy, at the Ordnance Survey office, Dublin. Passages inserted later are enclosed in square brackets. Diagrams and specimen forms are not included.)

No. 1 The interior survey of Ireland is to be performed on a scale of six inches to one English mile; and the plans are to be drawn with all the accuracy and minuteness of detail which that scale admits.

2 The interior survey is to be performed by districts.

3 The districts are to be distinguished by the letters of the alphabet.

4 The books, plots, sketches, plans &c. performed in a district are to be marked with the district letter.

5 Each district is to be placed under the superintendence of the senior officer employed in it; and he is to keep regular accounts of every thing done in the district, to be responsible for the execution of all orders, and for the accuracy of all the work performed in it.

6 Each district commanding officer is to send regular reports to the officer superintending the survey at Mountjoy; and to give him regular information of the state and progress of the work.

7 When a district commanding officer has reported that any plan or separate portion of the work is completed, and that such plan or portion is ready for delivery, the officer superintending the survey at Mountjoy is to direct that such plan or portion shall be forwarded to the office by some secure conveyance, taking care that the means of replacing any such plan or portion is left in the district until the plan &c. has arrived safe at Mountjoy.

8 Each district is to be furnished with a standard chain, and proper marks are to be laid off from the standard chain by means of which the lengths of the working chains may be regularly compared.

9 The position of these marks is to be carefully noticed, and their accuracy ensured by frequent comparisons with the standard chain.

10 The working chains are to be compared every morning, and their errors (if any errors exist in them) are to be recorded and rectified.

11 Each working chain is to be marked with a number by which it will be distinguished, and this number is to be entered in the field book on the day the chain is used.

12 The instruments used on the Irish survey are all to be marked with distinctive numbers or letters; and regular registers are to be kept of them both in the districts to which they belong, and at Mountjoy.

13 When instruments are in use, they are to be regularly examined every morning, and if they are out of repair, or any way defective, the accident or other cause of their becoming so is to be noted.

14 When any instrument gets out of repair, so as to become unserviceable in a district the circumstance is to be reported to the officer superintending the survey at Mountjoy.

15 The officer superintending the survey at Mountjoy is not to allow any unserviceable instruments to remain in the districts; but to order them to be sent to the office that they may be examined and either repaired or condemned and returned to the ordnance.

16 The field books are to be of an uniform size and marked with a number in addition to the district letter.

17 These numbers are to be written when the field books are delivered out by direction of the district commanding officers for use in the districts. Thus, the field books of each district will be distinguished by regular numbers proceeding from unity to the number of books that have been used.

18 A register of the field books is to be kept in each district according to the prescribed form.

19 The date inserted in the register of field books is to be the date of the commencement of the work in the book. But each days work is to be dated in the field book itself.

20 The name of the officer, non-commissioned officer or private who has performed a survey is to be noted in the days work in the field book; and if more than one has been employed the name of the senior in rank is to stand first.

21 The name of the senior in rank only is to be inserted in the register of field books, he being deemed principally responsible for the accuracy of the work.

22 When it becomes necessary to transfer a field book from one person to another, the date of the transfer and the name of the person to whom it has been transferred are to be inserted in the register.

23 The contents of the field books are to be clearly indicated in the fourth column of the register. The register will then shew what roads, boundaries or other lines are contained in each book for the convenience of reference.

24 The field books are to be kept as much as possible upon an uniform system; and when any innovations are introduced as improvements they are to be carefully registered in the remarks in the register of field books, that the field books may be intelligible to all persons.

25 In addition to the bearings and distances which are absolutely required to lay down the work, the field books are to have recorded in them, such other bearings or distances as may afford the best and most convenient checks for ascertaining and ensuring the accuracy of the work itself, and for connecting it with the surrounding portions of the survey.

26 The plotting is to be performed on sheets capable of containing at least ten or twelve square miles.

27 In order to connect the field work and prevent any twist or distortion, the trigonometrical points are to be pricked off on the paper before the plot is commenced.

28 The bearings and distances directed by art. 25 are to be laid down on the plots and penned in with light blue

lines that they may shew the relative accuracy of the work, without giving the plot (which will of course be penned in black) a confused appearance.

29 Such bearings or distances are not to be altered or omitted in consequence of any apparent disagreement with the plot.

30 The name of the person laying down each plot and the numbers of the field books from which it is taken are to be inserted on the plot.

31 All plots and field books are to be carefully preserved and kept in a proper state to be forwarded to the superintending officer at Mountjoy when he demands them.

32 When more than one plot is laid down for a single plan, the plots belonging to that plan are to be regularly numbered in black – the plan number being inserted on them in red.

33 The persons employed on the survey are to endeavour to obtain the correct orthography of the names of places by diligently consulting the best authorities within their reach.

34 The name of each place is to be inserted as it is commonly spelt, in the first column of the name book: and the various modes of spelling it used in books, writings &c. are to be inserted in the second column, with the authority placed in the third column opposite to each.

35 The situation of the place is to be recorded in a popular manner in the fourth column of the name book.

36 A short description of the place and any remarkable circumstances relating to it are to be inserted in the fifth column of the name book.

37 In order to ascertain the contents of the townlands &c. when reduced to an horizontal plane, it will be requisite to measure several elevations and, for reference, the extremities of the station lines must be marked on the plots with letters, when the points to which they refer are either of such different elevations as to require noting, or when those lines are to be used in calculating areas.

38 To prevent confusion among the references, the capital letters are first to be used, then the small letters, next the capitals with a dash over them (A^1) then the small letters similarly marked (a^1); and if these four alphabets be found insufficient, the figures 2, 3, 4 &c. are to be successively substituted for the dash. $(A^2, A^3, a^2, a^3$ &c.).

39 In towns, villages, mineral and manufacturing districts &c. where the work is so extremely close and intricate that the reference letters and other matters cannot be inserted together on the plot in a distinct manner, the plot is either to be pricked off and the lines and references required for the content and altitudes only inserted on the new sheet; or, a second plot of the work itself is to be laid down in such a scale as will admit of complete distinctness and proper accuracy for obtaining the required areas. The second sheet or plot thus formed is to be marked in the same manner as the original plot, with the additional mark No. 2 placed under it, and the original plot in these cases will have the mark No. 1.

Thus, A.2.4. and A.2.4.
  No. 1   No. 2.

40 The boundaries of the several legal and ecclesiastical divisions of Ireland are to be pointed out to the officers acting under the direction of the master-general, by persons authorised and directed to shew them by his excellency the lord lieutenant and the district officer is to send to notify the time and place where this person's services are required according to a form which will hereafter be prescribed.

41 The person appointed by the lord lieutenant will go round the boundaries of the several legal and ecclesiastical divisions with one of the officers attached to the survey having at least two of the sappers under his orders who will set up the temporary additional marks on the boundaries, which may be required for the survey. No boundary is to be received from the person appointed by the lord lieutenant unless its situation is definitely marked on the ground, either by a ditch or wall &c. denoting the boundary, or by fixed objects marking the extremities of straight lines.

42. The officer going round any legal or ecclesiastical boundary with the person appointed by the lord lieutenant to shew it, will carry with him a small book for remarks. In this book he will note the day of the month, the name of the person shewing the boundary, and the names of non commissioned officers, privates or other persons who may accompany him during the perambulation of the boundary. He will also describe in it the nature of the several boundary marks, and any accidental circumstances which may lead to the future definition of the boundary; as, for instance, portions of it lying in the direct line between two churches &c. He will also most particularly notice any doubts which may be entertained in the country respecting the real position of the boundary line on the ground. These original boundary remark books are to be regularly numbered and carefully preserved.

43 In the progress of the survey still further information will be obtained about the boundary lines, and more mature descriptions of the marks &c. may be written. A boundary register book is therefore to be kept in each district, in which such descriptions are to be inserted, together with the names, dates and other essential circumstances extracted from the original boundary remark books.

44 Having ascertained the boundaries over a sufficient portion of country to commence a survey, an officer or cadet &c. will direct such other station marks to be set up as may afford the most advantageous disposition of the lines to be measured &c.

45 The lines on the ground must be so disposed with reference to the trigonometrical points that no sensible error can be introduced or remain undetected.

46 Paper being liable to very considerable alterations from the effects of expansion and contraction, it will contribute to the correct determination of the areas required, to compute them from lines actually measured on the ground instead of from those measured on the plots. The lines are therefore to be disposed with reference to this object, that nothing beyond the minute portions of area inclosed by very crooked boundaries may depend on measurements from paper.

47 The disposition of the lines may also be frequently modified to suit the inequalities of the ground: when they

can be so disposed (without introducing any more important inconvenience) as to avoid the necessity of reductions to the horizontal plane, some time will be saved, and liability to mistakes prevented.

48 The areas of baronies, parishes &c. are required to be correctly ascertained as well as those of townlands &c., it will therefore be requisite to guard against the commission of errors which would become sensible if the areas of the larger divisions were derived from the summation of the areas of the minor divisions. This will be done by disposing (art. 46) the content lines principally with reference to the larger divisions; the areas of the minor divisions being made to depend on the several parts of the same lines together with such subsidiary lines as their boundaries may require.

49 The officer &c. laying out the ground (art. 44) will attend to those lines which require to be reduced to the horizontal plane, and to those points whose altitudes are required. For these purposes levelling marks must be put up at the proper stations to which vertical angles are to be taken.

50 The levelling marks must be distinguished by letters of reference (art. 38), and it will be convenient to make them the same height as the instruments, which may be regulated by an uniform standard, to save trouble and prevent mistakes.

51 The ground being properly set out for the survey according to the foregoing articles; an officer or cadet [or other qualified person acting under his directions] will proceed, with a theodolite to the several levelling stations, to take the reciprocal angles of elevation and depression &c. It being necessary to ensure accuracy that the corresponding angles should always be reciprocally taken.

52 The theodolite being set up of the regulated height and properly adjusted, great care is to be taken in the observation of the angles. The adjustment of the optical axis, parallelism of the level, and zero of the vertical arch will have been made at the morning inspection; but as some alterations will unavoidably take place in these delicate adjustments, the officer or cadet [or other qualified person acting under his directions] who observes the vertical angles will (after noting the letter of the levelling mark at which he stands in the first, and the letter of the mark to be observed in the second column of his field book) set down, in the third, the reading when the telescope is levelled in the direction of the object to be taken; the fourth column will contain the apparent elevation or depression of the object, the fifth the number of links to be subtracted as shewn by the instrument, and the sixth is left for remarks.

Among these remarks a few horizontal angles should occasionally be inserted to serve as a check on the chain survey. The field books used in levelling are to be subject to the regulations in the former articles relating to field books. The only alteration being the obvious one in the column of contents in the register.

53 The stations &c. being laid out, and the measurement of the elevations and depressions in progress, the chain surveyors are to commence their operations, noting in their field books the letters of the levelling marks when they come to them, and taking care not to disturb those marks. Among the chain surveyors one at least should have accompanied the officer or cadet when laying out the ground.

54 The station and levelling marks are to be removed by direction of the officer superintending in the field when he is satisfied that all the requisite precautions to insure accuracy have been properly attended to, and, that the continuance of those station marks would be no longer useful.

55 In cases where the distances are short and the relative altitudes are not required, the reductions of the lines to the horizontal plane, previously to their being used in plotting, are to be made by reference to the column of links in the levelling field book. But when the distances are long, or the relative altitudes required, logarithmic computations must be used, and those distances with the corresponding angles must be entered with the computations for further reference, in a book called a register of horizontal and vertical distances.

56 In the first column of this register the designations of the plans and plots in which the points or lines are contained will be entered.

The second column will shew the point or line; if a line, its measured length in links is to be written between the letters marking its extremities, thus, A1942B. The third column will shew the mean elevation or depression of the second object deduced from the reciprocal angles in the levelling field book, after applying the corrections indicated in the third column of that book, and those for curvature and refraction when very long distances render their effect sensible. The fourth column will contain the logarithmic cosine of the angle in the preceding column and the logarithm of the distance; the natural number answering to the sum of these logarithms will be entered in the fifth column. The sixth column will contain four or more figures of the constant logarithm 9.81954394, the logarithmic sine of the angle, and the logarithm of the distance; the number answering to the sum of these 3 logarithms will be entered in the seventh column.

The eighth column will contain absolute altitudes above the low watermark. Those obtained from the trigonometrical survey or by levelling are to be distinguished by being entered in red, and the words "trig. 1 survey" or "by levelling" opposite them in the column of remarks; those obtained by the addition or subtraction of the altitudes in the preceding column being entered in black. Here it is to be remarked that the altitudes in this column are to be proved by always commencing at some point whose altitude is known either from the trigonometrical survey or by levelling, and proceeding in a regular series of additions or subtractions to some other point of which the altitude is also known in like manner.

57 Having arrived at that part of the instructions which is to treat of the mode of registering the data for finding the contents of the legal and ecclesiastical divisions of Ireland, and other more advanced objects of the work, it becomes necessary to state that detail has been avoided in drawing up these instructions, as much as the development of a general system, and the adoption of a mode of registry which may both afford the information required and shew the degree of authenticity the survey possesses would admit.

The details of the survey must be adapted to the peculiar circumstances of the ground, and it would be impossible to give any general directions which would facilitate mere local operations; these must be left to the skill and arrangement of the district commanding officers and those employed under their orders and it is expected that nothing which may conduce to the perfection of the work will be neglected.

[Addition to Art. 57, 21 June 1831

In the original instructions for the Irish survey, I had not contemplated the demarcation of the boundaries of bog and uncultivated land with reference to their utility in the valuation; and I had not therefore laid down any specific rules to regulate the survey of them. It has since appeared that the valuators require the boundaries of uncultivated land as additional lines by which lands of different quality may be separated and the respective areas of each quality computed. All roads, streams and other lines and objects on the plans are used by the valuators for similar purposes; and it is consequently necessary that no line or building should be placed on a plan without due care and accuracy. The increase of labour and the expenditure of time and money incident to the survey of the uncultivated lands is to be reported to me as soon as a fair average can be obtained by experience. But in order to abridge the time required for seeking out the boundaries of cultivation where it is progressive and uncertain, in all such cases the nearest fence bounding cultivated land will be surveyed as the boundary, though cultivation may have partially extended beyond it. And all patches of about five acres or less will be considered as too trivial for notice, whether they be of uncultivated land in the midst of cultivation, or of cultivated land enclosed in masses of bog or uncultivated land except where such patches are so situated as to be surveyed without any loss of time. It being a general rule that everything which contributes to the perfection of the map should be inserted when it can be done without delay and expense.

Upon this principle though the boundaries of various qualities of uncultivated land are not absolutely essential, it will always be desirable where it can be done by the officer in his local examinations or in any other way in the course of the work (without delaying its progress) to indicate rocky land, turbary, or morasses by distinctive marks, though these particular qualities should not be bounded on the plans by lines which, (not being positively accurate), might mislead the valuators.

This order will have reference to all future surveys; but those plans which have already been revised, and in which the boundaries of cultivation have already been accurately surveyed according to the best of the division officers judgement will not be resurveyed as a consequence of this order.]

58 In order to facilitate the subsequent formation of correct county books, a book for registering the contents of the legal and ecclesiastical divisions in each district is to be kept in the following manner:

The first column to contain the designation of the plan, the second the name of the legal or ecclesiastical division, and the third the letters referring to the triangles or trapeziums on the outline plan. The figures in the fourth, fifth and sixth columns are to denote, respectively, the lengths* of the sides referred to by the first and second, first and third, and second and third letters in the preceding column. Except in cases where the base and perpendicular of a triangle, or the base and perpendicular of a trapezium are used in the computation of the area. In such cases the letters are to be so arranged in the third column that the two last may always denote the extremities of the base, and the perpendicular or perpendiculars are to be in red ink. The seventh column will shew the content, in square chains to three places of decimals, deduced from the preceding data, and the eighth column will shew the total area of the division or subdivision in English acres, roods and poles.

[The example, sent with article 58 requires the accompaniments of the diagram to render it completely intelligible to those who have not previously considered the subject.

I remember having taken great pains to devise a method of finding and registering the contents of the several divisions of Ireland, which might preclude the liability to important general errors which would be likely to result from misplacing figures. On that account, I had reduced the content in chains to a single column, using only additive quantities for the greater divisions; conceiving, as the plans are directed to be coextensive with the parishes, that the lines for finding the area might be all measured within the parish.

Independently of the inconvenience and liability to error arising from casting contents with positive and negative quantities, it seemed most proper that each person should work within his own parish, and thus, that the effect of any accidental error should be confined to a single parish.

The contents of the parishes are found in this method entirely by additive quantities, and the summation of all the triangles from which these contents are found may be verified by comparing it with the summation of the areas of the great triangles &c.

The areas of the separate townlands within a parish will be found by means of some of the triangles already used for the content of the parish, together with such small subsidiary ones as may be rendered necessary by the boundaries of those minor divisions. As the sum of the areas of the minor divisions must be the same as the area of the parish, a check is immediately afforded to this part of the operation. Even in this inferior matter positive and negative triangles are not to be indiscriminately introduced nor with the signs of + and −. But the whole of the positive triangles are first to be set down in regular order, beginning with those already used for the parish, and those having been summed up, as in the example; the whole of the negative ones are to be set down, and their sum subtracted from the former gives the area of the townland in square chains which is then to be converted into acres &c. and placed in the last column.

In short, the area of the parish is to be found by the simple addition of the areas of the triangles and trapezia which compose it; and, as it would be needless to repeat the work of the same triangles over and over again; the area of the parish is to be subdivided into the areas of its separate townlands either by single additions, or by two additions and a subtraction as the case may require, taking care however that no sums are converted into acres &c. but those which give the resulting area of some division or subdivision – the example contains a specimen of each case.]

59 Each district will be furnished with one theodolite of a superior description, and one good spirit level. The subsidiary triangulation for determining the interior points for regulating the survey being to be performed by the district officers; who will combine with that operation the determination of a good series of altitudes, from which the following extracts are to be made in the register of horizontal and vertical distances. viz. The height of the rise and fall of the tide both at springs and neaps at various places on the coast &c. The altitude above low water

---

* The horizontal distances are to be used in finding the content.

(spring tides) of some conspicuous part of each of the points which has been trigonometrically determined; and of a sufficient number of other points, found by levelling &c., to check and prevent the accumulation of error in the altitudes given in the register.

60 By article 49, the officer &c. laying out the ground, has been directed to attend to those points whose altitudes are required, and the register of horizontal and vertical distances, being furnished, in obedience to the last articles* with a great number of very accurate heights at small distances from one another, all over the country, it will be easy to render this part of the work complete and subservient to future local improvements without devoting much extra time to this object. Not only the heights of hills, but also those of the lowest parts of the necks which connect them should be given; also the heights and depths of lakes, and the altitudes of rivers and streams in various parts of their courses. As churches are usually very permanent objects in a country, the heights of the ground on which their towers or belfrys are erected should be given as points of future reference. And a knowledge of the altitudes of mines, and mineral deposits and of manufactories, towns, and villages will tend to facilitate internal improvements.

The heights of canals should be given at all the locks, and the heights of the summit levels of roads and when it can conveniently be done, the height over which a new canal or road must unavoidably pass to connect a valuable mineral deposit, or principal market or manufactory with some adjacent harbour, navigable river or existing canal.

61 The plans are to be coextensive with the parishes, each plan containing a single parish, except in cases where parishes are so small that two or more may conveniently be put together on a sheet of moderate size. These parish plans are to be drawn in outline, and regularly numbered for convenience of registry. Thus, in the A district, A.1 or A.2 &c. and in B district B.1 or B.2 &c. and so forth.

[But if a parish be so large in the east and west direction, that it cannot be drawn in a single sheet of double elephant paper, the western part bounded by some townland boundary is to be drawn on one sheet and marked with the plan number &c. and put down as part 1,

Thus, A.2, part 1,

and the eastern part on another sheet of paper, and marked part 2,

thus A.2, part 2,

and so on.

And if the parish extends also to the southward, the portions to the southward are to be drawn on separate sheets numbered from west to east in continuation from the northern portions, and marked in a similar manner for reference.

Thus, A.2 part 1, A.2 part 2, may be the northern portions of a plan and A.2 part 3, A.2 part 4 &c. the southern portions.]

62 In cities, towns and other particular places where continuity is essential to the perfection of the representation and where the division of parishes interrupts this continuity in the parish plans, subsidiary plans are to be laid down containing as much of the adjoining parishes as will render the representation complete. These subsidiary plans are to be distinguished from the original parish plans from which they have been laid down, by being marked with the small letter instead of the capital letter denoting the district. And the successive numbers of those original parish plans are also to be inserted on them. Thus, a.4, 5, 6 &c.

63 All plans are to be drawn with their tops to the north, so that the writing may lie in parallel directions from west to east, with the exception of the names of rivers, canals, chains of mountains &c. which require to be adapted to their natural sinuosities:—

Names of cities, towns, villages &c. are to be commenced on the east side of the places to which they refer, when no special obstacle occurs to interfere with this arrangement.

64 The disposition of the writing requires considerable ingenuity, and it is always to be borne in mind that the utility of a plan depends very much on that facility of reference which is obtained by the relative keeping of the names. The particular distinctive characters to be used will be shewn in the plates of characteristics, but the size of the letters must depend on the situations in which they can be placed, and it is to be considered as a general rule that the names are to be so written as to be legible at distances proportionate to the importance of the places. Thus, county names must be legible at greater distances than those of baronies, villages than single houses, gentlemen's houses than cottages &c.

65 In the first article of these instructions it is directed that the survey shall be performed on a scale of six inches to a mile and with all the accuracy of detail which that scale admits. It is not, however, intended to put in the fields generally, but with this exception, everything attached to the ground is to be inserted on the plans. Cabins built of mud &c. are to be distinguished from houses built of brick or stone by using indian ink instead of carmine. The boundaries of counties, baronies, parishes, townlands &c. are to be distinguished from each other by particular marks which are shewn in the plates of characteristics. Those plates also contain specimens of distinctive marks for exhibiting several other kinds of information required from the survey.

66 The plans directed by the preceding part of these instructions will be left entirely in outline, no sketching having as yet been provided for; and outline plans being most convenient for general use, and also for the subsequent reductions which would dirty and destroy the effect of shaded plans.

The hills and mountains are to be correctly sketched, and the sketches are to be properly penned in, and regularly numbered so as to correspond, in a similar manner to the plots, with the outline plans to which they refer. The drawing of complete finished plans with the ground properly shaded will be accomplished according to instructions which will be given when the outline work is in a much more advanced state, and when plans can be formed of proper dimensions to suit the exhibition of the features of the country.

67 A register of plans is to be kept in each district. This register will be divided into 12 columns, the first of which

---

* The accounts of anything relating to the trigonometrical operation will of course be kept separately; what is directed in art. 59 being merely such extracts from those accounts as are required for particular objects in the interior survey.

will contain the number of the plan in black, if it be an original parish plan, or the successive numbers, in red (art. 62), if it be a subsidiary plan. The second column is for the name of the parish or parishes, the third for the names of the townlands, the fourth the barony, the fifth the county, the sixth, the number of the sheet of the general reduced ordnance map of Ireland; the seventh, the numbers of the ordinary and levelling field books relating to the plan, the eighth, the number of plots and sketches belonging to it, the ninth, the names of the persons who drew it, the tenth, the name of the district officer under whose command it was completed, and the eleventh the date of its completion. The twelfth, is a column for remarks in which the place in which the plan, sketches &c. are deposited is to be inserted, as well as any incidental circumstances respecting them.

68 Each officer, employed in the districts, is to keep a journal in which he is to insert all the local information he can obtain relative to communications by land and water, manufactories, geology, antiquities or other matters connected with the survey.

69 A remark book is to be kept in each district, in which observations taken from the journals are to be properly classed and regularly entered.

70 As it is necessary that a particular account of the triangulation (art. 59) for fixing the points on which the survey depends should be published and that every facility should be given for reference and the re-examination of the work at any future period: the district officers are to take care to have all their stations properly marked and correctly described. Stations on the ground may be marked by sinking a large stone with a hole a few inches deep bored in it to shew the centre, and by measurements to permanent objects which may happen to be near them. Those on buildings require no particular marks because they may be accurately described by proper measurements. In addition to these means of rediscovering the stations, angles are to be observed between a few near objects of a permanent nature when any such happen to be in view.

71 The boundary surveyor appointed by his excellency the lord lieutenant having signified to the commanding officer of a district that he has marked out several boundaries, particularly mentioned according to the regular form for that purpose: the district officer is to consider which of those boundaries so mentioned can be most conveniently surveyed in the first instance, and he is to send a requisition of the following form (a) to the boundary surveyor, specifying the boundaries or portions of boundaries he requires to have pointed out, and the time and place for the attendance of the meresman. The letters of information from the boundary surveyor, and duplicates of the requisitions for the attendance of meresmen are to be preserved in regular order according to their numbers, to be bound up as records.

72 The district commanding officer having filled up a requisition as directed in art. 40 & 71 and sent it (by some confidential person to ensure its delivery), to the boundary surveyor &c. is to direct the attendance of an officer at the time and place he has appointed for the meresmen, and if any delay is occasioned either by the neglect of the officer or of the meresman he is to report the circumstance immediately to the officer superintending at Mountjoy, and to lose no time in giving information to the boundary surveyor of any difficulties or loss of time which may arise from the incompetence or inattention of the meresmen.

73 The officer who has been directed to attend to the pointing out of boundaries is to take the certificate brought by the meresmen from the boundary surveyor, and having examined it and found that it is properly filled up and attested according to the established form, he is to proceed with the meresmen according to art. 41, taking care however not to allow any meresman to point out any boundaries or portions of boundaries which are not mentioned in the boundary surveyor's certificate. The boundary surveyor's certificates to be preserved in regular order to be bound as records.

74 When the district commanding officer is satisfied that the meresmen have pointed out the boundaries mentioned in the boundary surveyor's certificate, in a sufficient manner for the purposes of the survey, he is to give them a certificate of the following form (b). But if any complaint has been made to him by the officer in attendance, or it appears that the time employed is greater than the extent of boundary warrants, he is to withhold the certificate until he has explained the circumstances to the boundary surveyor, and conferred with him as to the modification which the case demands, adding after the word 'days' in the certificate his opinion of the time actually required, taking into consideration the state of the weather, and any other unavoidable causes of delay. Duplicates of these certificates are to be sent to Mountjoy.

Appendix IV:
Ordnance Survey
Contours 1847–1890

(TABLE FROM WINTERBOTHAM, *The National Plans*, pp. 46–8)

INSTRUMENTAL CONTOURS

Period	Policy	Date	County	Remarks
(1)	25 and 50 ft.	1847	Wigtown	
1847	From 50 ft. to 400 ft. at 50 ft. V.I.	1847	Lancashire	From 1,200 ft. to 2,600 ft. at 200 ft. V.I.
to				
1856	From 400 ft. to 600 ft. at 100 ft. V.I. From 600 ft. to 1,200 ft. at 200 ft. V.I.	1852	Island of Lewis	400 ft. intervals from 1,200 ft. to 2,400 ft.
		1853	Kirkcudbright	do.
		1856	Yorkshire	do.
(2)	From 25 ft. to 100 ft. at 25 ft. V.I.	1854	Haddington	
1854	From 100 ft. to 500 ft. at 50 ft. V.I.	1855	Fife, Kinross and Edinburgh	
to	From 500 ft. to 1,000 ft. at 100 ft. V.I.	1856	Linlithgow	
1869	From 1,000 ft. to highest point at 250 ft. V.I.	1857	N.E. Corner of Berwick	See para. 3, 1857
		1858	West Dumfries and small part of East Peebles	do. 1859 do. 1858
		1859 –60	Small parts in N.E. and S.E. of Durham	do. 1859
		1869	North and South parts of Ayr	do. 1869
(3)	50 and 100 ft.	1857	Main part of Berwick ..	See para. 2, 1857
1857	From 100 ft. to 1,000 ft. at 100 ft.			
to	V.I.	1858	Main part of Peebles ..	do. 1858
1869	From 1,000 ft. to 2,000 ft. at 250 ft. V.I.			
	From 2,000 ft. to highest point at 500 ft. V.I.	1859	East half of Dumfries and whole of Westmorland	See para. 2, 1858
		1859 –60	Main part of Durham ..	See para. 2, 1859
		1861	Renfrew	
		1862	Lanark, Roxburgh and Selkirk	
		1864	Cumberland, most of Stirling and Dumbarton* and S.E. of Perth* and Clackmannan and Northumberland	See para. 4, 1864
		1867	Centre of Ayr	See para. 2, 1869
(4)	As above except only contoured	1864	East part of Perth*	See para. 3, 1864
1864	instrumentally up to 1,000 ft.	1865	Middlesex and S.E. of Forfar*	
to	Above 1,000 ft. water level contoured	1866	Islands of Bute, Great Cambrae, Little Cambrae and Inchmarnoch	
1890	at 250 ft. V.I. to highest point, but these are not published on the six-inch	1867	Part of Isle of Man	Remainder not contoured for six-inch except sheets 6 and 9, which were water levelled
		1868	Kincardine* Surrey	Except small part in West
		1871	Low lying districts in Banff* and Nairn*	Remainder Water Level contoured
		1872	Kent and Flint	
		1873	N.E. of Aberdeen*	Remainder Water Level contoured
			Elgin (low lying parts*)	do.

*Against a county indicated that the remainder of the county was water level contoured.

INSTRUMENTAL CONTOURS – *continued*

Period	Policy	Date	County	Remarks
		1873–5	N.E. Part of Inverness*	do.
		1874–5	North and East parts of Caithness*	do.
		1874	Hants.	
		1875	Cheshire	
		1877	Sussex, Denbigh and East part of Ross and Cromarty*	Round Cromarty Firth
		1878	Essex and Herts.	
		1879	Berks.	
		1880	Stafford	
		1881	Derby, Glamorgan and Monmouth and certain Orkney Islands*	See note below concerning Orkney Islands
		1882	Bucks, Oxford and Gloucester	
		1883	Bedford and Shropshire	
		1884	Leicester	
		1885	Rutland, Northants, Worcester, Cornwall and Scilly Islands	
		1886	Nottingham and Hereford	
		1887	Norfolk, Suffolk, Somerset, Wilts and Dorset	Lincoln, see Note 2 below
		1887–8	Cambridge	
		1888	Montgomery, Warwick and Huntingdon	
		1889	Anglesey, Merioneth, Brecknock and Pembroke and Devon	
		1890	Cardigan, Carnarvon, Radnor and Carmarthen	

Notes

(1) In 1881 Orkney islands of Papa Westray, Westray, Stronsay, Shapinsay, Kirkwall, Burray and South Ronaldshay were contoured up to 400 ft. only and Water Level contoured above 400 feet.
ORKNEY CONTOURS NOT PUBLISHED ON SIX-INCH SHEETS.

(2) Lincoln was contoured in 1887 at 25 ft., 50 ft. and 100 ft., and at 100 ft. intervals up to 500 ft.

(3) A 20 ft. contour was surveyed in 1926 in the Ouse drainage area and has been published on all sheets concerned in Norfolk, Suffolk, Huntingdon and Cambridge.

*Against a county indicated that the remainder of the county was water level contoured.

CONTOURS SKETCHED WITHOUT INSTRUMENTS

	Policy	Date	County	Remarks
(1)	Intermediate Contours at 25 ft. intervals from 75 ft. to various heights. See remarks column. All published on six-inch sheets	1847	Wigtown	Up to 1,200 ft.
		1847	Lancashire	Up to 2,625 ft.
(2)	As above but at 50 ft. intervals above 1,200 ft. All published on six-inch sheets ..	1852	Island of Lewis	Up to 2,650 ft.
		1853	Kirkcudbright	Up to 2,650 ft.
		1856	Yorkshire	Up to 2,550 ft.
(3)	All contours sketched without instruments. NOT PUBLISHED ON SIX-INCH SHEETS	1866	North part of Isle of Arran	
		1871–4	Sheets 96 and 97 Aberdeen	

WATER LEVEL CONTOURING
NOT PUBLISHED ON SIX-INCH SHEETS

Period	Policy	Date	County	Remarks
1860 to 1882	50 and 100 ft. .. .. From 100 ft. to 1,000 ft. at 100 ft. V.I. From 1,000 ft. to highest point at 250 ft. V.I.	1860	North part of Stirling North part of Dumbarton Outer Hebrides Island of Skye	

WATER LEVEL CONTOURING – *continued*

Period	Policy	Date	County	Remarks
		1866	Main part of Argyll	But see Isle of Arran under Sketched Contours, para. 3
		1867	Kincardine	Small part in West
		1868	N.W. Perth	
		1868	N.W. of Forfar	
		1870	Isle of Man Sheets 6 and 9	
		1872	Main part of Nairn	
		1873	S.W. of Aberdeen	But see under Sketched Contours, para. 3
		1874	Main part of Banff and South Elgin	
		1875	Majority of Inverness and West Caithness	
		1876–7	Sutherland	
		1878	Main part of Ross and Cromarty	
		1881	Shetlands	
		1881–2	Orkneys	(Except islands mentioned under instrumental contouring)

Note All counties mentioned under paragraph 4 of instrumental contouring were water level contoured above 1,000 feet where necessary.

Appendix V: Recommendations of the Dorington Committee

We offer the following summary of the leading recommendations which we have made in the preceding pages:

1 That the 1-inch map be produced in the following forms:
    a. An engraved outline map with contours in black.
    b. A black engraved map, with hill-shading either in black or in colour.
    c. A coloured map on thin paper, adapted to military purposes, but also on sale to the public.
    d. A cheap map by transfer to zinc or stone.

2 That the character of the roads on the 1-inch map be shown in four classes with distinct characteristics.

3 That parish boundaries be omitted from the 1-inch map.

4 That the contours of the sea bottom round the coast-line and the depths of inland waters be shown.

5 That experiments be made in the practical application of heliogravure, and that, if results not inferior to an Austrian specimen map which we have seen be produced, that process be substituted for the existing method of engraving hills and for so much of the country as is then uncompleted in its hill engraving.

6 That special arrangements be made to revise the 1-inch map within the next four years independently of the maps on the larger scales, and that subsequently the map be constantly revised within periods of 15 years.

7 That the cadastral maps be revised and brought up to date in the next 10 years, and that subsequently they be kept revised within periods of 15 years.

8 That the publication of these revised maps be carried out by contract, if necessary.

9 That detail, such as single trees, footpaths in gardens, &c., be omitted.

10 That the skeleton and coloured forms of the 25-inch and town maps be abandoned and the uses of both be combined in one edition having the houses cross-hatched.

11 That the reference numbers to parcels of land on the 25.344-inch plans be abandoned on revision.

12 That to a limited extent contour lines be added to the 6-inch map.

13 That on the 6-inch map the contours be always in black.

14 That certain of the engraved plates of the 6-inch map which are not now filled up beyond the county boundary be as soon as possible filled up to the margin of the plate with the detail of the adjoining county.

15 That the cost of the engraved sheets of the 6-inch map and that of the quarter-sheets of the photo-zincographed 6-inch map be equalised by a change of their respective selling prices.

16 That the Welsh names be gone over and corrected before the first revision of that map.

17 That the cadastral maps on the town scales be no longer entirely made or revised at the cost of the State, but that the town authorities be required by statute to maintain these maps.

18 That around towns and in tourist districts the existing sheets of the Ordnance Survey on the 6-inch and 1-inch scales be united so as to form special maps of such districts, and that advantage be taken of these maps to introduce any novelties in cartography that may be thought desirable as these maps are not required to be joined to the general maps of the United Kingdom.

19 That certain authorities be placed under statutable obligation to supply information to the Ordnance Survey Department in order to enable current revision to be better carried on.

20 That in future the term 'revision' should be confined to the bringing up to date on its existing scale of a map already published, and that the term 're-survey' be applied to the operations necessary for the production of maps on a scale larger than that on which they were originally published.

21 That the Ordnance Survey Department be allowed to control its own supply of paper and printing material.

22 That the map on the scale of 4 miles to an inch be revised as soon as the 1-inch map is out of hand and be completed with hill-shading.

23 That great freedom be allowed to private publishers desirous of bringing out other classes of maps than those specially published by the Survey Department, and that transfers of the maps on the 1-inch and smaller scales be supplied to publishers at cost price, a small sum being paid as an acknowledgement, and that all other reproduction of Ordnance Survey maps be prohibited.

24 That certain recommendations as to indices and catalogues be carried out.

25 That a book or pamphlet of information as to the Ordnance Survey be published, general in its main features

and special for each county, containing the county indices or diagrams (on a reduced scale) and the information formerly contained in the parish area books, and also the table of parish areas now printed on the index of the 6-inch map, which table should in future be omitted from that map, and that copies of the small indices in this pamphlet be freely distributed for public information.

We have the honour to be,
Sir,
Your obedient servants,
(Signed) JOHN E. DORINGTON
ARCH. GEIKIE
A. C. COOKE, Lieut.-General
H. W. PRIMROSE
W. MATHER
C. FORTESCUE BRICKDALE

To the Right Hon. Herbert Gardner,
President of H.M. Board of Agriculture
31st December 1892

Appendix VI: Recommendations of the Davidson Committee

1 That the 1:2500 scale should be retained.

2 That the 1:2500 survey should be recast on National instead of county sheet lines on a National projection, and that, while this work is in progress, there should be a general overhaul of the plans to eliminate the errors which have crept into the original survey in course of revision.

3 That a National grid should be super-imposed on all large scale plans and on smaller scale maps, with certain exceptions, to provide one reference system for the maps of the whole country.

4 That the international metre should be adopted as the unit on which the grid should be based.

5 That the large scale maps in the new National Series should be square in shape.

6 That the 1:2500 plans when re-published in the new National Series should cover one kilometre square of country.

7 That the one-inch to the mile and smaller scales should be retained in their existing form.

8 That the existing six-inch plates should be retained for printing on demand for special purposes.

9 That the scale of six inches to the mile should be retained, and that maps on this scale should be produced in the new National Series in a square shape and containing 25, 1:2500 plans.

10 That a new medium scale of 1:25 000 should be tried out experimentally in certain selected areas, and, if successful, should be extended to cover the whole country in a National Series.

11 That when the revision of the 1:2500 plans has been completed, further investigations should be carried out with a view to establishing whether the requirements of urban areas would not be more adequately met by a survey on the 1:1250 scale.

12 That when a suitable opportunity occurs, additional contours should be introduced.

13 That the numbering of parcels should be discontinued as soon as the National grid is introduced.

14 That the Ordnance Survey should continue to publish archaeological maps.

15 That the existing arrangements for revising the one-inch and smaller scales should continue.

16 That a system of continuous revision should be adopted for the large scale plans as soon as practicable.

17 That short term contracts to civil firms, for aerial photographs, should not be continued as a permanent policy and that the Government should consider the formation of a special Air Survey unit, capable of satisfying the requirements of the Ordnance Survey. We would emphasize that, in view of the potential value of air photography, it is desirable that such a unit should be created as soon as practicable.

18 That the position of the Ordnance Survey should be reviewed annually with a view to the maximum practicable recruitment, until such time as the recommendations we have embodied in this report have become effective, and that thereafter such work should be adequately maintained.

We are, Sir,
Your obedient servants,
DAVIDSON (Chairman)
D. F. ANDERSON (Major-General)
C. B. COLLINS
R. N. DUKE
H. W. S. FRANCIS
H. G. RICHARDSON
W. R. L. TRICKETT

C. F. COLBECK
M. O. COLLINS (Captain, R.E.)
(Joint Secretaries)
3rd February, 1938

Index

Abbreviations: f = footnote, Pl = Plate

1:1250 scale maps
  accuracy tests, 333
  Davidson Committee, 259, 263
  field document, 293
  post-war programme, 286
  programme planning, 293–4
  survey methods, 293–4, 332–4, Pl 25
1:2500 scale maps. *See also* 1:2500 scale maps of Ireland; Overhaul revision.
  archaeological survey, 173–5, Pl 12
  authorized, 124, 126
  drawing for reduction, 178–9
  enlargement to 1:1250, 206
  experimental revision, 182
  format 2km × 1km, 305
  function and content, 168
  National Coal Board programme, 294, 301, 325
  national projection, 261
  reduction of ornament, 328–9
  replotted counties, 183, 210
  Short Term Plan, 292
  survey method, 169–71, 336–7
  wartime revision, 283
  zincography, 179, 203
1:2500 scale maps of Ireland, 210
  Dublin, 150–1
1:10 000 scale maps. *See* Six-inch map of Great Britain.
1:25 000 scale maps
  1973 Committee, 356–7
  Davidson Committee, 262–3
  GSGS 3906, 291–2
  Provisional Edition, 291–2
  Provisional (Revised) Edition, 299
  Second Series, 328, Pl 24
1:50 000 scale maps, 352–3, Pl 27
1:250 000 scale maps. *See* Quarter-inch map of Great Britain.
Aberfan disaster, 325
Académie des Sciences, 12, 16, 17, 40
Accounting
  cost accounting, 244–5
  management accounting, 355–6
  Trading Fund, 357–8
Account of the Methods and Processes of the Ordnance Survey, 165
  hill drawing, 173
  place names, 175
Account of the Principal Triangulation, 139
Account of the Trigonometrical Survey, 33, 35, 68, 72
Accuracy
  chain survey 1:2500, 169
  Old Series, 60
  Overhaul, 337
  standards, Ireland, 87
Accuracy tests, 304
  1:1250, 333
  contours, 336
  six-inch, 334–6
Adair, John, 10
Adare, *Lord*, 93
Addison, G. H., *Maj-Gen*, 276
Adhémar, *Comte d'*, 14
Administrative Name Books, 175
Admiralty
  charts, copyright, 75
  complaints by, 101
  engraving for, 243
  pressure for Irish map, 79
Admiralty Hydrographic Service, 69, 87, 101–2, 131, 281, 315, 345

Advance Revision Information, 265, 301, 329
  on microfilm (SIM), 353
  renamed SUSI, 353
Advisory Committee on Oceanographical and Meteorological Research, 315
Advisory Committee on Surveying and Mapping, 293, 322
Aerofilms Limited, 258
Agents. *See* Map agents.
Agriculture, Board of, 181, 185–6. *See also* Departmental Committees.
Agriculture and Fisheries, Ministry of, 245–7, 323–4. *See also* Agriculture, Board of; Departmental Committees.
  abolition of engraving, 242–3
  Advisory Committee, 322
  Irish survey, separation, 233
  metrication, 327
  ministerial responsibility for Ordnance Survey, 323–4, 350
  post-war programme, 287
  responsibility for military, 245–7, 274
Ainslie, John, 57
Aircraft Operating Co, 249
Air Map of Salisbury, 234–5
Air Ministry, 235, 249
Air Photo Division, 292
Air photography. *See also* Cameras, air.
  archaeology, 238
  civil contract, 324
  infra-red, 340
  MTCA flying unit, 299, 324
  navigational systems, 258, 294, 312f, 344
  Ordnance Survey photographic unit, 265, 288, 324
  RAF photography, 288, 299
  World War I, 220
Air photo mosaics, 234–5, 292, 299
Air survey, 234, 248–9, 265, 294–5, 303–4. *See also* Cameras, air; Stereoplotters.
  1:1250, 332–4, Pl 25
  air-assisted Overhaul, 303, 324–5
  air-graphic, 294
  air-ground method, 325
  Air Survey Branch, 304, 324–5
  Arundel Method, 249
  Birmingham experiment 1935, 258
  Brighton experiment 1928, 249
  contouring, 335
  Eastbourne experiment 1925, 248–9
  Oxford experiment 1953, 303–4
  six-inch, 334–5
Air Survey Committee, War Office, 234, 249
Air Survey Company, 249
Airy, G. B., *Prof*, 88, 115–6, 311
  spheroid, 39, 141, 143–4, 270
  transit instrument, 311
  zenith sector, 115, 140, 143–4, 147, Pl 10
Alphabet controversy, 252
Amalgamated Society of Lithographic Artists, 243
American Boundary Commission, 135, 154
Anastatic process, 130
Ancient Wiltshire, 64
Anderson, D. F. *Brig.*, 258, 262
Anglesey, *Lord* (Master General), 119
Antiquity, 238
Antonine Wall, 62, 328
Appel, Rudolf, 130f
Arago, J. F. D., 29, 41, 145
Archaeological survey, 62–65, 173–5, 237–40, 340–3, Pl 12
  air photography, 238–9
  archaeological officer, 234, 237–40, 340
  Crawford, O. G. S., 237–40

Archaeological survey (*cont.*)
   errors, 174–5
   field survey, 342–3
   Gothic type, 64
   honorary correspondents, 238
   Instructions 1884, 174
   Old Series, 63–65
      sheet 14, 64–65
   period maps, 239, 328, Pl 17
   research and recording, 341–2
   Roy, William, 13, 62–63
   site antiquities, 65, 174
Arc of latitude, European 1860, 144
Arcs of meridian
   30th meridian, 271
   British Isles, 7, 12
   Cayenne, 33
   Dunnose-Clifton, 29, 40
   Franco-Spanish, 30
   Lappland, 33
   Peru, 33
   Picard 1671, 33
   Roy's proposal for India, 21
   West European 1816–23, 40–42
Area measurement. *See also* Six-inch map of Ireland, content
      survey.
   automation, 304
   parcels, 248, 264
   scale and trace, 304
Armstrong, Andrew, 11
Arnold, Matthew, quoted on
   one-inch map, 134–5
   scales dispute, 134
Arrowsmith, Aaron, 4, 6, 57, 103
Arrowsmith, John, 100
Artillery, 2–3. *See also* Royal Artillery
Artillery boards, 223–5
Artillerymen in Ordnance Survey, 15, 17, 30f, 35
Artillery survey, 221–3
   1st Survey Coy RA, 246
   Artillery, School of, 246
   flash spotting and sound ranging, 222
   map shooting, 221, 223
Arundel Method, 249
Ashmead, A. W., 232
Asses' skin, 59
Association of Government Geographers and Allied Tech-
      nicians, 299
Astronomer Royal. *See* Airy, Darwin, Maskelyne, Pond.
Atkinson, R. d'E., *Dr*, 311
Atterbury, F., 225
Automated cartography, 353–4
   Experimental Cartography Unit, 353

Bacon, George, 196
Bailey, C., *Lieut*, 102
Bailey, W., *Lieut*, 135
Baker, Benjamin, 69–70, 101, 105
Baker, Henry, 10
Baker, J., 69
Baldamus, C. F. C., 130f
Bald, William, 79
Banks, *Sir* Joseph, 1, 6, 13–16, 29
Barr & Stroud, 249
Bartholomew
   competition from, 225–7
   evidence to Dorington Committee, 189, 191
Bases. *See also* Belhelvie Sands, Caithness, Fort Revers-The
      Dunes, Hounslow Heath, Lossiemouth, Misterton
      Carr, Rhuddlan Marsh, Ridge Way, Romney Marsh,
      Salisbury Plain, Sedgemoor.
   calculated lengths, Principal Triangulation, 142
   Hotine, quoted, 269
   marking ends, 33–34, 37
Battersbee, T., *Lieut*, 103
Bayly, John, *Lieut Col*, 159
Bazley, H. A., *Major*, 275

Beaton, James, *Sgt*, 120
Beauclerk, Topham, 22
Beeching, *Lord*, 113f
Beighton, Henry, 10
Belhelvie Sands Base, 37, 142–3
Bench mark lists, 316–7
Bench marks, 88, 217, 316, 325–6. *See also* Fundamental
      Bench Marks.
   flush brackets, 217–8, 271
Benoit, J. R., 214, 270
Bentley, F. G. C., 294, 323
Berge, 40
Bergstrand, Eric, *Dr*, 309
Bessel, F. W., 144f
Bevan, Aneurin, 245
Bevis, John, 13
'Big Bertha', 249
Bilby tower, 271–2
Biot, Jean-Baptiste, 30
Bird, John, 13
   imperial standard 1760, 41
Black, A & C, 184
Black, A. N., *Prof*, 310
Black Letter Prayer Book, 164
Blagden, Charles, 13, 15–17
Blamire, W., 126
Board of Agriculture. *See* Agriculture, Board of.
Board of Celtic Studies, 326
Board of Health. *See* Health, Board of.
Board of Ordnance. *See* Ordnance, Board of.
Board of Works. *See* Works, Board of.
Bomford, G., *Brigadier*, 344
Bonne projection, 147, 164, 251
Bonnycastle, John, 9, 28
Borlase, William, 64
Boscawen, *Sir* Arthur, 230
Bouguer, Pierre, 36
Boulnois, P. K., *Col*, 276–7
Boundaries. *See also* Six-inch map of Ireland.
   Boundary Department, 159, 161, 163
   Survey Act, 110–1
Bourne, Ebenezer, 69–70
Bowen, Emmanuel, 10
Boyce, E. J., *Capt*, 183
Boyce, Henry, 52
Bradley's transit instrument, 36
Bragg, W. L., 222
Brickdale, *Sir* Charles, 189
   correspondence with Close, 227–8
British Association, 87–8, 92, 94
   address by Crook, 186
   memorial from, 102f
   test of triangulation, 205, 214
Brooke, A. F., *Maj-Gen*, 263
Brown, George, 290. *See also* Inter-Departmental Commit-
      tee on Survey Staffs 1950.
Brownlow, *Earl*, 105
Brown, R. L., *Maj-Gen* (Director General), 294, 298–300,
      319
Bryce, *Sir* Alexander, 15, 85
Budgen, Charles, 49, 51, 100–1, 104–5
Bull, Lucien, 222
Burdett-Coutts, Miss, 154
Burdett, Peter Perez, 11
Bureau International des Poids et Mesures, 214
Burgess, James, 193
Burgoyne, *Sir* John, 119, 122–3, 125–6
Burnaby, B., 133
Bury, *Viscount*, 133
Butler, Pierce, *Rev*, 157
Butt-joint plates, 293, 300

Cadastral survey, 80, 120–1, 168, 178, 209. *See also* Land
      registration.
   parish surveys, 85, 168
Cairns, *Lord*, 178
Caithness Base, 308–9

Calderwood, *Lieut-Col*, 34
Cambridge Instrument Company, 249
Cambridge & Paul, 217
Cambridge University Committee for Air Photography, 342
Cameras, air
    F8, 249
    F49 (Williamson Eagle IX), 288, 332, 334
    Fairchild K17, 288, 334, 340
    Wild RC8R, 334
    Zeiss 30/23 RMK, 334
Cameron, John, *Maj-Gen* (Director General), 88, 111, 123–4, 147, 166–7, 210
Campbell, J. D., *Col*, 274
Cardwell, Edward, 159
Carey, C. P. *Col*, 133, 179
Carey, L. F. de Vic, *Maj-Gen* (Director General), 301, 305
Carlisle, Nicholas, 105–6
Carmichael-Smyth, *Sir* James, 52, 91
    Board of Ordnance Inquiry 1828, 85
Cartographic Draughtsman Class, 290
    cartographic assistants, 321
    Fulton proposals, 351
    reconstruction competition, 290
Cartography, commercial publishers, 9–12, 29, 73–76
Cartography, Ordnance Survey maps, one-inch (in chronological order). *See also* Relief.
    Old Series, 104–5
    Ireland, 147–8, 151–2
    one-inch map in colour, 201, Pl 13
    Popular Edition, England and Wales, 231, 251–2, Pl 16
    Popular Edition, Scotland, 251
    Fifth (Relief) Edition, 252–3
    Seventh Series, 305, Pl 21
    Tourist maps, 231, 328
Cartography, Ordnance Survey maps, other than one-inch. *See also* Relief.
    1:25 000
        Provisional (revised) edition, 299
        Second Series, 328, Pl 24
    1:50 000, 352–3, Pl 27
    half-inch, 202
        edition of 1912, 206, 231–2
        Second Series, 328
    quarter-inch, 202
        Ireland, 152
        Third Edition, 232
        Fourth Edition, 253
        Fifth Series, 305, Pl 22
Cary, John, 69, 74, 76
Casgrain, P. H. du P., *Capt*, 200
Cassini de Thury, César François, 33f
    1783 Mémoire, 14, 33
Cassini de Thury, Jacques Dominique, *Comte de*, 17, 33f
Cassini, Giovanni Domenici, 33f
Cassini, Jacques, 33f
Cassini Projection, 143f, 164, 251, 268
Cavendish, Henry, 15, 15f
Cecil, William (*Lord* Burghley), 3
Celtic Studies, Board of, 326
Chadwick, Edwin, 113
Chain survey, 169–171
    after 1945, 332
    Ireland, 83, 86
Chamberlain, Thomas, 46
Chaplin, Charles, 55
Charteris, Francis (*Lord* Elcho), 121–2
    memorandum 1853, 124
    memorandum 1855, 129
Chatham, *Lord* (Master General), 25
Chaytor, John, *Lieut*, 87
Cheetham, G., *Maj-Gen* (Director General), 277, 286–294
    memorandum to Ministry of Agriculture, 287
Chelmsford Method, 294–5, 299, 337
Chronometers, 12. *See also* Longitude.
    transport of, 141
Church Temporalities Commission, 150–1
Circumferentor, 57

Civil Aviation, Ministry of, 288
Civilian Staff. *See also* Departmental Committees of 1881, 1888, 1891, 1911; Ireland, Ordnance Survey of; Pay; Staff Associations; Staffiing.
    classification, normal and special, 242
    engraving abolished, 242–3
    grievances, 136, 163–4, 242, 289
    pensions, 136, 163, 204
    recruiting policy, 247, 289–91
    relations under Close, 205
    role of civilians 1840, 115
    wartime experience, 291
Civil Service Commission, 298
Civil Service Department, 324, 356
Clarke, A. R., *Col*, 139–46, 185, 270, 311
    Geodesy, 145
    spheroids, 143–5
Close, *Sir* Charles (Director General), 29, 204–7, 224–8, 230–5
    archaeology, 237–9
    correspondence with Brickdale, 227–8
    engraving abolished, 243
    Ireland, 212
    magnetic survey, 216–7
    quoted
        on air survey, 234
        on Clarke, 145–6
        on economies, 228
    small scales, 227
    South Africa, 204
    transfer of meridians, 215–6
Clough, A. B., *Brig*, 277
Cobb, M. H., *Col*, 308–9
Coddington, A. B., *Capt*, 159
Colby, Thomas, *Maj-Gen* (Superintendent), 25, 27–28, 30–31, 51, 80–95, 99–107, 109–117
    accident, 28
    appointments, 27–28
    Blue Book, 83–84, App III
    character, 27–28, 116–7
    Colby papers, 27f
    Compensation Bars, 83, 140, Pl 9
    Greenwich-Paris connection 1821–23, 40–1
    Ireland, 81–95, 147, 149
    Precis of the Progress of the Ordnance Survey, 100
    quoted, on revision, 149
    quoted, on Royal Sappers and Miners, 136
    reforms in Gr3at Britain, 99–107
    Select Committee 1824, Evidence, 80–81
    six-inch scale, 109
    staffing and training system, 84, 89, 181
    Welsh place-names, 61–62
Collins, C. B., 258
Colonial Empire, Central Organization for Surveys, 287–8. *See also* Overseas Surveys, Directorate of.
Colonial surveys. *See also* Colonial Empire
    Topographical and Statistical Department, 135
Commission of Military Enquiry 1811
    commercial cartography, 29, 72
    costs and revenue, 72
    'professional surveyors', 52
    Trigonometrical Survey, 28
    Trigonometrical and Topographical Surveys, 45
Commonwealth Survey Officers Conference, 310
Comparison of standards, 145. *See also* Standards of length.
Compass, 57, 59
Compensation bars, 83, 140, 233, Pl 9
Compton, Mr, 101
Computers, 304, 334, 354. *See also* Automated cartography.
    ACE, 304, 334
    computerized planning, 354
    DEUCE, 334
    ICL 1902, 354
    ICL 1904, 354
Condition equations
    initial levelling, 145
    Principal Triangulation, 142

Condition equations (*cont.*)
  Retriangulation, 273
Consultation with users, 293, 358. *See also* Advisory Committee on Surveying and Mapping; Inter-Departmental Committee on Repayment Services; Local Authority Associations; Map Users' Conference.
Continuous Revision, 295, 300–1, 337–9. *See also* Advance Revision Information.
  Davidson Committee, 257, 265
  field methods, 337–8
  Kardex, 300
  manpower needs, 318–9
  planning and control, 338–9
Contouring, 126, 126f, App IV. *See also* Ireland, Ordnance Survey of.
  air survey, 335–6
  Committee on Contouring 1854, 126–7
  Dorington Committee, 190
  first application in United Kingdom, 126f
  flat areas, 335–6
  interpolation, 172
  methods of survey, 171–2
  metric contours, 264, 287, 352
  Select Committee on map of Ireland, 125
  sketched, 172–3, App IV
  water-levelled, 172, App IV
Conybeare, W. D., *Rev*, 61
Cooke, A. C., *Maj-Gen* (Director General), 167, 179–80
  Dorington Committee, 189
  expansion of the Survey, 179
  revision, 182
Cooke Transit Instrument, 311, 346
Cooke, Troughton & Simms, 271, 309f, 312–3. *See also* Simms, Troughton & Simms.
Cook, Hammond & Kell, 354
Copyright, 74–6, 117
  administered by Director General, 300
  Copyright Act 1911, 198, 207
  Crown copyright, 198
  Davidson Committee, 259–60
  Dorington Committee, 191, 193
  legal situation 1816, 75
  revenue increased, 323, 355
  Stationery Office, 198
  Treasury Minute 1887, 184
Cornish Bros, 227
Cornwallis, *Lord* (Master General), 24, 46, 68
Cost Accounting, 244–5
Costs. *See* Progress and costs
Cotswold Method, 294–5, 299, 336–7
County surveys and maps, 7, 9–11
County triangulation, 143, 169, 210. *See also* Ireland, Ordnance Survey of.
  rectangular co-ordinates, 143f
  transfer of meridians, 215–6
Cox Son & Barnett, 70
Crabwood House, 274, 279, 350
Craster, J. E. E., *Lieut-Col*, 233
Crawford, O. G. S., 234, 237–40, 340–1
Crimean War, 135
Crocker, Edmund, 55, 64
Crocker, John, 52–53
Crocker, Philip, 52–53, 64
Croker, J. W., 80
Crook, Henry T., 186–9
  Criticism of
    lack of revision, 187
    pricing mechanism, 187
    quarter-inch map, 202
    Treasury, 186–7
  importance, 193
  Maps of the Ordnance Survey as they are and as they ought to be, 188
  unpopularity of maps, 186–7
Cross-Channel connections
  1787, 16–17, 35–36, Pl 1
  1822, 30, 40–42

  1861, 144
  1951, 307, 312
  1963, 345, Pl 23
Cubbitt, Thomas, 46
Cumberland, *Duke of*, 4–6
Cunnington, William, 64–65
Currie, T., 189
Curwen, E. Cecil, *Dr*, 238
Cyclic Revision. *See* Revision
Cyclometer, 57

Da Costa, A. F. H., *Lieut*, 111
Dalby, Isaac
  Account of the Trigonometrical Survey, 33
  appointments, 17, 22
  quoted on
    field survey, 30
    Mudge, 25
    Williams, 23
  theorem, 39
Dalgleish, William, 90, 148
Dalrymple, Alexander, 21
Darwin, *Sir* George, 205
Davidson Committee, 257–66
  MacLeod's memorandum, 261
  terms of reference, 258
Davidson Committee – Final Report, 260–6, App VI
  1:1250, 263, 286
  1:2500 national series, 261
  1:25 000, 262–3
  air survey, 265
  continuous revision, 265
  decimal scales, 261–2
  manpower expansion, 265, 274
  metric contours, 264
  metric grids, 261
  parcel numbering, 264
  repayment work, 264
Davidson Committee – Interim Report, 258–60
  copyright, 259–60
  staff increase, 259
Davidson, *Sir* John, 257–66, 275
Davies, L., 183
Davies, *Rev*, 107
Davy, *Sir* Humphrey, 30
Dawson, Robert, 49, 51–52, 55, 74, 100, 107
  Course of Instruction, 51, 59, App II
  memorandum on relief depiction, 126
  representation of relief, 51–52
Dawson, Robert Kearsley, *Lieut-Col*
  Assistant Commissioner, Tithe Commission, 112, 117, 121
  contouring, 125
  correspondence with Treasury 1855, 129
  height 'zones', 60
  Ireland, 81, 88, 92
  Lincolnshire, 102
  Select Committee 1856, 130
  triangulation of Scotland, 30
Debbeig, Hugh, 5, 6
Decca navigational system, 294
Decimal Scales, 261–2, 327, 352
Defence, Ministry of. *See also* War Office.
  repayment work, 329–30
De Gomme, *Sir* Bernard, 3
Degree, length of, 12, 38–39
De Grey and Ripon, *Lord*, 154
De la Beche, Henry, 93, 104, 147
Delambre, Jean-Baptiste, 141
Denison, *Mr*, 183
Denmark, Geodetic Survey, 272
Departmental Committees
  1881, on pay and conditions, 163–4
  1888, on pay and classification, 181
  1891, on civil assistants, 181–2
  1892, on the present condition of the Ordnance Survey. *See* Dorington Committee.
  1895, on the sale of Ordnance Survey maps, 196–7

1911, on pay and classification, 204–5
1914, on the sale of small scale maps, 225–7, 231
1935, on the Ordnance Survey. *See* Davidson Committee
1953, on coastal flooding, 315
Department of Health for Scotland. *See* Scotland, Department of Health.
Depot of Military Knowledge, 71, 135
Descriptive pamphlets, 203
A Description of the Ordnance Survey Small Scale Maps, 232
Deviation of the vertical. *See* Local attraction.
Dewing, R. H., *Maj-Gen*, 277
Digges, Leonard, 4
Dillwyn, Lewis Weston, 61
Directorate of Military Survey. *See* Military Survey, Directorate of.
Directorate of Overseas Surveys. *See* Overseas Surveys, Directorate of.
Director General, responsibilities, 135, 159, 220, 224, 247, 276–7
Domesday Book, 164–5
Donald, Thomas, 68
Dorington Committee, 189–93, 358
    contours, 190
    Director General's reports, 192–3
    district maps, 191
    maps in colour, 190–1, 201
    Minute of Board of Agriculture, 192–3
    private publications, 191
    quarter-inch, 202
    revision
        of 1:2500, 190
        of one-inch, 189–90
        of replotted counties, 190
    town plans, 190
    Welsh place-names, 191–3
Dorington, *Sir* John, 189
Dot, George, 326
Downes, G. B., *Lieut*, 88
Dowson, A. H., *Maj-Gen* (Director General), 301–2, 319
Drawing materials
    anodised aluminium plates, 293
    Astrafoil, 300
    celluloid-coated paper, 248
    coated glass, 304–5
    enamel-coated zinc, 274, 293
Drewitt, B. D., 323
Drummond, Thomas, *Capt*, 81, 85, 93–94, 117
    limelight, 82, 140
Duke, R. N., 258
Duke of York's Military School, 111
Duncan George, 152
Duncan, James, 89–90, 148
Duncan, *Viscount*, 130
Dundas, David, 5
Dundas, William, 5
Dunkirk evacuation, 275–6
Earth, figure of, 12, 33, 40, 143–5. *See also* Geoid; Spheroids of Reference.
East India Company, 21–22, 25
Ecclesiastical Name Books, 175
Edge, R. C. A., *Maj-Gen* (Director General) 320, 326, 330, 346, 350, 353
Edgeworth, William, 79
Edinburgh, *Duke of*, 350
Edinburgh Review, quoted, 29
Eire, Ordnance Survey of, 233, 345
Elcho, *Lord. See* Charteris, Francis
Electric power, 185, 200
Electro-magnetic distance measurement, 309–10. *See also* Geodimeter, Tellurometer.
Electrotype, 90, 121, 135, 149, 164
Elkington, E. B., *Lieut-Col*, 275
Ellesmere, *Earl of*, 126
Ellice, Edward, 158
Elliot, T. H., 193
Elphinstone, John, 4f

Emery, Charles, 293
Empire Survey Review, 241
Engineers (Ordnance Corps), 2. *See also* Ordnance, Board of; Royal Engineers.
    military establishment 1717, 3
    qualifications 1683, 3
    ranks, 5f
    Survey Company 1784, 9f
English Place-Names Society, 326
Engraving
    abolition, 242–3
    differential etching, 70f
    hills, 173
    in the Tower, 69–70
    Ireland, 86, 89–90
    pay of engravers, 70
    quality, 105, Pl 7
    technique, 69–70
Esoteric terms, 299
Essex map 1805, 8, 45, 47–48, Pl 4
    engraving, 69
Estimates Committee 1962–63, 302, 319–24, 352
    consultation, 321–2
evidence of IPCS, 319
    marketing and revenue, 322–3
    ministerial responsibility for Ordnance Survey, 323–4
    staffing, 319–21
European datum, 312
Evans, E. Estyn, 91
Evans, J., 73
Expenditure and revenue, 72f, 228, 323, 355

Faden, William, 8, 11, 46–47, 58, 67–69, 73–74, 99–100
    map of Kent, 46–47, 68
Fanshawe, *Brig*, 225
Farquharson, John, *Col* (Director General), 183, 195–6, 201
    change of name, 195
    evidence to 1895 Committee, 196
    service after retirement, 195
Farr, *Mr*, 125
Feachem, R. W. de F., 341
Fergusson, James, 154–5
Fiddes, James, *Lieut*, 15–17
Field Books, 169–72
    chain survey, 169
    destruction 1872, 58f
    eighteenth century, 57
    Old Series, 58–59, 101
Field, John, 55, 100
Field Survey Battalions RE, 222. *See also* Royal Engineers; Survey Battalion.
Field Survey Companies RE, 222. *See also* Royal Engineers; Survey Companies.
Figure of the Earth. *See* Earth, figure of.
Finance (1909–10) Act, 206
Fisher Unwin, T., agent, 197, 232
    Departmental Committee 1914, 225–6
Flamsteed, John, 12
Flash spotting. *See* Artillery survey.
Foot, Thomas, 46, 68–69
Fort Revers – The Dunes Base, 36
Foster, Arnold, 196
Fourcade, H. G., 249
Fox, Charles James, 14
Fox, Charles R., *Maj-Gen*, 111
Francis, H. W. S., 258
Freeman, T. W., 91
Frome, E., 59
Fryer, R. E., *Brig*, 277
Fuller, J. F. C., *Maj-Gen*, 221
Fulton Committee on Civil Service, 351
Fundamental Bench Marks, 205, 217–8, 314, 316, 348, Pl 14

Galton, Douglas, 119, 161
Gardner, James, 41, 59, 100
Gardner, William, 11, 45–48, 59, 67
Gascoigne, Joel, 10

Gauss, K. F., 268
Gazetteers, 252–3
Geddes Axe, 235, 243, 260, 265
Geddes, *Sir* Eric, 235
Geikie, *Sir* Archibald, 189
Geodimeter, 309–10, 345, Pl 23
  connection to Ireland 1969, 345
  Malvern-Graz traverse, 347
Geographical Association, 198
Geographical Section, General Staff, 234, 241, 246, 254, 263, 276–7
Geoid, 143, 218, 346–7
Geoidal sections, 347
Geological maps, 91, 93, 103–4, 202
Geological Sciences, Institute for
  gravity survey, 348
  repayment work, 329–30
Geological Society of London, 104
Geological Survey of Great Britain, 103–4, 202–3. *See also* Ireland, Ordnance Survey of.
George III, 6, 15
  resumption of trigonometrical survey, 22
Gordon, Alexander, 62
Gosset, W., *Capt*, 111, 124–6
Government Printing Establishments, Committee of Enquiry into, 244
Graham, George, 13, 23
Grant, S. C. N., *Col* (Director General), 195–6, 201
Grattan & Gilbert, 100
Gravity survey, 254
  International Gravity Standardization Net, 348
  National Gravity Reference Net, 348
  Worden gravity meters, 348
Gream, Thomas, 46
Greenwich-Paris connection. *See also* Cross-Channel connections.
  Kater, 40–42
  Roy, 14, 33–36
Greenwich, Royal Observatory, 2, 12
  Airy's Transit, 311
  Cooke's Transit, 311, 346
  geodetic connection, 311
  latitude and longitude, 33
Greenwood, Anthony, *Rt Hon*, 350
Greenwood, Christopher, 74
Gregory, Olinthus, *Dr*, 9, 28–29
Grids on maps. *See also* National Grid.
  metric, 261, 266
  military, 225
  one-inch Fifth Edition, 252
Griffith, Richard, 79, 81, 84, 86–87, 94, 148, 150–1
Grimes, W. F., 340

Half-inch maps, 202
  Ireland, 212
  layered and shaded, 202, 206
  layered edition of 1912, 227, 231–2
  Ministry of Transport road map, 245
  revision, 253
  Second Series, 328
  tourist map, 328
Hall, Joseph, 174
Hall, L. A., *Col* (Superintendent), 111–27, 136, 147–9
  appointment of Clarke, 139
  evidence
    on contouring, to Select Committee on map of Ireland, 125
    to Metropolitan Sanitary Commission, 120
    to Select Committee on Army and Ordnance Expenditure, 120
    to Select Committee on Ordnance Survey of Scotland, 121
  quarrel with Yolland, 122–4
Hampshire Independent
  article on James, 166
Harris, George, 70
Harrison, John, 12

Hasty, surveying vessel, 101
Hawkins, J. S., *Lieut-Col*, 135
Hayes-Fisher, William, 196–7
Health, Board of, ten-foot plans, 114
Health, Ministry of, 250
Hearson, *Brig-Gen*, 234
Heathrow cannon, 284–5
Height datums. *See also* Ireland, Ordnance Survey of.
  Liverpool, 145, 316
  Newlyn, 218, 316, 347
  Normaal Amsterdam Peil, 347
Helicopters
  Highlands detail survey, 325, 335
  triangulation, 308
Heliozincography, 200, 242, 242f
  Ireland, 210
Hellard, R. C., *Col* (Director General), 183, 195
Hemming & Partners, 258
Henrici, E. O., *Capt*, 216
Herstmonceux, 311, 346
Hewitt, J., 346
Highland and Agricultural Society of Scotland, 109
Hilger & Watts, 303
Hill sketching
  field sketching, 172–3
  hill drawing, 173
  Old Series, 60, 102
  scale of shade, 60, 173
  vertical and horizontal systems, 60
H M Queen Elizabeth II, 350
H M Stationery Office, 159, 162, 193, 196, 244
  crown copyright, 198, 300
  map distribution, 183–4
Hoare, *Sir* Richard Colt, 64–65
Hobbs, J., *Capt*, 103
Hodges, Figgis & Co, agents, 184, 197
Hodges & Smith, agents, 90, 161
Hornby, P. J., *Lieut*, 111
Horsley, John, 62
Hotine, Martin, *Brig*
  Air Survey Committee, 249
  post-war planning, 286–8
  quoted, 261
  Retriangulation, 268–73, 307–9, 310
  World War II, 277
Hounslow Heath Base, 14–16, 142
  measurement, 33–34
  remeasurement 1791, 29, 37
Housing and Local Government, Ministry of, 322, 356f
  rights of way, 302
Howe, William, *Viscount*, 47
Howlett, Samuel Burt, 53
Howse, *Mr*, 5
H R H Princess Mary, 223
Hull-Preston line, 57, 114, 115
Hume, Joseph, 135
Hunt, Henry A., 161
Hutton, Charles, *Dr*, 9, 23, 28–29, 61
  first use of contours, 126f
Hyett, William, 49

Inclosure Act 1845, 112–3
India, Survey of, 234. *See also* East India Company.
Information, Central Office of
  Ordnance Survey house style, 355
Inspector General of Fortifications, 24
Institute of Printing, 320
Institut Géographique National
  Cross-Channel connection 1951, 307
Institution of Professional Civil Servants, 298–9, 320–1, 351
  evidence to Estimates Committee, 319
Institut Marey, 222
Instruments. *See also* Cameras, air; Geodimeter; Levels; Stereoplotters; Tellurometer; Theodolites.
  alidades, telescopic, 335
  automated cartography, 353–4
  deal rods, 34

eighteenth century, 57
glass rods, 34
Invar tapes, 214, 272, 308–9
Macca Base Equipment, 309
tacheometer, Kern DK-RT, 333
Thompson stereocomparator, 249
zenith sector (Airy), 115, 140, 147, 167, Pl 10
zenith sector (Ramsden), 29, 37, 40, 111, 140, Pl 3
Inter-Departmental Committee on Repayment Services, 293. *See also* Advisory Committee on Surveying and Mapping.
Inter-Departmental Committee on Survey Staffs (Brown Committee) 1950, 290, 293, 320, 352
Inter-Departmental Committee on Survey Staffs 1965, 320
Inter-Departmental Working Party on Survey Staffs 1967, 320
International Association of Geodesy, 326, 345–8
levelling classification, 218, 313
International Cartographic Association, 326
International Geographical Congress, 202, 239
International map 1:1 million, 202, 253
International Union for Geodesy and Geophysics, 254, 310
Invar, 214, 217, 272, 308–9, 314–5
Ireland
early surveys
bog survey 1809, 79
Down survey 1654, 79
Grand Jury maps, 79
Strafford survey 1636, 79
land reform
county cess, 79
Land Commission 1881, 209–10
Rundale system 209–10
tenement maps, 209
townlands, 79
Ireland, Ordnance Survey of, 79–95, 147–52, 209–12. *See also* Half-inch maps; One-inch maps; Quarter-inch maps; Six-inch map of Ireland.
geology, 91, 93
Report on Geology of Londonderry, 93
headquarters, Dublin, 82
heights and levels
contouring, 88, 149, 151,
contours at octonal intervals, 149
contours sketched, 149
hill sketching, 88, 152
initial levelling, 87–88
mean sea level, 88
Poolbeg Lighthouse datum, 88, 149, 210
relevelling, 210
spot heights, 83
vertical angles, 83, 87
Irish Survey Acts, 81
map publication transferred to Southampton, 94–95
Select Committee on Survey and Valuation of Ireland, 80–81
statistical data, 91–93
Colby's intentions, 91
Larcom's questionnaire, 91–92
memoir controversy, 92–93
publication of *Templemore Memoir*, 92
Topographical Department, 92
training and staffing
civilians, 82, 84–5
Colby system, 84, 89
engravers, 89–90
Irish surveyors, 80
officers, 81
Royal Sappers and Miners, 81–82
transfer to Republic of Ireland, 212, 233
triangulation, 82–83, 147–8
base measurement, 83
secondary and tertiary, 83, 86, 210
uses of Ordnance maps, 91
Irish Poor Relief Act, 91
Ironside, *Sir* William, 277
Irwin, B. St G., *Maj-Gen* (Director General), 353–4, 358

Isle of Man, 158–9
Survey Act, 110

Jack, E. M., *Brig* (Director General), 241–2
abolition of engraving, 243
air survey, 234, 248–9
metrication, 257
one-inch, Fifth Edition, 252
period maps, 239
research officer's role, 234
World War I, 220–3
Jackson, H. M., *Lieut-Col.*, 204
Jackson, *Mr*, 99
James, *Sir* Henry (Director General), 116, 127, 129–37, 158–67
archaeology, 174, 239
Director, Topographical and Statistical Department, 135
evidence to
Board of Works Committee of Enquiry, 161
Ordnance Survey Commission 1857, 132
Select Committee 1861–62, 133
Select Committee on Ordnance Survey of Scotland 1856, 131, 183
Irish survey, 150–2
justification for 1:2500 scale, 168
report to War Office and Office of Works, 159–60
scientific publications, 137, 146, 165
survey of Jerusalem and Sinai, 154–7
Jerie Analogue Computer, 308, 334
Jersey and Guernsey, survey of 1787, 45
Jerusalem, survey of, 135, 154–6, 158
Jervis, T. B., *Major*, 135
Johnson, *Dr*, 23
Johnston, Duncan, *Col* (Director General), 189, 195, 199–201, 203
Johnston, W. & A. K., main agent, 161, 197, 296
Johnston, W. J., *Lieut-Col*, 214, 243, 251, 270
standardization of bar O1₁, 214, 270
Joint Survey Service, 320
Jolly, H. L. P., 216, 233–4, 254, 296
Jones, R. O., *Maj-Gen*, 159

Kane, Robert, 91
Kardex, 300
Kate Base, East Africa, 272
Kater, Henry, *Capt*, 40–42
Keeling, B. F. E., *Major*, 216–7, 223
Keiller, Alexander, 238
Keleher, Jack, 278
Kent, 1801 map, 45–46, 68, Pl 4
Killarney District map, 206, 212, Pl 15
Killarney style, 206, 231, 252
Kitchin, Thomas, 10
Knight, *Mr*, 69

Lallemand, Charles, 218, 314
Land and Natural Resources, Ministry of, 319, 322, 324, 350
Landed Estates Court, 150–1, 209
Land registration, 198–9, 227–8, 250, 283, 326–7. *See also* Cadastral survey.
Committees on the Ordnance Survey and H M Land Registry
1898, 198
1899, 199
1901, 199
1905, 199
Departmental Committee 1928, 250
quoted, 199
enlargements to 1:1250, 206
extension of, 259, 294, 310, 327
General Map, 199
Land Registration Act 1925, 250
Land Registry Act 1862, 134
Land Registry Series, 199
Land Transfer Act 1875, 178
Land Transfer Act 1897, 198
reorganized 1968, 327

Land registration (*cont.*)
  repayment, 329–30
  Survey and Mapping Department, HM Land Registry, 198–9
Land Valuation Act 1931, 250–1
Land Valuation Department, 206, 251
Laplace azimuths, 310–1, 345–7
Larcom, Thomas, *Major*, 85, 88–95, 117, 147
  differences with Colby, 94–95
  on contours, 88, 126
Latitude
  calculation – Mudge, 40
  calculation – Roy, 36
  comparisons – Mudge and Retriangulation, 39
  comparisons – Roy and Kater, 42
  Principal Triangulation, 140, 143
  six-inch map of Ireland, 86
Leach, George, *Lieut-Col*, 95, 147
  revision, six-inch map of Ireland, 148–9, 336
  Secretary to Board of Agriculture, 181, 186
Least squares, 142, 145, 218
Lee, Richard, 3
Legendre, Adrien Marie, 17
  theorem, 41, 216
Leland, John, 62
Letts Son & Co, 161
Levelling. *See also* Bench marks; Contouring; Height datums; Ireland, Ordnance Survey of.
  Axmouth-Portishead experiment, 87–88
  causes of errors, 313
  computation in geopotential units, 347
  connections with Europe, 347–8
  curtailment proposed 1973, 356–7
  fen wastage points, 284
  hydrostatic, 347
  initial levelling of Great Britain, 145
  levelling cycles, 316, 325–6
  Roy's, 36
  Second Geodetic, 205, 217–8, 312–3
    accuracy, 218
    calculation, secondary and tertiary, 316
    dynamic heights, 218
    fundamental bench marks, 205, 217–8, Pl 14
    levels, 217
    levelling staves, 217
    orthometric heights, 218
    Scotland, 284, 312–3, 316
  Third Geodetic, 313–6
    calculation of secondary and tertiary, 316
    publication of results, 316
    readjustment, 348
    systematic error, 315
    transfer of levels, 314
Levelling staves (Invar), 217, 314–5
Levels
  eighteenth century, 57
  Zeiss, 217
Lewis, Isle of, 110, 130
Leybourn, William, 57
Light, velocity of, 309–10
Limelight, 82, 140
Lincolnshire. *See* One-inch map, Old Series.
Lind, James, *Dr*, 13
Lithography. *See also* Heliozincography; Photozincography; Vandyke Process.
  in Quartermaster-General's Department, 72f
Liverpool Datum, 145, 316
Lloyd, John, 13, 15
Local attraction, 33, 143–4
  Clarke's calculation, 144
  Dunnose-Clifton arc, 40
Local authorities, liaison officers, 322
Local authority associations, conferences with, 321–2
Local Government Act 1898 (Ireland), 211
Local Government Board
  Maps of civil divisions, 165
  parish names, 176

London County Council, 291
London map trade, 1, 10
  opposition from, 99
  relations with Board of Ordnance, 73
London Passenger Transport Act 1933, 253
London Passenger Transport Map, 253
London Review, 134–5
'London Shop Window', 323
London, survey of, 120, 159–60
Longtitude, 12, 140–1
  calculation, Principal Triangulation, 143
  comparisons – Mudge and Retriangulation, 39–40
  comparisons – Roy and Kater, 42
  electric telegraph, 141, 144
  Essex map 1805, 40f
  Greenwich-Feaghmaan, 141, 144–5
  Mudge's error, 38–39
  Roy's error, 36
  six-inch map of Ireland, 86, 147–8
Longitude, Board of, 12f, 23
Longitudes, Bureau de, 30
Longman & Co, 161
Long Term Plan
  1:1250 resurvey, 293–4
  1:2500 Overhaul, 294–5
  publication, 295–6
Lossiemouth Base, 205, 214–5, 308
  remeasured, 272
Lough Foyle Base, 83, 140, 142–3 214–5
Lund, O., *Brig*, 277

Macca Base Equipment, 309
McCall, W., 319
McCulloch, John, 26, 73, 103
MacKean, K., *Capt*, 183
Mackenzie, Robert, 47
McLauchan, *Mr*, 45
McLauchlan, Henry, 104
MacLeod, M. N., *Maj-Gen* (Director General), 246, 257–66, 276–7, 292
  air survey, 234
  artillery survey, 246
  Davidson Committee, 257–66
    memorandum to, 261
  post-war planning, 286–7
  World War I, 222
  World War II, 276–7
Macpherson, I. C. *See* Farquharson, John.
Magnetic survey, 216–7, 254
Malvern-Edinburgh traverse, 347
Malvern-Graz traverse, 347, Pl 23
Manchester Geographical Society, 186
Manson, John, 5
Map agents, 74, 99–100, 160–1, 183–4, 196–7. *See also* Faden, William; Fisher Unwin; Stanford, Edward.
  Arrowsmith, John, 100
  Black, A. & C., 184
  Cook, Hammond & Kell, 354
  Departmental Committee 1914, 225–7
  Gardner, James, 100
  Government map shop, 161, 183
  Grattan & Gilbert, 100
  HMSO responsible, 183–4
  Hodges Figgis & Co, 184, 197
  Hodges & Smith, 90, 161
  Johnston, W. & A. K., 161, 197, 296
  Letts, Son & Co, 161
  Longman & Co, 161
  Menzies, 197, 225
  Nelson & Sons, 296
  Post Office, 161, 196–7, 226
  sole agencies, 183–4, 196–7
  wholesaling from Southampton, 197, 354–5
  Wyld, J., 158, 161
Map covers, 232, 244
Map finishing, 329
Mappa Britanniae, 63

Maps. *See* Town plans, and under various scales: e.g. 1:1250, six-inch etc.
Maps in Europe, publication, 67f
Maps of the Ordnance Survey as they are and as they ought to be, 188
Maps published by Board of Ordnance, 67–77
  soliciting for orders, 99
Maps published by private firms, 67, 73–77, 190–1. *See also* Copyright; Map agents.
  bought by Board of Ordnance, 68
  trigonometrical data, 74
Maps – sales. *See* Map agents; marketing.
Map Users Conferences, 322
'March routes', 110
Margan, James Clarence, 92
Marketing. *See also* Map agents; Revenue.
  by subscription, 76–7, 103
  Estimates Committee recommendations, 322–3
  review of map market, 352, 355
Marles, A. C., *Major*, 325
Martin, A. R., *Major*, 280
Martin, Ellis, 232, 244
Maskelyne, Nevil, *Dr*, 23, 29, 33
  first use of contours, 126f
  formula, 38
Mason, William Shaw, 80
Mathematical model, large scale mapping, 354
Mather, William, 189
Matheson, *Sir* James, 110
Mathieson, John, 206
Mathieu, C. L., 41
Matson, *Col*, 127
Méchain, Pierre, 17
Melville, Robert, *Capt*, 62
Mémorial Topographique et Militaire, 51
Menzies, main agent, 197, 225
Meridians. *See also* Arcs of meridian; County triangulation.
  county meridians, Ireland, 86, 148
  county origins, Great Britain, 143, 215–6
  plotting one-inch, Old Series, 39–40, 57–58
  transfer of, 215–6, 230
Metcalf, Edward B., 49, 100
Metford, F. O., *Brig*, 294
Metric maps, 257, 327, 352
  1:50 000, 352–3
  contours, 264, 287, 352
  review of map market, 352, 355
Metropolitan Sanitary Commission
  evidence of Hall and Yolland, 120
Mew G. H., *Capt*, 233
Microfilm
  35mm, 353
  printing from 70mm, 329
Military Antiquities of the Romans in Britain, 63
Military mapping
  1:20 000, 263
  1:25 344 of East Anglia, 263
  Board of Ordnance, 2–9
  British national style, 51
  Crimean War, 135
  diversion of resources to, 1860, 133
  for RAF and USAF, 282
  invasion of Europe, 281–3
  Napoleonic War, 67–68
  Rearmament Series, 281
  Scotland, military survey 1747, 4–5
  South African War, 204
  World War I, 220–5
  World War II, 280–3
Military Survey, Directorate of, 277, 320
Military system, justification for, 245–8
  Board of Works Committee of Enquiry, 162–3
  Brown Committee, 290
  Cooke's and Stotherd's arguments, 179–80
  Estimates Committee, 319–20
  James, 159–60
  Roy, 8, 15

Milne, Thomas, 68
Ministry of (Agriculture etc). *See* (Agriculture etc), Ministry of.
Misterton Carr Base, 37–38, 142–3
Montefiore, *Sir* Moses, 156
Moore Brabazon, *Lieut-Col*, 234
Morse, Robert, *Gen*, 28, 70
Mudge, John, 23
Mudge, Richard, *Capt*, 54, 102, 104–5, 107
  correction of errors, 100–1
  on meridians, 58
Mudge, Thomas, 23
Mudge, William, *Maj-Gen* (Superintendent), 23–29
  cadet training, 50–51
  Commission of Military Enquiry, 28
  Essex map, specification, 47
  Greenwich-Paris connection 33, 35
  Hounslow Heath Base, 29
  international contacts, 29–30
  Mudge's Circular, 54
  place-names, 60
  plural offices, 25
  private publishers, 73–77
Mulcaster, *Sir* Frederick, 93–94, 109, 212
Mulgrave, *Earl of* (Master General), 70–71, 73, 76
Muller, John, 3
Murchison, *Sir* Roderick, 137
Murphy, Hastings, *Lieut*, 117
Murphy, L. P., 350
Murray, David, 175
Murray, Herbert, 161, 163

Names. *See* Place-names.
Napoleon III, 133
Napoleonic War, 24, 48–50, 67, 70–71
National Coal Board programme, 294, 301, 325
National Economy Committee, 244
National Grid, 268–9
National Institute of Oceanography, 347
National Parks and Access to Countryside Act 1949, 291
  rights of way, 302
National Physical Laboratory, 304
  ACE and DEUCE, 334
  velocity of light, 310
Nature, velocity of light, 309
Nelson, Thomas, & Sons, main agent, 296
Newlyn Datum, 218, 316, 347
Nicolson, J. B., *Flight-Lieut*, 278
Nimmo, Alexander, 79
Normaal Amsterdam Peil, 347
Norreys, *Sir* Denham, 125, 132
North-East London Polytechnic, 352
Northern Ireland, Ordnance Survey of, 233
  drawing for Ordnance Survey of Great Britain, 325
  repayment work, 330
Nottingham University, 345–6
Nye, A. E., *Brig*, 277

O'Beirne, Thomas, 296
O'Curry, Eugene, 92
O'Donovan, John, 89, 92–93, 239
Office of Woods and Forests. *See* Woods and Forests, Office of.
Office of Works. *See* Works, Office of.
Ogilby, John, 10
Olivier, *Sir* Sydney, 225
Oman, *Sir* Charles, 239
One-inch map series (in chronological order). *See also* Cartography; Revision.
  Old Series, 57–65, 100–7, 160, Pl 5, 7
    accuracy, 60
    archaeology, 63–65
    defects, 60, 100–2, 105, 134–5
    fieldwork, 58–60, Pl 5
    hill sketching, 60
    Kent and Essex, 45–48, Pl 4
    Lincolnshire, 76–77, 101, 104–5

One-inch map series (*cont.*)
  Old Series (*cont.*)
    place-names, 60–62, 105–7
    sheet lines, 58
  New Series, 164, 200–1
    Advance Edition, 188
    brown engraved hills, 201
    engraving, 164
    projection, 164
    reduction from six-inch, 185
    sheet lines, 164
  Ireland, 147–8, 201
    colour, 211
    hill sketching, 147
    latitude and longitude, 147–8
    projection, 147
    reduction from six-inch, 148
    revision, 211
    sheet lines, 147–8
    tourist maps, 212
  Scotland, 164
    projection, 164
    sheet lines, 164
  in colour, 201, Pl 13
    large sheet series, 201
    method of production, 201
  Third Edition, 201
    defects, 227
  Popular Edition, England and Wales, 231, 251–2, Pl 16
  Popular Edition, Scotland, 251
    Gaelic glossary, 244
  Fifth Edition, 252–3
    special sheets, 253
    unshaded, 253
  Sixth Edition (New Popular), 266, 292
  Seventh Series, 305, 352, Pl 21
    pilot sheet, 295
  Tourist/District, 231, 328
    Killarney district map, 206, 212, 231, 252, Pl 15
  War revision, 252, 284
One-inch scale. *See also* One-inch map series.
  choice of, 11
  proposal to leave to trade, 109
Ordnance Bars
  O_1, 141, 145, 214, 270
  $O1_1$, 145, 214, 270
  $O1_2$, 214
  O_2, 141
Ordnance, Board of, 2–3, 135
  Inspector General of Fortifications, 24
  Master General, 2
  survey of Ireland, 80–81
  triangulation 1787, 16–17
Ordnance, Board of – Committees of Enquiry
  1828 (Carmichael-Smyth), 85
  1829, 85
  1833, 86
Ordnance Board Transfer Act 1855, 135
Ordnance House, 200
Ordnance Survey
  first use of name on maps, 71
  house style, 355
Ordnance Survey, Committee on the, 1970, 355–8
  Royal Society letter, 357
  The Times, correspondence, 357
Ordnance Survey from a business point of view, The, 188
Ordnance Survey – internal organization
  Colby system, Ireland, 81–85, 89–90
  engravers, 69–70
  Field Directorate, 294, 300
  military control, 136, 179–80
  Old Series fieldwork, 100, 102
  post-war management structure, 287–8
  reorganization
    1787, 44–45
    1935, 259
    1953, 300

    1958, 304
    1970, 351
  Royal Military Surveyors and Draftsmen, 48–49, 55
Ordnance Survey offices. *See also* Tower of London.
  Chessington, 279–80, 285
  Hinchley Wood, 279–80
  Nottingham and Derby, 279
  Southampton, 111
    Air Raid Precautions, 277–8
    air raids, 277–80
    Crabwood site, 274, 279
    dispersal 1941–43, 279–80
    new headquarters, 350–1, Pl 26
  Waddon, 279–80
Ordnance Survey Review Committee 1978
  terms of reference, 359
Oriani, method of, 42
'Ornament', 70, 178, 328–9
Osmond, S. P., 320
Overhaul revision
  air-assisted, 303
  air-ground, 325
  by-passed plans, 301
  Chelmsford Method, 294–5, 299, 337
  Cotswold Method, 294–5, 299, 336–7
  Davidson Committee, 261
  priority, 294
Overseas Branch of the Ordnance Survey, 223
Overseas Surveys, Directorate of, 320. *See also* Colonial
    Empire, Central Organization for Surveys.

Paget, E. C. T., *Maj-Gen*, 277
Palestine Exploration Fund, 157
Palmer, Arthur, 232
Palmer, E. F., *Prof*
  Sinai survey, 157
Palmer, H. S., *Capt*
  Sinai survey, 157
Palmer, John, 69
Palmerston, *Lord*, 129, 133
Panmure, *Lord*, 130, 135
Parker, C. L. Y., *Lieut-Col*, 279, 286
Parsons, R. M., *Capt*, 135
Paterson, Daniel, 11, 73
Pay
  civilian staff, 136–7, 179, 181–2, 204–5, 242, 298, 351
  Director General, 180
  engravers, 69–70, 136–7
  Royal Military Surveyors and Draftsmen, 49
  surveyors, 45, 47–48, 101–2, 112–3, 137
Peake, E. R. L., *Brig*, 277, 286
Peake, H. J. E., 237
Pearson, William, 28
Peart, Frederick, *Rt Hon.* 350
Peel, *Sir* Robert, 93, 95, 110
Period maps, 239, 328, Pl 17
  Mappa Britanniae, 63
Petrie, George, 92
Petty, William, 79–80
Philip, Stanley
  Departmental Committee 1914, 225
  evidence to 1895 Committee, 196
Phillips, C. W., 340–1
Philosophical Transactions
  Greenwich-Paris connection, 14, 17, 33
  Hounslow Heath Base, 16
  research, 12
  white lights, 16
Photography, 137, 165. *See also* Air photography.
  one-inch map, 148, 185
  six-inch map, 178–9
  War Office Committee 1858, 137
Photozincography, 137, 165, 185. *See also* Heliozincography;
    Vandyke process.
  1:2500, 179, 203
  Domesday book, 164
  six-inch map, 178–9

Picard, Jean, 33
Piecework, 101–2, 126
    James's system, 130, 136
Piggott, *Mr* (Controller of HMSO), 196
Pink, George, 46
Pipon, J. K., *Lieut*, 111
Pitt, Moses, 10
Pitt, William, 22
Place-names, 60–62, 105–7, 175–6. 326. *See also* Six-inch
        map of Ireland.
    Administrative Name Books, 175
    competent authority doctrine, 326
    Dorington rules, 192f, 193
    Ecclesiastical Name Books, 175
    Gaelic names, 193, 206–7, 326
    Instructions to Field Examiners, 176
    Object Name Books, 174–6
    policy statement, 326
    Welsh names, 61–62, 106–7, 191–3
Plane table, 57, 59–60
    six-inch air survey, 335
Planning. *See* Long Term Plan; Production planning; Short
        Term Plan.
'Plans' (fair drawings) two-inch scale, 58
Plot, Robert, 10
Plymouth map 1784, 45
Point M., 36
Policy statements, 299
    Basic policy, 330
    place-names, 326
Pond, John, 41
Poolbeg Lighthouse, 88, 149, 210
Poor Law Commission 1834, 113–4
    town plans, 114
Popinjay, Richard, 3
Portlock, J. E., *Lieut-Col*, 81, 87, 91–93, 147
    quoted, 104, 116–7
Post Offices, map sales, 161, 196–7, 226
Post-war programme, 286–8. *See also* Long Term Plan, Short
        Term Plan.
    air photography, 288
    approved by Parliament, 288
    Cheetham memorandum, 287
    manpower, 288–91
    organization, 287
Powell, James, quoted, on sheet lines, 58
Precis of the Progress of the Ordnance Survey, 100
Presentation copies, 74, 90, 161–2
Prices of maps, 74, 90, 116, 187, 191, 231, 244–5, 323
    basis of calculation, 161, 322–3
    'Bill of Prices', 73
Primrose, Henry, 189
Principal Triangulation, 139–43, Pl 11
    adjustment, 142–3
    calculation, 142
    latitude and longitude, 140–1, 143
    lengths of bases, 142–3
    observation procedure, 140
    test of triangulation, 205, 214–5
    use for mapping, 143, 210
Pringle, J., *Capt*, 91
Printing. *See also* Six-inch map of Ireland.
    in Tower, 70
    microfilm, 329
    photo type-setting, 329
    printing paper, 227
    zinc printing, 178–9, 200
Printing Company RE, 221
Printing, Institute of, 320
Prismatic Bar, 36, 41, 141
Private map publishers. *See* Maps published by private
        firms.
Private surveyors, employment of, 52–53, 55, 80, 84–85,
        121, 130, 179
Production planning
    field programme, 300
    computerized, 354

co-ordination of surveying and drawing output, 294, 302,
        325
Progress and Costs
    1791–1846, 115–6
    1833 Ireland, 86
    1846 Ireland, 87
    1846 Great Britain and Ireland, 116
    1856 Scotland, 131
    1858, 132–3
    1858–62, 158
    1864–70, 160
    1870–80, 164
    1904–09, state of revision, 203–4
    1922–33, 248
    1934, 257
    1949, 1:1250 resurvey rate, 294
    1960–61, 1:1250 output by different methods, 304
    1962–63, effects of winter, 318
    1973–75 digital mapping, 354
Projections
    Bonne, 147, 164, 251
    Cassini, 143f, 164, 251, 268
    National, 261
    Old Series, 57–58
    Transverse Mercator, 252–3, 268–70
    Universal Transverse Mercator, 312, 344
Proofs
    circulation of, 60–62, 64, 101–2
    from copper plates, 70
Public Accounts Committee, 245
Publicity. *See also* Descriptive pamphlets.
    advertisements, 72–73, 99, 232
    advertising campaigns, 355
    Estimates Committee, 323
Pulkowa Observatory, 144

Quarter-inch maps
    Great Britain, 185, 202
        Atlas, 253
        Fifth Series, 305, Pl 22
        First and Second Editions, 202
        Fourth Edition, 253
        Third Edition, 232, 253
    Ireland, 152, 211
    Railway map, 94
Quartermaster-General's Department, 2, 6, 71–72
    Depot of Military Knowledge, 71, 135
    rivalry with Board of Ordnance, 24, 71

Radio Research Station, Slough, 346
Railway map, 94
Railway surveys, 113
Ramsden, Jesse, 13, 17, 29
    brass scale, 36–37, 41
    chains, 34, 36–37
    prismatic bar, 36, 41, 141
    theodolite B. O., 21–22, 34, 36
    theodolite R. S., 16, 34–36, Pl 2
    zenith sector, 29, 37, 40, 111, 140, Pl 3
Ramshaw, *Mr*, 111
Ranging Section RE, 1st, 221
Read, *Sir* Hercules, 237
Rectangular co-ordinates. *See also* National Grid.
    calculation, 18th century, 57
    Cassini, 143f
    meridians for plotting, 57–58
Registration and Conveyance Commission 1850, 121
Reid, William, *Major*, 81, 85
Relief, representation of, 60, 88, 149, 171–3, 206, 328, Pl 5,
        Pl 7, Pl 13, Pl 15, Pl 22, App IV
    Dawson's principles, 52, 126
    rock depiction, 305, 328
    triotint, 148, 152
Rendel, James, 126
Rennell, James, *Major*, 1, 21
Renny, H. L., *Lieut*, 103
Repayment work, 329–30
    Davidson Committee, 264

Repetition angles, 140
'Replotted counties', 182–3
  'revision', 190
Report on the Geology of the County of Londonderry, 93
Reports on the Progress of the Ordnance Survey, 137, 165,
  203
Representation of the People Act 1867
  maps for Commissioners, 159,
Research Officer, 233–4, 254, 307–8. *See also* Scientific
  Adviser.
Retrenchment in Public Expenditure, Committee on, 1916,
  230
Retriangulation, 261, 268–73, Pl 18
  adjustment figures, 270, 272–3
  adjustment, scientific, 270, 344–6
  analytical aerial triangulation, 334
  azimuth observations, 310–1
  base measurements, 308–9
  Bilby tower, 271–2
  comparison with Principal Triangulation, 311
  computation, 272–3
  cross-Channel connection 1951, 307, 312
  cross-Channel connection 1963, 345
  geoidal sections, 347
  Greenwich and Herstmonceux connections, 311
  helicopters, 308
  Ireland connection 1952, 312
  Ireland connection 1969, 345
  Jerie analogue computer, 308, 334
  observation of angles, 271–2
  primary, 269–72
  St Kilda connection, 311
  scale errors, 310
  scale and orientation, 269
  Scotland, 307
  secondary, 307–8
  standards of length, 270
  station marks, 270–1
  town control, 308
Revenue. *See also* Copyright; Marketing; Prices of Maps.
  1791–1846, 115–6
  1970–74, 355
  Estimates Committee, 322–3
  Sales
    1800–10, 72
    1866–71, 161
    1907–11, 197
    1965–69, 323
Revision. *See also* Continuous revision; Overhaul revision;
  Six-inch map of Ireland.
  1:2500 cyclic interval, 162, 193, 206, 230–1
  1:2500 experimental, 182
  card revision, 151, 203
  Crook's criticism, 187
  derived maps, 319
  Dorington Committee, 189–90
  field trace, 203
  Lancashire and Yorkshire, 182–3, 190
  land valuation, 206, 250–1
  Leach's doctrine, 336
  Old Series, 101–4
  one-inch revision, 189–90, 339
  one-inch road revision 1925, 251–2
  shining-up, 203, 336
Reynolds, *Sir* Joshua, 23
Reynolds, Thomas V., *Capt*, 67–68
Rhuddlan Marsh Base, 37, 142
Richard of Cirencester, 174
Richardson, H. G., 258
Richmond, *Duke of* (Master General), 3, 6, 11–13,
  24, 67
  reorganization of topographical survey, 45
  resumption of trigomometrical survey, 21–23
  Sussex map, 46
Rider, L/Cpl, 137
Ridge Way Base, 272, 308–10
Rights of way, 302

Road maps
  Ministry of Transport half-inch, 245
Robbins, A. R., 347
Robe, A. W., *Lieut*, 102, 117
Robinson, W., *Lieut*, 111
Roby, Henry, 189
Rock depiction
  1:2500, 328–9
  six-inch pilot sheet, 305
Rocque, John, 10
Rodriguez, *Don* Joseph, 29
Rods, deal, 34
  Fort Revers – The Dunes Base, 36
  Hounslow Heath Base, 34
Rods, glass, 34
Rogers, John, 3
Roman Empire map. 1:1 million, 239
Roman sites
  1:2500, 174–5
  Old Series, 64
  Roy, 62–63
Romney Marsh Base, 16–17, 34
Rosedew, Richard, 26
Rowe, H. G., & Co
  copyright infringement, 207
Rowland, *Mr*, 191f
Roy, William, *Maj-Gen*, 3–9, 13–18, 33–36
  archaeology, 13, 62–63, 239
  brass scale, 34, 37, 41
  dispute with Ramsden, 16–17
  Greenwich-Paris connection, 16–17 33–36, Pl 1
  Hounslow Heath Base, 15–16, 33–34
  Instructions in Surveying, 9, App I
  London residences, 13
  national survey, 6–8, 18
  plane table, 59
  Royal Society, 13
  Scotland map, 1747, 4–5, 57
Royal Air Force, 249, 258
  Central Interpretation Unit, 279
  maps for, 277, 282
  survey photography, 288, 299
Royal Artillery, 2, 15, 220–3, 225, 257
Royal Astronomical Society, 214
Royal College of Art
  Experimental Cartography Unit, 353
Royal Commission on Ancient and Historic Monuments
  (Scotland), 343
Royal Commission on the Ordnance Survey 1857, 132
Royal Engineers Journal, obitury for James, 166
Royal Engineers (Survey), 179–80, 245–8. *See also*
  Engineers; Royal Sappers and Miners.
  16th Survey Coy disbanded, 204
  19th Field Survey Coy, 246, 275
  522 (Ordnance Survey) Coy, 280, 287, 291
  cadet training, 50, 52
  Military Staff, Ordnance Survey, 280
  Royal Sappers and Miners incorporated, 135
  School of Military Survey, 352
  Survey Battalion, 246, 271, 275
  Survey Training Centre, 275
  World War I, 220–3
  World War II, 275–7
Royal Flying Corps, 221–2, 237–8
Royal Geographical Society, 156–7, 195, 252, 265
Royal Institution of Chartered Surveyors, 320, 358
Royal Irish Academy, 93, 210
Royal Military Academy, Woolwich, 3, 9, 23
  Mudge's appointment, 25
Royal Military College, High Wycombe, 22, 51, 71
Royal Military Surveyors and Draftsmen, 48–53, 55
Royal Radar Establishment, Malvern, 346
Royal Sappers and Miners, 81–82, 107, 110
  13th, 14th, 16th Survey Coys, 82f
  19th Survey Coy, 113
  changing role, 115, 136
  transfer to Corps of Royal Engineers, 135

Royal Scottish Geographical Society, Place-Names Committee, 193, 206–7, 326
Royal Society, 3, 12–13
  archaeological mapping, 63
  brass scale, 34, 37, 41
  correspondence with Secretary of State 1973, 357–8
  Greenwich-Paris connection, 14–18
  Jerusalem survey, 156
  magnetic survey, 216
  Rodriguez, *Don* Joseph, 29
  Royal Society Club, 13
  Sinai survey, 157
  test of triangulation, 205
  theodolite, three-foot, 16, 34–35, 37–38, 139, 278–9, Pl2
Royal Society of Arts. *See also* Society of Arts.
  Wilson's paper, 188
Rucker, *Sir* Arthur, 216
Rundale system, 209–10

Sackville, *Lord* George, 5
St Joseph, J. K. S., *Prof*, 342
St Paul's Cathedral
  observing platform, 120
Salisbury Plain Base, 37–38, 140, 142–3, 372
  test of triangulation, 214–5
Salt, J. S. A., *Lieut*, 249
Sandby, Paul, 5
Sandby, Thomas, 5
Sanitary Reform, 113–4, 154. *See also* Health, Board of; Poor Law Commission.
Satellite geodesy, 346–7
  Malvern-Edinburgh traverse, 347
  Malvern-Graz traverse, 347
  satellite tracking unit, 346
Saunders, Trelawney, 100
Saxton, Christopher, 4
  atlas, 4
Scale and trace, 304. *See also* Area measurement.
Scales dispute, 114–5, 119–22, 124–7, 129–34
  1851 Select Committee on Ordnance Survey of Scotland, 121–2
  1853 Charteris's memorandum, 124
  1853 Treasury circular, 124–5
  1854 Treasury circular, 125–6
  1854 Treasury Committee, 126
  1854 (15 July) Treasury minute, 126, 129
  1855 (18 May) Treasury minute, 129–30
  1856 Select Committee on Ordnance Survey of Scotland, 130–1
  1857 (June) 1:2500 scale discontinued, 132
  1857 Royal Commission on Ordnance Survey, 132
  1858 (11 Sept) Treasury minute, 132
  1861–2 Select Committee on Cadastral Survey, 133
  1863 Treasury minute, 133
School of Scottish Studies, 326
Schools, maps for 198, 352
Schumacher, Heinrich, 29
Science Museum, South Kensington
  exhibition of scientific apparatus, 167
Scientific Adviser, 296
Scotland, Department of Health
  1:25 000, 291
  NCB programme, 294
Scotland, military survey 1747, 4–5, 57
Scotland, one-inch map. *See* one-inch map.
Scotland, survey of Southern, 1819, 103
Scott, A. de C., *Col*, 137, 179–80
Scottish Geographical Magazine
  Crook's paper, 186
  place-names, 206–7
Scribing, 304–5
Searle, Richard, 51
'Secret Circular', 181
Sedgemoor Base, 37–38
Sedgwick, *Prof*, 61

Select Committees
  1824, on Survey and Valuation of Ireland, 30, 53, 81
    Colby's evidence, 80–81
  1837, on Survey of Parishes, 112
  1849, on Army and Ordnance Expenditure, 120
    Hall's evidence, 120
    Southampton office, 111
  1851, on Ordnance Survey of Scotland, 121–2
    Hall's evidence, 121
  1853, on map of Ireland, 125, 147
    Hall's evidence on contours, 125
  1856, on Ordnance Survey of Scotland, 130–1
    James's evidence, 131, 183
  1861 and 62, on Cadastral Survey, 133
  1878, on Land Titles and Transfer, 178
  1918, on National Expenditure, 230
Seller, John, 10
Serpell, *Sir* David, 359
Seven Years War, 5
Severndroog Castle
  initial azimuth 1787–89, 36
Sextants, 57, 59
Seymour, Digby, 136
Seymour, *Lord*, 129
Shadow programme, 287–8
Sheet lines
  1:50 000, 352
  large scales, 170, 261, 305
  one-inch
    Fifth Edition, 253
    Ireland, 147–8
    Large Sheet Series, 201
    New Series, 164
    Old Series, 58
    Popular Edition, Scotland, 251
    quarter-inch, Third Edition, 253
    six-inch, Ireland, 86
Shetlands, arc of meridian, 30
'Shining-up', 203, 336
SHORAN, 312, 344
Short, James, 13
Short Term Plan, 291–2, 295, 299
Shuckburgh, *Sir* George
  brass scale, 141
Sibbald, *Sir* Robert, 10
SIM. *See* Advance Revision Information.
Simms, William, 82. *See also* Troughton & Simms.
Sinai, survey of, 135, 157
Sisson, Jonathan, 13
Site antiquities. *See* Archaeological survey.
Six-inch map of Great Britain, 109–10, 129. *See also* Scales Dispute.
  1:10 000, 327
  County Series
    photozincography, 178–9
    quarter-sheets, 179, 251
    reduction by photography, 178–9
    town maps in colour, 231
  National Grid Series
    1959 specification, 302, Pl 19
    air survey, 303–4
    Provisional Edition (County Series, gridded), 292
    Provisional (National Grid sheet lines), 292, 299
    Regular Edition pilot sheet, 295
    rock depiction, 305
    Scottish Highlands, basic scale, 300
Six-inch map of Ireland, 79–91
  boundaries and valuation, 81, 84–87, 151, 209
    field boundaries, 80, 87, Pl 6
    requirement defined 1833, 86
  content survey, 83, 85
    paper computing, 85
  engraving, 89–90
    electrotyping, 90
    heliozincography, 210
    mechanical aids, 90
    plotting on copper, 86

Six-inch map of Ireland (*cont.*)
  methods of survey, 83–87. *See also* Ireland, Ordnance
    Survey of, heights and levels, triangulation.
    accuracy standards, 87
    chain triangulation, 83, 86
    fences, 87
    Instructions for the Interior Survey of Ireland, 83–84,
      App III
    secondary triangulation, 83
    traversing, 84, 86
  place-names, 89, 210
  printing, 90
    by contract, 90
    division of labour, 90
    presentation copies, 90
  revision, 148–9, 151, 209
    card revision, 151
    for one-inch map, 148
  specification, 83–84
    conventional signs, 89
    field boundaries, 80, 87, Pl 6
    parishes combined into sheets, 85–86
  uses, 91
Sketching. *See also* Hill sketching.
  Old Series, 58–59
Skinner, Andrew, 11
Slum Clearance Act, 250
Smeaton, John, 15
Smith, Walter P. (Director General), 358
Smith, W. H., & Son, 226
Smyth, *Mr*
  evidence to 1895 Committee, 196
Society of Antiquaries of London, 63, 174
Society of Antiquaries of Scotland, 174–5
Society of Arts, 10–11, 67. *See also* Royal Society of Arts.
Somerset, *Lord* Granville, 110
Sound ranging. *See* Artillery survey.
South African War, 204
Speed, John, 9, 175
Spherical excess, 34–35
Spheroids of reference, 143–5
  Airy's, 39, 141, 143–4, 270
  Bouguer's, 36
  Clarke's 1858, 144
  Clarke's 1866, 145
  Clarke's 1880, 145
  Clarke's United Kingdom, 144
  Kater's use of, 42
  Oriani's, 42
Spring Rice, S. E., 193
Spring Rice, Thomas, 80, 92–93
Staff Associations, 205, 232–3, 243, 321, 351. *See also*
  Association of Government Geographers; Institution
  of Professional Civil Servants.
Staffing. *See also* Cartographic Draughtsman Class; Civilian
  staff; Ireland, Ordnance Survey of; Royal Engineers;
  Royal Sappers and Miners.
  1851–1918 expansion and reduction, 132, 136, 163–4,
    167, 178, 180–2, 185, 192, 204, 228
  1918 cessation of recruitment, 230
  1935 expansion, 259, 265
  1946 post-war recruitment, 289–91
  1947 manpower ceilings, 290
  1949 reconstruction competition, 290
  1950 reductions, 298
  1951 maximum post-war strength, 290
  1951 recruitment competition, 298
  1966 expansion, 319
  Junior Temporary Civil Assistants, 275, 290
  promotion of technical staff, 320–1
  staff suggestions awards, 207
  sub-division of work, 181
  women, employment of, 275, 352
Standards of length. *See also* Ordnance bars.
  Bird's 1760 imperial standard, 41
  brass scale
    Ramsden's, 36–37, 41

    Royal Society's, 34, 37, 41, 141f
    Roy's, 34, 37, 41, 141
    Shuckburgh's, 141
  comparison of, 145, 214
  international metre, 214, 270
  prismatic bar, 36, 41, 141
  retriangulation, 270
Stanford, Edward, 100, 134, 161, 183–4, 197, 284, 296, 323,
    354
  evidence to 1895 Committee, 196
  evidence to Dorington Committee, 189
  The Ordnance Survey from a business point of view, 188
Stanley, *Dean*, 154
Stanley, William, 49, 51, 53, 55, 100
Stationery Office. *See* HM Stationery Office.
Steel, James, *Sgt*, 115, 120
Stereoplotters
  Barr & Stroud ('Big Bertha'), 249
  Fourcade stereogoniometer, 249, 279
  Santoni Stereo-Simplex, 303, 334–5
  Thompson-Watts, 303, 334, Pl 20
  Wild A5, 249, 279, 302–3
  Wild A6, 303–4, 334–5
  Wild A8, 303, 334
Stevens, Henry, 49, 55, 58f, 100–1
Stewart-Wallace, *Sir* John, 250, 259
  1928 Committee, 199, 250
  quoted, on Winterbotham, 250
Still, Henry, 175
Stokes, Charles, 61
Stotherd, R. H., *Col* (Director General), 179–80, 185
  HMSO, 183
  revision, 182–3
Struve, F. G. W. von, 144
Stukeley, William, 62
Suez Canal, 154
Suirbheireacht Ordenais, 233
Surrey, Lindley & Crossley map, 46
Survey Act 1841, 110–11, 154, 175
Survey Battalion RE, 246, 271, 275
Survey Companies, 82f, 110, 112–3, 132, 192, 204. *See also*
  Royal Engineers; Royal Sappers and Miners.
Surveying methods. *See* Air survey; Chain survey;
  Tacheometric survey; Traversing.
SUSI. *See* Advance Revision Information.
Sussex map, 1778, 1792, 11–12, 46
Symonds, J. F. A., *Lieut*, 155
Syrian Improvement Committee, 156

Tacheometric survey, 302–4, 333, Pl 25
  Banstead experiment, 302–3
Tapes, Invar, 214, 272
Taylor, George, 11
Technical conservatism in Ordnance Survey, 302
Technology, Ministry of
  Joint Standing Committee on Metrication, 327
Tellurometer, 308, 310, 345
  connection to Ireland 1969, 345
  cross-Channel connection 1963, 345
Templemore Parish Memoir, 92
Theodolites
  Ramsden's 18-inch, 36, 44, 120 139 351
  Ramsden's 3-foot
    'Board of Ordnance', 21–22, 34, 36, 38, 82, 139, 167
    Kater's modifications, 41
    observing procedure, 35, 38, 140
    'Royal Society', 16, 34–35, 37–38, 139, 278–9, Pl 2
  Tavistock
    3½-inch, 270
    geodetic, 271
  Two-foot, 139–40, 167
  Wild T4, 311
The Times
  articles
    choice of Southampton, 111
    death of James, 166
    unsatisfactory maps, 189, 202

correspondence
  from 'a Sapper', 136
  from Crook, 189
  on Committee on the Ordnance Survey, 357
  on Jerusalem survey, 156
  on one-inch map, 134
Thomas, Alfred, 107
Thomas, *Lieut* RN, 116
Thompson, E. H., *Prof*, 249, 303
Thompson, N. S., 278
Thorpe, *Sir* Edward, 216
Tidal stations, 205
  Dunbar, 217–8, 313, 315
  Felixstowe, 217–8, 313, 315
  Ireland – Airy's investigations, 88
  Newlyn, 217–8, 313, 315
  Poolbeg Lighthouse, 88, 149, 210
Tide lines survey, 339–40
Tithe Commutation Act 1836, 112
Tithe commutation surveys, 112–4, 121
  classification of surveys, 113
Topographical Department – Ireland, 92
Topographical Sections RE, 222
Topographical and Statistical Department of the War Office,
      135, 159
Topographical Subsection GHQ, 220
Topographical surveying methods, 57–60, 169–73, 332–6.
      See also Air survey; Chain survey; Revision; Six-inch
      map of Ireland; Tacheometric survey; Traversing.
  1:1250 comparative accuracy, 333
  'J' points, 206
  plan assessment rating, 334
  tide lines survey, 339–40
  town traversing, 170, 206, 294
Topographical Survey organization. *See also* Royal Military
      Surveyors and Draftsmen.
  civilians hired 1805, 52
  hill sketching, 102
  piecework system, 101–2
  reorganization 1787–88, 44–46
  survey of southern Scotland, 103
  unauthorized assistants, 101
Tovey, Richard, 69–70
Tovey, W., 69
Tower of London, 2
  drawing room, 3–4, 45–46, 49
  fire, 111
  map sales, 73–74, 99
Town and Country Planning Act 1925, 250
Town and Country Planning Act 1932, 250, 257–8
Town and Country Planning, Ministry of, 293
  1:25 000, 291
  National Coal Board programme, 294, 301, 325
Town plans
  1:500 scale, 129, 171
  Dorington Committee, 190, 203
  five-foot scale, 114, 124
  Ireland, scales, 86, 150
  Land Registry Series, 199
  London 1848, 120
  ten-foot scale, 114, Pl 8
Towns Improvement Clauses Act 1854, 150
Trading Funds Bill 1973, 357–8
Traherne, J. M., *Rev*, 61
Training and Information Division, 321
Training surveyors and draughtsmen, 4, 50–51. *See also* Ire-
      land, Ordnance Survey of.
  Basic Training Wing, 290
  National Certificates, 351–2
  'Newbury' courses, 352
  North-East London Polytechnic, 352
  post-war recruits, 289–90
  Training and Information Division, 321
  training needs 1965, 321
Transport, Ministry of
  half-inch road map, 245
Transport and Civil Aviation, Ministry of

Flying Unit, 299, 324
Transverse Mercator Projection, 252–3, 268, 270
Traversing
  1:1250, 294, 332–3
  1:2500, 170
  Old Series, 59
  prejudice against, 170
  Scotland, 1747 survey, 57
  six-inch map of Ireland, 84, 86
  town plans, 170
Treasury
  1840 six-inch map, 109
  1843 one-inch map of England, 109
  1843 six-inch scale, 114–5
  1851 six-inch scale, 122, 124
  1852 one-inch map of Ireland, 147
  1853 twenty-four inch scale, 124
  1853 circular on scales, 124–5
  1854 circular on scales, 125–6
  1854 (15 July) minute on 1:2500 scale, 126, 129
  1854 Committee on large scales, 126
  1855 (18 May) minute on basic scales, 129–30, 132–3
  1856 (25 Nov) minute on basic scales, 132
  1858 (11 Sept) minute on basic scales, 132–3
  1863 (18 March) minute, final authority on basic scales,
        133
  1882 1:2500 revision, 182
  1886 1:2500 revision, 182
  1887 copyright, 184
  1887 1:2500, Ireland, 210
  1890 criticized by Crook, 186–7
  1897 one-inch map in colour, 201
  1911 Crown copyright, 198
  1915 retrenchment, 228
  1928 staff for land registration, 250
  1938 minute on Establishment and Finance Officer, 323
  1944 memo on post-war Civil Service, 289
  1953 Organization and Methods Unit on continuous revi-
        sion, 300
  1961 Working Party on Survey Staffs, 321
  1963 marketing maps, 323
  1965 Organization and Methods Unit on land registration,
        327
  1967 Joint Survey Service, 320
  1970 management accounting, 356
Trench maps, 221–4
Trench, W. le Poer, *Lieut*, 133
Trevelyan, *Sir* Charles, 114–5, 126, 129, 147
  on cadastral survey, 168
Triangulation. *See also* County triangulation; Cross-Channel
      connections; Ireland, Ordnance Survey of; Principal
      Triangulation; Retriangulation.
  1787–89, 34–36, Pl 1
  1791–1822, 37–38, 40–42
  1792 secondary and tertiary, 44
  1838 Scotland, triangulation resumed, 107
  'interior' triangulation, 59
  military requirements, 24
  records, 216–7
  restoration, 216
  Royal Sappers and Miners, 115
  use by private mapmakers, 74
Triangulation stations
  heights, 36, 271
  marking, 35, 41, 270–1
  signals
    Drummond light, 82, 140
    electric beacon lamps, 271
    Fresnel lamps, 41
    heliostats, 82, 140
    white lights, 16, 35
Triangulation, test of the, 214–5
Trickett, W. R. L., 258
Trigonometrical Survey 1791–1823, 21–23, 28–31
  international contacts, 29–30
  objects, 28
  scientific uses, 29

Trimontium, Roy's identification, 62–63
Triotint, 148, 151–2
Troughton, E., 141
Troughton & Simms, 83, 139, 141, 216. *See also* Cooke, Troughton & Simms.
Tucker, Henry, *Lieut-Col*, 124–5, 127, 147
Tudor, H. H., *Brig-Gen*, 223
Turkish Government, 154–5
Twenty-five inch map. *See* 1:2500 scale map.
Two-inch scale, fair drawings, 58

Unified Survey Service proposed, 287
United States Air Force
  maps for, 282
  SHORAN, 312, 344
United States Army Map Service, 309
United States Coast and Geodetic Survey, 271
Universal Transverse Mercator Projection, 312, 344

Valuation. *See also* Six-inch map of Ireland.
  1855 Act, 131
  1909–10 Finance Act, 206
  1931 Act, 250–1
Vandyke, *Conductor*, 200
Vandyke process, 200, 203
Van Gorkum, J. E., *Col*, 173
Variation of co-ordinates, 272–3
Verney, *Sir* Henry, 106
Vetch, J., *Col*, 166
Victor, J. C., *Lieut*, 103
Vignal, J., 314
Vignoles, Charles, 126, 131
Vivian, *Lord* (Master General), 109–10

Wadley, T. L., *Dr*, 310
Walker, George, *Col*, 246
Walker, George, *Dr*, 216
Walker, James, 114
Warburton, John, 10
War Office, 135, 158–9, 164, 245–8, 275–7. *See also* Air Survey Committee; Defence, Ministry of.
  cost-accounting, 244
  Davidson Committee, 263
  Military Map of the United Kingdom, Committee on, 1892, 188
  military surveys in Great Britain 1939–45, 283–4
  reorganization 1868, 159
  repayment work, 329–30
Washington, F. P., *Col*, 183, 198–9
Washington, John, 131
Watson, David, *Col*, 4–5, 62
Watson, W. J., *Dr*, 206
Watts, B., 279
Waverley, *Lord*, 315
Wellcome, *Sir* Henry, 238
Wellesley, *Lord*, 80
Wellingborough project, 298–9
Wellington, *Duke of* (Master General), 26, 30, 100, 103, 109
  Colby's appointment, 28
  Ireland survey, 80–81, 147
  place-names, 61
  reduction of six-inch survey, 81
  scales dispute, 114
Western Front 1914–18, 220–3
West European Sub-Commission for Satellite Triangulation, 346
Westminster Abbey, 120
Wheeler, R. P., *Brig*, 295
Wheler, E. G., 189
Whitley, J. H., *Rt Hon*, 232
Whitley System, 232–3, 242
  Ordnance Survey Departmental Whitley Council, 351
Whitlock, G. F. A., *Col*, 232
Wilde, W. E., 279

Willatts, E. C., *Dr*, 291
Williams, C., *Rev*, 157
Williams, Edward, *Col* (Superintendent), 23, 67
Williams-Freeman, J. P., *Dr*, 237
Williams, John, 5
Willis, J. C. T., *Maj-Gen* (Director General), 301, 303–5
Wilson, *Sir* Charles (Director General), 180, 184–8, 195
  Dorington Committee, 189–93
  Ireland, 209–11
  revision, 182–3
  survey of Jerusalem and Sinai, 154–7
Winterbotham, H. St J. L., *Brig* (Director General), 221–3, 234, 241–2, 250–3, 257
  quoted on
    cost accounting, 244
    Fifth Edition, 252
    half-inch map, 202
    Popular Edition, 231
    Public Accounts Committee, 245
    replotted counties, 183
    Research Officer, 234
    Royal Engineers, 247
    sheet lines, 253
    survey legislation, 250
    transfer of meridians, 216
Withycombe, J. G., *Capt*, 252
Wollaston, W. H., 41
Women, employment of, 275, 352
Women's Army Auxiliary Corps, 223
Woods and Forests, Office of
  geological survey of Great Britain, 104
  Irish geological survey, 93
Woolcot, Simon, 22, 25, 53f
Worden Gravity Meter, 348
Wordsworth, William, quoted, 21
Works, Board of, Committee of Enquiry, 161–3
  Boundary Department, 161
  civil assistants' complaints, 163
  IIM Stationery Office, 162
  military system, 162–3
  minority report, 163
Works, Office of. *See also* Works, Board of.
  HM Stationery Office, 183
  Ordnance Survey transferred to, 159
  retention of Director General, 179
World War I, 220–8
  artillery boards, 223, 225
  Artillery survey, 221–3
  effects, 228
  maps from Ordnance Survey, 220, 224–5
World War II, 274–85
  air raids on Southampton, 277–9
  mapping for defence of Great Britain, 276–7
  map production table, 283
  military map production, 280–3
  mobilization, 275
  reorganization of military survey, 277
Wright, J. R., 103–4
Wrottesley, *Lord*, 132
Wyld, J., 158, 161
  Dorington Committee, 189

Yeakell, Thomas (elder), 11, 45–46
Yeakell, Thomas (younger), 46, 49, 55, 69–70, 100
Yolland, William, *Capt*, 111, 115, 119–24, 127, 139, 143, 147–8
  Bonne projection, 147, 164f
  Principal Triangulation, 139, 143
  quarrel with Hall, 122–4
Young, William, *Sgt-Major*, 136, 143

Zenith sector. *See* Instruments.
Zincography, 178–9, 200. *See also* Heliozincography; Photo-zincography; Vandyke process.